INVERTEBRATE PALEONTOLOGY

W. H. Easton, 1916-

University of Southern California

HARPER & BROTHERS, PUBLISHERS *New York*

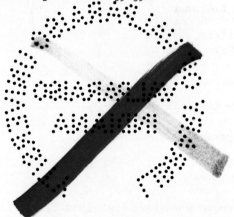

CONTENTS

Editor's Introduction   vii

Preface   ix

1. Introduction   1

> Value of Fossils
> Composition of Animal Kingdom
> Classification
> Nomenclature
> Fossilization
> Methods in Paleontology
> Evolutionary Theory
> Procedure in Paleontology

2. Single-Celled Animals   51

> Phylum I. Protozoa

3. Sponges and Spongelike Organisms   99

> Phylum II. Porifera
> Phylum III. Archaeocyatha

4. Lower Coelenterates (Including Graptolites, Stromatoporoids, and Conulariids)   123

> Phylum IV. Coelenterata

5. Higher Coelenterates (Mainly Corals)   155

> Phylum IV. Coelenterata (*Continued*)

v

6. Worms and Conodonts 214

Phylum V. Platyhelminthes
Phylum VI. Nemathelminthes
Phylum VII. Trochelminthes
Phylum VIII. Annelida

7. Bryozoans and Phoronids 239

Phylum IX. Bryozoa
Phylum X. Phoronida

8. Brachiopods 278

Phylum XI. Brachiopoda

9. Chitons, Pelecypods, and Scaphopods 325

Phylum XII. Mollusca

10. Snails 370

Phylum XII. Mollusca (*Continued*)

11. Cephalopods 407

Phylum XII. Mollusca (*Continued*)

12. Trilobites and Chelicerates 484

Phylum XIII. Arthropoda

13. Crustaceans and Insects 539

Phylum XIII. Arthropoda (*Continued*)

14. Attached Echinoderms 582

Phylum XIV. Echinoderma

15. Unattached Echinoderms 628

Phylum XIV. Echinoderma (*Continued*)

Comprehensive Questions 665

Index 667

EDITOR'S INTRODUCTION

Invertebrate Paleontology is a new book on an old subject which, with its sister discipline of stratigraphy, is again coming into at least a part of the prominence it once enjoyed. Prior to the advent of geophysical prospecting in the early 1920's, the average field geologist was regarded as inadequately trained if he were not something of a stratigraphical paleontologist. Now after about a quarter century of strong emphasis on the physical sciences as *the* supporting subjects in the education of a geologist, the biological and stratigraphical aspects of his training, in both the laboratory and in the field, are also taking on renewed significance. For this practical reason, as well as for many more scientific ones, the present text should prove an especially useful tool in the broad education of a modern earth scientist whatever his special interests or future assignments.

This book has been organized in such a fashion that the student who has had little or no formal biological training can nevertheless clearly grasp the important biological implications of the subject. Moreover, even the well-trained biologist may have his experience slightly enlarged through a close perusal of Easton's text, for in it he will find considerable information about the ancient ancestry and the extinct representatives of many of the living end products in whose study he may be engaged. There are, of course, a number of good American and foreign books on paleontology which provide the student with similar information. For the most part, however, the earlier works on the subject are either too condensed for effective use in semi-advanced collegiate courses or they are compendia somewhat too detailed for effective use as routine texts. *Invertebrate Paleontology* not only is different in organization from earlier works on paleontology, but it also has been designed to occupy a position intermediate between elementary texts and advanced treatments of the subject.

This text is an orderly work in that a bold scaffolding stands out prominently in each chapter. Thus even the casual student will find little difficulty in noting the essential facts regarding any or all of the invertebrates which have been incorporated in the fossil record. When taxonomic categories are used in their precise sense the word Genus, and all higher taxa, are capitalized. Moreover, standardized terminations for names of all the taxa from Subfamily to Superorder have been used in the hope that, as a result, students will more readily recognize the taxonomic status of many of the numerous names that must be employed.

For most of the major groups of invertebrates which are of some significance as fossils Dr. Easton has prepared "keys" which are constructed on simple, down-to-earth bases so that the student actually can use them readily and with profitable results. This is in itself refreshing because many keys tend to lock more doors to understanding than they open.

A short list of questions has been inserted near the end of each chapter. They are designed to entice both instructor and student to think about the real meaning of the chapter's facts and figures. In effect then they tend to magnify the significance of both theoretical and practical considerations and to play down the emphasis on memorizing names and terms which has plagued most courses in paleontology.

The bibliographies are not exhaustive, but are sufficiently extended that they should provide the average student with adequate materials for high-level term papers; and they will give the young research worker clues as to where next to search.

The style of the present text in part results from actual classroom and laboratory experience at the University of Southern California where, for a number of years, Dr. Easton has been testing materials and methods of presentation. The organization is also a result of the author's broad professional experience for Dr. Easton is not only an "academic" paleontologist, he is also an experienced field geologist and stratigrapher who has had opportunities to test paleontological principles and theories in many detailed field studies. Just prior to publication of this book the author was further enlarging his experience as a Guggenheim Fellow in England and France.

The reader may correctly judge that the editor has a particular interest in this present book in the Harper's Geoscience Series. This results not alone from the fact that Dr. Easton is a former student and that the subject itself is one which the editor has taught for many years. The editorial interest stems chiefly from the fact that the text is so well organized that it should help to make his own teaching tasks simpler. Other instructors concerned with paleontology and stratigraphy will, we hope, react similarly.

CAREY CRONEIS

The Rice Institute

PREFACE

The reception which people accord paleontology is somewhat analogous to their taste for kidney pie—there is either evangelical enthusiasm or case-hardened resistance, and there is very little uncommitted opinion. It has been my experience that people in general are most interested in paleontologic matters when fossils are presented as integral parts of actively changing situations. These vitalistic approaches are apt to generate enthusiasm among most students as well as among professional physical geologists and petroleum engineers, not all of whom are necessarily appreciative of the values of paleontology. On the other hand, detailed factual data on the anatomy, classification, and stratigraphic distribution of fossils are most earnestly sought by professional paleontologists and by advanced students who are already imbued with an interest in paleontology. For practical reasons, every geologist should be able to recognize the principle groups of invertebrates, to collect fossils intelligently for identification by specialists, and to understand and evaluate paleontologic reports.

It is a challenge to try to flavor the technical details in a systematic subject with continuity and interest. Various approaches to the problem were tried in paleontology classes at the University of Southern California over the past ten years, and then the methods selected for incorporation in this text were tested in lectures for two more years while modifications were being made in the manuscript. The book is planned for courses offering as much as one year of training, but the material should be equally adaptable to two-semester and to two- or three-quarter courses. It is assumed that students will have at least junior standing and that they will have studied Physical Geology, Historical Geology, and possibly Mineralogy. It would be commendable if all students of elementary paleontology also had studied Organic Evolution and Genetics, as well as General Zoology, but the realities of our educational system make it difficult to enforce such prerequisites.

The first chapter provides readers with a condensed review of some basic concepts in biology, zoology, and paleontology. In addition, it contains some controversial (and even some older discredited) ideas which are pertinent to an understanding of paleontologic thought, even though the ideas cannot be classed as basic. Considerable effort has been devoted to correlating the text of subsequent chapters with factors presented in the first chapter.

Subject matter in the remainder of the book is taken up systematically according to customary biologic classification. Students who are expected to learn the classification will find their task simplified because uniform endings are used for all taxa up through Superorders. Definitions and illustrations clarify the nature and limits of each taxon. In some sections morphologic information and illustrations are sufficient for readers to evaluate differences even at the generic and specific levels. In general, however, the presentation concerns arrangement of fossils in stratigraphic succession, or growth stages, or arbitrary morphologic series, or environmental adaptations, or their probable evolutionary progression. Only enough morphologic and zoologic information is presented in the systematic chapters to enable identification of members of the group or to enable recognition of one of the patterns of change in the group. Each of the foregoing patterns or series is not presented for each group. Instead, a particular series is utilized when an illuminating example of it is known. The amount of space allocated to the various systematic groups is governed in part by their usefulness in field work and by their suitability as teaching aids. For example, more space is devoted to foraminifers and brachiopods and less is devoted to sponges and cystoids than would be warranted by their relative taxonomic rank and their evolutionary significance.

Students of elementary paleontology commonly learn detailed stratigraphic ranges of fossils at the expense of more general paleontologic information. In view of this tendency, practically all stratigraphic information has been reduced to names of Systems for the Paleozoic and Mesozoic rocks and of Series for the Cenozoic rocks. Geologic ranges of fossils are illustrated with very simple abundance diagrams which are superimposed upon identical geologic time scales. It is hoped that the diagrams will promote greatest retention of the geologic significance of different fossils through simplified graphical presentation.

Illustrations have been selected not only for their morphologic value but also to depict common species from various geologic provinces in North America. Moreover, most of these species are readily available through purchase or exchange; therefore the illustrations can be utilized to advantage in laboratory work. It is hoped that citations of fossils from numerous states and provinces will impress readers with the feasibility of making collections in their own regions. Some soft-bodied organisms are illustrated so that readers may associate descriptive comments with actual forms, even within paleontologically unimportant groups.

Except for a few bryozoans, all previously published illustrations have been redrawn for purposes of clarity and uniformity. In many instances missing parts have been restored and imperfections have been omitted. Special effort has been expended to integrate the illustrations with the text. The source of each illustration is credited in appended explanations.

We are born into this world knowing nothing, and almost everything we do know has been learned from others. Having completed this book, the writer feels a great sense of indebtedness to all those whose ideas are transcribed herein. The works of many paleontologists are listed at the ends of the chapters, but additional contributions surely lie buried within the text, unintentionally lacking acknowledgment. In this latter category are ideas derived from others with whom I have shared wonderful days in the field and in the laboratories of many places. It has been my good fortune to work with many paleontologists of different professional inclination, who find their calling variously at universities, museums, exploration departments of oil companies, and state and federal geologic surveys. It would be gratifying if present and former associates were to recognize some of the fruits of our association in this book.

It is a pleasure to acknowledge the constructive criticism of various parts of the manuscript by Dr. Orville L. Bandy of the University of Southern California and Dr. Daniel J. Jones of the University of Utah. It is especially pleasant to acknowledge the assistance of Dr. Carey Croneis of The Rice Institute, for Dr. Croneis not only served as mentor during my student years, but has been the principal critic in the writing of this book. He read the entire manuscript and offered numerous suggestions for improvement of its style and content.

Information or assistance has been kindly furnished by Dr. C. H. Crickmay of Imperial Oil Limited, the late Dr. C. E. Decker of the University of Oklahoma, Dr. S. P. Ellison of the University of Texas, Dr. J. J. Galloway of Indiana University, Dr. J. S. Garth and Dr. Olga Hartman of Allan Hancock Foundation, Dr. N. T. Mattox of the University of Southern California, Dr. M. G. Mehl of the University of Missouri, the late Dr. J. B. Reeside of the U.S. Geological Survey, and Mr. F. C. Ziesenhenne of Allan Hancock Foundation.

Special thanks are due Mrs. Dorothy M. Halmos, Librarian of Allan Hancock Foundation at the University of Southern California, and to her staff. The courteous and dedicated services of these librarians made a pleasure out of normally onerous bibliographic work. Moreover, the writer greatly appreciates having permission to use the remarkable library of the Allan Hancock Foundation. Had it not been for the unique collection in this library, this book would most certainly not have been written.

About 400 illustrations of brachiopods, molluscs, and arthropods are the work of Mr. Gerhard Bakker, Jr., of Los Angeles City College. Mr. Bakker's drawings reflect his training as a biologist as well as his skill as an artist and his sensitiveness to the qualifications of illustrations intended for teaching.

Finally, the writer wishes to relieve his benefactors of any responsibility for errors which he may have inserted in this book. The coöperation of readers is earnestly invited in order to eliminate faults.

W. H. EASTON

December, 1959

INVERTEBRATE PALEONTOLOGY

Chapter 1

INTRODUCTION

A Cro-Magnon man who was buried 20,000 years ago with a string of Jurassic snails about his neck may rank not only as the first paleontologist but also as the first known scientist of any kind. Since his time, fossils have been noted by pre-Christian writers and by later men down through the ages, but the science of paleontology as a modern discipline dates only from about the middle of the nineteenth century. By that time the naturalists had described an abundance of fossils, and Darwin had suggested a rational explanation for the orderly and progressive changes of faunas through time.

Paleontology in its broadest sense is the study of all ancient life, but it is currently customary to speak of the study of plants as **paleobotany** and to refer to the study of animals as **paleontology.** Some purists correctly use **paleozoology** for the latter field and relegate paleobotany and paleontology to the position of subsidiary fields of paleobiology. **Vertebrate paleontology** and **invertebrate paleontology** are commonly differentiated as distinct fields. Moreover, the study of fossil foraminifers and of some other small fossils is widely referred to as **micropaleontology.** Indeed, the most enthusiastic students of foraminifers are apt to consider the words "paleontology" and "micropaleontology" as synonyms. The variation spelled "palaeontology" with a second "a" reflects continental influence and is rarely used in America. Finally, the study of plant spores, which may be undertaken as an adjunct of micropaleontology, is **palynology.**

Paleontology is dependent upon **zoology** for an understanding of fossils as parts of living, feeding, moving, reproducing organisms. Zoologists and paleontologists both face profound dilemmas. Zoologists can test genetic relationships of species, but they cannot test the actual succession of forms because ancestors and descendants live at the same time. Paleontologists, on the other hand, can observe successions of forms but cannot test fundamental biologic relationships because fossil material lacks living tissues. When paleontologists and zoologists work in harmony, however, their studies are complementary. When no living organism resembles a fossil, as in the case of conodonts, controversies arise concerning the zoologic relationships of the fossils.

The study of adjustment of creatures to their environment is **ecology.** Recently it has become popular to speak of ecologic studies of fossil organisms as **paleoecology** because this word emphasizes the geologic significance of studies in which some life relationships are not represented.

As E. O. Ulrich once wrote, "Systematic paleontology without a stratigraphic basis is regarded as an absurdity"; hence, most paleontologists are almost equally interested in the aspects of physical geology which comprise **stratigraphy.** By knowing the sequence of sedimentary units which contain fossil faunas it is possible to establish ranges of those faunas through intervals of time. By accumulating enough information about stratigraphic ranges, a trained paleontologist becomes able to reverse the procedure and to identify stratigraphic and time units from the fossils which they contain. Even though a student geologist may not become a professional paleontologist, he will have to associate with paleontologists in stratigraphic work and to appreciate the problems encountered by paleontologists. Accordingly, this book is planned as an introduction to the once living organisms which paleontologists study, the methods used, and the advantages and limitations of various categories of fossils. These paleontologic factors in most cases are absolutely necessary in determining age relationships of sedimentary rocks; therefore, we may paraphrase Ulrich's maxim and say, "Stratigraphy without paleontology is an absurdity."

VALUE OF FOSSILS

Fossils provide the basis for four major lines of study. First, they are part of the physical stratigraphic record because they provide much of the substance which makes up sediment. Most commonly, entire or broken shells are scattered through some sedimentary matrix such as sand or mud. In some cases fossils make up entire stratigraphic units composed of mounds or of layers of shells. If fossils are broken up finely enough, their skeletons produce the grains of calcium carbonate from which many limestones were formed. Detailed study of the foregoing matters generally is undertaken by petrographers and by students of sedimentation.

Second, fossils enable one to recognize environments of sedimentation in cases where one can compare fossil remains with living relatives. This subject is treated briefly under a section on environments (pp. 28-31).

Fig. 1.1 *(opposite).* Geologic Time Scale.
Spacing of horizontal lines is proportional to the estimated duration of each Period or Epoch. The same background is used on all subsequent range charts, but only abbreviated chart symbols are used for the names of time divisions. (After Holmes, 1947, and others.)

Eras	Periods	Epochs	Chart Symbol	Length in Millions of Years	Age in Millions of Years
	Quaternary	Pleistocene	Q	1	
Cenozoic	Tertiary	Pliocene	T	10	
		Miocene		15	
		Oligocene		10	
		Eocene		20	
		Paleocene		15	— 71
Mesozoic	Cretaceous		K	54	
	Jurassic		J	25	
	Triassic		Ŧ	30	— 180
Paleozoic	Permian		Pm	21	
	Pennsylvanian		IP	30	
	Mississippian		M	30	
	Devonian		D	50	
	Silurian		S	35	
	Ordovician		O	60	
	Cambrian		Є	80	— 486
	Precambrian				

Third, fossils are the major bases for recognizing units of time in the geologic record. The proper concept of time is probably the most valuable contribution which paleontology offers to physical geology and to the biologic sciences. The simplified geologic time scale used hereafter in this book is shown in Figure 1.1.

Fourth, of almost equal importance to biology is the succession of extinct creatures which record the passage of time. Fossil organisms fill in many gaps in the evolutionary record. Moreover, it is only by understanding something of the relationship of creatures to time that evolutionary changes in lineages can be assigned rate and duration. Time is one factor which cannot be used in sufficient amounts by zoologists to test how descent operates among living creatures; but changes in the fossil record are readily referable to units of time.

COMPOSITION OF THE ANIMAL KINGDOM

When someone embarks upon a new project, he needs to have some idea of how large a subject he faces and what its general composition is. Thus, a potential paleontologist presumably would like to know how many animals are available for study and how many of these comprise the materials of the science of paleontology. At least three major evaluations of the composition of the Animal Kingdom may be made. One can count the number of living species and add to them the number of extinct species which have actually been described thus far; or one can estimate the total number of species in the world, knowing how many have been described and the rate of new discovery; or one may estimate the volume of living material assignable to different species or to larger groups. All three of these approaches are beset with such difficulties that most tabulations of the composition of the Animal Kingdom are extremely inaccurate. For one thing, new species of insects, worms, and protozoans are being discovered so rapidly that they seem to be destined to exceed the other groups in numerical tabulations of names just as they apparently do volumetrically in nature. It has been guessed that as many as 4,000,000,000 different species of animals and plants have evolved since the dawn of life. Data presented in Table 1 indicate that about 1,135,000 species of animals alone have been described by scientists; and about 11 per cent (130,000) of the animals which have been described are extinct. It is probable that the paleontologic record ultimately will contain about 500,000 species of animals when descriptive work is essentially completed. It is likely that most of the vertebrates and most of the larger hard-shelled invertebrates have already been described. No doubt descriptive work on small fossils and on new collections will continue to occupy paleontologists for generations while

TABLE 1. Composition of the Animal Kingdom

Group	Number of Species			With Hard Parts	Per Cent of Total Species in Grand Total
	Living	Extinct	Total		
Protozoa	27,000	9,000	36,000	29,000	3.2
Porifera	2,240	1,760	4,000	3,500	0.4
Coelenterata	9,500	4,500	14,000	10,700	1.2
Worms	36,000	1,000	37,000	10,000	3.3
Bryozoa	3,050	3,000	6,050	5,500	0.5
Brachiopoda	225	15,000	15,225	15,225	1.3
Mollusca	81,150	40,400	121,550	121,000	10.7
Gastropoda	69,000	15,000	84,000	83,800	7.4
Pelecypoda	11,000	15,000	26,000	26,000	2.3
Cephalopoda	300	10,000	10,300	10,200	0.9
Other	850	400	1,250	1,000	0.1
Arthropoda	804,898	16,400	821,298	821,298	72.5
Insecta	746,298	12,000	758,298	758,298	66.9
Other	58,600	4,400	63,000	63,000	5.6
Echinodermata	5,344	14,329	19,813	19,700	1.7
Crinoidea	800	5,000	5,800	5,800	0.5
Echinoidea	867	7,200	8,067	8,067	0.8
Stelleroidea	3,700	479	4,179	4,179	0.3
Other	117	1,650	1,767	1,767	0.1
Chordata	33,640	24,360	58,000	56,000	5.1
Grand totals	1,106,749	129,749	1,132,796	1,091,923	99.9
	(1,105,000)	(130,000)	(1,135,000)	(1,090,000)	

SOURCE: Mostly from data by MacGinitie and MacGinitie, 1949; Mayr, Linsley, and Usinger, 1953; Shrock and Twenhofel, 1953; Muller and Campbell, 1954; Durham, 1954; Hyman, 1955.

the remaining faunas are discovered, descriptions are corrected and augmented, and species are split into smaller and smaller recognizable units. At the same time increasing numbers of paleontologists will probably turn to interpretative work in efforts to understand the evolution, habitats, and stratigraphic significance of known species. Enough material has been described and enough new material remains to be described so that ample opportunity exists for paleontologic work of many kinds.

Numerical representation of the various Phyla of the Animal Kingdom is presented in Figure 1.2. No doubt the most striking features of the graph are that arthropods comprise 72.5 per cent of all the 1,135,000 known animals in the world, living and fossil, and that insects alone account for 67 per cent of all known species. It seems that we live in the Age of Insects, if one wishes to consider our position from a strictly numerical standpoint!

Considered from a paleontologic standpoint, Figure 1.2 seems at first glance to indicate a bleak prospect for research in fossil animals, for only about 11 per cent of the known animals are extinct. Of course, thousands of the living species also extend back into the fossil record, some as far as the Pliocene or even the Miocene; but adjustments in percentages to account for these ancient records probably would not affect the proportions of the graph notably. The fact is, however, that the fossil record of the Animal Kingdom

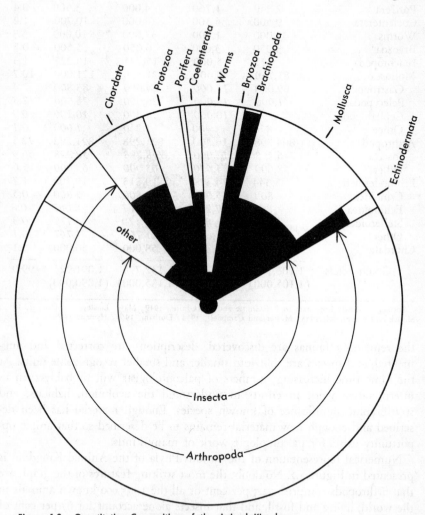

Figure 1.2. Quantitative Composition of the Animal Kingdom.
The complete circle represents the 1,135,000 known animals. The angle defining each sector is proportional to the per cent of the total number of animals represented by each group. Within each sector the shaded area represents the percentage of extinct animals in each group and the unshaded area represents the percentage of living animals. Numerical data are given in Table 1.

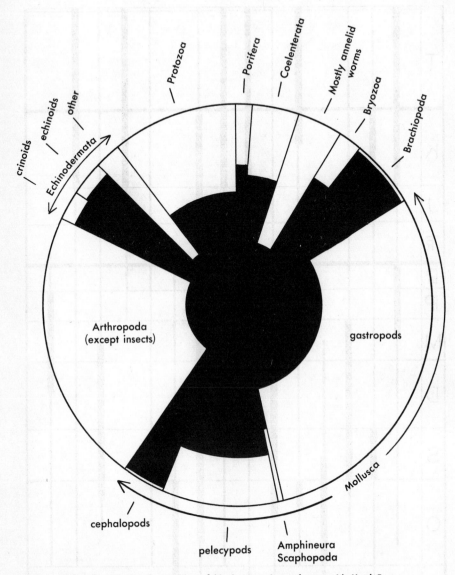

Figure 1.3. Quantitative Composition of Noninsectan Invertebrates with Hard Parts.
The complete circle representing 278,000 species of invertebrates is divided into sectors according to the percentage represented by each Phylum or Class. Shaded areas indicate about 130,000 species which comprise the known fossil invertebrates. Numerical data are presented in Table 1.

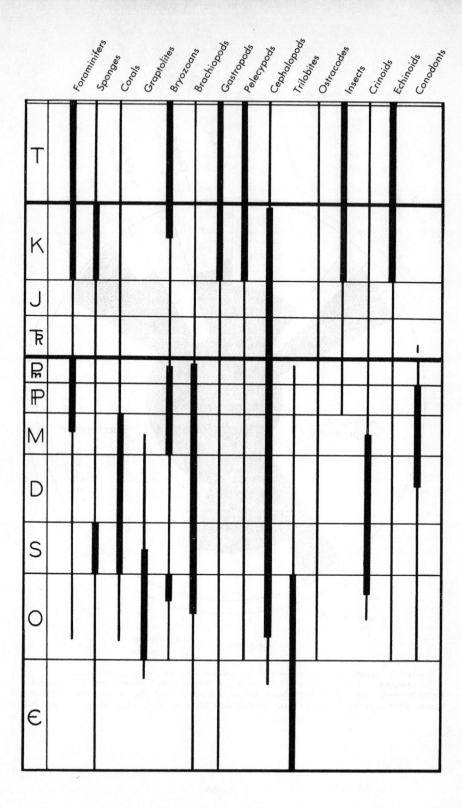

is not constructed of anything like proportionate parts of the various living groups. Insects and worms, for instance, are rarely found as fossils, and relatively few of the many protozoans are fossilized. Accordingly, a fairer picture of the composition of the fossil record is obtained if one selects the data so as to exclude those forms which have no hard parts or which are rarely preserved as fossils.

Figure 1.3 depicts the proportionate composition of only the invertebrate groups after some arbitrary adjustments have been made in the numerical data in order to eliminate animals without appreciable hard parts. After eliminations of this sort it is clear that molluscs dominate the fossil as well as the living populations of invertebrates in number of species. In addition, brachiopods and echinoderms are especially important paleontologically. Available numerical data still do not depict paleontologic materials realistically because the graphs cannot portray how creatures are distributed in time, or geographically, or according to local environmental controls such as depth, temperature, salinity, turbulence, or sedimentary features. Crinoids, for instance, were diverse, abundant, and widespread in the Paleozoic, but are relatively uncommon in Recent faunas. Conversely, foraminifers are tremendously abundant in Cenozoic sediments, but were only important locally during the Paleozoic.

Figure 1.4 shows the general distribution of the main groups of fossils during geologic time. From this figure it becomes apparent that even the world of fossils is divisible into two parts according to the major development of various groups. Members of one assortment reach their peak of development during the Paleozoic Era, but members of another group dominate Cretaceous and Cenozoic faunas. Minor fractions of both groups, however, range up or down into the opposite groups.

CLASSIFICATION

Human beings, having the ability to reason out differences among organisms, and wishing to pass this information along to others in intelligible form, have sought for over 2000 years to organize their knowledge of natural history. Accordingly, we recognize that even as early as the time of Aristotle (384-322 B.C.) a collection of descriptions was undertaken. But a collection without an index, or a key, or some method of grouping similar things together borders on the chaotic; therefore, a prime prerequisite of any collection

---

Figure 1.4 (opposite). Stratigraphic Ranges of Common Groups of Fossils.
Vertical lines represent over-all ranges of selected Phyla and Classes. Heavy portions of the range lines signify highly subjective estimates of the intervals during which particular groups reached the peak of diversity, abundance, and paleontologic usefulness. (Data from many sources.)

is to be arranged in some kind of orderly fashion. **Classification** is the arrangement of things in categories or assignment of things to their proper categories. In common parlance we say that we are identifying or that we are
classifying a collection of fossils. As more and more information has become
available over the centuries, certain procedures, rules, and practices have
become established so that scientists speak of the process of classification as a
distinct subdivision of biology named **taxonomy.** Application of the rules of
taxonomy has enabled us to systematize our knowledge and to facilitate the
study and utilization of collections. In any science, but most particularly in
biologic sciences, the taxonomic process is often spoken of as **systematics.**

In this text, for instance, the subject matter is presented as systematic
paleontology, meaning that the various groups are taken up in the order of
their increasing complexity. Other kinds of paleontologic study could be
based primarily upon stratigraphic, ecologic (environmental), or geographic
considerations.

Various kinds of classification are possible. Creatures can be grouped according to the kind of environment they occupy, such as fresh water, land,
and the various marine depth zones. Or they can be classified by their method
of locomotion, or by their sensitiveness to light, or by their physiologic activities. Most creatures, however, are classified according to their relationship to one another. These "blood relationships" are truly genetic only within
an interbreeding population. Various sorts of cats, such as lions and house
cats, although they do not interbreed, are supposedly more closely related to
each other than they are to any of the dogs; therefore, the concept of genetic
groups is expanded to express various diminishing degrees of relationship.
This kind of classification is termed a "natural classification" in order to
distinguish the more or less genetic kind from some purely "artificial classification" based upon characteristics such as habitat, size, depth distribution, or
geographic distribution. It should be realized from the first, however, that
no classification exists in nature. Classifications originate and exist only in
the minds of human beings who devise them in order to communicate ideas
to each other. Evolution is the basis of natural classification and species are
the building blocks of evolution. Evolution of a strain of creatures is like a
stream of water, and species have no more reality in the stream of evolution
than have cubic feet of water in a river. We describe a river by taking samples
and making measurements of water over its surface and down through it. In
like fashion we detect evolution by describing species in the stream of life. If
we decide that members of a group of species share some fundamental
feature, we assign that assemblage a higher rank in the classification. It can
be seen, then, that the degree of complexity of a classification depends upon
what depth of understanding of creatures is desired. No one classification is
"right" and another "wrong," but instead the classifications reflect abstract

concepts like "good" and "bad" which change with time and custom.

In biologic systems of classification organisms are grouped into units (**taxa,** sing. **taxon**) of decreasing importance, starting with the great Kingdoms of *Vegetabilia* and *Animalia.* The Kingdom *Protista* is used by some authors for those very simple organisms near the plant-animal boundary. In earlier years, another Kingdom, *Lapides* or minerals, was recognized, as is shown by the fact that we still speak of "species" of minerals or of the isometric Class of crystal forms. There are no rules governing the choice of features which determine the rank of each taxonomic category; therefore, all sorts of different groupings are available according to the individual ideas of specialists. One may compare, for instance, an arbitrary classification of automobiles with equally arbitrary classifications of a human being and a brachiopod, in which each object is referred to the same taxonomic categories.

TABLE 2.   Comparative Classifications

Taxon	Man	Brachiopod	Car
Kingdom	Animalia	Animalia	Machines
Phylum	Chordata	Brachiopoda	Transportation devices
Class	Mammalia	Articulata	Automobiles
Order	Primatida	Telotremida	Gasoline-powered
Family	Hominidae	Spiriferidae	Sedans
Genus	*Homo*	*Spirifer*	Two-door
Species	*sapiens*	*increbescens*	disc wheels
Individual	John Jones (Social Security No. —)	a specimen (Museum No. —)	a car (Motor No. —)

The foregoing parallelism should help to establish the relative sizes of categories higher than species and Genera when classifications of unfamiliar creatures are presented later in this book. At the Class level, for instance, the differences among automobiles, airplanes, and ships are comparable to the differences among mammals, birds, and fish. At the Order level the degree of difference between gasoline and electric cars is analogous to the degree of difference between primates and carnivores. And so the comparisons might be continued for the other categories, but someone is apt to object to the classification of cars used above because it ignores the manufacturer's name, which they think should be placed in between "sedans" and "gasoline-powered" as either a Suborder or a Superfamily; or perhaps "sedans" should be raised to the rank of Suborder and "manufacturer" put in its place as a Family name. Far from being a flippant diversion from the subject of the development of taxonomic classifications, the foregoing remarks give an accurate idea of the different opinions among biologists on the classification of animals and plants. As more and more information becomes available, new

categories are erected, so that "Sub-" this and "Super-" that need to be augmented by "Sections," "Tribes," "gens," and so forth. Moreover, there has
been a persistent trend by experts in systematics to raise each category below
Phylum to an ever higher position, so that, for instance, animals comprising
different Classes of worms a decade or so ago are now generally referred to
separate Phyla or Subphyla. Unfortunately, the grand differences by which a
moderately well-informed person was formerly able to recognize a group have
mostly been submerged in a welter of details which now seem to require exceptional material, intricate technique, or superior equipment for recognition.
Genera recognized by Linnaeus now correspond more or less to Families and
Orders. It seems to be a regrettable corollary of our wonderful increase in
knowledge that the interest of many amateurs declines as technical complexity increases.

Unfortunately for the newcomer to biology, he is faced with recognizing
names of numerous taxa above the rank of Genus, but ordinarily there are
few aids which enable him to recognize degrees of difference among the
names. If the same endings were used for the same taxa above the rank of
Genus, then a reader could recognize at a glance the magnitude of the category with which he is confronted. On the other hand, only a trained paleontologist is apt to recognize Trepostomata, Foraminifera, Scleractinia, and
Spatangida all as being names of Orders, because the words have different
terminations (*-ata, -a, -ia,* and *-ida*). The same problem affects other higher
taxa, many of which commonly are given the same terminations, even though
they occupy different levels in classification. There has been very little
standardization of the endings for names of taxonomic categories, but interest in the problem is increasing; hence, some formal action may be taken
by the International Zoological Congress in the near future. Official rules
currently require that Family names must be formed from the name of the
typical Genus, to the root of which has been added the suffix *-idae* (e.g.,
Spiriferidae, Arcidae, Orthidae, Halysitidae, from *Spirifer, Arca, Orthis,* and
Halysites). Likewise, names of Subfamilies must end in *-inae*. There are no
rules governing endings of names of any higher categories, but a provisional
arrangement largely derived from an analysis of current practices has been
proposed (Stenzel, 1950).

Inasmuch as the terminations of names for Family and Subfamily have
been formally adopted by biologists, it seems desirable to extend some of the
same terminal letters of these words into the ordinal level. Thus, *-ina* corresponds to *-inae,* and *-ida* corresponds to *-idae*. The use of *c* in the endings
for Superfamily and Superorder follows the custom of many biologists and
also enables one to preserve the form of the three terminations in each group.
All terminations at the ordinal and familial level have been standardized in
this text in the hope that the practice may help students to recognize the

taxonomic levels of these numerous names. It is not so difficult to recognize names of Classes and of Phyla because there are not many names at those levels. Moreover, some exceedingly common names would be changed if the terminations of Phyla and Classes were standardized. The terminations used herein, as applied to the Genus *Spirifer,* are:

Taxa	Terminations	Examples
Superorder	-ica	Impunctica[a]
Order	-ida	Protremida
Suborder	-ina	Spiriferina
Superfamily	-icae	Spirifericae
Family	-idae	Spiriferidae
Subfamily	-inae	Spiriferinae

[a] Impunctica as used here is a fictitious name designed to illustrate a particular suffix. No Superorder is currently recognized for spiriferoid brachiopods.

In order to stress the usage of taxonomic categories in their rigid sense, the word Genus and all higher taxa are capitalized in this text. This practice corresponds to the capitalization of formal names such as Epoch, Series, Period, System, and Era in stratigraphic terminology.

Many people like to render formal Latin names in English so that the words are less formidable and do not require any command of Latin etymology for their proper use. When Latin terms are converted into English adverbs, the general rule is to use the ending *-id,* when reference is being made to a definite taxonomic category, particularly a Genus or a Family. Thus, spiriferid brachiopods are those which belong in the Genus *Spirifer* or to the Family Spiriferidae; arcid pelecypods belong to the Family Arcidae; orthid brachiopods belong to the Orthidae; and halysitid corals are in the Halysitidae. If an inexact English adverb is desired, then the ending *-oid* is used with some root. In this way spiriferoid brachiopods may comprise not only the Spiriferidae, but the Atrypidae and perhaps even some brachiopods which look like Spiriferidae but are really in some other group. Orthoid brachiopods, for instance, do not necessarily have to be orthids, for they can be merely something which resembles orthids. The suffix *-oid* connotes "like" in English, whereas *-id* conveys "related to" or "the same as."

NOMENCLATURE

The basis of any scientific enterprise is to have names for the things being studied. Centuries ago it was realized that names for the same plant or animal vary from place to place, so a descriptive diagnosis of each organism was written in order to clarify each identity. Collections of descriptions into encyclopedias constituted the beginning of natural history, and an educated man was one who could quote extensive parts of these encyclopedias from memory. One of the most famous treatises was *Historia Naturalis* by Pliny the Elder, who died in A.D. 79. For the next 1500 years no great advances were made over classical treatises, but after the Renaissance a resurgence of interest in natural history began and many new descriptions were added to those in the older treatises. By the early eighteenth century so many animals, plants, and minerals were known that an index of some sort became necessary.

One of the best indices of the time was compiled by the Swedish scientist, Carl von Linné (1707-1778), who, in the fashion of educated persons of his time, Latinized his name to Linnaeus. He did not invent the system which made him famous, but he perfected it, used it consistently, and added so much to existing knowledge that his method quickly became accepted. Linnaeus himself said that he based his studies in natural history upon taxonomy and nomenclature. His taxonomy, or classification, was crude by present standards, but was a notable advance over previous attempts. His great contribution to science, however, was in perfecting a system of naming plants and animals. Under the method which Linnaeus popularized each old Latin description was shortened until it consisted of just two words—generally a substantive and a modifier; thus the two words *Homo sapiens* are merely the residue of a long discourse by some pre-Linnaean writer who was describing man in terms of man's intelligence, large head, erect posture, and so forth. In this system of **binominal nomenclature** (literally meaning "two-named naming system") the first name is the more general of the two and is the **generic name,** whereas the second element is of less importance and is the **specific name** (also commonly referred to as the **trivial name**).

In writing names according to the Linnaean method the generic name is always capitalized as a proper noun. The specific name is always written with a lower-case initial letter. Because the complete Linnaean name must consist of two elements, the official name, or **binomen,** is composed of the generic name, plus the specific name. By analogy one can see that a person's binomen may be William Jones, although we customarily write the generic element (Jones) last and put the specific element first. This analogy breaks down as an example of binominal nomenclature because our names refer to individuals, not to populations of individuals grouped into species or Genera. All Joneses, together with all other human beings, belong to the same Genus and species.

For centuries, educated people in Europe used Latin as their common language, just as it is common to use French today as the international language of foreign service. Thus, Linnaeus and all other early naturalists used Latin for scientific descriptions. In succeeding years we have recognized the international value of Latin in nomenclature by making it the only acceptable language. The custom is hard for some people to accept, possibly because of the increasing lack of familiarity with Latin. Nevertheless, many Latin or Latinized generic names are used in everyday conversation, such as *Geranium, Delphinium, Rhododendron, Hippopotamus, Alligator,* and *Junco.* Few people object to *Brontosaurus, Tyrannosaurus, Spirifer,* and *Eohippus* for names of extinct creatures because the words can be loosely translated into popular names such as "thunder lizard," "tyrant lizard," "spire-bearer," and "dawn horse." By the same token, less familiar Latinized taxonomic words also are equally accurately conceived. More importantly, however, all of these names have the decided advantage of referring to only one Genus of creatures. On the other hand, if a westerner in the United States encounters the word "gopher" he probably conjures up an image of a bur-rowing rodent often called a "pocket gopher" which belongs to the Genus *Geomys.* However, he might be thinking of one of the various "ground squirrels" belonging to *Spermophilus.* Contrariwise, residents in the Carolina pine barrens will think of a gopher as a burrowing tortoise, and in some places people refer to a particular snake as a gopher. One is reminded of how diversely the words "democratic" and "liberal" are used in different societies.

Stability in Latin nomenclature is arrived at by strict observance of the **Law of Priority.** By the time that the tenth edition of *Systema Naturae* ap-peared in 1758, Linnaeus had become so well known by his consistent appli-cation of binominal nomenclature that biologists agreed to use that particular edition as a starting point for recognizing the official names of creatures. Moreover, it was arbitrarily decided that this book should date from January 1, 1758.

Any Genus or species described after January 1, 1758, must be known by the first name given to it. When the same species is inadvertently described more than once, the later different names, when recognized as such, are sup-pressed as **synonyms** of the first name. When the same Latin words are used for two different species, the names are **homonyms.** In order to be sure whose Latin construction is under consideration, it is customary to write the name of the author after the generic or specific name and then to add the date of publication just to make absolutely sure of the citation. In this way, "*Leiorhyn-choidea* Cloud, 1944," means that a scientist by the name of Cloud described that Genus in 1944. If an author's name is sufficiently well known, his name may be abbreviated in the citation, as "*Spirifer* L., 1758," or "*Spirifer* Lin., 1758," the "L." or "Lin." meaning Linnaeus. The proper form for complete official names appears in the construction "*Meniscophyllum minutum* Simp-son, 1900." This means that the specific name *minutum* was first published in connection with *Meniscophyllum* by a scientist named Simpson in 1900. Very commonly the name of the author and the date are omitted when the data either are given elsewhere in the article or are not essential to the under-standing of the work (as in this text).

Commonly an author, when describing a new species, refers it to some particular Genus, but later workers find it necessary to transfer the species to another Genus for purposes of priority or merely because ideas on classification change. Biologists always indicate generic reassignment by placing the name of the author in parentheses. The citation *"Neozaphrentis tenella* (Miller, 1891)" means that Miller described a species in 1891; the specific name was *tenella,* but the generic name has been changed from something else (not apparent in the citation) to *Neozaphrentis.* (If Miller's 1891 publication is consulted, the curious systematist will find that Miller originally referred *tenella* to the Genus *Zaphrentis.*)

Some groups are studied in greater detail than are others and therefore require more careful subdivision in classification. In California, for instance, field geologists depend upon careful differentiation of fossil scallop shells to help them recognize subdivisions of the Tertiary strata. Many species of these scallops are now known which, although they all belong to *Pecten,* can be arranged into several groups on the basis of ornamentation. It is therefore desirable to erect a taxonomic category intermediate between species and Genus. In all such cases, Subgenera are created for the different groups, and the name of the Subgenus is enclosed in parentheses as *"Pecten (Lyropecten) magnolia* Conrad, 1857." It is also permissible to use either *Pecten magnolia* or *Lyropecten magnolia* for the species because most scientists will know what is meant.

When species are described, the author selects several specimens which show the range of variation. Some of these specimens he illustrates. These typical examples are called **type specimens,** and the single specimen which he cites as the average example is called the **holotype.** Holotypes are extremely valuable from a scientific standpoint because they constitute the absolute basis for understanding a species. A description may be erroneous, but the type specimens are valid by definition. Any subsequent scientist can restudy the type specimens when he wishes to verify a feature. Scientists agree that a species is what it truly is and, therefore, not necessarily what anyone says it is.

In all matters of nomenclature, paleontologists join with zoologists to follow rules and decisions laid down by the International Commission on Zoological Nomenclature. Deliberations of this committee of world-renowned scholars must be made official every four years when the International Zoological Congress meets.

FOSSILIZATION

Men had contemplated fossils for over 2000 years before they were in general agreement that fossils are natural remains of once living creatures rather than being inorganic, or freaks of nature, or supernatural objects. Although the tedious "fossil controversy" has been settled in the minds of all but the most implacably obstinate partisans since about 1800, many geologists still seem to be uncertain as to what material constitutes fossilized animals. At least the frequency with which pseudofossils are hopefully submitted to paleontologists for identification suggests that there is some indecision as to what constitutes a fossil. Common **pseudofossils** include septarian concretions, chert nodules, cone-in-cone, loess-dolls, bottom markings, dendrites, stylolites, clinkers, rillensteinen, conchoidal fractures, and travertine. To be sure, familiarity with members of the several Phyla generally enables geologists to select fossils in the field with intelligent confidence, but ignorance of the processes of fossilization on the part of the collector may still render a collection worthless because the necessary skeletal features may not be preserved. Thus, slabs bearing impressions of the exteriors of stony bryozoans are rarely instructive, but a uniformly calcified small fragment of such a bryozoan may be accurately identified. A spiral filling (**steinkern**) of a gastropod rarely can be identified even to Genus, but the internal mold of a trilobite is almost as good for identification as is the carapace itself. Accordingly, a careful collector needs to ask himself not only what features of a fossil are necessary for identification but whether or not the preservation of a particular specimen is potentially capable of providing information necessary for identification. Paleontologists, when driven by desperation, have sometimes become remarkably astute at determining stratigraphic position from fragmentary remains of fossils. Foraminiferal skeletons in some regions are so crushed and deformed along bedding planes that they cannot be referred to known species and Genera; nevertheless, nearly imponderable remains of this sort are sometimes referred to as "spots," the various shapes of which are discriminated one from another by numbers instead of by names.

In rare cases the actual soft tissues of animals have been preserved in ice or oil, or by desiccation. More commonly, soft parts and chitinous skeletons are preserved as films of carbon incrusting impressions of these tissues. Examples produced by the process of **carbonization** are represented by fossilized graptolites and leafy parts of plants. Two-dimensional materials such as these, whether carbonized or not, also produce slight indentations in the sediment which are commonly called **impressions.** Carbonization probably arises from the action of two agents—partial bacterial decomposition and distillation by heat which can be related to an increase in the thickness of overburden during sedimentation (the phenomenon of geothermal gradient) or to mountain building and vulcanism.

For all practical purposes, however, fossils occur as skeletal material or as impressions of skeletal material in sediments. In both cases alteration of the skeletal material begins immediately upon the death of the organism. If burial does not take place very quickly, the skeletal pieces become disassociated and reduced to sand by the abrasive action of currents or by the activities of scavengers. Assuming that burial does take place, then the skeletons are successively exposed to a variety of chemical environments as the overburden accumulates and interstitial water starts to migrate through pore spaces in the compacting sediments. Movement and chemical change in interstitial water can be visualized if a person imagines that an original marine deposit is lifted above sea level and truncated by erosion. Rainfall would then have access to the sediments and the original (connate) sea water would be flushed away by fresh water. Migrating masses of ground water are of different degrees of alkalinity or of acidity and contain various amounts of dissolved minerals which they acquire by solution as they flow along. Accordingly, both the sediments and the contained fossils are continually subject to alteration (**diagenesis**).

Most fossils originally consisted of calcium carbonate with minor admixtures of magnesium, phosphorus, strontium, and other salts. The principal noncalcareous fossils originally were composed of chitin. Chitin is a complex organic substance ($C_{32}H_{54}N_4O_{21}X$), from which the skeletons of insects are made, but it also occurs in other groups. Sometimes chitin is reinforced with calcium carbonate, as in the case of carapaces of crabs and lobsters. Chitin is not readily soluble in ground water, but it is destroyed by alkaline solutions and by bacterial activity.

The simplest change in fossils is **leaching,** in which calcium carbonate is progressively removed until the original pearly shell material becomes chalky. If the shell is removed altogether the void thus produced occurs between two **molds,** one on the outside and one on the inside where sediment has infiltrated hollow shells. Ordinarily molds make undesirable fossils because they are generally recovered incomplete or in coarse-grained sediments. On the other hand, molds in fine-grained sediment may record external features so faithfully that they are unusually valuable. It is customary to prepare **replicas** of the original shell from molds by squeezing gutta-percha or some clay into the cavity, or by filling molds with liquid rubber. These techniques enable a paleontologist to see delicate spines and other surficial sculpture which generally are lost from most other kinds of fossils.

If a void exists between internal and external molds, it can be filled with some mineral brought in naturally by ground water. In this way **casts** are formed. Casts commonly can be recognized because the mineral matter filled the voids by inwardly directed crystallization from the surfaces of the molds, and the terminations of euhedral crystals are visible in cross sections of the casts. Casts may provide accurate replicas of the surfaces of the original shell, but it is not possible to use casts for study of microstructure of the shell material proper. Calcite, dolomite, silica, gypsum, and pyrite are common minerals forming casts.

Minerals dissolved in ground water also may affect the original shell when it is still entombed in the sediment. Many porous skeletal parts, such as echinoderm plates, can be **indurated** by the deposition of more calcium carbonate in the open microscopic latticework of skeletal plates. Indurated fossils normally are heavier than their unaltered counterparts, but it is essentially impossible to tell them apart by their external appearances alone.

The last yet probably the most common and important method of fossilization is by **replacement.** In this process, the agent is again ground water, which transports some mineral compound in solution. It is not yet clear just why replacement operates the way it does, but the general fact seems to be that a molecule of the original shell substance is removed and its place is taken by a molecule of a new mineral compound. Original calcareous material is commonly replaced by dolomite or by silica and less commonly may be replaced by pyrite, marcasite, or hematite. Peculiar things about the process of replacement are that, although the process normally affects calcareous fossils, it may not alter the calcareous matrix around replaced fossils; or the process may affect brachiopod shells but not shells of other kinds of animals, such as gastropods, in the same block of rock. It is possible that very slight differences in trace compounds, or differences in crystallographic form or in orientation, must control the directiveness of replacement. It is known, for instance, that animals precipitate calcium carbonate in two polymorphic forms, calcite and aragonite. Aragonite is slightly more soluble in ground water than calcite is; therefore, aragonitic shells may be dissolved out of calcitix matrix, or aragonitic linings (such as some mother-of-pearl) may be dissolved out of pelecypod shells, thus leaving the calcitic layers behind. Moreover, the addition of small amounts of calcium phosphate to shells such as those of brachiopods renders them distinctly less soluble in ground water than are nonphosphatic shells.

It is likely that any shell subjected to the action of ground water has been affected by some replacement. It is very difficult to prove that the original calcium carbonate of a fossil has been replaced by other molecules of calcium carbonate (**calcification**) unless it is known that the original hard parts were composed of aragonite and the resulting fossil is composed of calcite. Moreover, the original skeletal tissues become indurated by calcite, and large pores in the shells also may be filled by calcite casts. Hence this common ensemble is produced by three processes of fossilization—replacement, induration, and filling of large voids.

Replacement by **dolomitization** is very similar to calcification because magnesium carbonate and calcium carbonate readily form a double salt ($MgCO_3 \cdot CaCO_3$), the properties of which resemble calcite. When a little magnesium carbonate is present in the double salt it is very difficult to recognize the effects of dolomitization, but when magnesium carbonate dominates the compound, dolomitization is readily recognizable. Most dolomitized fossils have a characteristic silky sheen in reflected light and their surfaces, as viewed with a hand lens, are covered with tiny rhombic crystals. Rhombic dolomite is the normal crystal form; but calcite crystals normally are terminated by scalenohedrons, and rhombic calcite crystals are rather rare. Thorough dolomitization usually affects the matrix as well as the fossils. Inasmuch as the process not only involves volumetric changes but also seems to go hand in hand with recrystallization, dolomitized fossils commonly are distorted or are intergrown with their matrix. Consequently, preservation of delicate microscopic features should not be expected in dolomitized fossils. The major exception to poor preservation resulting from dolomitization takes place on the sea floor in warm water while the sediments are being deposited. This is a form of **penecontemporaneous replacement,** that is, "almost at the same time" as primary dolomitization; this condition is in contrast to secondary dolomitization which results from action of ground water.

Pyritization produces attractive fossils such as occur in the Tully limestone of New York and in association with coal beds at many places. Unfortunately, pyritized fossils are opaque and therefore are difficult to use for the study of microscopic features. Moreover, pyrite commonly is accompanied by the ferrous iron sulfide, marcasite, which first decomposes to form an iron alum and then expands and breaks up the fossils as the alum becomes hydrated.

Either ferrous or ferric iron oxides (limonite and hematite) may replace fossils, but these compounds are rarely encountered except in the well-known Clinton iron ore of the Appalachians. Fossils and oolites in that sedimentary rock have been neatly altered to hematite. More commonly, however, fossils composed of iron oxide are pseudomorphs after pyrite or marcasite.

Silicification in limestone commonly affects only the fossils without altering the calcareous matrix. Therefore, silicified fossils can be recovered as an insoluble residue from limestone blocks which have been digested by weak acids. Fossils from insoluble residues not only retain the most delicate ornamentation, but the interior as well as the exterior features are readily observable. Dentition of bivalves, the loops and spires of brachiopods, growth stages of arthropods, and muscle scars of many groups are more readily seen in silicified residues than in material which has been prepared by hand. Increased attention is being devoted to silicified fossils as systematists use smaller and smaller differences for the discrimination of species. For instance, paleontologists cooperating in the restudy of the Permian faunas of Texas have processed about 12 tons of limestone blocks through acid vats in order to obtain the best possible material for study. Oddly enough, some disadvantage arises from having extraordinarily good collections, for criteria based upon such superior material may not be applicable on other occasions to specimens of even better than average preservation.

Silicification seems to progress from the exterior of a specimen to the interior. When silicification takes place only in a surficial layer less than 1 centimeter thick on an outcrop, the exposed portion of a fossil may be thoroughly silicified but the buried portion of the same fossil may retain its calcareous composition. In other instances specimens may be thoroughly silicified several feet back into a stratum. Silicification commonly involves an intermediate stage of completion in which delicate felted mats of acicular quartz crystals occupy much of the mass of the fossil. In other cases the silica gathers in concentric layers to form intergrown, botryoidal, or ringlike clusters of spherules 1 or 2 millimeters in diameter which are called **Liesegang rings** or **Beekite rings**. These rings sometimes are mistaken for oolites or for foraminifers. In the most extreme examples of silicification the silica may obliterate all but the vaguest traces of the original fossil. In less extreme cases it may be difficult to differentiate between silicified fossils and casts composed of silica.

Occasionally **tracks, trails, borings**, and **burrows** are discovered. Animals such as worms may ingest large quantities of sediment and then void the material in contorted strings called **castings**. In like fashion fecal matter termed **coprolites** may occur as pellets or as small patches of disassociated organic debris on otherwise unfossiliferous bedding planes. All of these phenomena are classed as fossils although they constitute only indirect evidence of life.

In some cases two or more methods of fossilization operate to produce a fossil specimen. Thus, limestone molds may be replaced so that a fossil may be represented by a dolomitized mold or by a silicified mold. It is important for a field geologist to recognize the manner of preservation and the composition of shells or molds when he collects them so that he can select material suitable for identification in the laboratory.

METHODS IN PALEONTOLOGY

A paleontologist is primarily a historian whose task is to arrange the multitude of fossil species in orderly fashion according to how he interprets natural laws. Classification is related to the deciphering process, for it segregates the chaotic mass of species into similar-appearing groups which are called species and Genera. A paleontologist seldom can prove that he is dealing with a species as long as species are defined in some way such as "an interbreeding population." Instead, a paleontologist can only collect shells from a bed and then define a species as that group whose members resemble each other more than they resemble members of any other group. He may be confident that his "species" has every attribute possessed by an analogous living "species," but he also has to rely to a certain degree on faith that members of the group had a blood relationship in life. The result is that paleontologists deal fundamentally with physical changes in form or distribution, and then they interpret these changes as evidence of specific difference. It is apparent, however, that the majority of biologically trained scientists now accept such physical changes as being proof of systematic genetic change —that is, of organic evolution.

The foregoing remarks may help to explain the peculiar dilemma of paleontologists that in trying to understand genetic changes they must deal to a large extent with nongenetic changes. This dilemma explains the consistent preoccupation of paleontologists with arranging things in orderly systems of various kinds. A paleontologist draws upon his training in physical geology when he arranges his materials into **stratigraphic series**, **geographic series**, and **environmental series**; or he draws upon training in biologic sciences when he arranges species into **developmental series**, **morphologic series**, and **evolutionary series**. By arranging as many series as possible, a paleontologist hopes to learn enough about the several species of a fossil fauna so that they constitute a harmonious assemblage having attributes of a living population.

Stratigraphic Series

The stratigraphic series commonly is the easiest to arrange because it is based upon application of the elementary Law of Superposition. In structurally simple regions, such as prevail in much of the midcontinent, collections of fossils can be made from successively higher beds in a stratigraphic succession and then classified into Genera and species. From this information it is possible to establish the vertical extent or **stratigraphic range** of each species. Finally, species which are abundant and are easily identified can be chosen to typify that portion of the stratigraphic succession in which they occur. In this fashion a series of **faunal zones** is established as the units in a stratigraphic series. A faunal zone consists of a bed or a succession of beds which contains a particular recognizable assemblage of fossils. It is customary to name faunal zones after the name of a characteristic fossil in the assemblage—thus we recognize the *Olenellus* zone in the Cambrian of many countries or the *Nonionella cockfieldensis* zone in the Tertiary of the Gulf Coastal Plain. Names for successive zones may be derived from any common fossils in the assemblages; therefore successive zones of one stratigraphic series may bear names derived from a brachiopod, a sponge, a gastropod, two bryozoans, and another brachiopod. Or another stratigraphic series may consist entirely of names of foraminifers or of graptolites. It is all a matter of convenience. Stratigraphic series are employed very commonly in applied paleontology as devices for purposes of rapid correlation. They can be set up for very adequate local use by any stratigraphic paleontologist who has studied a region, and the zones can be recognized by anyone who can identify fossils in an assemblage.

Stratigraphic ranges are made known by collecting from numerous localities. There is no reason why different species in the same fauna should have the same stratigraphic ranges inasmuch as they can have originated at different times, evolved at different rates, and constantly migrated back and forth in response to their need for perfect adjustment to their changing environments. When new information is consistent with previous knowledge, there is justification for making stratigraphic range charts such as are shown graphically in Figures 1.5 and 1.6. The two examples have been chosen in order to illustrate the relationship of stratigraphic ranges of fossils to formations in regions of very different sedimentation and environment.

Formations shown in Figure 1.5 exemplify the widespread, persistent, blanket type of sediments which accumulated in the central part of the continents, particularly during the Paleozoic Era. Individual formations shown in the figure rarely exceed 100 feet (30 m) in thickness. Physical characteristics of the formations (such as lithology, thickness, and position in the succession) enable one to subdivide the succession in more detail than one can by using paleontologic data. The advantage of physical criteria in this case is shown by the fact that stratigraphic ranges of most of the fossils shown in the figure cross several formational boundaries. Correlation of formations such as these, within one basin of deposition, is about as uncomplicated as it can be if one is able to see a sequence of several lithologic units. Paleontologic assistance in recognizing formations under the foregoing circumstances is necessary only when outcrops are far apart, small outcrops are available, or the strata have been extensively faulted and folded. Data shown in Figure 1.5 indicate that only the Golconda formation and the Renault limestone (of Illinois) are readily recognizable paleontologically, although the Chester Series could be subdivided into three ascending groups which are characterized by the range of *Talarocrinus,* the overlap of *Camarophoria explanata* and *Eumetria vera,* and the range of *Spirifer increbescens.*

Formations shown in Figure 1.6 typify the extremely variable formations of the Tertiary System in California. Thousands of feet of sandstone at one locality may be represented by an equal or different thickness of shale at another locality only a few miles distant. Under these circumstances it is in most cases almost impossible to recognize lithologic units over much area, so formational names have tended to fall into disuse and to be supplanted by Age or Stage divisions. These latter divisions bear geographic names based upon outcrops containing the species characteristic of two or more zones of foraminifers. In Figure 1.6 the zonation based upon gastropods, pelecypods, and echinoids is also shown. It is convenient to use the megafossils for corre-

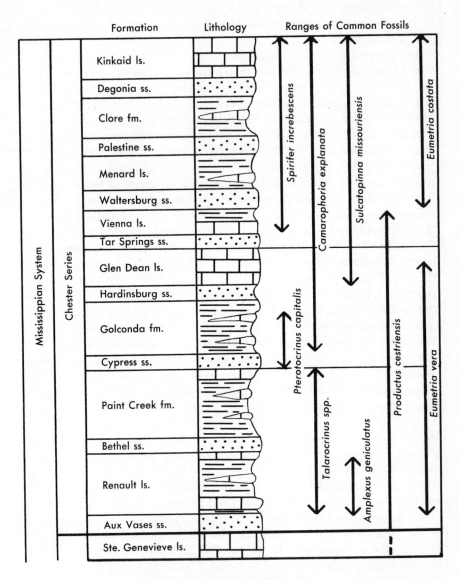

Figure 1.5. Ranges of Fossils in the Continental Interior.
    Stratigraphic succession and vertical ranges of some common fossils are shown in the Chester Series (Upper Mississippian) of the Eastern Interior Coal Basin (Illinois, Indiana, and Kentucky). Stratigraphic thickness is between 1000 and 1500 feet (330 to 500 m). (Based on data from Weller, et al., 1948.)

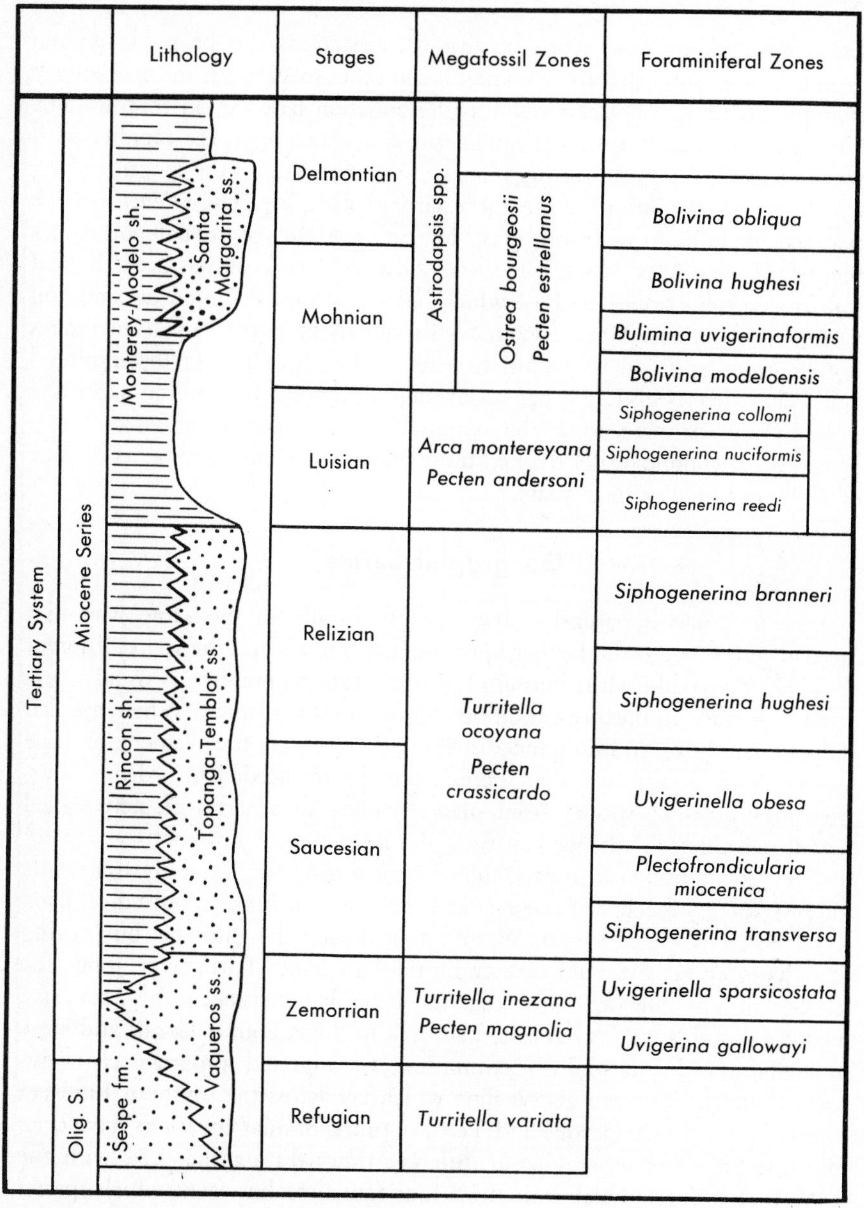

	Lithology	Stages	Megafossil Zones	Foraminiferal Zones
	Monterey-Modelo sh. / Santa Margarita ss.	Delmontian	*Astrodapsis* spp. / *Ostrea bourgeosii* *Pecten estrellanus*	
				Bolivina obliqua
		Mohnian		*Bolivina hughesi*
				Bulimina uvigerinaformis
				Bolivina modeloensis
		Luisian	*Arca montereyana* *Pecten andersoni*	*Siphogenerina collomi*
				Siphogenerina nuciformis
				Siphogenerina reedi
	Rincon sh. / Topanga-Temblor ss.	Relizian	*Turritella ocoyana*	*Siphogenerina branneri*
				Siphogenerina hughesi
		Saucesian	*Pecten crassicardo*	*Uvigerinella obesa*
				Plectofrondicularia miocenica
				Siphogenerina transversa
	Vaqueros ss.	Zemorrian	*Turritella inezana* *Pecten magnolia*	*Uvigerinella sparsicostata*
				Uvigerina gallowayi
	Sespe fm.	Refugian	*Turritella variata*	

Left margin labels: **Tertiary System** — **Miocene Series**; **Olig. S.**

Figure 1.6. Ranges of Fossils in the Pacific Coast.
The highly variable stratigraphic succession of part of the Tertiary of California is shown graphically, along with mollusc and echinoid megafossil zones and the standard foraminiferal zones. The succession is locally as much as 18,000 feet (6000 m) thick. (Based on data from Kleinpell, 1938.)

lation when doing field work because identifications can be made on the spot. It is interesting that the zonation based upon megafossils in the Tertiary example depicted is not as refined as the zonation based upon foraminifers. The time included in different faunal zones depends upon the rapidity with which a particular group of organisms evolved and upon the length during which suitable conditions existed at a particular locality. The *Olenellus* zone spanned 25 million years or more, but some Mesozoic cephalopod zones represent only 300,000 years. The Ordovician of New York has been divided into 20 graptolite zones, each of which has an average duration of 3 million years. The common Mississippian fossils shown in Figure 1.5 have ranges lasting from 1 million to 7 million years, and each of the 14 foraminiferal zones shown on Figure 1.6 has an average duration of 1 million years. As a very rough estimate, it can be assumed that stratigraphic series of fossils consist of paleontologically defined units which represent increments of time of the order of 3 million years.

Geographic Series

Ancient faunas apparently varied geographically in the same way that Recent faunas do, so the farther apart the two faunas are, the more different they are. Geographic distribution of animals (**zoogeography**) is usually presented on maps to portray conditions at one instant of time. When coupled with the study of stratigraphic distribution, however, the element of time assumes such significance that successive maps are needed in order to illustrate movement of species from place to place in a series of steps called **faunal migration.** Thus, we can trace the migration of numerous groups of invertebrates southward toward the equator during the late Cenozoic while the Ice Age approached. *Pecten (Patinopecten) caurinus,* for instance, lived as far north as Puget Sound, Washington, during the Pliocene, but during the Pleistocene it lived no farther north than Santa Barbara at about the latitude of Los Angeles. Now that the extensive Pleistocene glaciers have melted again this species has migrated back to Puget Sound. Corals and large multichambered foraminifers (nummulites) migrated progressively westward along the Tethyan geosyncline which lay across the southern Eurasian continent during Cretaceous and Tertiary times. Similar invasions have been recorded for different regions at different times during the past, with the result that we customarily recognize four **faunal realms** from which species migrated into North America. The Atlantic and Indo-Pacific faunal realms bound the continent on the east and west, whereas the Arctic and Mediterranean faunal realms lie to the north and south.

In addition, every region seems to have its own native faunas which comprise the **endemic population.** *Archimedes,* a peculiar screw-shaped axis of a bryozoan, is an endemic midwestern American Genus in the Mississippian, but it migrated westward to Nevada by Pennsylvanian time and entered the Indo-Pacific faunal realm, finally reaching Russia where it became extinct in the Permian.

Aucella is a characteristic Jurassic and Cretaceous clam which occasionally migrated down into both the United States and Russia from the northern polar regions. It would be erroneous to consider this Arctic species as necessarily indicating a cold-water fauna, however, so the word **boreal** is used to signify any northern fauna and **austral** is used to indicate any southern fauna, irrespective of what climate existed at a particular time.

Estimates of the rate of faunal migration are very important paleontologically because they help us to understand whether species can populate a considerable area in a geologically short interval of time. The faunal zones established by stratigraphic studies are conceived of primarily as time zones; hence, their validity is only as good as the speed with which their respective populations migrated. It has become apparent to paleontologists that the most widespread faunas are composed of graptolites and cephalopods, both of which were capable of drifting freely on the ocean currents whether they were alive or dead. Inasmuch as the equatorial current flows about 15 nautical miles a day, it would be theoretically possible for a specimen suspended in that current to have drifted around the world in four years. It should be remembered, of course, that there were few continental obstructions near the equator during much of geologic time.

On the other hand, bottom-dwelling organisms are known to migrate rather slowly, except when their larval forms are carried by oceanic currents. Perhaps the classic example in which the rate of migration has been measured is that of the common periwinkle, *Littorina littorea*. This periwinkle is naturally endemic to Europe, but probably was transported to North America on the bottoms of ships. It was first discovered in the western hemisphere along the coast of Nova Scotia in 1840. By 1892 specimens had been discovered as far south as Atlantic City, New Jersey. In 52 years the species had spread along 750 miles of coastline, which means that it migrated at the rate of about 15 miles per year. At this rate, *Littorina littorea* is theoretically able to migrate a distance equal to the circumference of the earth in about 1700 years. Inasmuch as estimates of the average rates of marine sedimentation range between 1 foot in 800 and 1 foot in 2500 years, it follows that a faunal zone characterized by any species with the migratory capability of *Littorina littorea* could spread around the world while only a foot of sediment was accumulating. Therefore, faunal migrations within sedimentary basins, and even between adjacent sedimentary basins, are, for all practical purposes, considered by paleontologists to have taken place instantaneously.

Environmental Series

Faunas which inhabit different environments characteristically are different. For instance, differences due to change in depth usually are apparent in a short distance, but changes in faunas at the same depth may only occur over a great horizontal distance. Inasmuch as depth zones intersect the ocean floor approximately parallel with coastlines, fossil bottom-dwelling faunas can be traced parallel with ancient shorelines more readily than they can be traced progressively farther offshore.

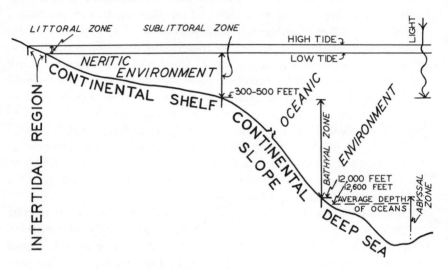

Figure 1.7. Marine Environments and Depth Zones.
Named portions of the sea floor, depth zones, and marine environments are shown on a generalized diagram of a continental margin. No definite vertical or horizontal scales are implied, except that the vertical scale is exaggerated. (Adapted from Hedgpeth, 1957.)

Environmental (also called bionomic) classifications are based upon the adaptations of creatures. Thus, we find that living invertebrates are marine, fresh water, or terrestrial; they inhabit shallow or deep water; they prefer cool or warm water; they require normally saline sea water or they can tolerate various salinities; they like clean or muddy water, firm or soft substratum, light or dark surroundings, and quiet or turbulent waters.

Most of the important invertebrate groups other than insects are marine; therefore, the marine realm has been subdivided on the basis of several varying physical properties. Subdivisions of the sea floor, depth zones, and the marine environments are shown in Figure 1.7. The sea floor consists of the **intertidal region, continental shelf, continental slope,** and **deep sea,** plus a variety of depressions and high regions which render the topography of the sea floor nearly as irregular as that of the land surface.

Corresponding to the regions of the sea floor are depth zones of the overlying water. These are the **littoral zone,** which extends between high tide and low tide; the **sublittoral zone,** which extends down to the outer edge of the continental shelf at a depth of between 300 and 600 feet, depending upon local conditions; the **bathyal zone,** extending down to 6000 or 12,000 feet, depending upon which of two main usages is followed; and the **abyssal zone,** which comprises waters deeper than the bathyal zone. Inasmuch as the average depth of the oceans is near 12,000 feet, it seems desirable to consider this depth figure as the upper limit of the bathyal zone.

The waters of the oceans which overlie the continental shelf comprise the **neritic environment,** and the waters of the open ocean beyond the break in slope of the shelf comprise the **oceanic environment.** Marine animals and plants are especially abundant in the upper 600 feet of the oceans because that is the region in which most of the sun's radiant energy is concentrated. Accordingly, most marine animals also inhabit the sublittoral depth zone, dwell within the neritic environment, and may rest upon the continental shelf. Moreover, the creatures that lived in the ancient seas which flooded the continents generally seem to resemble those creatures which inhabit the present neritic environment; hence, the neritic environment is being carefully studied today for evidence which will help to interpret sediments and animals of the geologic past. In some cases it is convenient to classify marine animals according to their relationship to their environment. Thus, **benthos,** or benthonic animals such as corals, rest upon the sea floor; **nekton** is composed of active swimmers such as cephalopods; and **plankton** consists of floaters such as jellyfish. Many other categories are recognized, but there is much difference of opinion about the definition of most of the bionomic terms, including those shown in Figure 1.7.

Ordinarily there has been little interest in arranging various creatures in actual series based upon their differing adaptations. Instead, biologists have been greatly impressed by the tenacity with which a certain species or even a group will confine itself to one set of conditions. This widespread environmental stability has led paleontologists more often to recognizing an individual environment than to demonstrating shifts of environment. In fact, the stability factor probably has been overemphasized if expressions such as "the present is the key to the past" are interpreted to mean that creatures never have changed their environmental position. There is no reason to doubt that natural laws which operate today are the same laws which operated in the past, but conditions of the present and the past are not the same. Accordingly, glass sponges migrated out of the sublittoral zone where they lived in Early

Paleozoic time into the bathyal and abyssal zones where they may be found today.

Fossil invertebrates are assigned one or another bionomic status according to how closely the fossil animal resembles its living counterpart. Unfortunately, resemblance of extinct organisms and living organisms decreases approximately in proportion to the length of time which separates them, so it is difficult or impossible to decide which environment was preferred by some creatures. Nevertheless, ancient faunas usually contain some animals whose habits can be guessed, so the results of paleontologic studies have been used for over 100 years to determine marine versus fresh-water conditions, and shallow versus deep water. During this time a great body of data has been assembled which indicates that most marine sediments entombed animals which lived in less than 1000 feet (300 m) of water. This interpretation usually applies equally well to thick accumulations of sediments in geosynclines along the margins of continents and to widespread thin sedimentary blankets and broad basinal deposits of the continental interior.

Some notable exceptions are known to the general rule of neritic faunas, for paleontologists have been accumulating faunal evidence which indicates that some Cenozoic sediments were deposited in water 5000 feet (1500 m) or more deep. Examples are to be found on the seaward margin of the Gulf Coastal Plain and in the centers of small but deep coastal basins on the Pacific Coast such as the Los Angeles Basin. It is now recognized that there is so much variation in sediments (**lithofacies**) and so much variation in faunas (**biofacies**) between neritic and bathyal zones that neither the sediments nor the fossils may resemble each other enough to warrant direct comparisons. Instead, detailed studies of the relationship of creatures to their environment (**ecology**) are necessary before the geologic record can be interpreted intelligently. More attention has been devoted to studying biofacies along the Gulf Coast in Texas and in Louisiana than at any other place in North America, although considerable emphasis is now being given to these studies in California. Geologists on the Gulf Coast are interested in biofacies because there is an intimate relationship between organisms and lithofacies; and, to complete the story, it is widely believed that oil accumulation in sediments of the Gulf Coastal Plain is largely confined to lithofacies of the neritic region. The relationships between lithofacies and several zones of foraminifers (*Marginulina, Heterostegina,* and four zones of *Discorbis*) are shown in Figure 1.8. Although wells 1 and 3 on the diagram will penetrate similar thicknesses of continental sediments, and both will enter the same neritic lithofacies, well 3 will test a much greater thickness of strata than will be tested by well 1. The function of a micropaleontologist working on the Gulf Coastal Plain is to advise drilling contractors of the strata which can be expected ahead of the drill and whether or not the well is passing

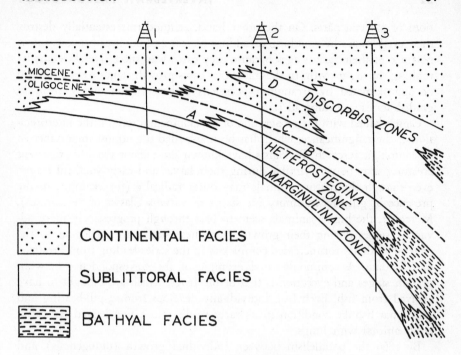

Figure 1.8.   Foraminiferal Zones on the Gulf Coastal Plain.
Cross section of part of the Oligocene and Miocene (Anahuac—Upper Catahoula) deposits in Texas and Louisiana showing lithofacies and foraminiferal zones. Thickening of the sequence is toward the Gulf of Mexico. Positions of three drill holes are indicated by numbers. Curvature of the dashed line represents post-Oligocene down-warping. The A part of the *Discorbis* zones is the lateral equivalent of the upper part of the *Heterostegina* zone, but the B, C, and D portions of the *Discorbis* zones occupied positions above the *Heterostegina* zone during the marine regression. (After Lowman, 1949.)

through lithofacies of the age and environmental condition known to produce oil nearby. Studies of the distribution of planktonic or benthonic fossils in regions of noteworthy marine transgressions and regressions include some of the most valuable and complex investigations now being carried on by paleontologists.

Developmental Series

Growth stages comprise the simplest biologic series because successive stages can be placed in the correct order by observing living animals. Growth of an animal throughout its life usually is called its **ontogeny.** Growth stages of many extinct animals are preserved in several ways. Early stages of snails and bivalved animals are preserved at the apex or beak of a shell, but early stages of ammonoids and corals may be concealed beneath later accumulations of skeletal parts. On the other hand, echinoderms essentially destroy their early stages by resorbing or adding plates; and adult arthropods retain no trace of their early stages because they cast away successive skeletons by molting during growth. In these last two cases growth stages sometimes can be approximated by arranging specimens collected from one stratum in graded series according to size.

Closely allied with the recognition of developmental series is the interpretation of their significance, which has been accorded the utmost importance in paleontologic research. Biologists have known since about 1800 that different creatures may be very similar during their larval and early youthful stages, even though the mature animals may differ radically (for example, in the presence of gill slits in embryonic stages of various Classes of vertebrates). Moreover, the higher animals seem to pass through progressively more advanced stages during their growth; and these stages are analogous to the general tendency for increased complexity in the series leading from Protozoa to Chordata. A commonly cited example of the correspondence between growth stages and evolution is that of the frogs, which are thought to have evolved from fish. Each frog individually develops from a gill-bearing and somewhat fishlike condition in its early youth into a four-legged terrestrial adult animal with lungs.

By 1866 the parallelism between individual growth (**ontogenesis**) and racial development (**phylogenesis**) was formalized as a natural law by the eminent German zoologist, Ernst Haeckel. The most important proposition in Haeckel's doctrine (otherwise known as the Biogenetic Law) is that "ontogenesis is a recapitulation of phylogenesis." Haeckel further suggested that the mature characters of one generation are succeeded in later generations by even more advanced characters so that the former adult stage tends to be pushed backward into earlier and earlier growth stages as time progresses. Eventually the early adult characters should be represented in the larval stages, and the history of the race should be written in the growth stages.

Unfortunately, detailed investigations of early growth stages, especially by embryologists, have revealed several flaws in the "theory of recapitulation." In the first place, the crowding of stages may become so severe that many stages are omitted during the short larval period of representatives of some groups and thus the record becomes erratically incomplete. Second, new stages in some cases originate during the larval period—perhaps as a response to adaptive requirements—which never were present in ancestral adult forms. Third, stages may appear in the wrong order in the larval period. So impressive were these and other objections to the theory of recapitulation that by 1900 many zoologists had essentially abandoned the theory as being unworkable. In fact, this negative attitude persists in many quarters.

Many, if not most, paleontologists, on the other hand, have found much in the recapitulation theory which is attractive and useful, although they may not subscribe to the theory in exactly its original form. Instead, many paleontologists and zoologists believe that recapitulation generally applies to development of specific organs and commonly applies to over-all growth of individuals. They maintain that the essential features of phylogeny should be expected in ontogeny, although specific minor departures from the rule may take place. In particular, paleontologists have been swayed by the evidence presented by students of cephalopods. Numerous races of ammonites, in particular, seem to offer monumental proof that the individuals pass through stages in their youth which were characteristic of the race in earlier times. Moreover, there is strong stratigraphic support for recapitulation among ammonites because successive fossils in proposed evolutionary sequences occur in progressively younger deposits. Similar noteworthy evidence has been adduced from the study of some corals, graptolites, brachiopods, and several other invertebrate groups, but is almost lacking among trilobites and ostracodes, for instance.

It is no exaggeration to say that the theory of recapitulation has had more effect upon paleontologic thought than has any doctrine aside from that of organic evolution itself. Moreover, while some zoologists were developing apprehensions about recapitulation, most paleontologists were assembling more and more developmental series which seemed to support recapitulation. Insofar as most paleontologic interpretations have been concerned, it was better to explain exceptions to the rule as being special adaptations, or in some other way being unusual, rather than to challenge the accumulating mass of supporting data. In all fairness, however, it should be pointed out that some paleontologists continue to be skeptical of the validity of any series based upon recapitulation. The bases of some classic vertebrate lineages have been shaken or disproved, and several recent students of cephalopods and trilobites find no value for their studies in the theory of recapitulation. Under these circumstances, investigations into the validity of the Biogenetic Law remain a fertile field for research.

Morphologic Series

A morphologic series is a group of organisms arranged in arbitrary fashion in order to show a systematic change in some anatomical or skeletal feature. Next to arranging species in progressive stratigraphic sequence, perhaps the most common function of a paleontologist is to organize fossils into morphologic series. Series of this kind ordinarily are based upon change in size, shape, spinosity, or the number of some ornamental or skeletal features such as ribs, segments, or lobes. In its most elementary condition a morphologic series is merely a working hypothesis concerning possible steps which a succession of species might have followed during an evolutionary progression. A morphologic series does not contain any implication of actual descent or genetic relation, although genetic relation is not necessarily excluded. Perhaps the arbitrary nature of a morphologic series is best understood by noting that the species which illustrate a changing feature may or may not belong to the same Genus and may or may not come from successive stratigraphic units. In its most perfected state a morphologic series assumes the status of an evolutionary series, for all evolutionary series are morphologic series; but only an evolutionary series can be proved to be within a genetic lineage.

Evolutionary Series

An evolutionary series represents the peak of scientific accomplishment in organizing fossil invertebrates. It purports to show an orderly progression in morphologic changes among related creatures during successive intervals of time. Starting with an admittedly hypothetical morphologic series, a paleontologist selects for each stage those specimens which also comprise a stratigraphic series. He tries to use specimens from the same faunal realm, and he may even be able to check his work by studying the systematic changes which take place in early developmental stages of species. Refinement in the selection of specimens is continued by a succession of approximations so long as new information and material become available, until an orderly series seems to have been arranged.

Much of the difficulty about accepting evolutionary lineages arises because of the nature of the proof required. If genetic proof is the only acceptable basis, then evolution seems doomed to remain an abstraction. On the other hand, if systematic modification of living varying organisms in ways harmonious with all natural laws is accepted as proof, then evolutionary lineages are capable of proof.

Evolutionary series of fossil organisms have been subjected to three kinds of criticism. First, they are primarily morphologic series which might be ingeniously assembled using only those individuals in a plexus of similar animals which support a hypothetical sequence and leaving out the numerous equivocal and problematical individuals which do not seem to fit the series. Second, the lineages which are being proposed usually are suggested by an evolutionary theory, yet the lineages purport to prove the theory—thus representing reasoning in a circle. Third, changes in appearance of organisms in successive overlying beds usually are thought to reflect progressive descent, yet species are known to live so long that an ancestral species and its descendant species can persist side by side through an appreciable thickness of strata. In view of this it is possible in the accidents of field work to collect only the ancestor from high beds and only the descendant from low beds in a sequence, thus imparting inverted evidence on the direction of modification! In spite of these objections, evidence continues to accumulate which supports most evolutionary series. Scientists have faith in the validity of the method as long as consistent concepts of morphologic, stratigraphic, geographic, environmental, and theoretical evolutionary lineages are maintained. When flaws in proposed evolutionary series have been revealed, scientists have made necessary rearrangements or have abandoned the particular series as being invalid.

EVOLUTIONARY THEORY

Darwinian Evolution

It has been just a hundred years since Darwin presented an orderly arrangement of the factors which have generally come to be accepted as the demonstration of organic evolution. After the theory was proposed scientists expected that the fossil record would afford indisputable proof of descent with modification. It was even hoped that stratigraphic columns could be divided into great zones in which the Phyla were represented in orderly succession with the Protozoa at the bottom and the progressively more advanced Phyla in successively younger deposits. By now, however, it must be apparent to all interested scientists that fossils were not preserved in sufficient abundance for adequate study until the beginning of the Cambrian, by which time many of the major events in organic evolution had already taken place. Paleontologists, therefore, rarely deal with evolution of the grandest groups, but must pay close attention to detail in order to discern how one dominant group yields in time to the dominance of its descendants. Paleontologists have enjoyed some gratifying results at this task. In the course of innumerable studies of myriad kinds of animals, paleontologists have revealed incontrovertible evidence of the systematic modification of groups of organisms during the passage of time.

Naturally, paleontologists, in believing that they are dealing with evolutionary series, try to understand the process of organic evolution by reference to the so-called factors in the Darwinian theory. All of these factors bear upon fossil as well as living organisms. The basic theory can be combined into a few factors which can be arranged into a logical order as follows:

1. Heredity
2. Variation
3. Prodigality
4. Competition
5. Natural selection and survival of the fittest

HEREDITY

Heredity is the constancy factor in evolution. It is the obvious manifestation that like begets like. We accept the factor of heredity as a fact and use simple ratios to predict results in hybridization experiments such as are used to advance agricultural science; but heredity has not been understood this well very long. In fact, Darwin had to accept heredity without understanding it at all because Mendel did not publish the first laws of inheritance until three years after Darwin published the *Origin of Species*. Moreover, Mendel's results lay unheeded in an obscure journal until the article was "discovered" in 1890.

VARIATION

Variation is the tendency toward change in nature. Although like begets like, offspring of the same parents are generally so different as to be readily identified. There is a simile which implies that two things "are alike as two peas in a pod." But peas in the same pod are commonly unlike; indeed, it was from actually observing differences in peas that Mendel derived the laws of inheritance.

It appears that creatures vary in all sorts of ways, as if a species were at the center of an explosion. In this way some variants are "good," some are "bad," and some are "indifferent." Darwin thought that the myriad little plus-and-minus variations, such as large bodily size versus small size, were the material changes which enabled evolution to take place. Darwin called these fluctuating variations, and other biologists have called them indeterminate variations. It is known now that many of the fluctuating variations are noninheritable and are therefore extraneous to the evolution theory. Two kinds of large genetic variations, however, are thought to be significant in evolution. **Indefinite variation** is the tendency of an organism to vary genetically in numerous ways, some of which may provide the organism with competitive advantages. Thus, a parent species inhabiting water of moderate depth may produce a range of numerous variants, one end point of which is capable of moving into deeper water and the other end point of which is capable of inhabiting shallower water than the parent group can. **Definite variation** is the consistent genetic tendency of some feature of an organism to vary in a particular direction. For example, progressive increase in size is a common definite variation.

PRODIGALITY

Prodigality is the factor of abundance of life. Darwin relied to a great extent upon prodigality because he was greatly impressed by the concept of overabundance as expressed by Malthus in his essay "On Population." According to the Malthusian principle, creatures reproduce at rates far in excess of the capacity of the world to support them. Spectacular population dynamics can be envisaged if one contemplates what would happen if all the progeny of some simple organism survived and reproduced at the same rate as the parent, thus creating a geometric increase which soon would reach astronomic proportions. Obviously, something happens to reduce the number of offspring that survive to adulthood.

The prodigality concept has an additional application in paleontology, for it helps to explain the successful dispersal of marine organisms in numbers such as enable them to be collected over considerable areas. A fossil, in order to be useful in correlations, must be common and widespread, so prodigality bears directly on these qualities.

COMPETITION

We are led inevitably from the Malthusian principle of overpopulation into the factor of competition, or struggle for existence. Creatures struggle for space, food, air, light, moisture, and all the commodities necessary for growth, reproduction, and dispersal. Biologically the struggle of a dense patch of seedlings for survival is identical in import with the competition among multitudes of oyster spat for the few clean objects on which to settle and with the demand of overpopulated countries for resources and tillable land. Some struggles take place silently and essentially inadvertently, whereas others involve willful violence.

NATURAL SELECTION

Some creatures vary in some slight degree from the average of their fellows and thereby are able to start growth sooner, grow faster, assimilate food and moisture quicker, run more swiftly, react sooner, or do any one or more of the myriad things living organisms do in such a way that they have an advantage over their fellows. This is to say that they are better adapted for some condition or conditions than are their fellow creatures. Accordingly, from having an advantage, their chances of survival are improved. Obviously, the race is propagated only by the survivors, or, to word it another way, by the best-adapted creatures. Natural selection is the tendency of variations to survive according to their degree of adaptation to natural conditions. As applied to changes in faunas, the factor of natural selection can be viewed in two ways. If the environment of the home area remains constant, then the species will be dispersed into new environments if the variants are adapted to those environments. In this case the typical form stays in the same area; variant forms move away into new areas. On the other hand, if there are advances or retreats of the oceans, the typical species must migrate with changing conditions. The variants, on the other hand, might be adapted to the new conditions which came into existence and might remain in the home area. In general, under natural selection, indefinite variation is apt to encourage diversity, whereas definite variation is apt to lead to restrictions.

SURVIVAL OF THE FITTEST

This factor is so intimately related to natural selection that the subject of survival has already been mentioned in the foregoing section. Survival of the best adapted is another way of interpreting survival of the fittest, for fitness in evolution generally means being fit for some place in the balance of nature. In essence, however, survival serves only one biologic purpose, and that is reproduction of the species. Whereupon the Darwinian logic can be applied anew to the next generation.

Mutation Theory

According to the Darwinian theory, evolution progressed by a succession of minute changes, through numerous generations, over a long period of time. Contrasted with this is the mutation theory of Hugo De Vries, which explains how a new species can originate by one great change, in one generation, over just one year or reproductive period. De Vries was a Dutch experimental botanist who observed (about 1890), among a population of evening primroses, that some plants produced "sports" or "saltations" which not only differed significantly from the other plants of a new generation but comprised a pure genetic strain. These new forms, which he ranked as species, he called mutants—hence the mutation theory. At first it was supposed by some biologists that perhaps Darwin's evolutionary theory might be replaced by that of De Vries, but current ideas are that both theories are valid and are complementary to each other. De Vries' theory shows that variations of any magnitude can take place, and Darwin's theory shows how variants can be preserved.

It is probable that the causative mechanism of variation is now known because man has been able to produce variations artificially with high intensity radiation. It is likely that cosmic rays have been a significant factor in evolution throughout geologic time because cosmic rays constantly bombard the genes of living cells at the present and presumably always have done so.

Paleontologists are sensitive to the implications of the mutation theory because they cannot be sure whether newly introduced species in the faunal succession are the result of rapid mutations of local species or of migration into the area by slowly evolving species.

Evolutionary Patterns

Whenever the rudiments of any theory of evolution appeared in pre-Darwinian times, the sequences almost invariably were thought of as sweeping linear ascents from simple to complex; hence, we customarily speak of any evolutionary series as a **lineage** (Fig. 1.9.1). Lamarck conceived the idea that evolutionary patterns were really very complex, and in 1809 he published the idea of a "tree of life" or **phylogenetic tree** (Fig. 1.9.6) in which the various taxa can be traced by a succession of junctures from the outermost twigs (species) down to the major limbs (Phyla). This kind of presentation remains the most popular graphic method of presenting the interrelationships and systematic classification of creatures. It is primarily a succession of lineages, any one of which can be traced back to the "roots" of the Animal Kingdom.

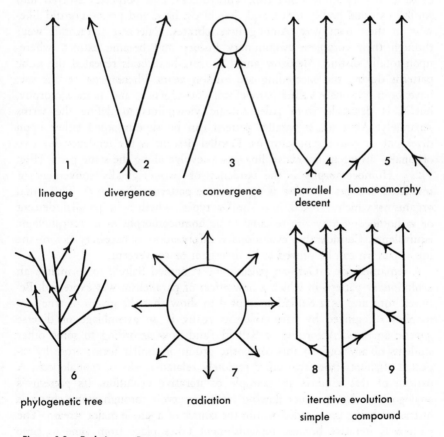

| 1 | 2 | 3 | 4 | 5 |
| lineage | divergence | convergence | parallel descent | homoeomorphy |

6	7	8	9
phylogenetic tree	radiation	iterative evolution
		simple	compound

Figure 1.9. Evolutionary Patterns.

When examined with care, a phylogenetic tree proves to be a complicated thing in which several small patterns are discernible. **Divergence** is the general tendency for a species to separate into two or more lineages which depart during their evolution ever farther from the ancestral type (Fig. 1.9.2). Every branching of a phylogenetic tree is an example of divergence. **Convergence,** on the other hand, is the tendency for two unrelated species to produce lineages which evolve into ever more similar forms (Fig. 1.9.3). Most evolutionary events can be spoken of as lineages, divergences, and convergences. In addition, however, many different lineages evolved along the same lines as if they were vehicles traveling to the same destination but on parallel highways. In some cases the different lineages lived in the same region, and in others they lived in different regions. Lineages may have been closely related or totally unrelated. Moreover, they may have been contemporaries, or they may have lived at very different times. Every student of earth history knows that fish, ichthyosaurs, and porpoises evolved into similar external bodily forms and that birds, bats, and pterosaurs did likewise in their own way. Among invertebrates, Paleozoic tetracorals went through their complete evolutionary history and became extinct, whereupon totally distinct Mesozoic and Cenozoic hexacorals repeated the same patterns during the succeeding 180 million years. Phenomena of this sort have been variously called parallelism, convergence, and homoeomorphy, but it is desirable from paleontologic viewpoints to define the terms separately. After all, a parallel pattern can be superimposed either upon divergent or convergent patterns. **Parallel descent** is the tendency for two originally divergent or related lineages to evolve along the same paths (Fig. 1.9.4). **Homoeomorphy** is the tendency of two originally convergent or unrelated lineages to evolve along the same patterns (Fig. 1.9.5). The actual organisms which evolved into similar types, whether in parallel descent or in homoeomorphy, are referred to as **homoeomorphs** or as **morphologic equivalents.** Considerable evolutionary information is necessary before the initial pattern can be proved to be divergent or convergent.

It remained for a German paleontologist named Salfeld to formalize an evolutionary pattern in which a new effect of parallelism was expressed. Between 1913 and 1922 Salfeld attempted to show that the group of true ammonites recognized by paleontologists really is an assemblage of diverse genetic ancestry. According to Salfeld (and now according to some other students of ammonites) this composite group of similar forms arose by repeated offshoots from two other remotely related stocks of cephalopods. A pattern of this kind is an example of **iterative evolution.** Its pattern is analogous to that of water flowing into a reservoir through many channels instead of being impounded within the course of a single major stream. The pattern is iterative because replenishment takes place from time to time from the same source or sources. When a taxonomic group is derived by repeated offshoots from a single stock the result is **simple iterative evolution** (Fig. 1.9.8). When a taxonomic group is derived by offshoots from two or more stocks the result is **compound iterative evolution** (Fig. 1.9.9). Another way of thinking of these patterns is to consider them examples of repeated parallelism, simple and compound. Iterative evolution should not be confused with any causative theory of evolution such as those which were proposed by Darwin or De Vries. Instead, iterative evolution is merely a method of depicting patterns which organic evolution has followed. Iterative evolution might, however, emphasize the materials for a test of why straight-line evolution takes place.

Parallelism is usually explained as the adaptation of different creatures to the same environment. This is a reasonable hypothesis in the case of swimming or flying creatures, and it more or less serves to explain why many unrelated colonial organisms adopt a hexagonal pattern for packing together bundles of tubular skeletons. Instances of this sort may be thought of as obligatory parallelism which does not require any particular biologic explanation. Nevertheless, similarities in environment are not apparent in some cases of parallelism; hence, additional theories have been proposed to account for similarity of evolutionary patterns.

One of the latter theories which profoundly affected paleontologic thought is called **orthogenesis,** or the concept of straight-line evolution. According to orthogenetic philosophy there is an inherent tendency in some groups of animals which causes them to evolve along certain lines rather than to vary in all directions and then to adapt themselves to the random situations to which they may be suited. Darwinian patterns of variation are fundamentally radial, whereas the pattern in orthogenesis is essentially linear (*ortho* means straight). Orthogenesis was originally proposed by Eimer in 1896 in order to account for the systematic change in color patterns of butterflies. Eimer suggested that the wing patterns evolved through several stages from horizontal stripes, through horizontal and vertical stripes, and finally to solid color; and he pointed out that this sequence of patterns also is followed during the ontogeny of some individual butterflies and reptiles. The theory of orthogenesis was seized upon by vertebrate paleontologists, particularly in America, to explain the evolution of the horse and to explain why different strains of titanotheres which lived at different times all produced one or two extra sets of horns as they increased in size.

Much opposition to the theory of orthogenesis has arisen, principally from zoologists, but more recently from paleontologists. For example, some stages in supposed orthogenetic series have been found to be in the wrong stratigraphic order. It has also been said that "examples" of orthogenesis have been selected because they fit the theory, whereas other examples which did not fit the theory were left out. Or the theory has implications of super-natural forces or of predestination and therefore is not subject to scientific evaluation.

Zoologists despair of finding any genetic mechanism which can account for orthogenesis. In the absence of a genetic causal mechanism, some biologists have thought that perhaps orthogenesis is caused by adaptation to an environment. Organisms subject to variation must adapt themselves to suitable conditions, but there does not seem to be any way in which the adaptation itself can cause variation in the organism's genetic make-up. It also has been suggested that orthogenesis is really nothing but orthoselection, in which successive generations of diverse variations are refined by natural selection so that only those individuals survive which vary in a particular consistent way. In this respect orthogenesis can be shown to be the same as "definite variation."

No matter whether the phenomenon is called orthogenesis or orthoselection, the record of invertebrate paleontology abounds with evidence that many different creatures seem to march along rigidly circumscribed courses in their evolution. Moreover, some trends seem to have progressed to specialized extremes far beyond what appear to be optimum modifications. Few paleontologists openly support orthogenetic theories today, but much paleontologic literature cannot be evaluated intelligently unless there is an appreciation of the underlying philosophical tenor of straight-line evolution.

About the same time that the doctrine of orthogenesis was proposed, a collateral hypothesis was suggested in Europe by Dollo. It was Dollo's belief that evolution was always progressive—that is, that creatures, once they started down a certain evolutionary path, never retreated nor could they resume a former condition. In 1893 he proposed these concepts as the Law of Irreversibility of Evolution. As an example he cited the well-known shapes of nautiloid cephalopods which range from straight, to curved, to loosely coiled, to tightly coiled, and finally to involute. Dollo did not know of any instances in which a reversal of shape changes took place among cephalopods, but several are believed to have been discovered since his time (Fig. 11.5); therefore the law can be said on an absolute basis to be false. Moreover, it is well known that aquatic vertebrates gave rise to terrestrial vertebrates and that these latter reverted to aquatic types as in the cases of whales and ichthyosaurs. The result is that many biologists prefer to interpret Dollo's law in such a way that organs lost during the course of evolution cannot be regained in a structural form homologous with their original condition, even though the apparent direction of evolution is reversible.

PROCEDURE IN PALEONTOLOGY

Paleontology is so wedded to stratigraphy that the two disciplines are almost inseparable. Many stratigraphers are also paleontologists, and almost all paleontologists are also stratigraphers. To be sure, some stratigraphers deny the need for paleontologic assistance, and some paleontologists survive happily without a thought for field relationships of their faunas. On the other hand, most geologists use paleontologic information as the principal means of dating the formations with which they are dealing and thereby help to establish the order of succession of formations. It is true that paleontologic control is not needed for recognition of every outcropping stratigraphic succession or for correlation of the formations encountered in every oil well. For instance, if one maps along a consistent succession of outcrops of distinctive appearance, one is reasonably sure that the ages remain the same for all practical purposes from outcrop to outcrop. Even so, the age relationship of every outcropping or subsurface unit ultimately rests upon paleontologic dating of some stratigraphic succession somewhere. But if beds are not laterally continuous, if new beds come into a succession, if strata grade laterally from one lithology to another, if there are severe structural complications, or if one is dealing with a monotonous succession of similar lithologic units, then the services of a paleontologist become desirable or even indispensable to solution of a stratigraphic problem. By the same token, changes in subsurface conditions are equally vexatious in the absence of paleontologic control. Many oil companies make it a practice to study microfaunas from every wildcat well and from at least one well in every geographic Section in a pool or field being developed; the policy assures their geologists the opportunity to avoid some costly errors of miscorrelation. The petroleum industry provides many stories of failures due to miscorrelations, some of which could have been avoided if all available information, including paleontologic, had been evaluated.

There is a widespread belief that two categories of paleontologists exist—the academic and the practical—but it would be difficult to establish finite differences between the two, if indeed there are any. Basic research in one or more of the methods discussed earlier in this chapter (that is, morphologic series, stratigraphic series, evolutionary series, and so forth) usually has been carried on at universities, museums, and state and federal organizations, plus some research organizations of oil companies. Applied paleontology has been practiced by all sorts of geologists, many of whom may not fully recognize their dependence upon their academic colleagues. Increase in available species, stability of nomenclature, orderliness of classification, and validity of methods used are unquestionably academic subjects without which applied paleontology could not function intelligently. Conversely, if there were no application for paleontologic research, the academic pursuits would probably dwindle significantly and would represent the research of a few dedicated and purely academic workers who served theoretical biology while satisfying their own insatiable curiosity.

Specifically, the so-called practical paleontologist usually is engaged in using one or more of the physical or biologic methods in order to identify the age or identity of the rocks from which the fossils came. Employment of the most advanced method, the evolutionary series, may be used for an example. Each species in an evolutionary series is like a frame in a motion picture. Accordingly, a paleontologist tries to understand the flow of evolution by piecing together the several successive stages of a series in a way such that the stages make a rational and continuous picture of changes which transpired during an interval of time. If we phrase paleontologic work in a pseudo-mathematical fashion, we can say that paleontologists try to equate time in terms of evolutionary position. Having done this, they can work the relationship in reverse and place a species in its proper evolutionary position in a known series; then it becomes apparent when the species lived. In like fashion a paleontologist commonly identifies other geologic, geographic, and environmental qualities by reference to known series of fossils. But first he must have fossils.

Field Techniques

Large fossils (**megafossils**) such as molluscs, corals, brachiopods, and echinoids are used most commonly in studies of outcrops because their skeletal remains are easily seen and may be identified on the spot by a well-informed geologist. Field geologists in a particular region usually develop a repertoire of common fossils which are present and whose names and stratigraphic ranges they know. Thus, these men are able to function as paleontologists from outcrop to outcrop without having to collect fossils, carry them around all day, and then wait for days or weeks until a paleontologic report is sent to them. Field geologists commonly are able to assist professional paleontologists by adding new information on the occurrence of various species.

When a mapping program is started a field geologist can obtain much information on stratigraphy and paleontology by consulting a paleontologist. In particular, a field geologist usually can be furnished with illustrations of useful fossils or even with a small collection of actual fossils which are diagnostic of some of the formations known to be present in nearby regions. The field geologist then is able to carry his field work into his area from these nearby regions or even to start work in the middle of a new area and still recognize some common formations. He uses the observed physical evidence of composition and appearance, plus fossils he collects and identifies with his preliminary paleontologic information, in order to recognize nearby formations which extend into his area. Many field geologists prefer to send representative suites of fossils to a paleontologist for identification after detailed stratigraphic studies are under way. That is, geologists collect fossils while they are measuring stratigraphic sections. Or they may invite a paleontologist-stratigrapher to go into the field with them in order to verify ages and names of strata in the region. In these ways technical problems of stratigraphic nomenclature are settled before detailed mapping begins.

Fossil collections should be restricted to one apparent bed, if possible, because strata that look very much alike may be of different ages. It is better to make several collections containing similar faunas than to make one mixed collection with an impossible association of species. Specimens should be taken from the actual outcrop, if possible, in order to eliminate contamination by rock falls from overlying beds. The temptation to pick up cleanly weathered specimens from talus slopes is insurmountable, but at least a collection of this sort should be labeled with the customary term "float," to indicate that it was not *in situ*. Not only do specimens work down slopes by gravity, but geologists are notorious for carrying around odd rocks and then tossing them aside. A good fossil locality is apt to be visited by many geologists, some of whom will arrive there carrying one or more fossils from some other locality. In order to take away a pocket full of material, a visitor may throw the earlier specimens on the ground where some later collector will have the ill fortune to pick them up and send them in to a laboratory for identification. A professional paleontologist's life sooner or later is enlivened by controversy over whether he has misidentified a fauna entrusted to his care or some colleague erred in making the collection.

Once having made a collection, the collector puts the specimens in a suitable bag. Two kinds are very popular—cloth bags with glazed tags and a drawstring around the neck and heavy paper envelopes with a metallic band which will hold closed a rolled portion of the mouth. In either case the bag should have some sort of collection number on it, which can be used in reference to the fauna. Either the bag or the field notes should carry the date, the probable formation, the lithology, the precise stratigraphic position, the geographic description (Section, Township, Range, County, State), and a descriptive statement as to how to get to the locality (distances and bearings from roads, buildings, creeks, or other landmarks). Collecting localities should be indicated on topographic maps or on aerial photographs whenever it is possible. The foregoing information enables a paleontologist to save time in searching for the proper publications which he must consult. The information also enables anyone to check or to augment the collection if he wants to do so. With regard to collections without data, they test not only the ingenuity and professional resources of a paleontologist, but also his temper.

Samples for micropaleontologic examination should be put only in clean sacks and tied tightly around the neck of the bag in order to prevent contamination. Moreover, the sample should be taken from well below the surface of an outcrop in order to obtain unweathered and uncontaminated material. Calcareous shales commonly abound in microfossils, and shale partings in limestone strata are particularly rich in small fossils.

Finally, if a field geologist wishes to endear himself to his paleontologist, then he should send him an elegant collection. This means that there may be not only a score of exteriors of clams, but one nice hinge line with teeth; or a scallop with its ears attached; or a crinoid showing the posterior interray; or the interior of a brachiopod shell; and all of these rare things carefully wrapped against damage. In other words, paleontologists react kindly when they receive what they sorely need in order for them to do their work (which is work for the field man, after all). Students who arrive at the end of a paleontology textbook should at least be aware of the morphologic features which collections of various kinds of animals should display, even if this awareness is only a matter of selfish interest.

Subsurface Techniques

Collecting fossils in subsurface studies usually involves recovery of cuttings from drilling oil wells. It follows that almost all subsurface collections concern microfossils such as foraminifers, ostracodes, conodonts, and spores. Only in a few cases, such as when an exploratory well is being drilled in a new region, are there apt to be many cores taken from which megafossils can be recovered. Cuttings are recovered manually by sieving them out of the drilling fluid, or they are separated by a mechanical device. It is customary to separate sacks of cuttings representing successive 10-foot intervals of a drill hole. Sacks of cuttings are then sent to a micropaleontology laboratory ("bug lab") for processing, identification, and determination of age.

Laboratory Techniques

Megafossils received at a laboratory are cleaned of matrix by washing, chiseling, grinding, acidizing, or by use of vibratory tools equipped with needles for tiny chisels. Preparatory work usually is done by the paleontologist who is studying the collection, and he cleans up only as much of a specimen as is needed in order to assure its identification. If a fauna is to be described and illustrated, however, then much more extensive preparation is necessary. Some museums maintain staffs of skilled preparators who free the fossils from their matrix and catalogue the collection. Once the specimens are clean, they can be identified either by use of publications on similar faunas or by comparison with collections made previously. The paleontologist usually obtains a fairly good idea of the species which are present in a fauna while he sorts over the collection. The field notes will inform him of the name of the formation which presumably provided the material and where the outcrops were located. Of course, it is necessary to compare the unknown fauna with a known fauna from the same environment, because creatures which are of the same age but which occupied different environments may be very different. Suitable reference books or collections then can be consulted. Paleontologists have also discovered that, except for some free-floating or swimming organisms, most species are restricted to one sedimentary province or to a relatively restricted geographic region rather than being distributed world-wide. Therefore, it usually is necessary to compare collections with faunas from nearby areas in order to obtain the closest possible specific correspondence when identifications are being made.

Correlation

Having completed his identifications, a paleontologist prepares a faunal list in which all of the species are listed. He then compares this list with lists from other localities of known age, using several techniques. A very common and time-honored method is to look for some one or a few species whose positions in the stratigraphic zonation are well known—these species are the so-called **index fossils** or **guide fossils.** In many instances these highly diagnostic forms can be used with confidence to date faunas. Cephalopods and fusulinids in particular have been used as index fossils with great faith by many paleontologists.

A different method is to compare the entire fauna with another entire fauna and to see what degree of correspondence there is. This procedure is called **matching faunas.** The degree of correspondence commonly is stated numerically, as a ratio, or as a percentage. Thus, one may find that two faunas have 15 species in common; or that 15 of the species of fauna A are present among the 23 species of fauna B; or that 65 per cent of the species of fauna A are present in fauna B.

A third method is to consider not only the species which are present, but the abundance of each species. This is the **relative abundance** method and is a refinement of the matching method in that it attempts to evaluate natural relationships of the species in the population. Thus, a species (or even a Genus or higher taxon) may have had a long range but been particularly abundant at a certain time and is reasonably indicative of a certain formation if it occurs in abundance. It is from early considerations such as this that geologists used to name formations by such appellations as "Agoniatite formation," "Pentremital limestone," and "Archimedal limestone." Relative abundance may be stated as a ratio or as a percentage in order to indicate the importance of a species in the whole population.

The final method of paleontologic correlation is to evaluate the **evolutionary position** of one or more species in a fauna. If the evolution and stratigraphic occurrence of several species in a Genus are known in considerable detail, then it is possible to assign a species in a new collection to its proper place in the evolutionary sequence and thereby arrive at its stratigraphic range. This method requires exceptionally good information on evolution of the group and a high degree of skill by the paleontologist. The method is used very successfully with corals and cephalopods but probably reaches its acme of practical application with fusulinids.

None of the foregoing methods is very effective unless collections are made with an understanding as to how the paleontologist is going to have to operate. It therefore is desirable for the prospective collector to ask in advance what kind and how much material the paleontologist may require. Unfortunately, many collections are merely casual accumulations of fossils taken in the press of time, far from an automobile, and with more concern for lightness of load than for completeness of representation. Obviously, no paleontologist can use statistical methods in matching faunas or in studies of relative abundance if he does not have adequate material. The result is that meager collections force the use of inadequate methods. Perhaps it is for this reason that it is highly desirable to bring a paleontologist into the field where he can make his own collection and call upon his own enthusiasm and energy to get large suites of fossils back to civilization. Many a paleontologist has returned cross country deshabillé with important pieces of his clothing removed in order for them to serve as emergency luggage for fine collections of fossils!

Laboratory examination of microfossils is somewhat different from that of megafossils. Cuttings from a well or samples of shale from an outcrop are first washed through a set of graded screens at the laboratory. Many microfossils in a particular area are known by experience to occur within certain ranges of diameters; therefore, they can be concentrated between screens of proper meshwork. If the shales do not break down in water, they may have to be crushed, boiled, or treated chemically to disassociate the mineral particles and free the fossils. In some cases microfossils are separated from mineral grains by floating them off on heavy liquids which allow the slightly heavier mineral grains to settle out. In any case the concentrated sample is then "picked," which means that specimens of the various species are removed under a binocular microscope and are mounted on slides bearing a grid of numbered spaces. A paleontologist (who may do his own picking) then identifies the fossils and prepares a faunal list. After that he follows the same methods (index fossils, matching of faunas, relative abundance, or evolutionary position) as the student of megafaunas does in order to arrive at his conclusion as to the age of the fauna. With the advent of ecologic studies of microfaunas, it is becoming increasingly common for micropaleontologists to utilize information on depth and temperature of certain living species as evidence bearing upon the correlation of extinct faunas.

QUESTIONS

1. What bearing do parallelism, straight-line evolution, and irreversibility have on the correlation of faunas?
2. How can mutations be confused with effects of faunal migration?
3. How does a paleontologist recognize units of geologic time, and what phenomena are apt to confuse his decision?
4. Why are numerical data on distribution of Phyla in the Animal Kingdom not representative of the materials available to paleontologists?
5. Under what circumstances are fossils of most value in stratigraphy? Of least?
6. In what ways can manner of preservation of fossils affect the ability of a paleontologist to make identification?
7. Where and under what geologic conditions did environment influence marine faunas significantly in North America?
8. Give an example of faunal migration, stating the causes.
9. Why should the paleontologist, W. D. Lang, once say, "Confused nomenclature is fatal to clear thinking"?
10. Why should academic and practical paleontologists be dependent upon each other?

BIBLIOGRAPHY

Bequaert, J. C., 1943, The Genus Littorina in the western Atlantic: Johnsonia, v. 1, no. 7, pp. 1–27.
Dollo, L., 1893, Les Lois de l'Évolution: Bull. Soc. Belge Geol. Pal. Hyd. (Bruxelles), v. 7, pp. 164–166.
———, 1910, La Paléontologie Éthologique: Bull. Soc. Belge Geol. Pal. Hyd. (Bruxelles), v. 23, pp. 377–421.
———, 1922, Les Céphalopodes déroulés et l'irréversibilité de l'évolution: Bijdragen tot Dierkunde (Amsterdam), v. 22, pp. 216–226.
Durham, J. W., 1954, Echinodermata: Eleutherozoa, in Status of invertebrate paleontology, 1953: Bull. Mus. Comp. Zool. (Harvard), v. 112, pp. 151–160.
Emery, K. O., 1956, Marine geology of Johnston Island and its surrounding shallows, Central Pacific Ocean: Geol. Soc. America Bull., v. 67, pp. 1505–1520.

———, and Cox, D. C., 1956, Beachrock in the Hawaiian Islands: Pacific Sci., v. 10, no. 4, pp. 382–402.

Garstang, W., 1922, The theory of recapitulation: a critical re-statement of the biogenetic law: Jour. Linnean Soc. London, Zoology, v. 35, pp. 81–101.

George, T. N., 1932, Palingenesis and palaeontology: Cambridge Phil. Soc., Biol. Revs., v. 8, no. 2, pp. 107–135.

Grabau, A. W., 1913, Principles of stratigraphy: New York, A. G. Seiler and Company, pp. 450–461.

Hedgpeth, J. W., 1957, Classification of marine environments: Geol. Soc. America, Mem. 67, v. 2, pp. 93–100.

Holmes, A., 1947, The construction of a geological time scale: Trans. Geol. Soc. (Glasgow), v. 21, pt. 1, pp. 117-152.

Hyman, L. H., 1955, How many species? Syst. Zool., v. 4, no. 3, pp. 142–143.

Longwell, C. R., in Foose, R. M., et al., 1958, Geologic column and scale of time: Geotimes: v. 11, no. 9, pp. 13, 14.

Lowman, S. W., 1949, Sedimentary facies in Gulf Coast: Bull. Amer. Assoc. Petroleum Geologists, v. 33, no. 12, pp. 1939–1997.

MacGinitie, G. E., and MacGinitie, N., 1949, Natural history of marine animals: New York, McGraw-Hill Book Co., 473 pp.

Mayr, E., Linsley, E. G., and Usinger, R. L., 1953, Methods and principles of systematic zoology: New York, McGraw-Hill Book Co., 328 pp.

Moore, R. C., Lalicker, C. G., and Fischer, A. G., 1952, Invertebrate fossils: New York, McGraw-Hill Book Co., 766 pp.

Muller, S. W., and Campbell, A., 1954, The relative number of living and fossil species of animals: Syst. Zool., v. 3, pt. 4, pp. 169–170.

Shrock, R. R., and Twenhofel, W. H., 1953, Principles of invertebrate paleontology: 2nd ed., New York, McGraw-Hill Book Co., 816 pp.

Simpson, G. G., 1952, For and against uniform endings: Syst. Zool., v. 1, no. 1, pp. 20–22.

Stenzel, H. B., 1950, Proposed uniform endings for names of higher categories in zoological systematics: Science, n. ser., v. 112, no. 2899, p. 94.

Teichert, C., 1958, Some biostratigraphical concepts: Geol. Soc. America Bull., v. 69, pp. 99–120.

Teichert, Kurt, 1956, How many fossil species? Jour. Paleont., v. 30, no. 4, pp. 967–969.

Weller, J. M., et al., 1948, Correlation of the Mississippian formations of North America: Geol. Soc. America Bull., v. 59, pp. 91–196.

Chapter 2

SINGLE-CELLED ANIMALS

PHYLUM I. PROTOZOA

Although the Protozoa are the simplest members of the Animal Kingdom, they are not necessarily the smallest, nor is their simplicity such as to make them uninteresting. Protozoa range in size from minute organisms, the examination of which requires a high-powered microscope, to frilly, lenticular, calcareous discs such as *Neusina* which are 7.5 inches (19 cm) in diameter. Some diaphanous members of the Phylum which lack even a cell wall (such as the intestinal parasite, *Porospora gigantea*) grow to be an inch in length. Protozoa mostly consist of a single cell, although this cell may be distributed through numerous chambers of a complex skeletal system. The body itself is composed largely of cytoplasm or living tissue which contains a single nucleus or more than one nuclei (Fig. 2.4.1). Suspended in the cytoplasm are substances which perform the digestive functions of the cell, there being no digestive organs. Moreover, the products of the digestive process are carried to all parts of the cell body by vortical motion of the cytoplasm, there being no circulatory system of arteries and veins. Finally, the lack of a differentiated respiratory system requires that waste products of metabolic activity be passed out of the body (and oxygen passed into the body) by osmosis, which is diffusion through the wall or outer surface of the body. A major difficulty facing most protozoans is the tendency of the colloidal-like suspension called protoplasm to become infinitely diluted in the fresh-water or salt-water medium in which the animal lives. In order to prevent this disassociation of the body, the Protozoa commonly are able, by unknown means, to concentrate the water entering the body into localized centers called contractile vacuoles, which grow larger and larger until they break through the outer surface of the animal and empty their contents into the surrounding water. About as soon as one contractile vacuole has emptied, another is swelling up at another center. The action of these dewatering devices demonstrates that many Protozoa lack a membranous cell wall, but that their outer surface is rather like the tough surface on a thin custard pudding.

51

Food particles generally are taken into the body through the body wall. An *Amoeba,* for instance, flows across a tiny plant cell, sending out extensions of the body and ingesting the particle. After digestion the remnant of the food particle passes through the "rind" of the body and is left behind while the cell flows onward.

One of the best ways to evaluate the simplicity of Protozoa is by reference to the reproductive process. Protozoa are so unspecialized that they can reproduce either by use of the normal process of cell division which constitutes growth in higher animals or by means of special sex cells. In the first instance, cells divide so that each half contains a full complement of chromosomes and each half is just like the parent. In most Protozoa these cells separate by **fission** to form new individuals, whereas in higher animals the cells congregate to form the body of the organism. In the case of sex cells, division of the parent proceeds in a way that results in each daughter cell having only half of the full complement of chromosomes. In this case two cells must unite to form a new individual. These two processes of **asexual reproduction** and **sexual reproduction** are common to primitive plants as well as to primitive animals and seem to indicate a common origin for both of the Kingdoms. Moreover, both Kingdoms progress by increasing domination of sexual reproduction over fission.

Protozoa inhabit fresh, salt, and brackish water; moist earth; moist surfaces of plants and rocks; digestive systems of most animals; and even circulatory systems of vertebrates, as in the case of the malarial parasite in man. Some protozoans in their resting stages are blown about by winds, and the rapidly reproducing individuals quickly populate almost every available environment. Other protozoans constitute a major element of the food supply of larger creatures in aqueous environments. Marine protozoans with calcareous tests rain down upon the ocean floor in such numbers as to be important rock-formers. In former times also this skeletal rain contributed to the accumulation of rocks and now offers us a convenient source of some of the oil in sediments and of fossil tests for correlation of these sediments. Protozoans, therefore, are important in medicine, in petroleum exploration, and in the biologic balance of the seas.

CLASSIFICATION. Major subdivisions of the animal world are generally differentiated by symmetry, reproduction, and progressive development of respiratory, circulatory, and nervous systems. Protozoa, however, are basically asymmetrical (although they may approach true symmetry and exhibit false symmetry) and are otherwise too simple to lend themselves to further subdivision on the foregoing grounds. Instead, it is customary to group them largely in accord with locomotor devices plus other factors. The following short classification reflects these ideas as applied to those protozoans of major interest to paleontologists. Large numbers of zoologically important groups are omitted.

Phylum I. Protozoa
  Class A. Mastigophora
    Order a. Chrysomonadida
    Order b. Dinoflagellida
    Order c. Silicoflagellida
    Order d. Choanoflagellida
  Class B. Sarcodina
    Subclass 1. Rhizopoda
    Order a. Amoebida
    Order b. Testacida
    Order c. Foraminiferida
      Superfamily (1). Astrorhizicae
      Superfamily (2). Lituolicae
      Superfamily (3). Endothyricae
      Superfamily (4). Miliolicae
      Superfamily (5). Lagenicae
      Superfamily (6). Buliminicae
      Superfamily (7). Rotaliicae
    Subclass 2. Actinopoda
    Order a. Radiolariida
    Order b. Heliozoida
  Class C. Sporozoa
  Class D. Ciliata

PHYLUM I. PROTOZOA

Single cells or colonial aggregates of cells without differentiation of function, mostly asymmetrical, and reproducing chiefly by asexual methods.

Class A. Mastigophora

Those Protozoa which move by means of one or more long, thin, whiplike processes are included within this Class. Most of them are very tiny cells whose whiplike **flagellum** (pl. **flagella**) is so tenuous as to be almost invisible under a microscope. Only a few have a hard skeleton, so the group is not very important paleontologically. This Class has also been called the Flagellata in obvious allusion to the locomotor device. Less obviously, the word Mastigophora is derived from two Greek words meaning "whip-bearer."

Mastigophorans may ingest food particles and then digest them as most animals do, or they may live by producing their own food in the same way that plants do from red or green pigmented areas called **chromatophores.** It is at this point that our human-devised classification shows major weaknesses, for we cannot decide what to do with creatures that move about, but make their own food. They have variously been called animals or plants.

Other mastigophorans are parasitic, like the trypanosomes, and cause serious diseases in man and in creatures by infesting body cavities, blood, and muscle tissues.

The trend toward colonial habit shows up in Mastigophora which build erect colonies or which congregate in spherical masses, some of which may even be enveloped within a common sheath or cuticle of cellulose. Culmination of this communal action is seen in *Synura* (Fig. 2.1.18), in which cells making up a hollow sphere even indulge in some specialization of function to the advantage of the colony. Thus, some cells form one kind of reproductive body and other cells form a different kind. This is in contrast to the other Protozoa wherein reproductive bodies are all alike. *Synura,* it seems, foreshadows the coming of the higher animals and represents a morphologic stage along the evolutionary path.

Order a.   Chrysomonadida

Among the several groups of Mastigophora is this Order of biflagellate protozoans. The individuals may secrete a spherical skeleton consisting of many minute, discoidal, calcified bodies called **coccoliths** and **discoasters** (Fig. 2.1). These particles, which measure only from 1 to 15 microns (1 mu = 0.001 mm) in diameter, have been reported from sediments in many parts of the world. Although first noted in 1836 and named in 1858, their true nature was not known until 1861, and they were not extensively studied until after 1900. It is now generally accepted that they belong in this Order, although some scientists consider that various similar forms (possibly all discoasters) may be precipitated biochemically by algae. Much remains to be learned with reference to the coccoliths and they may not be correctly placed in the classification. By referring to the organisms which produced coccoliths as **coccolithophores,** it is possible to evade the problem of precise biologic assignment.

Coccoliths are circular to elliptical bodies with or without a perforation in the center of a central depression. Among the various kinds of coccoliths those called **rhabdoliths** are hollow club-shaped bodies. **Tremaliths** are perforate coccoliths (Fig. 2.1.9). **Lopadoliths** are hollow and rodlike coccoliths (Fig. 2.1.8). Some recent attempts have been made to organize our knowledge of coccoliths so that they may be useful paleontologically in correlation or in ecologic studies.

Their widespread distribution is a desirable feature, but their minute size reduces their usefulness. Magnifications of 400 diameters or more are desirable in their study.

Recent coccolithophores occur abundantly in the open ocean in temperate or tropical waters, mostly above a depth of 150 meters. Fossil coccoliths have been reported from the Cambrian to Recent of many lands, but only Jurassic to Recent reports are undoubted. They are abundant in the Cretaceous chalk deposits of Europe. In North America they occur in several stratigraphic bands in the Upper Cretaceous of the High Plains where they have been referred to by subsurface geologists as the specks in the "First Speckled shale," and "Second Speckled shale." This terminology is a utilitarian nomenclature left over from the time when their position in the organic or inorganic Kingdoms was not appreciated.

Discoasters are minute bodies in the size range of coccoliths and are often associated with coccoliths. As the name suggests, the plates are discoidal and star-shaped (Fig. 2.1.10–14). Discoasters may be produced by plants, instead of by animals, there being no very sound basis for their assignment either

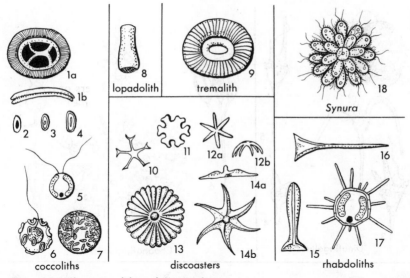

Figure 2.1. Chrysomonadida and Mastigophora.
1a, 1b. Plan and side views of a coccolith, 1000X, Eocene to Recent. 2-4. Coccoliths, 2000X, Recent. 5. Probable biflagellated coccolith-bearing organism with solid black nucleus and stippled chromatophores, 1000X, Recent. 6. Uniflagellate organism with a central capsule and coccoliths produced on outer surface, 1000X, Recent. 7. Test composed of coccoliths, 1000X, Recent. 8. Lopadolith, 625X, Miocene. 9. Tremalith, 1000X, Eocene. 10. *Discoaster* sp., 625X, Miocene. 11. *Discoaster* sp., 625X, Eocene to Miocene. 12a, 12b. Plan and side views of *Discoaster* sp., 625X, Oligocene to Pliocene. 13. *Discoaster* sp., 625X, Cretaceous or Paleocene. 14a, 14b. Side and plan views of *Discoaster* sp., 625X, Eocene. 15. *Rhabdosphaera* sp., 1000+X, Recent. 16. Rhabdolith, 625X, Eocene. 17. Cross section of *Rhabdosphaera* sp. with solid black nucleus and stippled chromatophores, 1000X, Recent. 18. *Synura* sp., a colonial biflagellated mastigophoran, 500X, Recent.
(1, 8-14, 16 after Bramlette and Riedel, 1954. 2-7, 15, 17 after Lohmann, 1902. 18 after Conn, 1905.)

way. This vagary arises because no unquestioned Recent discoasters are known. Unquestioned reports are from Tertiary sediments only.

Order b.   Dinoflagellida

Mastigophora with two flagella and a body wall made of cellulose have been referred to this Order. Dinoflagellates are principally distinguished because one flagellum springs from a longitudinal groove in the test, and the other flagellum lies within a transverse groove. The name, which means "terrible flagellates," refers to the spinosity of many members of the group, which do look forbidding under a microscope (Fig. 2.2.1–5). At certain times when these creatures are able to reach their full reproductive rate their bodies may be so numerous in the ocean that they color the water conspicuously. "Red tides" due to dinoflagellates and to diatoms (microscopic plants) are common along the coast of California and are also known off Florida.

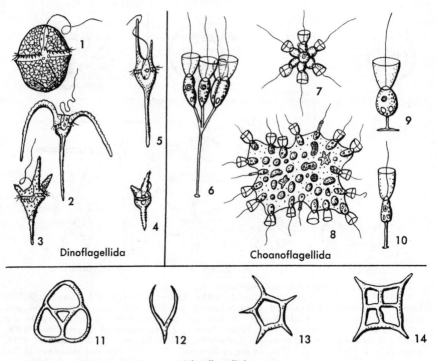

Figure 2.2.   Dinoflagellida (1-5), Choanoflagellida (6-10), and Silicoflagellida (11-14).
1. *Peridinium* sp., 115X, Recent.   2. *Ceratium* sp., 80X, Recent.   3. *Ceratium* sp., 100X, Recent.
4. *Ceratium* sp., 60X, Recent.   5. *Ceratium* sp., 105X, Recent.   6. *Codosiga* sp., 300X, Recent.
7. *Halisarca* sp., 535X, Recent.   8. *Proterospongia* sp., 335X, Recent.   9. *Monosiga* sp., 800X,
Recent.   10. *Salpingoeca* sp., 1200X, Recent.   11. *Corbisema* sp., 220X, Cretaceous.   12. *Lyramula*
sp., 285X, Cretaceous.   13. *Vallacerta* sp., 500X, Cretaceous.   14. *Dictyocha* sp., 380X, Cretaceous.
(1-10 after Kent, 1880-1882. 11-14 after Hanna, 1928.)

The Spanish explorer de Portola originally named the Gulf of California the "Red Sea" because of the red tide he encountered there.

Under rare conditions these creatures may be preserved in siliceous deposits such as chert. Thus, they have been identified from thin sections of Jurassic and Cretaceous strata in Europe.

Order c.   Silicoflagellida

Those mastigophorans which secrete a siliceous test have either been recognized as a separate Order or have been considered as a Family of the Chrysomonadida. Their skeletons are generally spinose rings or simple netlike structures requiring high magnifications (like coccoliths) in order to be studied (Fig. 2.2.11–14).

Since their discovery in 1838 there has been very little work done on them. In this country Hanna (1928) has reported them from the Cretaceous of California. They have been reported from the Cretaceous to the Recent. In modern seas they live near the surface as part of the plankton and drift widely.

Hanna suggested that their variability, abundance, distinctness, wide geographic range, and short stratigraphic range warrant their study as useful fossils. Accordingly, some recent work has been undertaken with them. On the other hand, their minute size and their general occurrence with other more attractive organisms such as radiolarians and diatoms have operated against their increased study.

Order d.   Choanoflagellida

Choanoflagellates bear one flagellum which is surrounded by a collar of protoplasm that stands like a circular wall above the main cell mass (Fig. 2.2.6–10). Food particles coming in contact with the collar are ingested into the cell in special vacuoles. Cells may be protected by a chitinous vaselike test or **lorica.** Under some circumstances the collar and flagellum are retracted and the cell assumes an amoeboid shape.

Simple, stalked choanoflagellates are known, but their most interesting feature is the trend toward colonial form, which is expressed in two ways. Arborescent growths such as *Codosiga* may arise, or separate collared cells may be scattered over and separated by a shapeless jellylike matrix as in *Proterospongia.*

Choanoflagellata are unknown as fossils, although the lorica is potentially preservable.

Class B.   Sarcodina

When early biologists wished to differentiate those creatures with a protoplasmic body or "sarcode" from higher animals, the name of this Class was

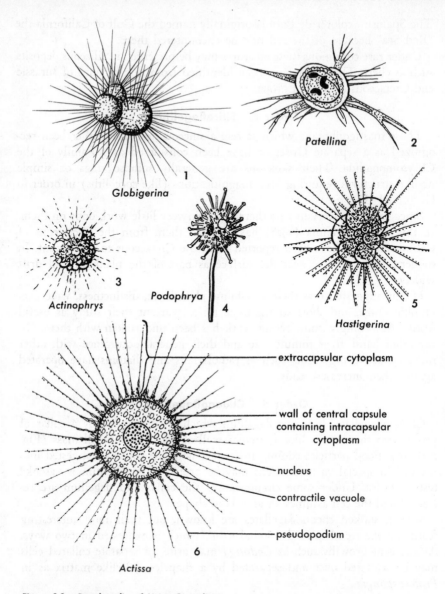

Figure 2.3. Pseudopodia of Living Sarcodina.
1. *Globigerina bulloides*, a foraminifer with filose pseudopodia, 25X. 2. *Patellina corrugata*, a foraminifer with anastomosing pseudopodia, 100X. 3. *Actinophrys sol*, a heliozoan, 170X. 4. *Podophrya* sp., a suctorian, 290X. 5. *Hastigerina pelagica*, a foraminifer with rodlike pseudopodia, 25X. 6. *Actissa princeps*, a radiolarian, 180X.
(1, 5 after Brady, 1884. 2 after Myers, 1935. 3, 4 after Conn, 1905. 6 after Haeckel, 1887, and Aberdeen, 1940.)

diagnostic, but now many other creatures with a sarcode are known. Sarcodina move by means of projections of the protoplasm, **pseudopodia,** and the various groups can be differentiated thereby. Among floating marine forms that change their depth systematically by day and night, some may alter the carbon dioxide content of gas vacuoles in their protoplasm and thereby change their buoyancy like a submarine.

SUBCLASS 1.   RHIZOPODA

Those Sarcodina with lobelike or netlike pseudopodia belong here. The name of the Subclass is an allusion to the rootlike appearance of some pseudopodia (as opposed to the stiff-rayed members of the other Subclass, Actinopoda).

Order a.   Amoebida

This group contains *Amoeba,* which is one of the commonest and best-known Genera of animals because of its widespread use in biology courses. Amoebas have no hard parts and are not known fossil. They move in their search for food by sending out **lobose pseudopodia,** into some of which the main mass of the body flows like an advancing lava flow; pseudopodia which advance in unprofitable directions are retracted.

Order b.   Testacida

Testacida have amoeboid bodies but they construct an external cover or **test** of mineral grains or of tests of other creatures, therefore the name

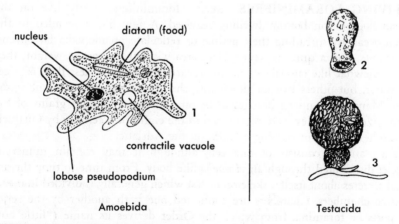

Figure 2.4. Amoebida (1) and Testacida (2, 3).
1. *Amoeba proteus,* shown as if moving to the left, 200X, Recent. 2. Test of *Difflugia* sp., 165X, Recent. 3. *Difflugia* sp. with pseudopodia, 125X, Recent.
(After Conn, 1905.)

Testacida. The Order has been reported as far back as the Eocene and is represented in the Recent by *Difflugia*.

Order c.   Foraminiferida

Herodotus may have been the first to record Foraminiferida when he suggested, in the fourth century B.C., that the discoidal tests of nummulites scattered about the pyramids of Egypt were fossilized lentils from the workers' food supply.

Foraminiferida are now so important paleontologically that, to many workers, the science of paleontology is essentially restricted to the study of "forams," as these protozoans have come to be familiarly known. Most economic applications of paleontology today are by oil companies who employ students of Foraminiferida as micropaleontologists. By knowing the vertical relationships of foraminiferal zones to known oil- or gas-producing strata, a micropaleontologist can predict the distance from a recognizable zone in a drilling well to a potential producing bed. Foraminifers, being quite small, are not all ground up when the teeth on the bit cut into rocks; hence, many remain in the "cuttings" to be studied at the surface.

Our knowledge of these protozoans is increasing so rapidly that the illustrated catalogue (Ellis and Messina) grows by the addition of 300 to 500 new pages every year to the 20-foot-long row of books in the catalogue. Perhaps 25,000 to 30,000 species are recognized currently, depending upon how many duplications (synonyms) are thought to exist. Special courses at many colleges enable a student to perfect his knowledge of this Order.

LIVING FORAMINIFERS.   Recent foraminifers mostly live on the ocean floor or on bottom-dwelling seaweed. A few live suspended in the open ocean by spreading their netlike or **reticulate pseudopodia** far beyond their tests, thus acquiring great surface area without increase in weight; they are somewhat like snowflakes in this regard. Most live in less than 600 feet of water, but others live far down into the abyssal regions to about 13,500 feet. Many wash up on beaches to become mixed with sand grains of the same size and so they were recognized in the eighteenth century by Gualtieri and other Venetians bathing at Lido on the Adriatic.

Each animal consists of one cell, although it may contain numerous nuclei distributed through an *Amoeba*-like body. From time to time the animal secretes about itself a skeleton or **test** which generally is divided into successive **chambers.** Chambers are connected one with another by the series of ports or **foramina,** from which the Order derives its name ("little hole bearers"). Protoplasm is extruded through the last foramen called the **aperture** and grows until another chamber is built around it. Chambered tests also may bear minute perforations on their surfaces from which tenuous filaments of protoplasm stream out to form the pseudopodia. These filaments ensnare food particles and also carry on such locomotor activities as are necessary (Fig. 2.3.1, 2, 5).

SKELETAL FEATURES. Tests are of two major types according to manner of origin. Many globular, tubular, or branching tubular foraminifers build **agglutinated** or **arenaceous** tests by cementing together tiny mineral grains or various foreign particles. About one-fifth of all foraminifers are arenaceous. The other and much more numerous type is of **calcareous** tests secreted by the organism. Several different calcareous subtypes are recognized, of which the most common are **hyaline** (or **perforate**), so named because their tests appear glassy, or because they bear minute holes. On the other hand, most tests of the **porcellaneous** (or **imperforate**) subtype are chalky and dull, and commonly lack perforations. Still other skeletal categories occur among the fusulinids (**complex**) or among smaller foraminiferal groups (**chitinous, fibrous, siliceous, granular**). It is probable that calcareous tests are secreted upon a chitinous framework.

SHAPE. The simplest forms of protoplasm may be either globular or elongate. In the first instance the resulting spherical test would have a **globular** shape. Simple modifications of this involve addition of a neck to the flask to become **lagenoid.** In the second case the extended form would be covered with a **tubular** test which might become branched (**arborescent**) or star-shaped (**stellate**) in modified forms.

By modifying the lagenoid shape most simply, a uniserial succession of spherical tests can be added to the initial chamber to form a **nodosarian** shape like a string of beads. In this and in all subsequent shape modifications, the initial chamber resembling a lagenoid foraminifer is called the **proloculus.** Other elongate shapes are the biserial V-shaped **textularian** and the triserial **tritaxian.**

In planispirally coiled foraminifers the test may consist of a few simple chambers (**rotalioid**) or of myriad complex chambers in a lenticular aggregate (**orbitoid**). Spindle-shaped tests like a grain of wheat, but still planispirally enrolled, are **fusiform.** When trochospirally coiled forms first start to grow along a helicoid axis they are **trochoid,** and when they are distinctly spired they are **spiral.**

Still more complex modifications are the **milioline** foraminifers, which add chambers spirally in such a way that the ranks of chambers coincide with imaginary rays radiating from the proloculus symmetrically. Thus, if chambers are added first on one side and then on the opposite side (180° rays) the shape is **biloculine.** If three rays (120°) are involved, the shape is **triloculine,** and if five rays (72°) are involved, the shape is **quinqueloculine.** Finally, in some foraminifers one or more early chambers are concealed beneath later chambers and the tests are said to be **dimorphine,** although they

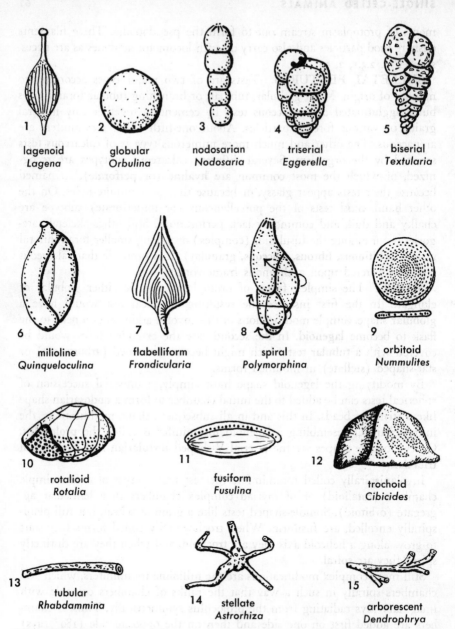

1 lagenoid
Lagena

2 globular
Orbulina

3 nodosarian
Nodosaria

4 triserial
Eggerella

5 biserial
Textularia

6 milioline
Quinqueloculina

7 flabelliform
Frondicularia

8 spiral
Polymorphina

9 orbitoid
Nummulites

10 rotalioid
Rotalia

11 fusiform
Fusulina

12 trochoid
Cibicides

13 tubular
Rhabdammina

14 stellate
Astrorhiza

15 arborescent
Dendrophrya

Figure 2.5. Shapes of Foraminifers.
Most of the figures are enlarged about 15X, except for Fusulina (about 5X) and Nummulites (about 3X).
(Mostly after Brady, 1884.)

are externally nodosarian or textularian in shape. Tests of leaflike shape which contain concealed chambers are **frondicularian** or **flabelliform.**

It has been a common custom among many micropaleontologists to speak of "smaller forams" and "larger forams." **Smaller foraminifers** consist basically of relatively few chambers which are arranged in a simple sequence. Thus, chambers of smaller foraminifers are arranged linearly, or in a planispiral coil, or in a whorl, or in an alternating pattern of the textularian kind. Most foraminifers are smaller foraminifers. **Larger foraminifers,** on the other hand, are composed of relatively numerous chambers which are produced simultaneously in several rows or layers. Resulting shapes are discoidal, globular, conical, and fusiform. It has recently been discovered that a third and exceedingly small size category of foraminifers exists. These tests are referred to as **microforaminifers** to distinguish them from smaller foraminifers. As a rule of thumb, most microforaminifers are about 0.01 millimeter in greatest dimension; most smaller foraminifers are about 0.4 millimeter in greatest dimension; and most larger foraminifers exceed 2 millimeters in diameter. Numerical systems, however, are inadequate to differentiate categories of foraminifers because some larger foraminifers may be within the size range of the smaller foraminifers, and vice versa.

SHAPE AND POLYMORPHISM. Foraminifers reproduce asexually most of the time. In this process a tiny bit of cytoplasm with one nucleus breaks away from the multinucleate cytoplasm of the parent and grows into a new individual. Tests formed in this fashion are characterized by the presence of relatively few chambers, but by a relatively large proloculus; hence, the tests are termed **megalospheric** (Fig. 2.14.4a, 7a). The same species of foraminifers can also reproduce sexually by union of two sex cells, in which case the resulting test consists of a relatively large number of chambers, but the proloculus is relatively small. Tests of this kind are termed **microspheric** (Fig. 2.14.1a, 3, 4b, 7d). Moreover, those species of Foraminiferida which may exhibit two bodily forms have been said to be **dimorphic;** and some specialists recognize three-bodied or **trimorphic** species. Until there is general agreement about the probable number of bodily forms in foraminifers, it is convenient to refer to foraminifers (and to some other organisms) which are represented by two or more bodily forms as animals which exhibit **polymorphism.**

Perhaps it is important to stress at this point that polymorphism is a separate phenomenon from size differences represented by smaller and larger foraminifers. Polymorphism is not very important among smaller forams, although some external differences may appear between a microspheric (Fig. 2.16.9a) and a megalospheric (Fig. 2.16.9b) test of the same species. On the other hand, polymorphism can be of great importance among larger foraminifers where an adult microspheric test (Fig. 2.18.12c) may be five times as large as an adult megalospheric test (Fig. 2.18.12b).

Polymorphism (particularly the strictly dimorphic type) is reflected in a more or less regular reproductive cycle in which sexual and asexual reproduction take place alternately. The phenomenon is called **alternation of generations.** Many simple animals and plants exhibit alternation of generations, but the phenomenon cannot take place in higher animals in which there is no asexual reproduction.

Much importance is attached to shape changes not only when differentiating groups, but when establishing the evolutionary position of particular specimens. For instance, an individual which is textularian in its later growth may be spiral in its initial stages. Or, in more elaborate compound shapes, some externally biloculine test may contain a triloculine or

Figure 2.6.   Apertures of Foraminifers.
All figures greatly enlarged.

quinqueloculine central portion. In all of these cases the assumption is that the initial stage represents the normal shape of the adult ancestral form and that the later shapes in the developmental series represent evolutionary advance over the ancestral condition. Expressed as the Theory of Recapitulation, this principle means that an individual records some of its evolutionary history as it grows.

Attention is also given in classification as to whether the aperture is circular, oval, slitlike, triangular, or quadrate; or whether it is open or partly closed by a tooth which may be simple, bifid, or trifid; or possibly the aperture may be lined in forms with needlelike spines to make a radiate type or may be perforated by a branching channel called cribrate. Moreover, apertures may be terminal, marginal, or basal, depending upon shapes of tests. Illustrations of foraminifers, therefore, customarily show an apertural view as well as a side or plan view.

ORNAMENTATION. From a basically smooth surface, the foraminifers developed ribs or ridges (**costae**), granules or nodes, spines, flanges, and pits.

Surfaces covered by a network of fine lines have **reticulate** ornament. These ornamental features are in addition to the fundamentally perforate or imperforate construction of the tests. The trace of the wall which separates adjacent chambers usually is visible on the exterior of the test as a **suture.** Positions of grooved sutures may be delineated by a depression, and **limbate sutures** may be accentuated by a ridge along one side of the suture.

CLASSIFICATION. No simple classification is generally acceptable because exceptions complicate almost every simplified grouping. Different shapes, chemical compositions, and test architecture occur in all sorts of combinations. For instance, even perforate and imperforate groups are not restricted to the calcareous foraminifers because agglutinated tests may be perforate. Systematists, by attempting to create exclusive categories, have increased the number of taxa until as many as 51 Families of Foraminiferida have been recognized. Inasmuch as only specialists need to be interested in all of these technicalities, the classification of seven Superfamilies proposed by Glaessner (1947) is adopted herein as an acceptable simplified grouping.

The following key to the Superfamilies of foraminifers suffices to differentiate most of the commonly encountered living and extinct forms, but it is inadequate for the assignment of a small percentage of mostly uncommon forms.

KEY TO SUPERFAMILIES OF FORAMINIFERIDA

I. Test arenaceous
   A. Nonchambered .... Astrorhizicae
   B. Chambered .... Lituolicae

II. Test calcareous
   A. Mostly imperforate, not hyaline
     1. Discoidal to fusiform, granular .... Endothyricae
     2. Milioline, porcellanous .... Miliolicae
   B. Mostly perforate, hyaline
     1. Chambers tend to lie in linear or planispiral series,
       particularly in early portions .... Lagenicae
     2. Chambers tend to lie in complex whorls
       a. Tests mostly helicoid around a main long axis . Buliminicae
       b. Tests mostly rotalioid .... Rotaliicae

Superfamily (1). Astrorhizicae

The **astrorhizids** consist of arenaceous tubes which are not divided into chambers. *Astrorhiza* is a stellate form ranging from Jurassic to Recent. *Involutina* (widely known as *Ammodiscus*) is a planispiral form which has been reported from Silurian to Recent. These arenaceous forms can be recovered from insoluble residues in the laboratory by gently decanting the fines from a block of limestone which has been dissolved in dilute acid.

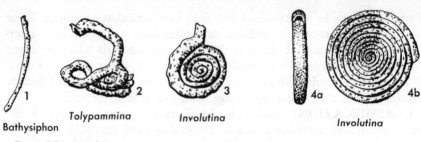

Bathysiphon   Tolypammina   Involutina   Involutina

Figure 2.7. Astrorhizicae.
1. *Bathysiphon parallelus,* 25X, Silurian.   2. *Tolypammina tortuosa,* 30X, Silurian.   3. *Involutina exsertus,* 30X, Silurian.   4a, 4b. Apertural and plan views of *Involutina.incertus,* 8X, Recent.
(1-3 after Dunn, 1942. 4 after Brady, 1884.)

Superfamily (2).   Lituolicae

Lituolids are chambered, arenaceous foraminifers. Principal morphologic
trends in the lituolids reflect changes in shape which are illustrated in Figure
2.8. Members of one group typified by *Cyclammina* and *Haplophragmoides*
possess coiled tests, whereas members of another group possess elongate tests.
Representatives of the latter category can be differentiated according to how
the chambers are distributed in different portions of the test (that is, according
to different developmental series). *Bigenerina* (Fig. 2.8.5a, 5b) changes from
biserial to uniserial. *Ammobaculites* (Fig. 2.8.2) starts out with a spiral apex
and becomes straight and uniserial later on, but *Spiroplectammina* (Fig.
2.8.7b) and *Textularia* (Fig. 2.8.3b) change from coiled into straight and
biserial. *Gaudryina* (Fig. 2.8.8a, 8b) is triserial near the apex and changes
later into biserial, but *Clavulina* (Fig. 2.8.4) changes from triserial to uniserial.

Much work needs to be done before there can be much confidence about
the interrelationships of these foraminifers, but certain working hypotheses
are currently in vogue. By applying the Theory of Recapitulation to the
lituolids we can refer to the developmental series above and conclude that
Ammobaculites, Spiroplectammina, and *Textularia* were all derived from
coiled ancestors. Also, the straight lituolids seem generally to have been derived from ancestors with biserial or triserial tests.

One or more offshoots developed into larger foraminifers in early Cretaceous time and slightly anticipated a similar development in other groups.

The lituolids extend back at least to the Silurian and reached the culmination of their development in the Cretaceous. They continue to be an important element of Recent marine faunas.

Superfamily (3).   Endothyricae

Endothyrid foraminifers constitute a catch-all of mostly granular, calcareous, planispiral forms, plus a few arenaceous representatives. The first larger

foraminifers arose from within the Endothyricae as the fusiform strain called **fusulinids.** These were so successful that they completely dominated Late Paleozoic protozoan faunas and provide some of the most biologically significant and geologically important index fossils in the whole Animal Kingdom. The Superfamily ranges from Devonian through Permian over most of the world.

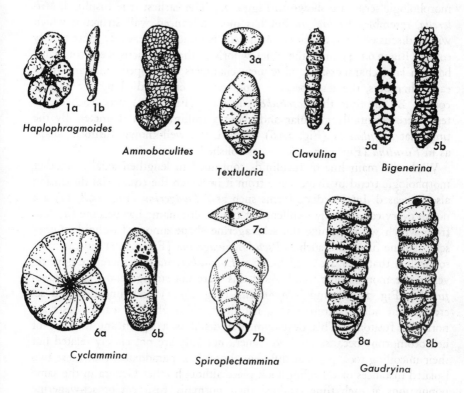

Figure 2.8. Lituolicae.

1a, 1b. Plan and edge views of *Haplophragmoides concava*, 30X, Cretaceous. 2. *Ammobaculites flariformis*, 20X, Eocene. 3a, 3b. Apertural view and side view showing completely biserial arrangement of *Textularia dibollensis*, 40X, Eocene. 4. *Clavulina parisiensis*, 25X, Eocene. 5a, 5b. Longitudinal section and side view showing change from biserial to uniserial in *Bigenerina nodosaria*, 25X, Miocene. 6a, 6b. Plan and edge views of *Cyclammina cancellata*, 8X, Recent. 7a, 7b. Apertural and side views of *Spiroplectammina mississippiensis*, 50X, Eocene. 8a, 8b. Different side views of *Gaudryina subrotundata*, which changes from triserial to biserial, 14X, Miocene to Recent.

(1 after Tappan, 1940. 2, 3, 7 after Bandy, 1949. 4-6, 8 after Brady, 1884.)

Primitive endothyrids are discoidal with rather rounded chambers and simple wall structure. This sort, typified by *Endothyra*, became a noteworthy rock-maker in Mississippian time (Salem limestone of Indiana) and persisted as a prominent constituent of calcareous sediments into Pennsylvanian time. A subsidiary strain separated from *Endothyra* in late Mississippian (Chester) time to become the fusiform group called fusulinids.

FUSULINIDS. Evolution of the endothyrids progressed very rapidly from the moderately tight coiling and discoidal shape of *Endothyra* (Fig. 2.9.9) to the fusiform shape of the typical fusulinids. Successive stages in this morphologic series are shown in Figure 2.9. The earliest true fusulinid, *Millerella,* resembles *Endothyra* but has more advanced wall structure which will be discussed later. Species of *Millerella* became progressively more tightly coiled (Fig. 2.9.1–4) until the inner whorls at the umbilicus were concealed beneath later chambers. As subsequent chambers overlapped more and more early chambers, the tests became progressively extended along the axis of coiling. By the time the *Eoschubertella* stage (Fig. 2.9.5) was reached, the tests were essentially globular and about 1 millimeter in diameter. By the time that *Fusulinella* (Fig. 2.9.6) evolved, the well-known **fusiform shape** as in *Fusulina* (Fig 2.9.7, 10) was established.

While the main line of fusulinids continued to lengthen axially, another morphologic trend in shape arose from it in which the equatorial dimension also increased. Intermediate forms such as *Schwagerina* (Fig. 2.9.8, 14) are not in every case notably swollen, but the generic name has become the root from which we recognize the **schwagerine shape** among fusulinids. Other schwagerine fusulinids such as *Pseudoschwagerina* (Fig. 2.9.13) have become so swollen that they are as globular as *Eoschubertella* and therefore have reversed the morphologic trend. As if this were not strange enough, *Codonofusiella* (Fig. 2.9.11) and *Nipponitella* (Fig. 2.9.12) both uncoiled and secreted their adult chambers in a flat sheet, although their earlier tests are normally fusiform. This developmental detail is a significant instance of homoeomorphy because the two Genera not only are not closely related but their uncoiling took place at different times. It is paradoxical that these two isolated instances of uncoiling took place although other Genera in the same populations at each time retained their normally fusiform or schwagerine shapes.

A second morphologic trend in fusulinids affected their size. Primitive fusulinids are about 0.5 millimeter in diameter, but later forms rather consistently increased in size until the group reached its average length of that of a grain of wheat (or up to about 10 mm). Continued extension of the axis led to very slender spindle-shaped tests which became as much as 60 millimeters (2½ in.) long and have the distinction of being among the largest Protozoa known. In the schwagerine line, some tests were as much as 12 millimeters (½ in.) in diameter.

Before taking up other trends among fusulinids it is necessary to establish some details of internal anatomy. These are illustrated in Figure 2.10. The

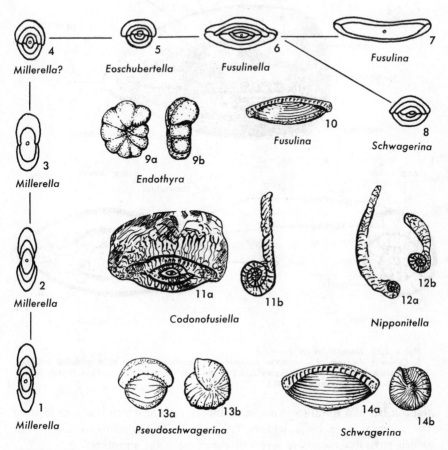

Figure 2.9. Shapes of Fusulinids.
1-6. Morphologic series in which tests become more elongate along the axis and the whorls become more involute. 7. Extreme elongation of the axis. 8. Extreme elongation of equatorial dimension in schwagerine forms. 9a, 9b. Side and edge views of *Endothyra* sp., 20X, Mississippian, Indiana. 10. Side view of *Fusulina acme* with fluted antetheca and fusuline shape, 5X, Pennsylvanian, Illinois. 11a, 11b. Axial and equatorial sections of *Codonofusiella* sp., 20X, Late Permian, Texas. 12a, 12b. Two equatorial sections of *Nipponitella* sp., 4X, Early Permian, Japan. 13a, 13b. Side and end views of *Pseudoschwagerina* sp., with schwagerine shape and unfluted antetheca, 3X, Permian, China. 14a, 14b. Side and end views of *Schwagerina diversiformis*, 4X, Permian, Texas.

(1-7, 12 after Thompson, 1948. 11 after Skinner and Wilde, 1955. 10, 13, 14 after Dunbar and Henbest, 1942.)

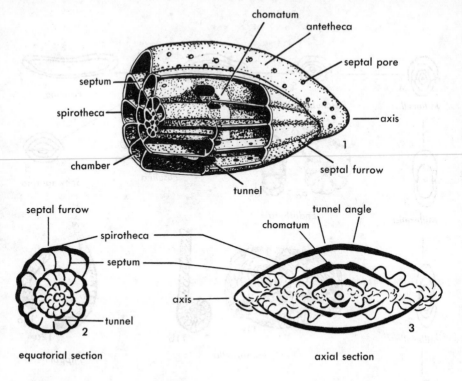

Figure 2.10. Morphology of Fusulinids.
1. Cut-away diagram of a primitive fusulinid. 2. Equatorial section of a primitive fusulinid.
3. Axial section corresponding to Figure 2.10.2. Septa near the tips of the test are slightly folded.
(After Dunbar and Henbest, 1942.)

test consists of a spiral sequence of chambers, each of which is separated from
the adjacent ones by a **septum** (pl. **septa**). The continuous spiral wall
which separates successive layers of chambers is the **spirotheca.**

The test consists of about 3 to 20 whorls of chambers which are separated
into layers by a planispiral wall, the **spirotheca.** Within each whorl the
chambers are defined by successive vertical partitions, the **septa,** which extend
like a curtain or wall between the two regions of a spirotheca that make up
the "floor" and "ceiling" of a whorl. Traces of septa on the exterior of a test
are **septal furrows.** The last or exposed septum at any stage of growth is
called the **antetheca.** It bears **pores,** but it and the preceding one or two septa
are not pierced by a foramen. This is a paradoxical situation, because each of
the other inner septa always bears the foramen (called a **tunnel** in fusulinids)
along its lower middle portion, as in the case with other foraminifers. It seems,
therefore, that the tunnel arises by resorption of skeletal material within the
interior of the living organism. On the spirotheca along both sides of the

tunnel of some fusulinids are thickened zones (**chomata**) which stand above the floor of the chamber like little levees. The angle at which the chomata diverge through successive whorls is the **tunnel angle.** It is useful in defining species.

One of the most important features of fusulinids is the microscopic structure of the wall (Fig. 2.11). The simplest, earliest, and presumably most primitive spirotheca (Fig. 2.11.1) consists of a thin median layer, the **tectum,** which is reinforced by two accessory layers of calcite, the **inner tectorium** and the **outer tectorium.** Secretion of the outer tectorium may lag slightly behind secretion of the inner tectorium; hence, some spirothecae of outer whorls may be only two-layered. The septa consist only of extensions of the inner tectorium. A wall of this type is called a **profusulinellid wall.**

The next more advanced wall (Fig. 2.11.2) is just like a profusulinellid wall except that a new and very transparent layer, the **diaphanotheca,** is developed between the tectum and the inner tectorium. All of the layers are perforated by minute **mural pores.** If deposition of inner and outer tectoria lagged behind growth, the outer whorls of the spirotheca may consist largely of tectum and diaphanotheca. A wall which has a distinct diaphanotheca is called a **fusulinellid wall.**

The most complex wall (Fig. 2.11.3) seems to have developed from the fusulinellid wall by thickening of the tectum and by loss of the tectoria and diaphanotheca. In their place is a very thick layer of tissue called the **keriotheca.** It consists of masses of tubules or spaces (**alveoli**) which are separated by narrow walls. In sections at right angles to a spirotheca the tectum resembles the back of a comb and the alveolar walls simulate the teeth of a comb. A wall which has a keriotheca is termed a **schwagerinid wall.**

There is some correlation between wall structure and shape of fusulinids. Profusulinellid and fusulinellid walls are most characteristic of fusiform fusulinids, whereas schwagerinid walls are most characteristic of fusulinids with the globose or schwagerine shape. Unfortunately, exceptions are common, and there may even be a reversion to the fusulinellid wall in strains which had previously advanced to the stage of a schwagerinid wall. It is apparent, however, that the three kinds of walls can be arranged in a stratigraphic series according to the first appearance of a particular structure. Thus, profusulinellid walls appear first and schwagerinid walls appear last. They overlap each other erratically, however, in their upper stratigraphic ranges.

Returning again to morphologic trends among fusulinids, we see a distinct change in appearance of septa. Early septa tend to be plane or slightly curved, like a flat screen or sheet hanging down from the ceiling of a room. Very early in their history, however, the septa begin to become pleated with draperylike folds. These are **fluted septa.** Fluting starts to affect septa near the ends of the axis of coiling and moves progressively toward the equatorial

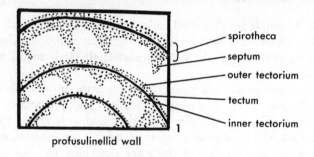

profusulinellid wall

spirotheca
septum
outer tectorium
tectum
inner tectorium

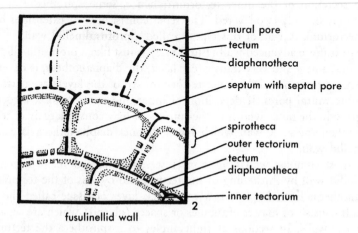

fusulinellid wall

mural pore
tectum
diaphanotheca

septum with septal pore

spirotheca
outer tectorium
tectum
diaphanotheca
inner tectorium

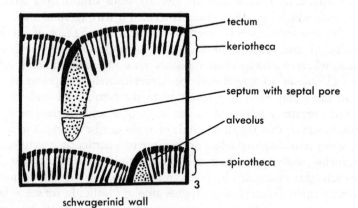

schwagerinid wall

tectum
keriotheca

septum with septal pore

alveolus

spirotheca

Figure 2.11. Wall Structure of Fusulinids.
1. Profusulinellid wall. 2. Fusulinellid wall. 3. Schwagerinid wall. All figures greatly enlarged.
(1 after Thompson, 1948. 2, 3 after Dunbar and Henbest, 1942.)

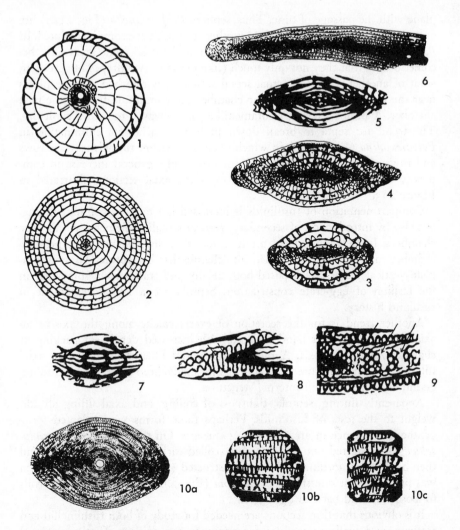

Figure 2.12. Internal Morphology of Fusulinids.

1-6. Variations in compactness. 1. Equatorial section of *Pseudoschwagerina gerontica*, 5X, Permian, Texas. 2. Equatorial section of *Verbeekina heimi*, 4X, Permian, China. 3. Axial section of *Paraschwagerina fosteri*, 5X, Permian, China. 4. Axial section of *Paraschwagerina gigantea*, 3X, Permian, Texas. 5. Axial section of *Wedekindellina matura*, 14X, Pennsylvanian, Utah. 6. Axial section of *Polydiexodina shumardi* with a nearly solid axial filling, 4X, Permian, Texas. 7-9. Fluting of septa as seen in tangential sections. 7. *Profusulinella munda*, 15X, Pennsylvanian, Texas. 8. *Parafusulina nosonensis* with arrows indicating cuniculi, 6X, Permian, California. 9. *Polydiexodina afghanensis* with arrows indicating accessory tunnels, 6X, Permian, Afghanistan. 10. *Lepidolina multiseptata*, Permian, Japan. 10a, axial section, 5X. 10b, transverse septula in axial section, 15X. 10c, axial septula between thicker septa in equatorial section, 15X.

(1 after Thompson, 1954. 2-10 after Thompson, 1948.)

plane with the passage of time. Thus, septa of *Profusulinella* (Fig. 2.12.7) are only slightly fluted, but those of most other fusulinids are complexly fluted. In *Parafusulina* (Fig. 2.12.8), for instance, the folds of adjacent septa have become so deep that they not only touch (like pleats in two drapes hung one in front of another), but the actual septal substance is resorbed at these places near the base of the septa and one chamber can communicate with the next chamber. A minor secondary foramenlike passageway is termed a **cuniculus.** The trend for septa to break down probably reaches its culmination in *Polydiexodina* (Fig. 2.12.9) in which distinct **accessory tunnels** traverse rows and rows of septa within the flanks of a test. The general increase in complexity of septal fluting is apparent from the axial sections illustrated in Figure 2.13.

Compartmentation of fusulinids is increased not only by complex fluting, but also by introduction of secondary, vertical septalike elements within true chambers. In *Lepidolina* (Fig. 2.12.10a, 10b, 10c), for instance, each primary chamber may be partially divided into chamberlets by **septula.** These incomplete vertical plates are disposed both axially and transversely somewhat in the fashion of egg-crate construction. Septula are a late development in fusulinid history.

Another trend is for the secretion of excess calcite along the axis as an **axial filling.** This goes hand in hand with increased density of packing of chambers along the axis. A morphologic series illustrating increased axial filling is shown in Figure 2.12.3-6. In its most advanced stage the axial filling essentially obliterates all internal structures.

Apparently fluting, septula, tightness of coiling, and axial filling all add weight to the tests of fusulinids. Perhaps these forms were adapted for a benthonic existence in areas of strong currents. On the other hand, *Pseudoschwagerina* started out with a tightly coiled early stage (**juvenarium**) and then became extraordinarily lightly constructed (Fig. 2.12.1). Perhaps it even was planktonic at one stage. *Verbeekina* (Fig. 2.12.2) grew from tight coils to loose coils and back to tight coils.

It is obvious that thin sections are needed for study of both fusulinellid and schwagerinid walls as well as for adequate recognition of other internal morphologic features. It is customary to prepare equatorial as well as axial sections for study and illustration. By determining features such as number of whorls, diameter of proloculus, degree of folding of septa, and wall struc-

Figure 2.13 (opposite).   Stratigraphic Distribution of Fusulinids.

Vertical ranges of the Genera typical of each zone are shown by dotted lines. Vertical extent of different shapes and wall structures are shown by arrows. Enlarged axial and equatorial sections of a species of each zonal Genus are shown alongside each zone.

The *Polydiexodina-Verbeekina* zone is indicated by the abbreviation *Poly.* The *Yabeina* zone is indicated by the abbreviation *Yab.*

(Compiled from data and Illustrations by Thompson, 1948 and 1954; Dunbar and Henbest, 1942; Knight, 1956; Zeller, 1950; Skinner and Wilde, 1955.)

Periods	Epochs	Fusulinid Zones	Shape and Wall Structure	Zonal Genera
Permian	Ochoa	Yab.		
Permian	Guadalupe	Poly.		
Permian	Leanoard	Parafusulina	schwagerine shape / schwagerinid wall	
Permian	Wolfcamp	Pseudo-schwagerina	fusiform shape / fusulinellid wall	
Pennsylvanian	Late	Triticites	profusulinellid wall	
Pennsylvanian	Medial	Fusulina		
Pennsylvanian	Medial	Fusulinella		
Pennsylvanian	Medial	Profusulinella	discoidal shape	
Pennsylvanian	Early	Millerella		
Miss.		Endothyra		
Devonian				

ture, a skilled paleontologist can use fusulinids with confidence in correlations. These fossils are no doubt the most important zonal indices of the Pennsylvanian and Permian; in fact, some paleontologists use only the fusulinids for correlation, even if other groups of useful invertebrates are also present in the same collections. Various strata consist almost entirely of fusulinids; hence the creatures were significant rock-makers in sediments of shallow or epeiric seas.

Stratigraphic distribution of fusulinids is shown in Figure 2.13. Zonation by Genera shown in that figure is used on a world-wide basis.

Superfamily (4). Miliolicae

Miliolid foraminifers are calcareous but imperforate, and most of them are coiled in some fashion. Many of the simple ones resemble seeds surrounded by husks, but the large ones tend to be discoidal. Some of the largest known Protozoa and some of the most effective rock-makers are miliolid foraminifers. They range in age from Triassic to Recent and were particularly abundant after the mid-Cretaceous.

Miliolids exemplify very well the differences between megalospheric and microspheric tests in alternation of generations. Moreover, three basic kinds of internal anatomy of the tests are recognized, and these can be arranged in a striking morphologic series. All of these features are shown in Figure 2.14. The simplest miliolids are typified by the *Quinqueloculina*. In this Genus five chambers are visible on the exterior of the test. Moreover, when a test is cut along the equatorial plane (Fig. 2.14.1a, 3), the successive chambers are arranged in spiral form with such necessary increase in size and spacing that the chambers tend to lie along five imaginary rays which radiate from the proloculus.

The next stage in the morphologic series is represented by *Triloculina*, in which three chambers are visible on the exterior of an adult test. Megalo-

---

Figure 2.14 (*opposite*).   Miliolicae.

1. *Quinqueloculina costata*, Recent. 1a, equatorial section of megalospheric test with completely quinqueloculine arrangement of chambers, 65X. 1b, side view, 25X.   2a, 2b, 2c. Apertural and two side views of *Quinqueloculina lamarckiana*, 25X, Recent. 3. Megalospheric test of *Quinqueloculina parvula*, 130X, Recent. 4. *Triloculina schreiberiana*, Recent. 4a, equatorial section of a megalospheric test showing completely triloculine chambers, 45X. 4b, equatorial section of a microspheric test showing quinqueloculine arrangement of the first eight chambers, 45X. 4c, 4d, apertural and side views, 30X. 5a, 5b. Apertural and side views of *Triloculina trigonula*, 25X Recent.   6a, 6b. Apertural and side views of *Pyrgo comata*, 25X, Recent.   7. *Pyrgo fischeri*, Recent. 7a, equatorial section of a megalospheric test with completely biloculine chambers, 20X. 7b, 7c, side and apertural views 15X. 7d equatorial section of a microspheric test with some of the biloculine chambers numbered, 20X. 7e, enlarged central portion of 7d showing quinqueloculine arrangement of first seven chambers and triloculine arrangement of chambers 8 and 9, 140X.

In all equatorial sections the proloculus is the central chamber. Walls of quinqueloculine chambers are black. Triloculine walls are stippled. Biloculine walls are outlined but unshaded.

(1, 3, 4, 7 after Schlumberger, 1891, 1893, 1894. 2, 5, 6 after Bandy, 1954.)

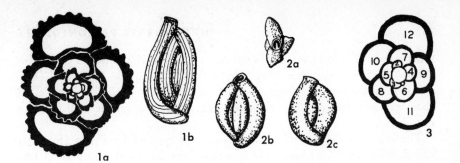

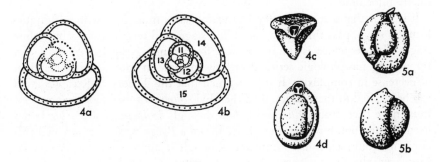

Quinqueloculina

Triloculina

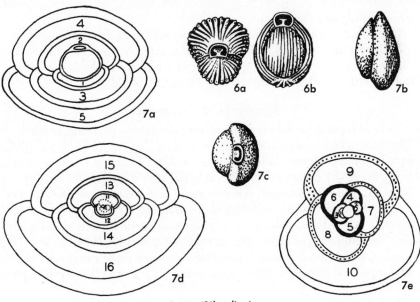

Pyrgo (Biloculina)

spheric tests (Fig. 2.14.4a) are completely triloculine down to the proloculus and the first two chambers. Microspheric tests of the species illustrated (Fig. 2.14.4b), however, are quinqueloculine up through about the first eight chambers and then are triloculine in adult stages through the final fifteenth chamber.

The last stage in the morphologic series is typified by *Pyrgo* (formerly called *Biloculina*) in which only two chambers are visible in an adult test. Megalospheric tests (Fig. 2.14.7a) are biloculine throughout. In the microspheric test (Fig. 2.14.7d, 7e enlarged), however, the proloculus and about the first seven chambers retain essentially a quinqueloculine symmetry. Chambers 0-10 are distinctly triloculine in arrangement, and chambers 11-16 are distinctly biloculine.

It is clear that a complete developmental series must start with a quinqueloculine stage, pass through a triloculine stage, and terminate in a biloculine stage. This sequence is the main basis for arranging the Genera in a corresponding morphologic series of orderly increase in complexity rather than of decrease in complexity. If it is assumed that the Theory of Recapitulation can be applied to these series, then the phylogenetic or evolutionary sequence must have been from *Quinqueloculina* through *Triloculina* to *Pyrgo*. It has been pointed out, however, that the center of a *Pyrgo* is not recapitulated precisely in quinqueloculine symmetry although it approaches that symmetry. Moreover, the three Genera cannot be arranged in a definite stratigraphic series because they appear more or less at the same time in the Jurassic. In view of these facts more research is required before we can be sure that we are dealing with an evolutionary series, even though the present evidence strongly indicates that we are.

One strain of larger foraminifers (alveolinids) arose from the miliolids in mid-Cretaceous time and still survives (Fig. 2.18.4-6). Several minor trends can be recognized within this group, one of which led to the development of tests remarkably like those of the long-extinct fusulinids.

Superfamily (5). Lagenicae

Tests of **lagenid** foraminifers typically are calcareous, perforate, and hyaline. The basic shape is flasklike as in the case of *Lagena* (Fig. 2.15.2-4), but equally common forms such as *Nodosaria, Dentalina,* and *Glandulina* (Fig. 2.15.7, 8a, 6, 5b) consist of elongate uniserial tests which might have sprung from a *Lagena*-like ancestor. Another strain is represented by *Robulus* (Fig. 2.15.9), which is spirally coiled; and by *Marginulina* (Fig. 2.15.10), which seems to be mostly uncoiled or at least to retain curvature only near the apex. One well-known specialized side branch is typified by *Frondicularia* (Fig. 2.15.11), which has a delicate, symmetrical, leaflike shape externally but may be complicated internally. Finally, *Guttulina* (Fig. 2.15.1) developed in paral-

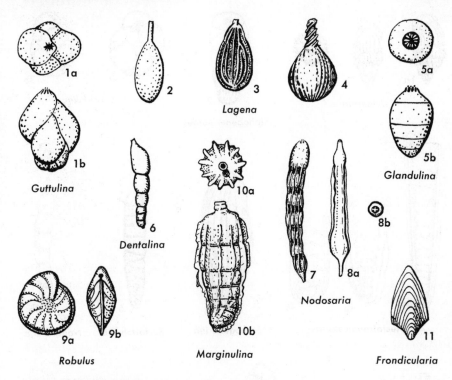

Figure. 2.15. Lagenicae.

1a, 1b. *Guttulina hantkeni,* 35X, Eocene. 2. *Lagena elliptica,* 75X, Eocene. 3. *Lagena humeri-fera,* 75X, Oligocene. 4. *Lagena sulcata spirata,* 75X, Eocene. 5a, 5b. *Glandulina conica,* 35X, Eocene. 6. *Dentalina communis,* 30X, Eocene. 7. *Nodosaria obliquata,* 30X, Oligocene to Recent. 8a, 8b. *Nodosaria latejugata,* 30X, Eocene and Oligocene. 9a, 9b. *Robulus euglypheus,* 12X, Eocene. 10a, 10b. Apertural and side views of *Marginulina texana,* 40X, Oligocene, Gulf Coastal Plain. 11. *Frondicularia goldfussi,* 15X, Cretaceous.

(1-6, 8, 9 after Bandy, 1949. 7 after Galloway and Heminway, 1941. 10 after Garrett and Ellis, 1937. 11 after Cushman, 1946.)

lelism with the miliolid, *Quinqueloculina,* but the chambers in *Guttulina* are arranged in an ascending spiral instead of in a plane.

Lagenids may extend back to the Cambrian, but they were insignificant until they appeared in great numbers during the Jurassic. They continued to be very abundant through the Cretaceous and are still relatively important in Recent sediments.

Superfamily (6).   Buliminicae

Buliminids typically are V-shaped, rather elongate, calcareous, perforate, and hyaline. Some partially coiled and some globular forms which are put here for evolutionary reasons tend to obscure the significance of the characteristic elongate shape of the other members of the group (Fig. 2.16).

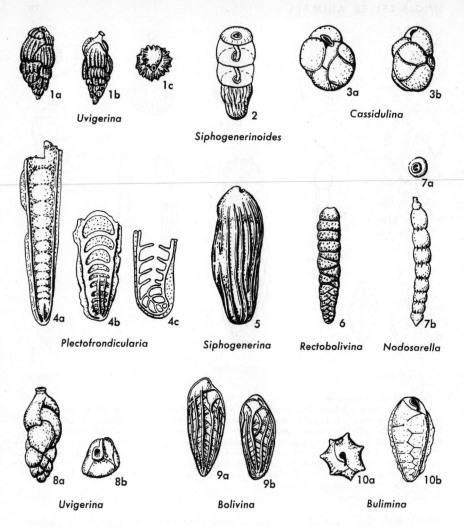

Figure 2.16. Buliminicae.

1a, 1b, 1c. Side and apertural views of *Uvigerina peregrina*, 30X, Pleistocene, California. 2. Cut-away view of *Siphogenerinoides* sp. showing the tube connecting successive chambers, enlarged. 3a, 3b. Two side views of *Cassidulina californica*, 25X, Pleistocene, California. 4. *Plectofrondicularia californica*, Pliocene, California. 4a, side view, 35X. 4b, side view, 45X. 4c, longitudinal section of microspheric form, 50X. 5. *Siphogenerina branneri*, 30X, Miocene, California. 6. *Rectobolivina monsouri*, 45X, Oligocene. 7a, 7b. Apertural and side views of *Nodosarella paucistriata*, 15X, Oligocene. 8a, 8b. Side and apertural views of *Uvigerina hughesi*, 50X, Pleistocene, California. 9a, 9b. Microspheric and megalospheric tests of *Bolivina interjuncta*, 30X, Pleistocene, California. 10a, 10b. Apertural and side views of *Bulimina jacksonensis*, 30X, Eocene, Gulf Coastal Plain.

(1, 3, 8, 9 after Galloway and Wissler, 1927. 2 after Stone, 1946. 4a, 4c after Cushman and Stewart, 1926. 4b, 5 after Kleinpell, 1938. 6 after Garrett, 1939. 7 after Galloway and Heminway, 1941. 10 after Bandy, 1949.)

Characteristic straight Genera are *Bulimina* (Fig. 2.16.10), *Bolivina* (Fig. 2.16.9), and *Uvigerina* (Fig. 2.16.1, 8). Some of these are biserial and some resemble bunches of grapes. Morphologic series commonly can be arranged according to changes in strength and number of external ridges and other ornament.

Plectofrondicularia retains a curved biserial apex (Fig. 2.16.4c) but is otherwise straight and uniserial (Fig. 2.16.4a, 4b). *Nodosarella* (Fig. 2.16.7a, 7b) resembles some of the nodosarian Genera (Fig. 2.15.6, 7, 8a) very closely, but *Nodosaria,* for instance, has a radiate aperture, whereas *Nodosarella* has a single tooth in the aperture. *Rectobolivina* (Fig. 2.16.6) changes from biserial to uniserial according to the same developmental series that its lituolid counterpart, *Bigenerina* (Fig. 2.8.5), follows. One of the most remarkable specializations to be found among any foraminifers, however, is the tube or siphon which is present in *Siphogenerinoides* (Fig. 2.16.2) and in *Siphogenerina* (Fig. 2.16.5). It extends down the axis from the aperture in a broad helicoid spiral and traverses all of the chambers in the test along its course.

Buliminids range from Jurassic to Recent and have been very abundant since Early Cretaceous. Numerous Genera have been described and many species constitute important guide fossils.

Superfamily (7). Rotaliicae

Tests of **rotaliid** foraminifers are characteristically discoidal, coiled, calcareous, perforate, and hyaline. Typical Genera are *Valvulineria* (Cretaceous to Recent), *Cibicides* (Cretaceous to Recent), *Globigerina* (Cretaceous to Recent), *Elphidium* (Eocene to Recent), *Rotalia* (Cretaceous to Recent), and *Nummulites* (Paleocene to Oligocene). It is a peculiar feature of many rotaliids that chambers on opposite sides of a test seem to be coiled in different patterns (Figs. 2.17.9a, 9c; or Fig. 2.17.13a, 13c).

Globigerina is perhaps the best-known foraminifer because it is the principal organic constituent of globigerine oozes. It has a close relative, however, named *Orbulina* which appears at first glance to consist of a spherical test with many perforations. If a translucent specimen is available, however, it may be seen that much of the interior of an *Orbulina* appears to be constructed like a small *Globigerina* (Fig. 2.17.3).

Among larger foraminifers belong several important Genera of orbitoids, including *Nummulites*.

The rotaliids are perhaps the most abundant and diverse of all the foraminifers. Moreover, numerous excellent guide fossils are represented in the group. Rotaliids appeared in the Late Paleozoic and attained a plateau of abundance and importance which has endured from mid-Cretaceous to the Recent.

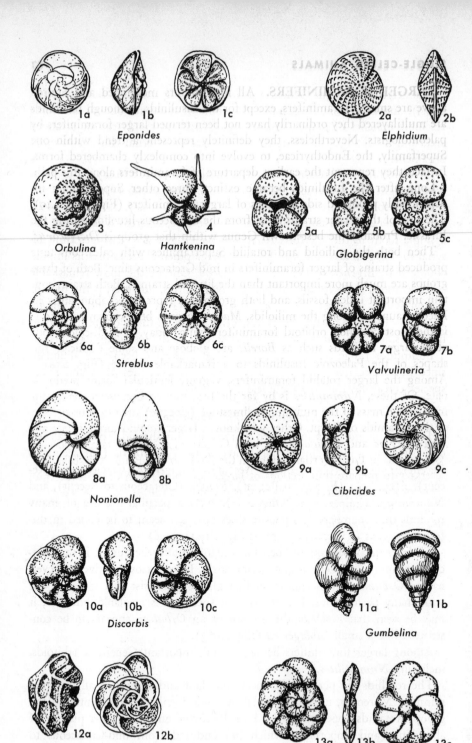

1a 1b 1c
Eponides

2a 2b
Elphidium

3
Orbulina

4
Hantkenina

5a 5b 5c
Globigerina

6a 6b 6c
Streblus

7a 7b
Valvulineria

8a 8b
Nonionella

9a 9b 9c
Cibicides

10a 10b 10c
Discorbis

11a 11b
Gumbelina

12a 12b
Globotruncana

13a 13b 13c
Planulina

LARGER FORAMINIFERS. All foraminifers mentioned and figured above are smaller foraminifers, except for the fusulinids. Although fusulinids are multilayered they ordinarily have not been termed larger foraminifers by paleontologists. Nevertheless, they definitely represent a trend within one Superfamily, the Endothyricae, to evolve into complexly chambered forms. In fact, they represent the earliest departure of foraminifers along this path.

Long after the fusulinids became extinct, three other Superfamilies independently produced side branches of larger foraminifers (Figs. 2.18, 2.19). The first of these later strains arose from the arenaceous lituolids during the Jurassic. Probably the best-known Genus within that group is *Dictyoconus*.

Then both the miliolid and rotaliid Superfamilies with calcareous tests produced strains of larger foraminifers in mid-Cretaceous time. Both of these groups are much more important than the lituolid strain is. Both strains contain important index fossils, and both groups are represented abundantly in Recent faunas. Among the miliolids, *Marginopora* is best known because it is the most common orbitoid foraminifer living today. It is discoidal, but other larger miliolids such as *Borelis* are globose and some duplicate the shapes of the Paleozoic fusulinids to a remarkable degree (Fig. 2.18.6). Among the larger rotaliid foraminifers, vaguely lenticular forms predominate. Of these, *Nummulites* is by far the best known because it makes up most of the mass of the nummulitic limestone (Eocene) used in construction of the pyramids of Egypt. Other well-known larger rotaliid foraminifers are *Heterostegina* and *Lepidocyclina,* both Genera of which contain important zonal fossils in Early Tertiary strata on the Gulf Coastal Plain. It is absolutely necessary to prepare thin sections of larger foraminifers in order to be confident of their identification. When this is done the multirayed internal symmetry of the miliolids (Fig. 2.18.4e, 5b) or the spiral construction of the rotaliids (Fig. 2.18.11a) usually becomes apparent. Experts in the study of larger foraminifers place special taxonomic value upon the various ways in which new chambers spring from the proloculus.

The most significant general feature of larger foraminifers, however, is their remarkable demonstration of parallel descent. It is probable that the

Figure 2.17 *(opposite).* Rotaliicae.
1a, 1b, 1c. *Eponides antillarum,* 30X, Recent. 2a, 2b. *Elphidium crispum,* 20X, Recent. 3. *Orbulina universa* showing globigerine early test within spherical outer test, 35X, Recent. 4. *Hantkenina alabamensis,* 25X, Eocene, Atlantic Coastal Plain. 5a, 5b, 5c. *Globigerina bulloides,* 35X, Eocene to Recent, world-wide. 6a, 6b, 6c. *Streblus beccarii,* 45X, Recent. 7a, 7b, *Valvulineria californica,* 50X, Miocene, California. 8a, 8b, *Nonionella cockfieldensis,* 60X, Eocene, Gulf Coastal Plain. 9a, 9b, 9c. *Cibicides choctawensis,* 55X, Oligocene, Gulf Coastal Plain. 10a, 10b, 10c. *Discorbis gravelli,* 30X, Oligocene, Gulf Coastal Plain. 11a, 11b. *Gumbelina plummerae,* 70X, Cretaceous, Gulf Coastal Plain. 12a, 12b. *Globotruncana arca,* 25X, Cretaceous. 13a, 13b, 13c. *Planulina taylorensis,* 25X, Cretaceous, Gulf Coastal Plain.

(1 after Bandy, 1954. 2, 6 after Galloway and Wissler, 1927. 3 after Brady, 1884. 4, 5 after Bandy, 1949. 7 after Kleinpell, 1938. 8 after Cushman, 1939. 9 after Galloway and Heminway, 1941. 10 after Garrett, 1939. 11-13 after Cushman, 1946.)

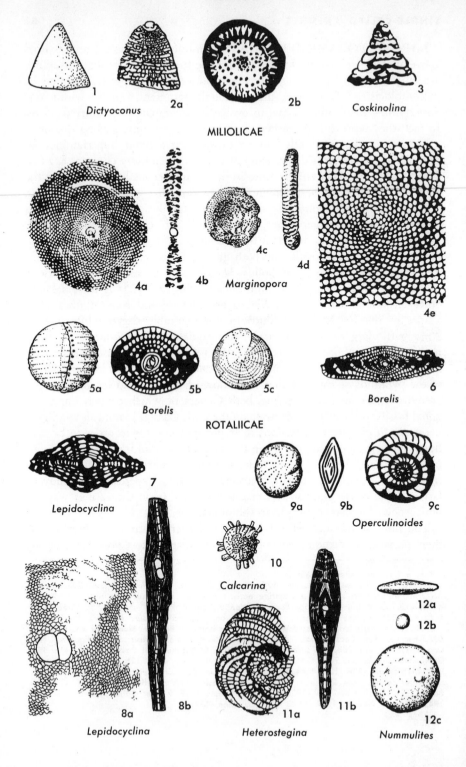

LITUOLICAE

1   2a   *Dictyoconus*   2b   *Coskinolina*   3

MILIOLICAE

4a   4b   4c   4d   *Marginopora*   4e

5a   5b   5c   *Borelis*   6   *Borelis*

ROTALIICAE

7   *Lepidocyclina*   9a   9b   9c   *Operculinoides*

10   *Calcarina*

8a   8b   *Lepidocyclina*   11a   11b   *Heterostegina*   12a   12b   12c   *Nummulites*

several Superfamilies had diverged into separate genetic strains anywhere from a few million to 200 million years before first one and then the other of the Superfamilies gave rise to larger foraminifers. In spite of the long genetic isolation, the fundamental differences in composition, and the differences in internal structure, many of the end products resemble each other to a remarkable degree in external appearance.

Post-Paleozoic larger foraminifers are studied extensively from Cretaceous and Lower Tertiary strata in Europe and Asia but are poorly represented in North America, except for local abundances around the margin of the Gulf of Mexico and the Caribbean Sea. The Vicksburg limestone (Oligocene) of Mississippi contains an abundance of *Lepidocyclina*. Orbitoids still live in shallow tropical waters in great numbers.

ORIGIN OF FORAMINIFERS. Opinions about the origin of foraminifers fall into two categories. According to one school of thought, the lagenid tests are the most primitive because they not only retain the simple flask shape which would be easiest for a globular cell to secrete, but the proloculus of other foraminifers resembles the lagenoid stage. According to this theory the most primitive test would have been chitinous, and later tests arose from it by addition of calcium carbonate to the chitinous form. Arenaceous tests may have evolved from calcareous tests still later by addition of mineral grains, or have evolved directly from chitinous forms. These theories have been reflected in the writings of J. J. Galloway, one of the foremost students of foraminifers.

According to the second theory, the arenaceous foraminifers passed through a stage in which mineral grains were suspended in a matrix of calcium carbonate. Then calcareous tests arose from arenaceous tests by loss of mineral grains. The primitive shapes, therefore, would have to have been tubular at first and then spiral, as in the astrorhizids. This theory is supported by facts of stratigraphic distribution because the arenaceous foraminifers are known

---

Figure 2.18 (*opposite*).   Larger Foraminifers.
Lituolicae: 1. Exterior of *Dictyoconus walnutensis*, 15X, Cretaceous, Texas.   2a, 2b. Longitudinal and transverse sections of *Dictyoconus americanus*, 10X, Eocene, West Indies and Florida. 3. Longitudinal section of *Coskinolina adkinsi*, 50X, Cretaceous, Texas.
Miliolicae: 4. *Marginopora vertebralis*, Recent, Bikini. 4a, equatorial section, 12X. 4b, axial section, 15X. 4c, surface, 6X. 4d, edge, 13X. 4e, equatorial section of region around proloculus, 25X.   5. *Borelis melo*, 30X Recent, Pacific. 5a, apertural side. 5b, axial section showing miliolid interior. 5c, end view.   6. Axial section of *Borelis schlumbergeri* showing remarkable similarity to fusulinids, 25X, Recent, Bikini.
Rotaliicae: 7. Axial section of *Lepidocyclina peruviana*, 24X, Eocene, Peru.   8. *Lepidocyclina mantelli*, Oligocene, Florida. 8a, equatorial section, 12X. 8b, axial section, 8X.   9. *Operculinoides vicksburgensis*, Oligocene, Florida. 9a, exterior, 6X. 9b, axial section, 8X. 9c, equatorial section, 10X.   10. Exterior of *Calcarina spengleri*, 7X, Recent, Bikini.   11. *Heterostegina texana*, Oligocene, Texas. 11a, equatorial section, 12X. 11b, axial section, 10X.   12. *Nummulites ghizehensis*, 2/3X, Eocene, Egypt. 12a, edge view. 12b, megalospheric test. 12c, microspheric test.
(1, 3 after Barker, 1944. 2 after Cole, 1942. 4, 6, 10 after Cole, 1954. 5 after Brady, 1884. 7-9 after Cole, 1944. 11 after Gravell and Hanna, 1937.)

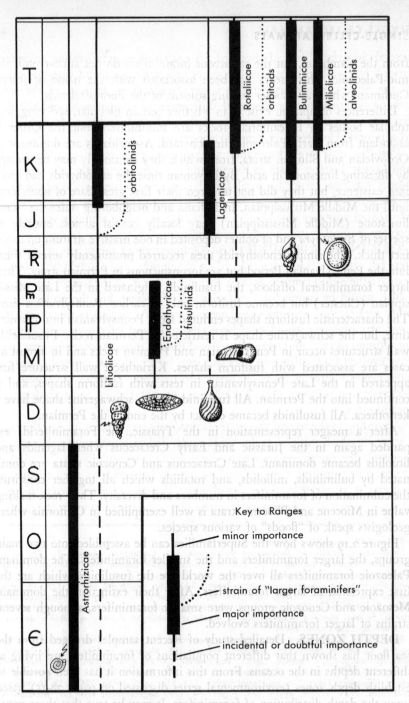

Figure 2.19. Stratigraphic Distribution of Foraminiferida. (Based on data from Glaessner, 1947.)

from the Cambrian, but the calcareous foraminifers do not appear until the mid-Paleozoic. This theory has been associated with the name of Joseph Cushman, who was another leading student of the Foraminiferida.

Differences of opinion exist as to whether certain globular, radiating, and tubular bodies in Precambrian rocks are foraminifers, but the Order is abundant from Early Paleozoic time onward. Astrorhizids are dominant in Ordovician and Silurian strata, from which they commonly may be isolated by digesting limestone in acid. By Devonian time the endothyrids had come into existence, but they did not undergo their first great flare of abundance until the Middle Mississippian. In Indiana and neighboring states the Salem limestone (Middle Mississippian) may locally consist almost entirely of species of *Endothyra* and of oolites deposited in one massive stratum up to 125 feet thick. The simple endothyrids then recurred prominently several times into the Pennsylvanian Period but are inconspicuous in Permian strata. Their larger foraminiferal offshoot, the fusulinids, originated in the Late Mississippian (Chester) but became fusiform only in earliest Pennsylvanian time. The characteristic fusiform shapes endured from Pennsylvanian into Permian time, but the schwagerine shape is restricted to Permian rocks. Fusulinellid wall structures occur in Pennsylvanian and Permian rocks and in almost all cases are associated with fusiform shapes. Keriothecal wall structure first appeared in the Late Pennsylvanian in tests with fusiform shapes, and it continued into the Permian. All fusulinids with a schwagerine shape have a keriotheca. All fusulinids became extinct by the end of the Permian.

After a meager representation in the Triassic, the Foraminiferida expanded again in the Jurassic and Early Cretaceous when lagenids and lituolids became dominant. Late Cretaceous and Cenozoic strata are dominated by buliminids, miliolids, and rotaliids which all together constitute the culmination of foraminifers in numbers and diversity. Their rock-making value in Miocene and Pliocene strata is well exemplified in California where geologists speak of "floods" of various species.

Figure 2.19 shows how the Superfamilies can be assembled into two main groups, the larger foraminifers and the smaller foraminifers. The dominant Paleozoic foraminifers all over the world are the fusulinids, which are the first expression of larger foraminifers. After their extinction the dominant Mesozoic and Cenozoic groups were smaller foraminifers, although several strains of larger foraminifers evolved.

DEPTH ZONES. Detailed study of Recent samples dredged from the sea floor has shown that different populations of foraminifers are living at different depths in the oceans. From this information it has been possible to establish depth zones (environmental series discussed on pages 28-31) based upon the depth distribution of foraminifers. It may be true that these zones really are temperature zones, because creatures seem to be more sensitive to lowered temperatures at depth than they are to pressure itself; but it also is probably true that ecologic foraminiferal zones represent complex effects on living organisms of temperature, pressure, light, salinity, turbulence, food, acidity, and suspended matter.

Many Recent species of foraminifers have been discovered in Upper Tertiary sediments; therefore depth zones based upon Recent species can be recognized in some stratigraphic successions. Moreover, knowledge of environments of Recent life zones makes it possible to interpret ecologic conditions which were in effect when some Tertiary sediments were being deposited. As we learn more about the habitat in which petroleum originated, we expect to be able to use fossils (particularly foraminifers) to recognize regions of encouraging geologic conditions in which to explore for oil and gas.

For instance, environmental considerations affect interpretations of deposits of marine Tertiary sediments which accumulated on the Gulf Coast or on the Pacific Coast. Exploration for oil is very active in both of these regions, so there is economic significance to the interpretations.

Perhaps the more elementary application of ecologic studies in paleontology is in correlation of faunas. If two populations in nearby regions are very similar it is commonly assumed that the strata in which the fossils occur are of the same age. Conversely, if two faunas are different, the strata commonly have been considered to be of different ages. The first of these working hypotheses is generally true, but the second needs to be qualified with ecologic information, because two faunas in different environments will always be different due to depth zonation, even though they lived at the same time. This is apparent in Figure 1.8, in which the *Discorbis* A zone lies between the *Heterostegina* zone and the *Discorbis* B zone in well 1. But in well 2 the *Discorbis* A zone is represented by the upper part of the *Heterostigina* zone, which is an offshore facies. Instead of interpreting the base of the *Discorbis* B zone as an unconformity in well 2 (because the A zone is missing), the contact really is conformable; sediments in the upper part of the *Heterostegina* zone were merely deposited in deeper water than were the sediments characterized by *Discorbis* A.

The more advanced application of ecologic information concerns interpretation of the history of a region. On the Pacific Coast, for instance, the Tertiary sediments accumulated in small depressions such as the Los Angeles Basin. It has been discovered during the geologic exploration of the Los Angeles Basin that oil fields there tend to produce only from sands which were deposited in the bathyal zone. Inasmuch as many of the same species or closely related species of Tertiary foraminifers still live in the Pacific Ocean today, it is possible to establish by comparison the depth of water in which the Tertiary sediments were deposited. Accordingly, it is recognized that the mid-Miocene sediments in the center of the Los Angeles Basin, for instance, accumulated in water about a mile deep. Thereafter the depth of water decreased progressively through Pliocene time until finally the basin ceased to exist as a site of marine deposition in Pleistocene time. Obviously, the environment on the sea floor changed radically as near-shore conditions shifted progressively toward the center of the basin with the passage of time.

Depth distribution of foraminifers also can be used in study of Tertiary sediments on the Gulf Coastal Plain, but in conditions which are somewhat different geologically from those which are present in the Los Angeles Basin. The Tertiary sediments of the Gulf Coastal Plain consist essentially of a long-continued sequence of regressive marine deposits in which there is an occasional transgressive tongue. Thus, on Figure 1.8, well 2 penetrated a notable transgression of the *Discorbis* D zone directed shoreward, or toward the left side of the figure. Other transgressive tongues are represented by the tongue of bathyal sediments in the offshore equivalents of the *Discorbis* D zone and in the *Heterostegina* zone. Differentiating between transgressive and regressive marine tongues in Cenozoic deposits on the Gulf Coastal Plain is of major economic value because most of the commercial oil accumulations there occur in sands deposited during transgressions. Doris Malkin and Dorothy Jung Echols have shown that occurrence of some foraminifers such as *Nonionella cockfieldensis* (Eocene) was not confined to one bottom condition. Instead, these foraminifers are present in near-shore sand, but in mud farther out to sea where water was deeper. As transgressions progressed, the fine-grained offshore sediments advanced shoreward and overlapped earlier accumulations of sand. *N. cockfieldensis,* however, being of short duration and free from control by bottom conditions, occurs in a narrow zone which crosses from sand into mud as the faunal zone is traced away from shore (down the initial dip). Consequently, a micropaleontologist who discovers that a zone of planktonic foraminifers (or other environmentally nonrestricted fossils) rises stratigraphically downdip, can interpret the phenomenon as evidence of a marine transgression.

The existence of a transgressive tongue can be detected on physical evidence such as grain size by correlating lithologic units in a linear series of several wells extending seaward, and then constructing a lithologic cross section such as is shown in Figure 1.8. Or the same transgressions can be detected on paleontologic grounds by recognizing the sequence of depth zones of foraminifers such as would be encountered near the base of well 3 on Figure 1.8. Israelsky has shown that the time of maximum submergence in an area can be established by calculating the percentage of brackish-water, shallow-water, and deep-water foraminifers present in successive samples taken vertically through a sedimentary sequence. The zone of greatest relative abundance of deep-water forms coincides with the time of greatest marine transgression.

Depth distribution of foraminifers is just as accurate a guide to changing physical conditions as is the lithology of the sediments which were deposited under those conditions. Moreover, if lithologies are very similar, ecologic studies may be the only practical way to recognize physical changes. It is apparent, therefore, that coordination of physical and biologic studies provides greater understanding of the geologic history of the foregoing regions than does the use of only one line of evidence.

ECONOMIC MICROPALEONTOLOGY. Foraminifers are collected by field geologists or are recovered by mechanical devices from the cuttings of drilling oil wells, after which they are stored in paper or cloth sacks with adequate locality data attached. Smaller foraminifers generally are freed from matrix of shale or impure limestone by prolonged boiling if the sediment cannot be simply washed away through a set of graded screens. This "bug washing" occupies a significant portion of the time of preparation in a micropaleontologic laboratory and is a source of summer or part-time employment for students contemplating careers in micropaleontology. Washed samples are "picked" under a binocular microscope by touching a damp camel's-hair brush with a sharp point to each desired specimen, which then sticks to the brush by adhesion to the moisture. Specimens then can be attached with any one of several water-soluble adhesives to slides for identification and storage.

In the case of larger foraminifers, thin sections must be ground on glass slides by lapidary techniques so that internal structures can be studied.

Highly skilled micropaleontologists may be sent to the location of a drilling oil well to "sit on the well" by making on-the-spot determinations of foraminifers brought up with the cuttings. Well sitting is especially necessary when the downward rate of progress of the bit is so fast that there is no time to obtain laboratory determinations before a potential producing zone or a dangerous high pressure gas or water sand might be encountered. Micropaleontologists cooperate with petroleum engineers by determining the depths to which wells are to be drilled and where important strata are apt to be encountered.

Smaller foraminifers have become of paramount value in the petroleum industry in all operational areas since the first commercial use of foraminifers on the Gulf Coast in about 1919. In California the monotonous Miocene succession of fine-grained sediments has been subdivided into foraminiferal zones so successfully that the names of ages and stages proposed by Kleinpell in 1938 for foraminiferal zones have become more generally used than the erstwhile lithologic names of formations (Fig. 1.6). Dependence upon micropaleontologic control in mapping or in stratigraphic work has become so widespread in areas such as the Gulf Coast and California that physical geologists and even engineers have developed a proprietary interest in

Foraminiferida, referring to them by such familiar appellations as "forams" and "bugs." Moreover, highly unorthodox abbreviations such as "*Val. cal.*" and "lower *Siphos*" (meaning *Valvulineria californica* and a zone of *Siphogenerina*) are bandied about in casual conversation not only by geologists and paleontologists but also by brokers and "tool pushers." No one denies that economic paleontology has sold itself for at least one systematic category.

SUBCLASS 2. ACTINOPODA

Pseudopodia of Actinopoda are arranged in stiff rays radiating from a central body (Fig. 2.3.3, 4, 6).

Order a. Radiolariida

Those marine actinopods with protoplasm differentiated into intra- and extracapsular portions constitute the radiolarians. Almost all have siliceous tests. Although their size is normally exceedingly small, some relative giants are large enough to be seen with the naked eye. In Recent seas they are common at most depths, whence their tests fall like a microscopic rain upon the sea floor.

The complete radiolarian animal (Fig. 2.3.6) consists of an inner, small, perforated **central capsule** containing the nucleus and dark **intracapsular cytoplasm** and a large, outer, perforated test containing pale protoplasm, or **extracapsular cytoplasm** from which radiate the pseudopodia. Tests are dominantly either spherical or helmet-shaped. In the latter instance long spines may project down from the rim, but these spines are commonly broken during mounting of the material. Tests are mostly opaline silica, but chitin commonly is present in the central capsule. A few radiolarians (Fig. 2.20.3) are composed of strontium sulfate (**acanthin**). Diversity of the shape and ornamentation of the test is so great that radiolarians are one of the most diverse groups of animals known; 4217 species were described in one report on the "Challenger" expedition alone!

Radiolarians are known to occur from Cambrian to Recent, with notable American occurrences in Devonian novaculite of Arkansas and Texas, Jurassic (Franciscan) chert or **radiolarite** of California, and Tertiary (Eocene and Miocene) **radiolarian earth** of the Barbados Islands, California, and Maryland. Perhaps the most important economic occurrence is in Miocene diatomite of California, which is the principal source of such insulating and filtering substances in America.

The extreme diversity of form, long stratigraphic ranges, microscopic size, and fragile nature militate against their stratigraphic use, but their abundance and potentially widespread distribution encourage their continued study.

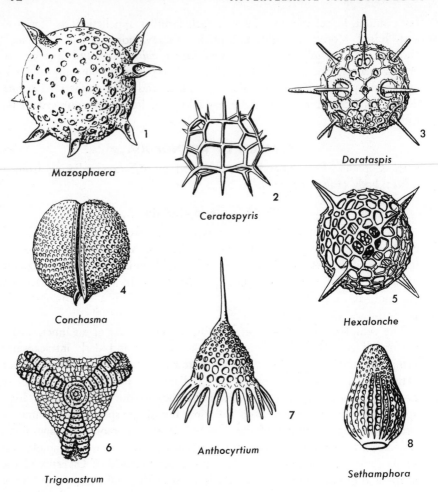

1

Mazosphaera

2

Ceratospyris

3

Dorataspis

4

Conchasma

5

Hexalonche

6

Trigonastrum

7

Anthocyrtium

8

Sethamphora

Figure 2.20.   Radiolariida.
1. *Mazosphaera* sp., 210X.   2. *Ceratospyris* sp., 150X.   3. *Dorataspis* sp., 200X.   4. *Conchasma* sp., 110X.   5. *Hexalonche* sp., 200X.   6. *Trigonastrum* sp., 50X.   7. *Anthocyrtium* sp., 140X.   8. *Sethamphora* sp., 145X.
(After Haeckel, 1887.)

Order b.   Heliozoida

A few actinopods possess only the outer capsule or test which is not generally preservable. Rayed pseudopodia (axopoda) are stiffened by axial filaments, thus warranting the common name "sun animalcules."

Heliozoans have been reported from Pleistocene lake sediments and peat in northern Europe. Recent occurrences are in both fresh and marine water (Fig. 2.3.3, 4).

Class C.   Sporozoa

Sporozoans are of major importance medically, inasmuch as the group contains parasites such as *Plasmodium,* the malarial organism. Locomotor devices are generally lacking. They also lack hard parts and therefore are unlikely to occur as fossils.

Class D.   Ciliata

Many protozoans move by means of myriad, minute, hairlike **cilia** which cover their bodies like the fabric pile of a piece of velvet or mohair. These Protozoa are sometimes referred to as the Class Infusoria, but more recently the tendency of zoologists has been to suppress Infusoria in favor of the word Ciliata. "Infusoria" is a relic of former beliefs that hay and water mixtures (infusions) produced living animals such as *Paramoecium* by spontaneous generation.

A few ciliates called **tintinnids** secrete an external, transparent, vaselike skeleton called a **lorica,** which can be fossilized. Some of the loricas are glassy, some have one or more prismatic central layers, and others are studded with mineral grains. Most have a flaring collar and a pointed caudal appendix. All are tiny, being 50 to 100 microns long.

Most of the Recent tintinnids occur in marine water, but a few are known

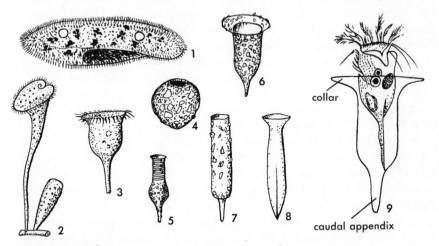

Figure 2.21. Cieliata.
  1. *Paramoecium* sp., 125X, Recent.   2. *Stentor* sp., 25X, Recent.   3. *Vorticella* sp., 250X, Recent.   4. *Stenosomella* sp., 100X, Recent.   5. *Codonellopsis* sp., 100X, Recent.   6. *Tintinnopsis* sp., 100X, Recent.   7. *Tintinnopsis* sp., 100X, Recent.   8. *Amphorellopsis* sp., greatly enlarged, Recent.   9. morphology of *Tintinnopsis* sp.
  (1, 3 after Conn, 1905. 2 after Kent, 1880-1882. 4-9 after Colom, 1948.)

in fresh water. Fossil species have been reported from Upper Jurassic and Cretaceous strata in the Mediterranean region of Europe. Cross sections of calcified tintinnids may be studied in thin sections of some limestone.

DISTRIBUTION OF RECENT MARINE PROTOZOA. Some Recent marine Protozoa occur in numbers such as to constitute a major source of sediments in the open oceans. Of principal interest are the planktonic foraminifers and the radiolarians, both of which are major inhabitants of the upper 600 feet of the ocean in most parts of the world. After these animals succumb, their tests drop to the ocean floor, either in shallow water or out in the deep sea. Although a large test of *Globigerina* may fall to the floor of the deep sea in a day, many days may elapse before tests of very small foraminifers or of radiolarians reach bottom (about 2.5 mi). Tests may not be apparent in near-shore deposits because so much land-derived sediment is also accumulating that the presence of protozoans is masked. Out in the open ocean, however, vast areas of the sea floor are blanketed with **oozes** of one sort or another which are formed primarily from the skeletons of minute animals, plus some admixture of other sediment.

The most common of the oozes is made up of planktonic foraminifers, of which *Globigerina* is the most abundant of several Genera; hence, **globigerine ooze** is well known. Globigerine ooze occurs at depths varying from about 7500 to 13,500 feet in different oceanic basins. It is the commonest deep-sea sediment throughout the Atlantic Ocean but is second in importance to red clay in the Pacific Ocean. Even so, the southern Pacific Ocean is mostly underlain by globigerine ooze. Locally, as on the flanks of some mid-oceanic ridges, so many pteropods (minute molluscs) are incorporated in the globigerine ooze as to warrant calling that variety a "pteropod ooze."

Below about 15,000 feet the solubility of calcium carbonate in sea water is so great that calcareous tests of foraminifers and pteropods are dissolved. Under these circumstances the siliceous tests of radiolarians remain. Moreover, they may be so abundant (over 20 to 25 per cent of the sediment) as to deserve the name of **radiolarian ooze.** Radiolarian ooze grades laterally into red clay below about 18,000 feet and extends down to at least 24,000 feet. One of the most striking patches of radiolarian ooze is a strip which seems to underlie the Counterequatorial Current just north of the equator in the Pacific Ocean.

Supposed fossil oozes which have been located in outcrop at a few places would seem to indicate that the deep sea has been uplifted into land. This would be contrary to a widely held geologic belief in the permanence of oceanic basins. Cretaceous chalk in England, for instance, is famous as a foraminiferal deposit by reason of Huxley's essay "On a Piece of Chalk." In this case, however, the ooze consists of bottom-dwelling organisms whose living counterparts inhabit shallow water today. The same is true of the geologically well-known Lomita marl (Pleistocene) in California. This is really a foraminiferal sand which was deposited in only 200 to 300 feet of water. And so it goes for other examples, with the result that no deep-sea foraminiferal oozes are known, even though rather deep-water associations of benthonic foraminifers occur. Therefore, the presence of foraminiferal deposits does not nullify the theory of permanence of oceanic basins.

Of the supposed fossil radiolarian (or diatomaceous) oozes, those of the island of Barbados in the West Indies resemble deep-sea deposits most closely.

It is certain, however, that some supposed oozes are not deep-sea deposits. Radiolarians are revealed in them because of the absence of masking sediments. Under such circumstances other supposed outcrops of deep-sea deposits are generally viewed with reservations. This brings us back to the original observation that, after all, the parent organisms live in the surficial waters of the ocean; hence, their tests can accumulate in waters of any depth under the proper conditions.

QUESTIONS

1. What characteristics favor the use of protozoans in stratigraphic studies?
2. What are the disadvantages of protozoans for stratigraphic studies?
3. It has become popular to ascribe more significance to fusulinids in studies of Carboniferous rocks than to other groups of animals. Why is their study enjoying such a vogue?
4. What does the occurrence of radiolarians in an outcropping sediment indicate as to the environment of deposition? The rate of sedimentation? The current velocity?
5. Why are micropaleontologists becoming increasingly concerned with Recent marine foraminiferal faunas?
6. How would the parallelism of shape between the four Superfamilies of larger foraminifers be explained by a proponent of orthogenesis? Of ortho-selection?
7. What reason is there to think that *Orbulina* is a close relative of *Globigerina*?
8. What characters make *Bigenerina* and *Rectobolivina* homoeomorphic species? Why are they placed in separate Genera?
9. How can ecologic distribution be used to recognize a marine transgression?
10. What is the nature of the proof needed to discover whether or not quinqueloculine foraminifers really are the most primitive miliolids?

BIBLIOGRAPHY

Aberdeen, E., 1940, Radiolarian fauna of the Caballos formation, Marathon basin, Texas: Jour. Paleont., v. 14, no. 2, pp. 127–139.

Bandy, O. L., 1949, Eocene and Oligocene Foraminifera from Little Stave Creek, Clarke County, Alabama: Bull. Amer. Paleont., v. 32, no. 131.

———, 1954, Distribution of some shallow-water Foraminifera in the Gulf of Mexico: U. S. Geol. Survey Prof. Paper 254-F, pp. 125–141.

Barker, R. W., 1944, Some larger Foraminifera from the Lower Cretaceous of Texas: Jour. Paleont., v. 18, no. 2, pp. 204–209.

Brady, H. B., 1884, Report on the Foraminifera, etc., Report on the scientific results of the exploring voyage of H. M. S. "Challenger," 1873–76: Zoology, v. 9.

Bramlette, M. N., and Riedel, W. R., 1954, Stratigraphic value of discoasters and some other microfossils related to Recent coccolithophores: Jour. Paleont., v. 28, no. 4, pp. 385–403.

Campbell, A. S., and Moore, R. C., 1954, Protozoa (chiefly Radiolaria and Tintinnina) in Treatise on invertebrate paleontology, pt. D, Protista 3.

Cole, W. S., 1942, Stratigraphic and paleontologic studies of wells in Florida—No. 2: Florida Geol. Survey, Bull. 20.

———, 1944, Stratigraphic and paleontologic studies of wells in Florida—No. 3: Florida Geol. Survey, Bull. 26.

———, 1954, Larger Foraminifera and smaller diagnostic Foraminifera from Bikini drill holes: U. S. Geol. Survey Prof. Paper 260-O, pp. 569–608.

Colom, G., 1948, Fossil tintinnids: loricated Infusoria of the Order of the Oligotricha: Jour. Paleont., v. 22, no. 2, pp. 233–263.

Conn, W. H., 1905, A preliminary report on the Protozoa of the fresh waters of Connecticut: Connecticut State Geol. Nat. Hist. Survey, Bull. 2.

Cushman, J. A., 1939, A monograph of the foraminiferal Family Nonionidae: U. S. Geol. Survey Prof. Paper 191.

———, 1946, Upper Cretaceous Foraminifera of the Gulf Coastal region of the United States and adjacent areas: U. S. Geol. Survey Prof. Paper 206.

———, 1948, Foraminifera, their classification and economic use: 4th ed., Cushman Lab. Foram. Res., Spec. Pub.

———, and Stewart, R. E., 1926, A new Plectofrondicularia from the Pliocene of California: Contr. Cushman Lab. Foram. Res., v. 2, pt. 2, no. 28, pp. 39, 47.

Dunbar, C. O., and Henbest, L. G., 1942, Pennsylvania Fusulinidae of Illinois: Illinois Geol. Survey, Bull. 67. (Contains information about collecting, sectioning, and morphology.)

Dunn, P. H., 1942, Silurian Foraminifera of the Mississippi basin: Jour. Paleont., v. 16, no. 3, pp. 317–342.

Ellis, B. F., and Messina, A. R., 1942–, A catalogue of the Foraminifera: New York, Amer. Mus. Nat. Hist.

Galloway, J. J., 1933, A manual of Foraminifera: Bloomington, Indiana, Principia Press.

———, and Heminway, C. E., 1941, The Tertiary Foraminifera of Puerto Rico: New York Acad. Sci., Scientific Survey of Puerto Rico and the Virgin Islands, v. 3, pt. 4, pp. 275–491.

———, and Wissler, S. G., 1927, Pleistocene Foraminifera from the Lomita Quarry, Palos Verdes Hills, California: Jour. Paleont., v. 1, no. 1, pp. 35–87.

Garrett, J. B., 1939, Some Middle Tertiary smaller Foraminifera from subsurface beds of Jefferson County, Texas: Jour. Paleont., v. 13, no. 6, pp. 575-579.

———, and Ellis, A. D., Jr., 1937, Distinctive Foraminifera of the Genus *Marginulina* from Middle Tertiary beds of the Gulf Coast: Jour. Paleont., v. 11, no. 8, pp. 629–633.

Glaessner, M. F., 1947, Principles of micropalaeontology: 2nd ed., New York, John Wiley and Sons.

Goodman, A. J., 1951, White specks in Colorado Shale: Bull. Amer. Assoc. Petroleum Geologists, v. 35, no. 11, pp. 2427–2433.

Gravell, D. W., and Hanna, M. A., 1937, The *Lepidocyclina texana* horizon in the *Heterostegina* zone, Upper Oligocene, of Texas and Louisiana: Jour. Paleont., v. 11, no. 6, pp. 517–529.

Haeckel, E., 1887, The Radiolaria: Report on the scientific results of the exploring voyage of H. M. S. "Challenger," 1873–76: Zoology, v. 18, pts. 1, 2, pls.

Hanna, G. D., 1928, Silicoflagellata from the Cretaceous of California: Jour. Paleont., v. 1, pp. 259–263.

Hofker, J., 1956, Foraminifera dentata: Spolia Zool. Mus. Hauniensis XV, Skr., Univ. Zool. Mus. (Copenhagen), pp. 9–13.

Israelsky, M. C., 1949, Oscillation chart: Bull. Amer. Assoc. Petroleum Geologists, v. 33, no. 1, pp. 92–98.

Jones, D. J., 1956, Introduction to microfossils: New York, Harper & Brothers.

Kent, W. S., 1880–1882, A manual of the Infusoria, etc.: London, David Bogue, 3 vols.

Kleinpell, R. M., 1938, Miocene stratigraphy of California: Amer. Assoc. Petroleum Geologists (Tulsa, Oklahoma).

Knight, R. L., 1956, Permian fusulines from Nevada: Jour. Paleont., v. 30, no. 4, pp. 773–792.

Loeblich, A. R., Jr., and Loeblich, H. Tappan, 1957, Correlation of the Gulf and Atlantic Coastal Plain Paleocene and Lower Eocene formations by means of planktonic Foraminifera: Jour. Paleont., v. 31, no. 6, pp. 1109–1137.

Lohmann, H., 1902, Die Coccolithophoridae, etc.: Archiv. für Protistenkunde, v. 1, pp. 89–165.

Lowman, S. W., 1949, Sedimentary facies in Gulf Coast: Bull. Amer. Assoc. Petroleum Geologists, v. 33, no. 12, pp. 1939–1997.

Malkin, D. S., and Jung, D. A., 1941, Marine sedimentation and oil accumulation. Transgressive marine overlap: Bull. Amer. Assoc. Petroleum Geologists, v. 25, no. 11, pp. 2010–2020.

Myers, E. H., 1935, The life history of Patellina corrugata Williamson a foraminifer: Bull. Scripps Inst. Oceanography (Univ. California), Tech. Ser., v. 3, no. 15, pp. 355–392.

Natland, M. L., 1933, The temperature and depth-distribution of some Recent and fossil Foraminifera in the southern California Region: Bull. Scripps Inst. Oceanography (Univ. California), Tech. Ser., v. 3, no. 10, pp. 225–230.

Revelle, R. R., 1944, Marine bottom samples collected in the Pacific Ocean by the "Carnegie" on its seventh cruise: Carnegie Inst. Washington Pub. 556 (especially pp. 8, 9, 42, 43).

Schlumberger, C., 1891, Révision des Biloculines des Grand Fondes: Mém. Soc. Zool. (France), v. 4, pp. 542–579.

——, 1893, Monographie des Miliolidées du Golfe de Marseille: Mém. Soc. Zool. (France), v. 6, pp. 57-80.

——, 1894, Note sur les Foraminifères des Mers Arctiques Russes: Mém. Soc. Zool. (France), v. 7, pp. 252–258.

Skinner, J. W., and Wilde, G. L., 1955, New fusulinids from the Permian of west Texas: Jour. Paleont., v. 29, no. 6, pp. 927–940.

Stone, B., 1946, Siphogenerinoides Cushman (Order Foraminifera, Family Buliminidae): Jour. Paleont., v. 20, no. 5, pp. 463–478.

Tappan, H., 1940, Foraminifera from the Grayson formation of northern Texas: Jour. Paleont., v. 14, no. 2, pp. 93–126.

Thompson, M. L., 1948, Studies of American fusulinids: Univ. Kansas Pub., Paleont. Contr., Protozoa, art. 1.

——, 1954, American Wolfcampian fusulinids: Univ. Kansas Pub., Paleont. Contr., Protozoa, art. 5.

Zeller, E. J., 1950, Stratigraphic significance of Mississippian endothyroid Foraminifera: Univ. Kansas Pub., Paleont. Contr., Protozoa, art. 4, pp. 1–23.

Chapter 3

SPONGES AND SPONGELIKE ORGANISMS

PHYLUM II. PORIFERA

Growth forms of sponges range from flat incrustations to hummocky balls, vaselike or hand-shaped erect growths, and fan-shaped expansions. The direction of growth is governed by vicissitudes of the substratum on which they grow and by the water currents which bathe them, so even the different individuals of one species cannot be expected to resemble each other closely in external form. The common bath sponges exemplify the variability of Porifera in external form, but soft sponges of this sort are typical neither of most of the common fossil sponges nor of all living sponges. Most sponges contain needlelike skeletal elements which are either scattered through the body tissue or are fused into a hard supporting boxwork.

Most sponges are marine, living in waters which vary greatly in depth, from the strand line to the abyssal zone. A few inhabit fresh water. Sponges are **gregarious,** that is, they tend to grow close together but in isolated patches. Accordingly, their occurrence in the stratigraphic record is erratic, but they may make good zonal fossils of very local nature. It is probable that fossil sponges are of more common occurrence than is indicated by paleontologic reports, because they are of indefinite shape and may be mistaken for concretions or for some vague sedimentary bulge on a bedding plane.

The body wall of a sponge is composed somewhat rudely of three layers, but these layers are not all the same as the three layers in higher animals. If the outer layer of the Porifera consists of a pavement of cells it can be termed **ectoderm,** as in the higher animals. Some sponges, however, are invested with a noncellular sheath or cuticle instead of an ectoderm. The inner layer of cells is composed of collar-bearing flagellated cells called **choanocytes** (Fig. 3.1.2). Rhythmic beating of the flagella creates currents of water which circulate through pores or passageways in the body wall of the sponge. Moreover, the flagella trap particles of food which are ingested into the choanocytes and are digested there. The layer of choanocytes corresponds roughly to the **endoderm** of higher animals. Between the ectoderm and the layer of choanocytes is the third layer of tissue, which is called the **mesenchyme.** It is analogous to the mesoderm of higher animals but scarcely resembles it. Instead, the mesenchyme of Porifera consists of a matrix of noncellular jellylike **mesogloea** in which are suspended various sorts of cells and a variety

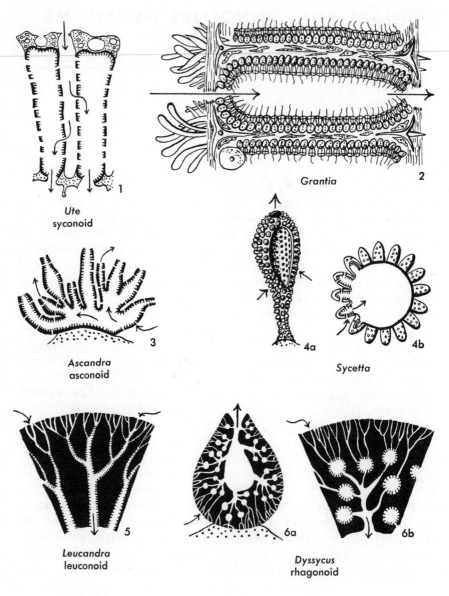

Ute
syconoid

1

Grantia

2

Ascandra
asconoid

3

Sycetta

4a

4b

Leucandra
leuconoid

5

Dyssycus
rhagonoid

6a

6b

of needlelike skeletal elements, the **spicules.** The spicules are secreted by one special group of amoeboid cells called scleroblasts (Fig. 3.2.2) which move through the mesenchyme. Another group of amoeboid cells assists in the digestive process and serves as a circulatory system by transporting nutriment to other cells; moreover, these same cells carry on all reproductive functions of the animals. A third group of cells, the spongioblasts, secretes the horny fibers of spongin which make up the main mass of a bath sponge. Still other cells serve as connective cells between the inner and outer layers, and a final group of contractile cells functions as muscles to close openings or to adjust the position of the sponge. Many of these cells migrate amoeba-fashion through the mesogloea, and even dermal cells may pass from one layer to another via the mesogloea. Cellular differentiation is so primitive that a cell may function as a choanocyte for a time, but then become amoeboid and migrate to another place and take on another function. It is apparent that sponge cells are not only individualistic but are amply adaptable to changing requirements. A sponge can be cut up into small pieces, each of which will continue to grow; and growing sponges can fuse together physiologically into larger colonies. Finally, if sponges are rubbed through a sieve and the separate cells are allowed to settle out suspended in their associated mesogloea, they will reorient themselves into a new colony and continue to grow.

The primitive state of organization of the sponges caused many early naturalists to classify these creatures among the plants. Sponges' occasional greenish color, lack of differentiation into organs, and completely sedentary habit lent credence to the early belief. As a result of the indecision as to whether sponges are plants or animals, they were appropriately known as "zoophytes" by other naturalists. The fact is, however, that Porifera are truly animals, being unable to survive for more than a few days without having access to some source of food. Sponges lack nervous, respiratory, circulatory, and locomotor organs; and only a simulated digestive apparatus is developed. Sponges are sort of superaggregates of protozoanlike cells in which interdependence of cells is at its lowest level. Some zoologists recognize the

---

Figure 3.1 (*opposite*). Morphology of Living Sponges.
Movement of water is shown by arrows. In all schematic figures the flagellated layer of cells is indicated with comblike hachures.
1. Cross section of wall of *Ute syconoides* showing typical syconoid architecture with its alternation of incurrent canals and flagellated chambers, the two connected by prosopyles, much enlarged. Inner and outer cortical layers are stippled. 2. Cross section of wall of *Grantia compressa*, 535X. Choanocytes line the flagellated chamber. 3. Vertical section of a colony of *Ascandra reticulum* showing asconoid type of architecture in a very simple calcareous sponge, about 5X. 4. *Sycetta primitiva*, a calcareous sponge with flagellated chambers protruding beyond the paragastric cavity. 4a, cut-away profile of a complete individual, 8X. 4b, oblique cross section, 4X. 5. Schematic transverse section of part of the wall of *Leucandra bomba*, a calcareous sponge with radial leuconoid architecture, 2X. 6. *Dyssycus ananas*, a calcareous sponge with the most advanced (rhagonoid) architecture. 6a, schematic longitudinal section, 2/3X. 6b, schematic transverse section of part of a wall, 2X.
(1 after Dendy, 1894. 2 after Kent, 1880-1882. 3-6 after Haeckel, 1872.)

singular status of Porifera by putting this group in a separate systematic Subkingdom, the Parazoa, to differentiate them from Protozoa on the one hand and from all higher animals, the Metazoa, on the other.

The most fundamental differences among sponges seem to be reflected in the complexity of the food-gathering system. In the simplest stage of sponge development the organism resembles a narrow-necked vase with its thin walls perforated by small **pores.** Usually several vaselike individuals grow together in a colony. The inner surface of a colony and in some cases the lining of the pores are paved with choanocytes (Fig. 3.1.3). Water enters the pores, flows across the blankets of choanocytes in the **paragastric cavity,** and passes out through the large excurrent pore **(oscule).** Sponges of this simple type are said to have the **asconoid** type of architecture. Asconoid architecture is not commonly seen in mature sponges, but it is represented in the very youthful developmental stages of some calcareous sponges.

Increase in the digestive ability of sponges is brought about simply by addition of new choanocytes rather than by perfecting a true digestive system through improved cooperation among cells. Mere addition of new paragastric chambers does not increase the digestive efficiency but only the size of the colony. Likewise, increase in size of each individual not only does not increase efficiency of food-gathering ability, but it limits the growth of an individual because the sponge wall is unable to support a large body. The result is that in sponges there have developed ingenious methods of folding the body wall so that the digestive area increases but the size remains the same, supporting strength is improved, and sediment has less chance of obstructing the choanocytes.

One simple method of folding the body wall is seen in *Grantia* and *Sycetta* (Fig. 3.1.2, 4). In *Sycetta* the body wall bulges out in moundlike nodes, the hollow centers of which bear all of the choanocytes; and the paragastric cavity has no digestive function at all. A more advanced and much more typical development is for the body wall to be accordion-pleated into pairs of passageways, one of which necessarily opens outward and the other opens inward (Fig. 3.1.1). Naturally, after pleating has taken place the choanocytes line opposite sides of the outfolded transverse chamber and the pores which were strictly external in ascon sponges now are arranged internally along the walls of the infolded transverse chamber. Water enters through the new incurrent pore, passes along an **incurrent canal,** then enters the flagellated **excurrent canal** through the true pores, and passes into the paragastric cavity through the new excurrent pore. Sponges of this rather common type are said to have the **syconoid** type of architecture.

Progressive compaction of the body wall and concentration of the flagellated chambers produce **leuconoid** architecture. In radial leuconoid sponges (Fig. 3.1.5) many small incurrent canals coalesce into a few large flagellated canals. Water still flows into a paragastric cavity and out through an oscule as in Figure 3.1.4a. The most advanced kind of sponge (Fig. 3.1.6) is a special leuconoid type in which the flagellated cells are confined to spherical chambers that are buried deeply in the body wall. These sponges sometimes are said to have **rhagonoid** architecture. In them the water passes through incurrent canals into the flagellated chambers, then through special excurrent canals into the paragastric cavity and out through the oscule. Nearly all living and fossil sponges are constructed on the most complex (leuconoid or rhagonoid) architectural plans.

In no sponge are any organs homologous with a stomach or with a digestive track. Nor are the external pores of asconoid sponges homologous with the external pores of syconoid or leuconoid sponges. It was the presence of the poriferous surface, however, which suggested the name Porifera for the Phylum. Curiously, although the sponges were known from classical times, the method of circulation of water through them was not demonstrated until 1825.

Sponges proliferate offshoots from the parent colony by **budding,** in which a new tubular extension grows up from the basal expansion or from the side of a previous growth. If, in rare cases, one of these new shoots should become detached, it can start a new colony; sponges, however, generally must rely on sexual reproduction for distribution of the group. Larval stages may last several days, during which time the free-swimming form may drift many miles on the ocean currents. Fresh-water sponges are capable of forming special aggregates of cells into a drought-resistant resting stage called a **gemmule.** When living conditions become adverse the gemmule breaks away from the parent and drifts off (possibly even to be blown about by winds!) to form a new colony after favorable conditions return and the gemmule can renew growth.

SKELETAL STRUCTURES. The necessity of keeping the canals open for circulation of water is correlated with the development of adequate supporting skeletal elements. To be sure, some simple types lack hard skeletons and are supported only by gelatinous mesenchyme. Other sponges, however, secrete a horny organic substance, **spongin,** as threads throughout the mesenchyme. Spongin is familiar as the substance present in bath sponges (all cellular tissue around the fibers having been removed prior to marketing). Unfortunately for the geologic record, spongin decomposes after the death of the organism and is not likely to be found fossilized.

Most sponge remains consist of minute siliceous or calcareous needles, hooks, or plates which are embedded in the tissues as interlocking **spicules.** These spicules may be so matted or even fused together that the original shape of the sponge is preserved after death, or the loose spicules may fall apart and be scattered over the ocean floor. Some sponges are able to pick up organic or inorganic foreign bodies. These include tiny skeletal elements of radiolarians, diatoms, and foraminifers; spicules of other sponges; or just mineral grains of fragments of broken molluscs. Debris of this sort commonly incrusts the surface, but the fragments also are transported by wandering amoeboid cells down into inner regions of the mesenchyme where they are incorporated into the natural skeletal system as peculiar erratics. Thus, a sponge may consist of spongin, of spicules, of foreign bodies, or of a combination of spongin and spicules.

Spicules are composed of two different chemical compounds, the most common being hydrous silica (opal) and the other being calcium carbonate (calcite). Calcareous spicules are commonly silicified after burial and thereby simulate natural siliceous spicules. Contrariwise, original siliceous spicules can be dissolved from argillaceous rocks by ground water and the molds may be filled secondarily with calcite (or with limonite) as casts which thereby simulate calcareous spicules.

Spicules attain two general sizes. The larger ones, **megascleres,** may be represented by silky strands several millimeters long, or they may be so small that they are barely visible to the unaided eye (about 0.3 mm long). Megascleres comprise the main mass of the skeleton of a sponge. A minute canal commonly occupies the axis of many megascleres. The smaller spicules, **microscleres,** are too small to be seen with the unaided eye (about 0.01 to 0.1 mm long). Microscleres serve as auxiliary reinforcement of bodies, particularly around pores in the body wall. Both megascleres and microscleres commonly are present in an individual sponge.

Specialists have named numerous modifications in the geometric construction of spicules, but the various kinds can be grouped into a few simple basic types, depending upon the number of axes or rays present. Thus, rays of sponge spicules grow along imaginary lines which are analogous to axes of symmetry of crystals. Some of the various kinds of spicules are illustrated in Figure 3.2.

Monaxon spicules are elongate needles, either straight or curved, smooth or spinose, pointed or blunt, and possibly even knobbed at one or both ends.

Triaxon spicules may form in one plane or in three dimensions. In planar spicules the three rays do not intersect, but diverge from a common point along three axes 120 degrees apart. One ray may be much longer than the other two, and the two shorter ones may converge at various angles to join one end of the long ray. One special kind of triaxon spicule is shaped like a tuning fork. In three-dimensional triaxon spicules, the three rays pass at right angles to each other through a common point and are analogous to the three axes of symmetry in the isometric system of crystallography. In these latter forms the six halves of the rays about the common point produce

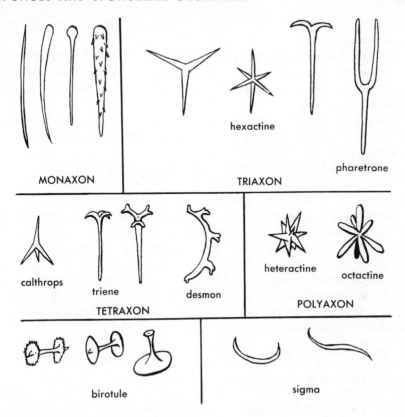

Figure 3.2. Types of Sponge Spicules.
All figures are greatly enlarged but not to the same scale.
(Schematic drawings from various sources.)

hexactine spicules. Hexactine spicules usually have one extremely long ray and two very short ones, and the skeletal elements seem at first glance to consist of bundles of spun glass (Fig. 3.6.2). One ray of a hexactine spicule may be aborted to form five-rayed spicules.

Rays of **tetraxon** spicules are arranged precisely like the four axes of symmetry in the tetragonal system of crystallography. The resulting spicule normally consists of four equally long rays symmetrically disposed about a common point; hence, a tetraxon spicule of this sort will always stand upon three rays and keep the fourth ray pointing straight up. These are **calthrops** spicules. In other tetraxons, referred to as **triaenes,** one ray is much longer than the others, or the remaining three rays are variously curved, recurved, or branched. Members of one extremely aberrant group of tetraxons, called **desmas,** have lost almost all evidence of fundamental tetragonal construction by adding shapeless secondary excrescences and auxiliary projections. These spicules commonly are fused together to form solid masses, but even then some trace of tetraxon symmetry may remain (Fig. 3.4.9).

Polyaxons, as the name implies, are multirayed. A ball-like aggregation of short spines is a **heteractine** spicule or an **asteractine** spicule. An eight-rayed form with six rays in one plane and two at right angles to this plane is called an **octactine** spicule.

Birotules consist of two buttonlike or star-shaped discs connected by a rod, the whole assemblage reminding one of two wheels on an axle.

Sigmas are S-shaped or C-shaped spicules.

CLASSIFICATION. Recognition of fossil sponges from chemical composition and shape of spicules alone is almost impossible, except in some extraordinary circumstance. If bodily shape is preserved, it is of some assistance in classifying groups in which individual variation is slight. Architectural features of the folded body wall are also important but usually are not preserved. Most classifications reflect efforts to incorporate the foregoing factors in some compatible fashion. The classification used here combines features of several classifications, but is weighted to emphasize groups commonly encountered as fossils. Because of the presence of choanocytes it is possible that the Porifera evolved from the Choanoflagellata through some transitional form such as *Proterospongia* (Fig. 2.2.8).

> Phylum II. Porifera
>> Class A. Demospongea
>>> Order 1. Myxospongida
>>> Order 2. Keratosida
>>> Order 3. Monactinellida
>>> Order 4. Tetractinellida
>>> Order 5. Lithistida
>>> Order 6. Heteractinellida
>> Class B. Hyalospongea
>> Class C. Calcispongea
>> Incertae sedis
>>> Receptaculites
>>> Ischadites

PHYLUM II. PORIFERA

Porifera are relatively undifferentiated organisms with pores for the entrance of water into canals and with digestion carried on by choanocytes. Skeletons consist of spongin fibers or of spicules.

Class A. Demospongea

Demospongea may lack spicules or have skeletons of spongin or silica or of mixtures of spongin and silica. Bodies are of the most advanced leuconoid architecture (rhagonoid).

Order 1. Myxospongida

These are the soft sponges without skeletal material. No fossils are known.

Order 2. Keratosida

Sponges with only spongin in their skeletons, such as the bath sponges, *Spongia* and *Euspongia,* belong here. No fossils are certainly known, but impressions assigned to the Keratosida have been reported from rocks as old as the Carboniferous.

Order 3. Monactinellida

The monactinellids are, of course, those sponges whose spicular symmetry is monaxon. Mixtures of spongin with the siliceous spicules are common. Monactinellid spicules abound in many Recent marine sediments and have been reported sporadically from strata as old as the Cambrian.

Cliona, the sulfur sponge, or boring sponge, is a well-known monactinellid representative in modern seas. It burrows into shells of oysters and other organisms, forming closely packed holes about 1 millimeter in diameter which ramify all through the substance of the shell (Fig. 3.3.2). Thoroughly infested shells may be so riddled that they fall apart readily when the sponge dies; thus, *Cliona* not only adds spicules to sedimentary deposits, but contributes to the disintegration of shells whose fragments then become part of the sediments. In Recent seas *Cliona* can infest shells of oysters so thoroughly as to make them unfit for market. Either the shells crumble during shipping or the sponge gives off a sulfurous odor which masks the delicate flavor of the oyster. Fossil specimens of *Cliona*-like borings from the Devonian have been termed *Clionolithes* and *Clionoides.*

Spongilla and *Myenia,* two common fresh-water sponges in the Recent, commonly produce both monaxons and birotules which may occur in lake sediments. Many fresh-water sponges related to *Spongilla* reproduce by gemmules (Fig. 3.3.6). Moreover, some members contain chlorophyll in their tissues and can manufacture part of their own food the way plants do. *Spongilla* has been reported from strata as old as the Jurassic.

Order 4. Tetractinellida

Spicules of the tetraxon type occur sporadically through the stratigraphic record, but the group is particularly notable in sediments ranging in age from Pennsylvanian to Recent (Fig. 3.3.7-9). Recognizable Genera have been found only rarely.

Order 5. Lithistida

Although lithistid sponge spicules are technically tetraxons, they fuse together to make durable skeletal masses which commonly retain their original

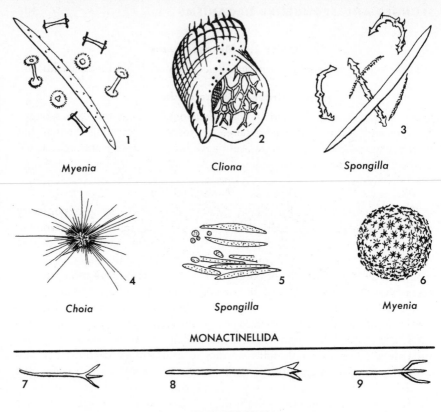

Myenia   Cliona   Spongilla

Choia   Spongilla   Myenia

MONACTINELLIDA

TETRACTINELLIDA

Figure 3.3.   Monactinellida and Tetractinellida.

1. Spicules of *Myenia millsi,* a fresh-water form, 130X, Recent.   2. Apertural region of a marine snail (*Buccinum undatum*) infested with *Cliona celata,* 2/3X, Recent. External perforations are visible on the inner margin or body side of the aperture. Ramifying tubules within the substance of the outer whorl are shown as if the shell were translucent.   3. Spicules of the fresh-water sponge, *Spongilla lacustris,* 130X, Recent.   4. Exterior of *Choia ridleyi,* 3X, Cambrian, British Columbia.   5. Spicules of a fossil fresh-water sponge, *Spongilla purbeckensis,* seen in thin section, 50X, Jurassic, England.   6. A gemmule of a fresh-water sponge, *Myenia fluviatalis,* bearing stellate birotules, enlarged, Recent.   7-9. Three spicules of tetractinellid sponges, 10X, Pennsylvanian; Illinois and Indiana.

(1, 3, 6 after Potts, 1888. 2 after Topsent, 1887. 4 after Walcott, 1920. 5 after Hinde, 1887-1893.)

Figures 3.4 (opposite).   Lithistida.

1. *Corallistes nolitangere,* 2/3X, Recent.   2. *Jerea tesselata,* 2/5X, Cretaceous, Germany. 3. *Leiodorella expansa,* 2/3X, Jurassic, Germany.   4. *Astylospongia praemorsa,* IX, Silurian, Tennessee.   5. *Caryomanon* sp., 1X, Silurian, Tennessee.   6. *Microspongia fibrosa,* Silurian, Tennessee. 6a, exterior, 1X. 6b, broken specimen showing radiate structure, 1X. 6c, silicified molds of canals with lateral chambers, 10X.   7. *Pachynion scriptum,* 40X, Cretaceous, Germany. 7a, 7b, side and plan views of typical tetraxial spicule. 7c, a desmon spicule.   8. Desmon spicule of *Hyalotragos patella,* 40X, Jurassic, Germany.   9. *Turonia constricta,* 40X, Cretaceous, Germany. Fused meshwork is typical of lithistids and retains traces of tetraxial construction.

(1, 3, 7-9 after Zittel, 1878. 2 after Steinman, 1882. 4 after Goldfuss, 1826.)

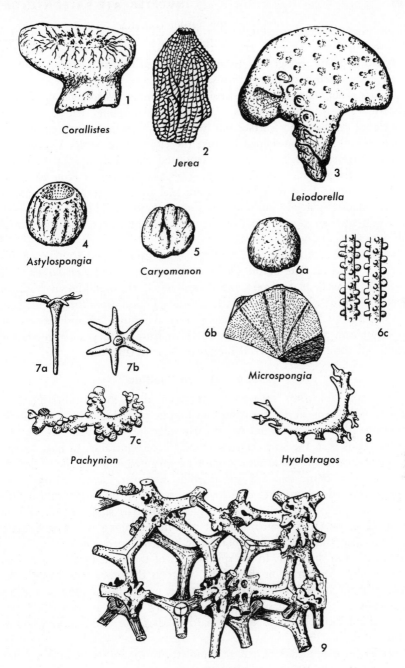

Corallistes 1

Jerea 2

Leiodorella 3

Astylospongia 4

Caryomanon 5

6a

6b

Microspongia

6c

7a 7b

Pachynion 7c

Hyalotragos 8

Turonia 9

shapes after death. Accordingly, this Order contains the most abundant of all fossil sponges. Spicules are of the peculiar and aberrant desma type. Lithistid or stony sponges are mostly globular to pear-shaped, but there are many cup-shaped and stalked forms.

The most abundant American fossil sponges are *Astylospongia* and its close relatives (Fig. 3.4.4-6). *Astylospongia* is a globular sponge with a very shallow cloaca on the upper surface into which the excurrent canals empty. The whole colony is melon-shaped because the sides are grooved. *Caryomanon* is like *Astylospongia,* but lacks the depressed cloacal cavity and may have less distinctly grooved sides. *Microspongia* (also known as *Hindia*) is also globular, but its long straight canals are met by short transverse canals to make a ladder-shaped succession of internal molds. These Genera occur locally in such large numbers as to be major rock-formers, as in the Middle Silurian of Tennessee.

No additional lithistids were common until Jurassic and Cretaceous time when the greatest flare of the Order occurred. *Jerea* and *Leiodorella* (Fig. 3.4.2, 3), as well as *Siphonia* and *Verruculina,* are well-known Mesozoic Genera, some of which lived into the Teritiary Period. *Corallistes* (Fig. 3.4.1) is a widespread Tertiary and Recent Genus. Although lithistid sponges are important constituents of Mesozoic rocks in Europe, they are relatively insignificant components of fossil faunas in North America.

Order 6.   Heteractinellida

Early spicular forms such as are represented in the Cambrian by the *Eiffelia* and *Chancelloria* bear from four to nine rays (Fig. 3.5.4, 5), although six in one plane are common. At an early stage in the sequence of Heteractinellida, however, the true octactine spicule is recognizable. In fact, sponges with this kind of spicule in some cases are segregated as a separate Order, the Octactinellida. Some so-called octactinellids, however, have lost one or two rays or have added an extra one, so they grade into other Heteractinellida. *Astraeospongium* is a well-known Genus in Silurian strata of the midcontinent (Fig. 3.5.3). It is an important rock-maker along with the lithistids in Tennessee and northern Illinois. The saucer-shaped colonies are about 1 to 3 inches in diameter. In the spicules, six of the eight rays lie in a plane parallel with the surface of the colony, whereas the other two rays are disposed at right angles to this plane; one ray is buried in the interior and one ray stands out freely. Inasmuch as the free ray usually is broken off, true symmetrical distribution of rays is hard to diagnose from cursory examination.

Increase in the number of axes of symmetry continues in the hexactinellids until eventually so many axes are present that no symmetry can be detected. These are the true heteractine spicules. No colonies have been recognized, but the peculiar spicules abound in some Carboniferous strata in North America

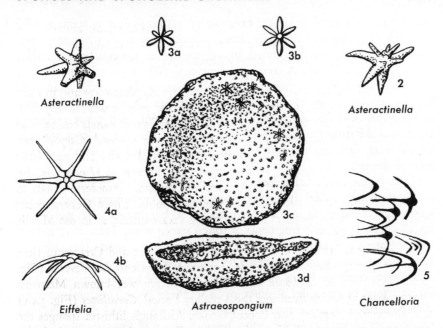

Figure 3.5.   Heteractinellida.
1. *Asteractinella* sp., 6X, Mississippian, Indiana.   2. *Asteractinella audax*, 8X, Pennsylvanian, Illinois.   3. *Astraeospongium meniscus*, Silurian, Tennessee. 3a, 3b, side and top views of a spicule, 5X. 3c, 3d, concave surface and side view of a colony, 2/3X.   4a, 4b. Plan and side views of a spicule of *Eiffelia globosa*, 4X, Cambrian, British Columbia.   5. Spicules of *Chancelloria eros* crushed on a bedding plane, 3X, Cambrian, British Columbia.
(2 after Weller, 1930. 4a, 5 after Walcott, 1920.)

and in Europe. *Asteractinella* is the most common Genus. Its spicules (Fig. 3.5.1, 2) are subspheroidal aggregations of stubby spines which resemble a medieval spiked ball carried by warriors. The Heteractinellida comprise a small Order which appeared in the Early Cambrian and became an important rock-maker in Silurian strata of North America and Europe. Its last sparse descendants succumbed in Late Permian time.

Class B.   Hyalospongea

Those sponges which have triaxon or modified triaxon siliceous spicules are commonly assigned to this Class. The typical spicular form is six-rayed (hexactinellid), but one or two rays in one axis may be suppressed to form five-rayed or four-rayed spicules. Recent hexactinellid sponges, such as *Euplectella,* are among the most beautiful and elegant of animals, their fibrous tubular skeletons being referred to as glass sponges (Fig. 3.6.1, 3).

The simplest hexactinellid spicules are the true hexactines with their three axes of symmetry and with six subequal rays. In primitive forms and in young stages the tips of rays in adjacent hexactines may overlap (Fig. 3.6.5), but in more advanced stages the neighboring rays may fuse to create a solid boxwork (Fig. 3.6.4). In both of these cases the hexactines are megascleres. Tiny microscleres are distributed among the coarse skeletal tissue in both of the foregoing forms. A trend for continual and excessive elongation of rays along two axes of symmetry eventually leads to the typically spun glass appearance of the glass sponges (Fig. 3.6.2). In this form each square orifice in the skeleton of living individuals was ringed with soft tissue around a pore; and this ring was supported by very numerous microscleres, some of which were tiny treelike forms (Fig. 3.6.12) whose tips pointed inward toward the pore.

Glass sponges with rather loosely arranged fibers outlining subrectangular perforations are called **lyassacine** sponges. They are represented by the spherical *Protospongia* in Cambrian rocks or by disassociated patches of spicules which resemble fragments of rotten screen wine. Then, after modest representation in Ordovician rocks, the group reached a spectacular culmination in the Late Devonian when *Dictyospongia, Hydnoceras,* and *Prismodictya* were common forms. Several great colonies of lyssacine sponges occur across a total of 150 miles of outcrops in southern New York and northern Pennsylvania. The 90 or more Devonian species which lived there inhabited sandy facies of the Chemung group, becoming rare in finer or more calcareous facies. Cross sections of these conical lyssacine sponges changed progressively from elliptical to hexagonal, and the smooth surface eventually became nodose or concentrically ridged during their evolution. Lyssacine sponges declined sharply in abundance in Early Mississippian time when they apparently migrated into deeper water. In Recent seas they are represented by the well-known "Venus' flower basket" which lives in abyssal waters. Inasmuch as the Devonian lyssacine sponges probably lived in no more than 300 feet of water, and possibly in much less, it is obvious that this group of sponges has undergone phenomenal change in its environmental requirements. Only rarely has a transition of this magnitude been discovered in ecology.

Figure 3.6 (*opposite*).   Hexactinellida.
1. Side view of a fragment of the skeleton of *Euplectella imperialis*, 1/2X, Recent. 2. Spicules of *Euplectella aspergillum*, 3X, Recent.   3. Complete specimen of *Euplectella oweni* with anchoring threads, 1/4X, Recent.   4. Fused megascleres of *Hexactinella tubulosa* with microscleres, 12X, Recent.   5. Unfused megascleres of *Farrea facunda* with microscleres, about 10X, Recent.   6. Reconstruction of *Protospongia monomera*, 1/2X, Cambrian, Quebec.   7. Spicules of *Protospongia fenestrata*, 2/3X, Cambrian, Montana.   8. Side view of *Hydnoceras phymatodes*, 1/3X, Devonian, New York.   9-13. Spicules of lyssacine sponges, 40X to 200X, Devonian, New York.   14. Side view of *Dictyospongia sceptrum*, 1/3X, Devonian, New York.   15. Side view of *Prismodictya prismatica*, 1/3X, Devonian, New York.   16. Side view of *Coeloptychium lobatum*, 1/2X, Cretaceous, Germany.   17. Side view of *Ventriculites gracilis*, a lychniskid sponge, 1/2X, Cretaceous, Germany.   18. Intersection of lychniskid spicules of *Coeloptychium*, 80X, Cretaceous, Germany. 19. Side view of *Tremadictyon reticulata*, a dictyonine sponge, 1/4X, Jurassic, Europe.
(1, 3 after Ijima, 1901. 2, 4 after Schulze, 1887. 5 after Marshall, 1875. 6 after Walcott, 1920. 8-15 after Hall and Clarke, 1898. 16, 18 after Zittel, 1876. 17 after Römer, 1864. 19 after Goldfuss, 1826.)

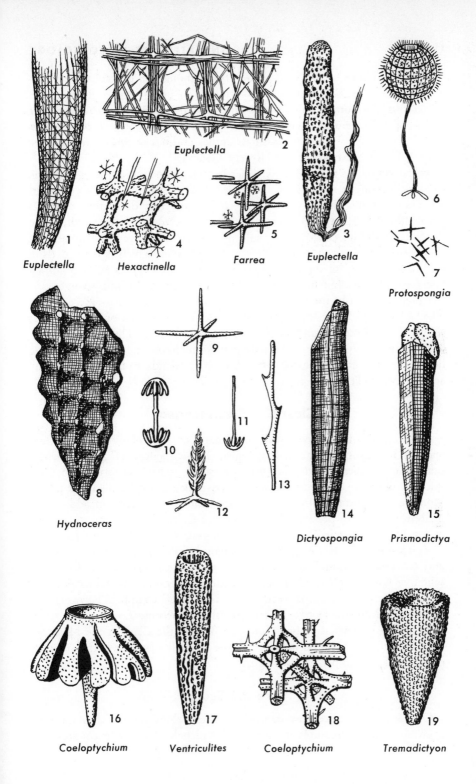

Euplectella

Euplectella

2

Euplectella

1

Hexactinella

4

Farrea

5

Euplectella

3

6

7

Protospongia

Hydnoceras

8

9

10

11

12

13

Dictyospongia

14

Prismodictya

15

Coeloptychium

16

Ventriculites

17

Coeloptychium

18

Tremadictyon

19

After the decline of the lyssacines, the glass sponges in general were unimportant until another branch, the dictyonines, underwent a flare in the Cretaceous. **Dictyonine** sponges resemble lyssacine sponges, except that their fibrous spicules delineate regularly arranged, quadrate pores. *Tremadictyon* (Fig. 3.6.19) is a European fossil example, and *Hexactinella* and *Farrea* (Fig. 3.6.4, 5) are characteristic Recent Genera.

At the same time that the dictyonines became abundant, a third group, the **lychniskid** sponges, underwent a notable increase in abundance. Lychniskid spicules resemble those of other hexactinellids, but distinctive diagonal braces like flying buttresses cross each of the twelve angles where the three axes intersect (Fig. 3.6.18). The resulting geometrical figure is like an ancient open-work Greek lamp; hence the name lychniskid, which is derived from the Greek word for lamp. *Ventriculites* (Fig. 3.6.17) is a well-known Cretaceous Genus, but Recent seas contain very few lychniskid sponges.

Taken as a whole, the hexactinellids are abyssal organisms in Recent seas. The "Challenger" expedition dredged 47, out of 100 species of hexactinellids recorded, from more than 6000 feet (2000 m) of water. The shallowest collection came from 870 feet and the deepest from almost 17,000 feet. The living hexactinellids are abundant near the Philippine Islands, in the Indian Ocean, and off Bermuda.

Class C.   Calcispongea

Architecture of the body wall and shape of the colony are important features in classifying the Calcispongea. These sponges (Fig. 3.7) secrete calcareous spicules but do not produce other skeletal materials. Of their spicules, the pharetrones are most distinctive, being restricted to this group. Moreover, monaxons, tetraxons, and other kinds of triaxons in addition to pharetrones may be present. Calcispongea, or Calcarea as they are sometimes called, are common in Recent marine waters shallower than 2500 feet.

Amblysiphonella from the Pennsylvanian and Permian of many countries, and *Girtycoelia,* from Pennsylvanian strata in the midcontinent, are representative Genera. *Girtycoelia* has a poriferous central tube surrounded by a poriferous outer wall, between which is a broad chamber. *Barroisia* is a common calcareous sponge in the British Cretaceous. *Eudea* (Fig. 3.7.7) represents a somewhat earlier (Jurassic) flare of the Class in the Mesozoic.

In Recent seas *Sycon* is notable because its wall structure is the standard example of the simply folded stage.

Incertae Sedis

One does not realize how dependent paleontology is upon zoology until a group of fossil creatures is discovered which has no living counterparts.

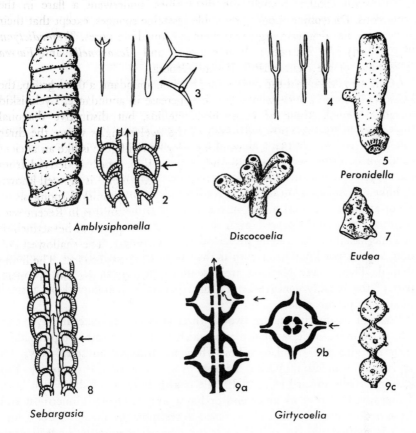

Figure 3.7.   Calcispongea.
1. *Amblysiphonella prosseri*, 2/3X, Pennsylvanian, Kansas and Nebraska.   2. Longitudinal section of *Amblysiphonella barroisi* showing double wall and probable course of water (arrows) through the pores, 1 1/3X, Carboniferous, Spain.   3. Five spicules of calcisponges, including characteristic triact shapes, greatly enlarged, Recent.   4. Three pharetrone spicules, 135X, Jurassic, England.   5. Side view of *Peronidella metabronni*, 2/3X, Jurassic, England.   6. Side view of *Discocoelia divaricata*, 1X, Jurassic, Germany.   7. Side view of *Eudea pisum*, 2X, Jurassic, England.   8. Longitudinal section of *Sebargasia carbonaria* showing sparse but large pores on inner wall and probable course of water (arrows), 1 1/3X, Carboniferous, Spain.   9. *Girtycoelia beedei*, Pennsylvanian, Texas. 9a, 9b, schematic longitudinal and transverse sections showing central canal and possible course of water (arrows), 3X. 9c, side view of part of a colonial string, 1X.
(2, 8 after Steinman, 1882. 3 after Dendy, 1894. 4, 5, 7 after Hinde, 1887-1893. 6 after Römer, 1864.)

By placing such groups each time in a special category, "Incertae Sedis" (position unknown), a systematist conveys their singular characteristics. In some cases the degree of our ignorance concerns position at the specific or generic level, but in other cases the magnitude of structural peculiarity may be much higher, even up to the ranks of Phylum or Kingdom. This latter condition is true of the organisms illustrated in Figures 3.8 and 3.9.

Receptaculites is the most common and widespread member of a group of 11 so-called Genera which have never been assigned with much confidence to any systematic group. Qualified observers have variously concluded that these strange creatures are protozoans, sponges, coelenterates, cystoids, tunicates, pine cones, calcareous algae, a transitional stage between sponges and corals, or a distinctive group not closely related to anything else. As commonly preserved in the rocks, *Receptaculites* seemingly consists of hollow, dishlike, globular, conical, or fingerlike calcareous bodies ranging from about an inch to almost a foot in diameter. It is doubtful if a complete individual has been discovered, even though specimens occur by the thousand at some localities. As usually preserved they seemingly lack any upper portion, so it is not known for sure if they were truly globular or were dish-shaped. Their lower portions are essentially hemispherical, but the axial part of the broadly concave central area generally is occupied by a small mound or protuberance.

Walls of receptaculitids are two- or three-layered. The external layer consists of rhombic or hexagonal plates which fit together rather tightly along their margins and simulate scales. They are arranged in spiral rows, the individual elements of which increase in size toward the periphery. Projecting radially inward from each scale is a shaft (Fig. 3.8.5b) which bears a four-rayed cross at its inner end or has a simple, tapered, innermost end. In some instances the shaft is shortened to resemble the shank of a cuff link, or it is aborted and the stellate cross is appressed against the under surface of the plate (Fig. 3.8.5c). The shafts seem to have been hollow cylinders in life, although they are now generally filled with calcite. Each shaft has a narrow neck just beneath the polygonal head, so that a zone of shallow chambers lies underneath the polygons. Matrix of sediment fills spaces between shafts as well as filling the aforementioned chambers and the central cavity of the colony; all of these outline potential circulatory paths through the wall and into a central cavity. Access of water would have to have been around the edges of the polygons.

Receptaculitids are placed with the sponges in this book because of their apparent circulatory passages, rudely spicular (modified triaxons?) shafts with heads and crosses, and because a thin layer of loosely matted needlelike spicules covers the polygons in thin sections observed from one specimen. This latter feature is like surficial mats of spicules on Recent sponges.

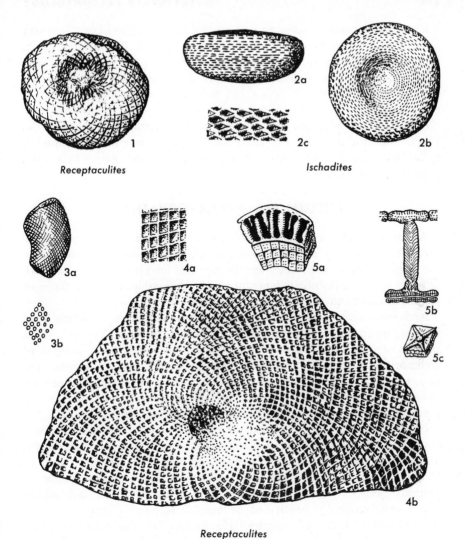

Receptaculites

Ischadites

Receptaculites

Figure 3.8.   Receptaculitids.
1. Surface of *Receptaculites occidentalis*, 2/3X, Ordovician, Tennessee.   2. *Ischadites iowensis*,
Ordovician, Minnesota. 2a, 2b, side view and surface, 1X. 2c, portion of surface showing
diamond-shaped cavities representing former hard parts, 3X.   3. *Receptaculites mammillaris*,
Ordovician, Nevada. 3a, side view, 2/3X. 3b, section tangential to surface showing outlines of
vertical tubular elements, 1X.   4. *Receptaculites oweni*, Ordovician, Minnesota and Missouri.
4a, portion of surface with head plates of tubular spiculelike elements removed, 2/3X. 4b, portion
of colony, 1X.   5. *Receptaculites neptuni*, Ordovician, eastern Europe. 5a, fragment of colony
showing tubular elements and head plates, 1/2X. 5b, vertical section of a spiculelike element,
1 1/2X. 5c, under surface of a surficial plate with cross-shaped ridges, 1 1/3X.
(2a, 2b, 4a, 4c after Winchell and Schuchert, 1895. 5 after Gümbel, 1876.)

Receptaculites was a major rock-maker in Medial Ordovician (Trenton) time in Minnesota, Wisconsin, and Missouri, and in Nevada and Utah. Moreover, the group flourished in other continents at the same time, being a fine example of widely distributed and readily identifiable fossils. The last descendants died in the Devonian, but only the Middle Ordovician flare is noteworthy.

Ischadites resembles *Receptaculites* but is almost always dolomitized (Fig. 3.8.2). Thus, the long shafts of spiculelike polygons were dissolved, leaving radial tubes in a dolomite matrix. These falsely resemble sponges even more than does *Receptaculites*.

PHYLUM III.   ARCHAEOCYATHA

Archaeocyathids are peculiarly qualified to titillate the curiosity of paleontologists because they not only occupy an anomalous systematic position in the Animal Kingdom, but they are the first reef-forming animals. Paradoxically, then, we are essentially ignorant of the relationships of one of the most abundant Cambrian organisms.

Archaeocyathids, as the name implies, are the "ancient cups," which stood balanced on the tips of open cones attached to the sea floor (Fig. 3.9). Cross sections of cylindrical forms vary between circular and ovate. Lengths of archaeocyathids range from about 1 inch (2.5 cm) to perhaps 4 inches (10 cm), but most specimens are less than 2 inches (5 cm) long. The exterior surface of the organism was composed of a thin **outer wall** which bore minute pores. Pore patterns are useful in classifying Archaeocyatha.

In many cases a cavity occupied the central region of the cone and was bounded by a poriferous **inner wall.** Some inner walls bore bars, rods, hooks, and so forth, and others were veneered with a layer of vesicular tissue. In fact, the vesicular tissue even filled the central cavity in some archaeocyathids. Between the inner and outer walls was a space, the **intervallum,** which was commonly subdivided by vertical perforate plates resembling septa of corals but termed **parieties** (sing. **paries**). In a few forms the intervallum was additionally subdivided by horizontal elements (**tabulae**), as well as by parieties, to form cubical chambers. All skeletal material is calcareous.

After a fashion reminiscent of receptaculitids, the archaeocyathids have been referred to a variety of systematic groups, but not with any widespread agreement among systematists. Calcareous algae, protozoans, sponges, and corals have severally been thought of as near relatives, but most opinion seems to be that archaeocyathids either constitute a Class of sponges or should be placed near sponges in classifications because both groups are porous. In recent publications Okulitch and some other paleontologists have

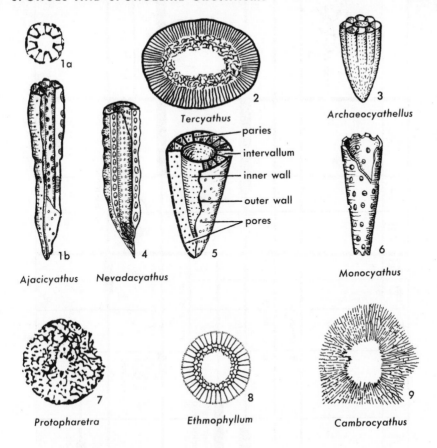

paries
intervallum
inner wall
outer wall
pores

Tercyathus

Archaeocyathellus

Ajacicyathus Nevadacyathus

Monocyathus

Protopharetra

Ethmophyllum

Cambrocyathus

Figure 3.9. Archaeocyatha.
1. *Ajacicyathus nevadensis.* 4X. 1a, transverse section. 1b, side view with part of outer wall and parieties removed.   2. *Tercyathus* sp., with complicated inner wall, 2X.   3. *Archaeocyathellus* sp., with a fluted outer wall, enlarged.   4. *Nevadacyathus septaporus,* with large pores in parieties and small pores in inner wall, 9X.   5. Schematic view of an archaeocyathid showing terminology of parts.   6. *Monocyathus* sp., with a single wall, enlarged.   7. *Protopharetra* raymondi, with narrow central cavity and vesicular intervallum, 3X.   8. *Ethmophyllum* whitneyi, with vesicular inner wall, slightly enlarged.   9. Cross section of *Cambrocyathus occidentalis,* 1/3X.
All material is from the Lower Cambrian, principally of Nevada and California.
(After Okulitch, 1943.)

raised the archaeocyathids to the rank of Phylum. This course is adopted herein.

North American archaeocyathids lived strictly during the Early Cambrian, occurring in association with the *Mesonacis* trilobite fauna, but a few descendants survived into the Medial Cambrian in Asia. The best-known occurrence is in Australia, where they became major rock-formers in the Early

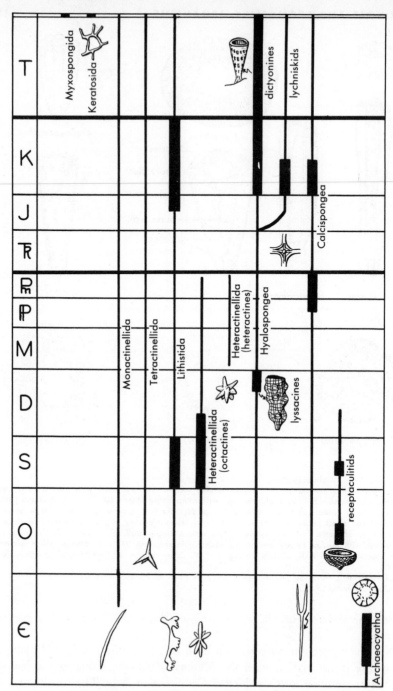

Figure 3.10.   Geologic Distribution of Sponges and Archaeocyatha.

Cambrian. Similar abundance over a smaller area is recorded from the Waucoba region just west of Death Valley, California.

Ethmophyllum is a common double-walled archaeocyathid with an open central cavity (Fig. 3.9.8). In *Protopharetra* the central cavity is almost filled with vesicular tissue which merges with the inner wall (Fig. 3.9.7).

QUESTIONS

1. What are the limitations in use of architecture, shape, chemical composition, and spicular form in classification of sponges?
2. How does the ecologic distribution of the Recent Hexactinellida affect the wording of the Law of Uniformitarianism?
3. Which features of Archaeocyatha resemble sponges?
4. Why are lithistid sponges rarely seen in zoologic collections?
5. From what group of Protozoa did the Porifera probably arise?

BIBLIOGRAPHY

Clarke, J. M., 1920, The great glass-sponge colonies of the Devonian; their origin, rise, and disappearance: Jour. Geol., v. 28, no. 1, pp. 25–37.

de Laubenfels, M. W., 1956, Porifera *in* Treatise on invertebrate paleontology, pt. E, pp. E21–E122.

Dendy, A., 1894, Studies on the comparative anatomy of sponges. V. Observations on the structure and classification of the Calcarea Heterocoela: Quart. Jour. Micro. Sci., n. ser., v. 35, pp. 159–257.

Goldfuss, A., 1826, Petrefacten: Düsseldorf, Arnz and Co., pt. 1, pp. 1–76.

Gümbel, C. W., 1876, Beiträge zur Kenntniss der Organisation und systematischen Stellung von Receptaculites: Abh. könig. bayerischen Akad. Wiss., v. 12, pt. 1, pp. 169–215.

Haeckel, E., 1872, Die Kalkschwämme: Berlin, Georg Reimer, 3 vols.

Hinde, G. J., 1884, On the structure and affinities of the Family of Receptaculitidae: Geol. Soc. London Quart. Jour., v. 40, pp. 795–849.

———, 1887–1893, A monograph of the British fossil sponges: Palaeontographical Soc. (London).

Ijima, I., 1901, Studies on the Hexactinellida, Contribution I. (Euplectellidae): Jour. Coll. Sci., Imp. Univ. Tokyo, v. 15, pp. 1–299.

Marshall, W., 1875, Untersuchungen über Hexactinelliden: Zeitschrift Wiss. Zool., v. 25, supp., pp. 142–243.

Okulitch, V. J., 1943, North American Pleospongia: Geol. Soc. America Spec. Paper 48.

———, 1956, Archaeocyatha *in* Treatise on invertebrate paleontology, pt. E, pp. E1–E20.

Potts, E., 1888, Contributions toward a synopsis of the American forms of fresh water sponges, etc.: Proc. Acad. Nat. Sci. (Philadelphia, 1887), v. 39, pp. 158–279.

Römer, F. A., 1864, Die Spongitarien des norddeutschen Kreidegebirges: Palaeontographica, v. 13, pp. 1–64.

Schulze, F. E., 1887, Report on the Hexactinellida, etc., *in* Report on the scientific results of the exploring voyage of H. M. S. "Challenger": Zoology, v. 21.

Scott, H. W., 1937, Siliceous sponge spicules from the Lower Pennsylvania of Montana: Amer. Midland Naturalist, v. 29, pp. 732–760.

Steinmann, G., 1882, Pharetronen-Studien: Neues Jahrb. Mineral Geologie u. Paläontologie Abh. (Stuttgart, 1882), v. 2, pp. 139–191.

Topsent, E., 1887, Contribution à l'étude des Clionides: Arch. Zool. Exp. Gen., v. 5, supp., Mem. 4.

Walcott, C. D., 1920, Middle Cambrian Spongiae: Smithsonian Misc. Coll., v. 67, no. 6, pp. 261-364.

Weller, J. M., 1930, Siliceous sponge spicules of Pennsylvanian age from Illinois and Indiana: Jour. Paleont., v. 4, no. 3, pp. 233–251.

Winchell, N. H., and Schuchert, C., 1895, Sponges, graptolites and corals from the Lower Silurian in Minnesota: Minnesota Geol. Survey, v. 3, pt. 1, pp. 55–59.

Zittel, K. A., 1876, Ueber Coeloptychium. Ein Beitrag zur Kenntniss der Organisation fossiler Spongien: Abh. könig. bayerischen Akad. Wiss., Math.-Phys. Cl., v. 12, pt. 3, pp. 1–80.

———, 1878, Studien über fossile Spongien: Abh. könig. bayerischen Akad. Wiss., Math.-Phys. Cl., v. 13, pt. 1, pp. 65–154.

LOWER COELENTERATES
(Including Graptolites, Stromatoporoids, and Conularioids)

PHYLUM IV.   COELENTERATA

THE LIVING ORGANISMS.   Coelenterates comprise not only the well-known corals and marine jellyfish, but also a host of small shrubby growths and the ctenophores which resemble ciliated gooseberries. Most coelenterates are marine, but others inhabit fresh water, and some of the latter even produce small jellyfish which occasionally astonish people who observe them in fresh water. The only coelenterates which secrete durable skeletons (corals, for instance) are strictly marine. They are especially abundant in shallow water where they comprise the principal reef-making organisms in the geologic record. Many coelenterates are sedentary throughout life so they depend upon free-living larval stages for their distribution. Others are planktonic creatures that may drift freely over the oceans. Still others become attached either to the bottom or to floating objects and therefore are secondarily planktonic.

Bodies of coelenterates consist of three layers reminiscent of those in sponges. The thin ectoderm and the thick endoderm are separated by the jellylike mesogloea. In jellyfish the mesogloea makes up almost all of the bulk of the animal, but in sedentary coelenterates such as corals the mesogloea is very thin, and the layer containing it becomes increasingly cellular.

The first real indication of differentiation of tissues into organs is found in the coelenterates. Their primary advance over Protozoa or Porifera, and the feature from which they derive their name, is the development of a true baglike digestive cavity or **coelenteron.** The simplest coelenterates ingest or swallow food through an **oral pore** directly into the coelenteron (Fig. 4.1.4), but more advanced coelenterates have a round or slitlike mouth which leads through a tubular **stomodaeum** into the coelenteron (Fig. 4.1.5). One or both ends of the oesophagus, or inside of the stomodaeum, bear ciliated grooves (**siphonoglyphs**). Other cilia lining the coelenteron create currents of water which transport food particles and also circulate digestive and nutrient solutions. In simple forms digestion is carried on by specialized cells in the body wall, but in advanced forms these cells are concentrated on the inner edges of radiating muscular partitions in the coelenteron which are called **mesenteries** (Fig. 5.1.1, 3). There being no digestive track, waste materials must be voided back through the oral pore with the assistance of water currents created in the siphonoglyphs. Although this digestive apparatus is distinctively advantageous over that of sponges, it is still not very efficient because it entails carrying on digestion in the presence of ingested water. Perhaps that is why most coelenterates contract their bodies tightly

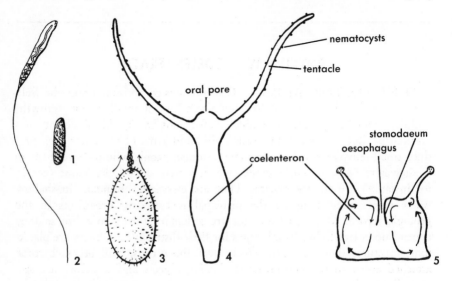

Figure 4.1.   Morphology of Coelenterates.
1. Nematocyst with hollow thread inside capsule, 400X, Recent.   2. Nematocyst with hollow thread extended, 400X, Recent.   3. Ciliated planula larva with arrows showing flow of water toward oral pole and granules, about 10X, Recent.   4. Schematic vertical section of *Hydra*, a very simple coelenterate, about 10X, Recent.   5. Schematic vertical section of a very young polyp of a coral to illustrate an advanced coelenterate with arrows showing circulation of water in the coelenteron, about 5X, Recent.
(1-3 after Lucaze-Duthiers, 1873. 4 mostly after Chun, 1891. 5 after Duerden, 1904.)

during digestion and thereby not only press the digestive glands against food but also squeeze most of the water out of the coelenteron.

No circulatory system is present, but digestive products are transported into the hollow tentacles by direct connection of these tubular arms with the coelenteron. Then the food is diffused through endodermal cell walls into the body of the animal. Coelenterates have a nervous system of primitive construction, it being a loose network of fibers dispersed through the tissue but in some cases it is concentrated at nodes where chemical- or light-sensitive cells are located. There is no respiratory system; transfer of oxygen and nitrogenous waste takes place through the body wall.

Most coelenterates have one or more rings of flexible **tentacles** around the oral pore. In most instances the tentacles are armed with batteries of adhesive cells or of stinging cells (**nematocysts**). Each cell, although only about 0.05 millimeter in length, contains a toxic fluid and a long tubular thread coiled up inside the cell (Fig. 4.1.1). When the nematocyst is properly stimulated (as by contact with prey), the cell ejects the thread by turning it inside out (as if one were peeling a glove off a hand). At the same time the poisonous contents of the cell are ejected through the inverting tubular thread. Nematocysts operate forcibly enough to penetrate scales of fish and are notable sources of irritation to people at some ocean beaches.

Reproduction by coelenterates can be very diverse and complex. In its simplest form, the growing tip of an individual divides vegetatively into two new individuals by **fission.** When division involves a lateral offshoot of a new individual from the wall of the parent the process is called **budding.** Both of these processes are asexual, of course. In sexual reproduction the fertilized egg develops into a ciliated, spherical, **planula** larva (Fig. 4.1.3) which swims about for a short time before assuming its mature characteristics.

Living coelenterates can be grouped into two categories, depending upon growth habit following the larval stage. If single individuals or colonies grow attached to the substratum they represent the **polypoid** or **hydroid** form. If bell-shaped free-swimming individuals such as jellyfish are produced, the **medusoid** form is represented. In its most complicated expression the life history of a coelenterate involves production of both bodily forms, and any single species can be said to be **dimorphic.** Thus, the hydroid form only reproduces sexually to form a medusa, and the medusa only reproduces sexually to form a new hydroid form. This manifestation of **alternation of generations** is reminiscent of reproduction among some Foraminiferida. The most successful animals tend to minimize and eventually to eliminate the asexual generation and to increase the dominance of the sexual generation.

Although many Coelenterata are devoid of any skeletal material, others develop internal or external hard parts. Hydroids commonly surround the vegetative and reproductive polyps with a perishable **perisarc** of transparent organic material. Sea-fans (gorgonids) and other related corals secrete a horny axis which may or may not contain calcareous spicules in its substance. When these corals die and the axis decomposes, the spicules are released. True corals secrete an external skeleton which grows inward from the base and sides to act like an internal skeleton. These are always calcareous skeletons which tend to be strongly constructed and are therefore readily fossilized.

CLASSIFICATION. The most significant feature of coelenterates for systematic purposes is the reproductive arrangement. Major taxonomic groups are differentiated according to how complex their reproductive processes. Minor taxa are defined on skeletal differences or on lesser anatomic features. At present zoologists differ among themselves as to what group is the most primitive depending upon which of two philosophies is involved. According to one idea, the medusoid forms are most primitive because they not only occur first in the geologic record, but they are the necessary sexually reproducing form. Hydroids, according to this view, are the subsidiary and nonessential form. On the other hand, the development of hydroids, as has been classically understood by zoologists, seems to indicate that medusae evolved from hydroids. In a sense the arguments are reminiscent of the conundrum "Which came first, the chicken or the egg?"

Other morphologic features of importance in classification are the presence and construction of nematocysts, nature and number of mesenteries, number of siphonoglyphs, presence of a stomodaeum, and nature and origin of septa and other skeletal features. Unfortunately, only the skeletal characteristics are observable in fossilized material. In the following classification the features of paleontologic importance are stressed, even though some resulting groupings are inconsistent with current zoologic interpretation and much more detail is shown in some groups than in others. The Classes Anthozoa and Ctenophora comprise the subject of Chapter 5.

Phylum IV. Coelenterata
  Class A. Hydrozoa
    Order 1. Hydroida
    Order 2. Hydrocorallida
    Order 3. Trachylida
    Order 4. Siphonophorida
  Class B. Graptozoa
    Order 1. Dendroida
    Order 2. Graptoloida
  Class C. Stromatoporoidea (including sphaeractinioids)
  Class D. Scyphozoa (including conularioids)
  Class E. Anthozoa
  Class F. Ctenophora

PHYLUM IV.   COELENTERATA

Coelenterates are essentially radially symmetrical animals with a coelenteron and a simple network of nerves; alternation of generations is common; calcareous skeletons with septa are important geologically; nematocysts are commonly present.

Class A.   Hydrozoa

Hydrozoa are Coelenterata which tend to reproduce by alternation of generations, but some species retain only the polypoid or only the medusoid form associated with this kind of reproduction. Medusae of Hydrozoa are characterized by the presence of an inwardly projecting shelf (**velum**) within the brim; by general small size (less than $1\frac{1}{2}$ in. in diameter); commonly by four or eight canals radiating from the coelenteron; and by four to sixteen tentacles around the brim. Inasmuch as many medusae are not correlated with any known hydroid generation, some systematists favor a dual classification of Hydrozoa in which members of each of the two generations could have different generic and specific names. The issue is avoided herein because few Hydrozoa are of any geologic importance.

Order 1.   Hydroida

Those Hydrozoa which are principally represented by the hydroid bodily form make up this Order. Some very simple hydroids without hard parts, such as *Hydra,* belong here, but most of the representatives are brushy colonies an inch or two in height which are stiffened by a thin, transparent, external perisarc. Zoologists find it convenient to subdivide hydroids on the basis of whether the polyps are covered by perisarc or are bare.

The simplest hydroids are represented by *Hydra* (Fig. 4.2.1), a Genus of tiny fresh-water coelenterates which is widely recognized as the prototype of the whole hydroid Order. It usually consists of a single individual but may bud off a new polyp from the wall of the coelenteron. *Hydra* reproduces sexually by ova and spermatozoa produced by the same individual. No skeleton is present.

Colonial hydroids originate by many *Hydra*-like individuals budding off one another to form a treelike colony (Fig. 4.2.2, 4b). Within each colony one can recognize two kinds of individuals. Feeding or vegetative polyps of *Hydra*-like form are called **hydrozoids,** and reproductive polyps are called **gonozoids** (Fig. 4.2.3, 4a). Each of these polyps is encased in a cuplike **theca** whose shape is consistent with the function performed by the polyp it encases; therefore, it is possible to recognize **hydrotheca** and **gonotheca.** In simple colonial forms such as *Campanularia* (Fig. 4.2.2, 3), the gonozoids typically have lost their tentacles and merely consist of long stalks (**blastostyles**) to which minute medusa buds are attached by stalks like parasols with handles, or like tiny mushrooms. Sexual reproduction takes place from ova and sperms released from medusa buds. In more complicated hydroids such as *Eucope* (Fig. 4.2.4) the medusa buds break away from the blastostyle and

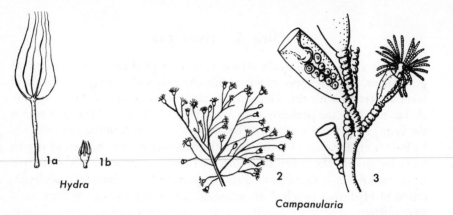

1a   1b

Hydra

2

3

Campanularia

hydrozoid
gonozoid

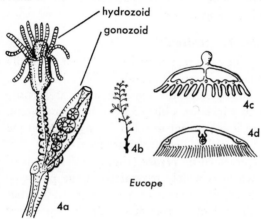

4b

4c

4d

4a

Eucope

5

Syncoryne

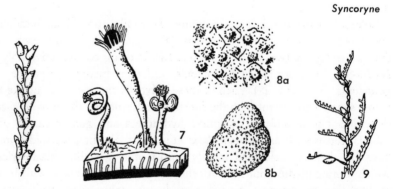

6

7

8a

8b

9

Thuiaria   *Hydractinia*   *Archaeoantennularia*

become free-living medusae. At first the stalk of the free medusa projects above the umbrella (Fig. 4.2.4c), but eventually the umbrella of the medusa turns inside out and the stalk then serves its proper function of stomodaeum (Fig. 4.2.4d). All sexual reproduction is carried on by the medusae as they drift along. Fertilized eggs develop into larvae which swim about for a short time before settling down to form new hydroid colonies. Thus, dimorphism is distinct and alternation of generations is well established. By continued emphasis of the medusoid form the Hydroida converge upon the Trachylida which is discussed as Order 3.

Of the occasional fossil hydroids which have been reported, the oldest occurs in Cambrian rocks of Australia. The only hydroid of much potential fossil importance so far described is *Hydractinia* (Fig. 4.2.7, 8). It has been reported questionably as far back as the Jurassic and is definitely represented in Tertiary rocks. Many colonial hydroids send out slender roots (**hydrorhizae**) over the surfaces they incrust, but in *Hydractinia* the roots pile up into a thin mat of chitinous or slightly calcified tissue. In Recent seas the mat always seems to occur as a thin chitinous incrustation on shells of gastropods which are, or have been, occupied by hermit crabs. Scavenging crustaceans such as crabs and lobsters habitually tear apart their food with their claws preparatory to tucking it in their mouths; therefore minute particles suspended in the water around the host provide for the sustenance of incrusting hydroids. Combinations of creatures eating at the same table, as it were, are said to be **commensal** organisms. A crab gets some advantage out of the association because the hydroid keeps other creatures away with its stinging cells. *Hydractinia* not only has reproductive and feeding polyps but also defensive polyps which are armed with the nematocysts (Fig. 4.2.7). There is no medusoid form.

The great abundance of Hydroida in Recent seas indicates that they probably were abundant in earlier times, but they are not capable of being preserved under normal marine conditions.

Figure 4.2 (*opposite*). Hydroida.
1a, 1b. Fully extended and fully contracted *Hydra carnea*, 2X, Recent fresh water. 2. Colony of *Campanularia edwardsi*, 1X, Recent. 3. Portion of colony of *Campanularia flexuosa* with feeding polyp on right and reproductive polyp on left (there is no medusoid generation), 15X, Recent. 4. *Eucope diaphana*, Recent. 4a, feeding polyp and reproductive polyp containing medusae, 15X. 4b, portion of colony, 1X. 4c, newly freed medusa with stomodaeum uppermost, 8X. 4d, mature medusa with stomodaeum beneath umbrella, 3X. 5. Medusa of *Syncoryne mutabilis* with well-developed velum, 4X, Recent. 6. Empty thecae in part of a colony of *Thuiaria argentea*, 5X, Recent. 7. Defensive (left), feeding (center), and reproductive (right) polyps of *Hydractinia polyclina* springing from an incrusting base on a gastropod shell (black), 10X, Recent. 8. *Hydractinia multispinosa*, Miocene, Maryland. 8a, portion of surface, 5X. 8b, gastropod completely incrusted, 2/3X. 9. Portion of a colony of *Archaeoantennularia byersi*, 3X, Devonian, Michigan.
(1 after Hyman, 1931. 2, 3, 5-7 partly after Nutting, 1901. 4 after A. Agassiz, 1865. 7 partly after L. Agassiz, 1862. 8 after Clarke, et al., 1904. 9 after Decker, 1952.)

Order 2.   Hydrocorallida

Some Hydrozoa secrete an incrusting basal skeleton rather reminiscent of that of *Hydractinia,* but consisting of distinctly calcareous tissue. These are the hydrocorallines, which are exemplified by the well-known recent "staghorn coral," or "pepper coral," *Millepora* (Fig. 4.3.1). Reproduction of hydrocorallines is by tiny medusae which either escape from or remain confined to spherical chambers **(ampullae)** just beneath the surface of the colony (Fig.

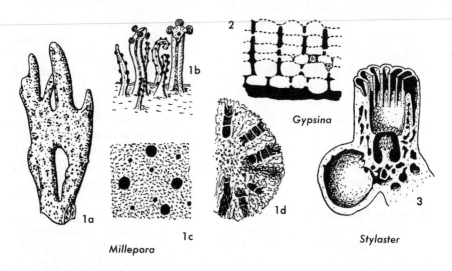

Figure 4.3.   Hydrocorallida.
1. *Millepora alcicornis,* Recent. 1a, part of a colony, 2/3X. 1b, gastrozoids (large) and dactylozoids (small) extended above the surface of a colony, 15X. 1c, gastropores (large) and dactylopores (small) on the surface of a colony, 10X. 1d, transverse broken section of a round fragment with tabulate gastropores, 25X.   2. Vertical section of *Gypsina plana,* 65X, Recent.   3. Longitudinal section of *Stylaster densicaulis* showing the brushlike axis in the base of the gastropore, about 25X, Recent. A semicircle of dactylopores lies on the far side of the gastropore, and a spherical reproductive ampulla lies at the lower left.
(1b, 1d after L. Agassiz, 1860. 2 after Hickson, 1934. 3 after Mosely, 1879.)

4.3.3). Hydrocorallines are commonly conspicuous in very shallow tropical seas and locally become components of coral and algal reefs. A few live at great depths.

Millepora sends up palmate to branched expansions from the incrusting basal portion, the whole colony attaining heights of several inches. The surface of a colony is characteristically perforated by two sizes of circular to scalloped openings. Feeding polyps called gastrozoids occupy the larger cavities **(gastropores)**, whereas irregular rings of elongate slenderer dactylozoids occupy the narrower **dactylopores.** Gastrozoids and dactylozoids are interconnected within the base of the calcareous colony by intergrown tubules, but as growth progresses the polyps seal off gastropores and dactylopores with horizontal floors (**tabulae**), after which the deeper tissue in a colony disintegrates (Fig. 4.3.1d).

In spite of the strongly constructed colonial skeletons, *Millepora* and its close relatives have only been reported rarely as fossils, possibly in rocks as old as late Cretaceous, and probably in a few Cenozoic strata.

Stylaster, a distant living relative of *Millepora,* resembles *Millepora* in most respects, but each gastropore is equipped with an axial column which extends up from the base a short distance to form a **gastrostyle** (Fig. 4.3.3). *Stylaster* and its close relatives are more solid than *Millepora,* so it is not surprising to find more of these Genera and more confident reports of their fossil occurrences than of *Millepora.* The earliest record for both groups is Late Cretaceous.

Gypsina is an incrusting hydrocoralline which has been referred by some authorities to the colonial foraminifers. Its principal features of importance are weak horizontal tabulae in successive floors which are traversed by strong vertical pillars (Fig. 4.3.2).

Order 3.   Trachylida

Zoologists have demonstrated that a few marine and some even rarer freshwater Hydrozoa lack or nearly lack the hydroid generation. Although these medusae resemble those of other Hydrozoa in major morphologic features such as shape and presence of a velum, they differ from those other medusoids by having some tentacles springing from the upper surface of the medusa instead of from around the rim; moreover, microscopic study reveals that some similar structures of the two medusae arise from different layers of the body wall; hence, the two groups are presumed to be quite unrelated. In some trachylid reproduction the planula larva gives rise to a special larval stage, the **actinula,** which is sessile like a hydroid, but is compartmented symmetrically like a medusoid. Actinula larvae are attached with the oral side up, and they bud off immature medusae in succession from the upper surface. These buds grow into adult medusae, so there is no true hydroid generation. Lack of a hard skeleton renders their preservation extremely unlikely.

Kirklandia, from the marine Cretaceous of Germany and Texas, is a presumed trachylid hydrozoan, and others have been reported doubtfully from Cambrian strata, but the recognition of a fossil trachylid poses difficulties not readily resolved.

Craspedacusta is one of the rare, Recent, fresh-water Genera whose medusae are known (Fig. 4.4.1).

Order 4.   Siphonophorida

The progressive tendency for new bodily forms to arise from the basic hydroid anatomy eventually led to differentiation into various kinds of

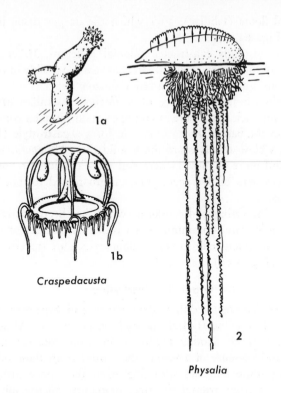

Figure 4.4.   Trachylida and Siphonophorida.
  1. *Craspedacusta ryderi,* Recent. 1a, hydroid generation, 25X. 1b, medusoid generation with three orders of tentacles, 2X.   2. *Physalia arethusa,* a small Portuguese man-of-war, 1X, Recent. (1 after Payne, 1924. 2 after A. Agassiz, 1865.)

feeding, reproductive, swimming, and defensive polyps, all of which became intergrown in a loose colonial aggregation. Therefore, more than being dimorphic like simple Hydrozoa, they are said to be **polymorphic.** The most well known of these, *Physalia,* is the infamous Portuguese man-of-war which can inflict stripes of very painful stings on the skin of swimmers. *Physalia,* as with most other siphonophorans, floats suspended by a hollow **pneumatophore,** from the under side of which the diverse individuals are suspended (Fig. 4.4.2). The pneumatophores, although commonly glassy like those of the Recent sail-bearing *Velella,* are tough enough to be preserved as impressions in sediments.

A few fossil siphonophorans are thought to have been discovered in rocks as old as Ordovician.

Class B.   Graptozoa

Graptozoans, or graptolites as they are most commonly called, are among the most instructive and useful fossils known. They reached their peak of abundance and diversity at about the same time that the trilobites reached theirs, but trilobites tended to be stay-at-homes, whereas graptolites were the original drifters. In technical terms the trilobites tend to be provincial and the graptolite faunas tend to be cosmopolitan. For instance, the graptolite zones on which Lapworth founded the Ordovician Period have been recognized all over the world.

Graptolites are remarkably useful guide fossils in Ordovician and Silurian rocks. Indeed, they exemplify most of the ideal qualities of good index fossils: they were abundant, widespread, rapidly evolving, and easily identified. It is no wonder, then, that their study progressed more rapidly and in more detail than did the study of many other groups. On the other hand, it is noteworthy that the problems of their morphology and their assignment to one or another Phylum have been most vexatious.

The most common matrix in which graptolites are preserved is dark gray to black, platy to fissile shale. The fossils themselves are usually preserved as flattened carbonaceous films which blend with the matrix and cannot be seen clearly unless the slab of shale is tilted until light is reflected off the jet-black surfaces of the graptolites. Colonies either lie spread out upon bedding planes or they occupy incipient fracture planes where they may be revealed by a judicious blow with a pick. Many shales are so strewn with myriad segments of graptolites that their very abundance interferes with their identification. Their common occurrence in black shales probably is due in large part to the absence of scavenging organisms in the environment of deposition. This would seem to indicate that the sediments accumulated in toxic waters of closed submarine basins or in lagoons in which circulation of water was impaired. Inasmuch as most graptolites were floating organisms, their bodies also rained down upon sea floors covered with sand and gravel, but in the usual environments in which coarse clastic sediments accumulated the graptolites were apt to be consumed by bottom-dwelling organisms or destroyed by abrasion. Moreover, they would be revealed on broken surfaces of nonfissile rocks only by accident. Some of the best material has been recovered as chitinous insoluble residues from the digestion of limestone or chert in appropriate acids.

Growth forms are all colonial, but sessile colonies are principally shrubby, and planktonic colonies consist of threadlike branches which radiate from a central origin. Colonies are termed **rhabdosomes,** each of which consists of one or more narrow branches (**stipes**). A stipe is composed of a uniserial or biserial arrangement of individual organisms, each of which is housed in a chitinous sheath or **theca.** Thus, rhabdosomes resemble hydroid generations of Hydrozoa and thecae resemble hydrothecae of Hydrozoa.

Two great Orders of Graptozoa are recognized by most paleontologists, and three minor groups recently have been raised to ordinal rank by some authorities.

Order 1.   Dendroida

Dendroid graptolites built fan-shaped rhabdosomes which are generally 1 to 3 or 4 inches (2 to 10 cm) in height and are a little less broad than high (Fig. 4.5.1). Many dendroid rhabdosomes were definitely attached to the substratum by basal expansions, but others apparently were suspended from some floating object by a threadlike filament.

Each stipe of a dendroid graptolite consists of as many as four different kinds of thecae. In one series which has been studied, an axial theca budded off a new axial theca directly ahead and at the same time it budded off a lateral theca on each side of the axial theca. Stipes are so slender, thecae are so small, and preservation is so inadequate, however, that these details are rarely seen. In fact, on many dendroid stipes it is difficult to see the serrated edges where the thecal apertures are lined up. When specimens are well preserved some details of the different kinds of thecae can be seen (Fig. 4.5.2). The largest thecae are tubular with circular apertures from which a single ring of tentacles protruded. These **autothecae** probably housed feeding polyps. Alongside many autothecae are elongate slender-tubed bithecae which also seem to have been ringed with tentacles. Bithecae are thought to have housed male reproductive polyps. Large hive-shaped or barrel-shaped bulges which are located at the point of branching of stipes are **gonothecae.** They probably housed female reproductive polyps. The fourth of the polymorphic thecae consists of minute tubular structures which seem to be scattered primarily over the surface of autothecae. These, the **nematothecae,** may have housed defensive polyps with nematocysts, or merely batteries of nematocysts.

Rhabdosomes grew by branching of stipes in dichotomous, or lateral, or irregular patterns. One featherlike rhabdosome budded off stipes alternately from a central axis. Stipes in various colonies either continued to grow free;

Figure 4.5 *(opposite).*   Morphology of Graptolites.
    1. Frond of *Dictyonema sociale,* 1X, Upper Cambrian, widespread.   2. Reconstruction of part of a dendroid graptozoan showing four kinds of thecae, greatly enlarged.   3. Schematic cut-away diagram of a dendroid graptozoan theca, greatly enlarged.   4. Reconstruction of a rhabdosome of *Diplograptus,* enlarged, Ordovician, widespread.   5. Sicula with dichograptid budding, greatly enlarged.   6. Sicula with diplograptid budding, greatly enlarged.   7. Sicula with mongraptid budding, greatly enlarged.   8. Base of a diplograptid stipe with bulbous graptogonophores, greatly enlarged.
    (1, 4 after Ruedemann, 1947. 3 after Kozlowski, 1947. 5-7 after Bulman, 1954. 8 after Elles, 1940.)

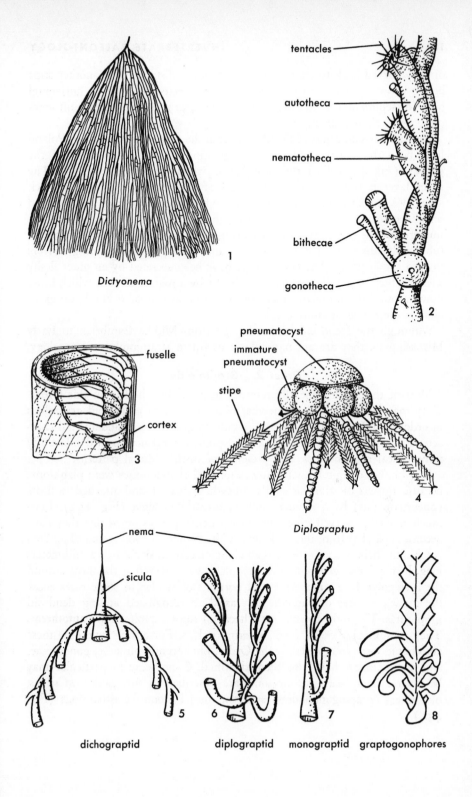

1

Dictyonema

2

- tentacles
- autotheca
- nematotheca
- bithecae
- gonotheca

3

- fuselle
- cortex

4

Diplograptus

- pneumatocyst
- immature pneumatocyst
- stipe

5

- nema
- sicula

dichograptid

6

diplograptid

7

monograptid

8

graptogonophores

or they curved back to engraft themselves for a distance with another stipe before growing free again; or they were connected by tenuous horizontal bars (**dissepiments**) as in *Dictyonema* (Fig. 4.5.1). Some species built complex, wide, ribbonlike stipes.

Unusually well-preserved Dendroida from the Lower Ordovician of Poland have been the source of detailed information on the construction of the perisarc (Fig. 4.5.3). Each theca consists of two layers of chitinous tissue. The inner layer is constructed of semicircles of skeletal tissue which interlock along two zigzag sutures. Apparently these half-rings or **fuselles** were secreted on alternate sides of the polyp, although irregularities in the pattern are numerous. The outer layer or **cortex** consists of several layers of transparent tubular sheaths which cover the fuselles and overlap each other progressively toward the aperture. The cortex must have been secreted by an outer fleshy sheath which originally covered the stipe or by a mantle of flesh which hung down around the lip of the aperture. A condition similar to the latter exists among some Recent stony corals.

Although the Dendroida range in age from Middle Cambrian to Early Mississippian, they are not particularly useful in stratigraphic paleontology.

Order 2.   Graptoloida

Most of the fossils generally referred to graptolites belong in this Order. They may be referred to (somewhat redundantly) as graptoloid graptolites in order to differentiate them from dendroid graptolites. Fundamental characteristics of the Order are planktonic habit, a tendency toward bilaterally symmetrical rhabdosomes, and presence of distinct thecal patterns.

It is known definitely that many graptoloid rhabdosomes were planktonic because clusters of stipes or single stipes have been found attached to floats (**pneumatocysts**) by a slender, hollow, threadlike **nema** (Fig. 4.5.4). Inasmuch as well-preserved stipes also have a nema, it is assumed that they have become separated from their pneumatocysts. Where the lower end of a nema reaches the base of a stipe there is an elongate conical **sicula** 1 or 2 millimeters long. It may have sheltered an embryonic stage or served as the theca around the first polyp in a stipe. Apertural portions of siculae in some cases show the zigzag sutures of fuselles such as were recognized among dendroid graptolites. The most conspicuous thecae of the Graptoloida are **autothecae**. They presumably housed food-gathering polyps. For a long time only these autothecae were recognized in the Order, but recently bithecae, gonothecae, and nematothecae have also been identified. Gonothecae in particular may be diverse in appearance, for some are described as tiny nodes on stipes, but others (**graptogonophores**) swell up into balloonlike expansions (Fig. 4.5.8).

TRENDS OF MODIFICATION. The evolution of different structures in any group of organisms may or may not take place at the same time or at the same relative speeds. The whole process is analogous to a great river which is fed by many tributaries. Just as an observer in an airplane can detect clean or muddy streaks of tributary water in a river, so it is possible by looking back in time to detect several main patterns of graptoloid evolution. Moreover, the speed at which one trend operated over another is analogous to the differences with which currents flow in the various channels of a river.

SHAPE OF RHABDOSOME. Although the entire rhabdosomes hung suspended from some floating object, the stipes could grow in four basic directions (Fig. 4.6.1-4). Stipes of **pendent** rhabdosomes hung down from the sicula; **horizontal** stipes grew laterally; **reclined** stipes grew obliquely upward somewhat in the reverse direction of pendent stipes; and **scandent** stipes grew straight up the nema. No doubt the shape of a rhabdosome influenced its chances for survival because of its effect upon structural strength and food-gathering ability. Loosely constructed rhabdosomes with many slender uniserial stipes probably were easily broken during life. Moreover, food-gathering ability is not increased most efficiently merely by lengthening stipes. The greatest compactness and strength and the greatest food-gathering ability in relation to size would seem to occur in the scandent forms. Most of these were biserial, but some early ones were quadriserial and some later ones became uniserial.

REDUCTION IN NUMBER OF BRANCHES. One general evolutionary pattern which is expressed in multitudes of organisms is the tendency toward reduction in number of items when many are present originally. This trend is expressed spectacularly by the Graptoloida because the number of stipes tended to decrease systematically. Usually the decrease took place simultaneously on both sides of the symmetrical rhabdosomes, but some instances are known in which the decrease operated asymmetrically and a rhabdosome might have seven, five, or three stipes.

THECAL SHAPE. Simple thecae of Graptoloida are straight and tubular, and they grew in a row *en echelon* (Fig. 4.6.5). At least three orderly trends have been recognized, starting with the simple, generalized thecal type. In the **sigmoid** morphologic series (Fig. 4.6.6-8) the straight tubes became S-shaped and even angulate. Increasing curvature caused the aperture to swing up until the polyp was crowded against the side of the overlying theca. Stifling of polyps was avoided by twisting the aperture over to one side (**introtorsion**). A second morphologic series simulated the sigmoid trend, except that thecae in the **lobate** series (Fig. 4.6.9–11) curved outward and downward in the reverse fashion to the sigmoid trend. In the extreme development of

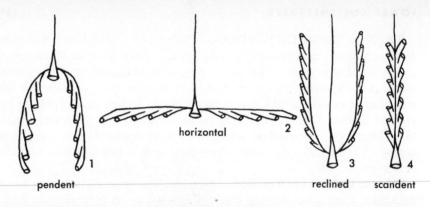

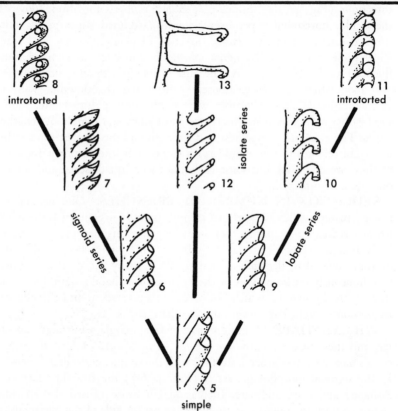

Figure 4.6.   Modification of Stipes and Thecae.

1-4. Schematic drawings of attitudes of pairs of stipes with siculae.   5. Simple thecae.   6-8. Apertures of sigmoid thecae.   9-11. Apertures of lobate thecae.   12, 13. Apertures of isolate thecae in *Rastrites*.   All figures are greatly enlarged. Heavy lines connect morphologic series in 5-13.

(After Elles, 1922, and Bulman, 1954.)

the lobate trend there was again a tendency for obstruction of apertures, but again introtorsion freed the polyps. The **isolate** trend (Fig. 4.6.12, 13) expressed progressive separation of thecae from each other until thecae of *Rastrites* were slender tubes spaced far apart.

BUDDING. Numerous stages in the origin of stipes from the siculae have been recognized, but three fundamental patterns will serve to illustrate this morphologic (and probably evolutionary) series. In the earliest **dichograptid** stage (Fig. 4.5.5) the first theca sprang from the side of the sicula and produced in turn two new buds; one bud continued to extend the original stipe, but the other bud crossed over the sicula to form the beginning of a new stipe which grew in the opposite direction. Thecae in all stipes were uniserial and the stipes were not reinforced along their backs. In **diplograptid** budding (Fig. 4.5.6) the first thecae sprang downward from the sicula as if it were going to form a dichograptid theca, but then it curved upward like a deep-bowled pipe. The first few theca budded off of each other alternately in herringbone pattern, but soon this pattern gave way to two parallel rows of theca in a truly biserial arrangement. Normally the thecae in each row were crowded closely together and the two rows backed up solidly against the nema. The nema and axial regions were then reinforced to form a solid rod, the **virgula.** In **monograptid** budding (Fig. 4.5.7) the first theca grew obliquely upward from the sicula and other thecae comprised a uniserial stipe like one-half of a diplograptid stipe. There was also a virgula along the back of each monograptid stipe.

EVOLUTION OF GRAPTOZOA. Synthesis of the various evolutionary currents into a stream which represents orderly development of all graptolites is shown in Figure 4.7. Graptolite evolution may have stemmed from Dendroida such as *Dictyonema* (Fig. 4.7.1) in the Medial or Late Cambrian. Even by earliest Ordovician time two independent planktonic strains of graptolites had arisen—the pendent and the horizontal. *Bryograptus* and *Clonograptus* combine the thecal construction of the dendroids with the planktonic habit and simple branching of the graptoloids; hence, specialists variously assign *Bryograptus* and *Clonograptus* to one or the other Order. Indecision as to their proper assignment is merely illustrative of their position as "missing links" in the evolution of graptolites. *Bryograptus* is a drooping form which grew outward along three rays, whereas *Clonograptus* branched dichotomously eight or nine times and became a generalized multirayed colony.

In the pendent strain (Fig. 4.7.2-5), *Bryograptus* evolved into *Tetragraptus* through some reduction of branches, and thence into *Didymograptus* by further reduction of branches before the end of the Early Ordovician. Pendent *Didymograptus* survived into the Medial Ordovician and

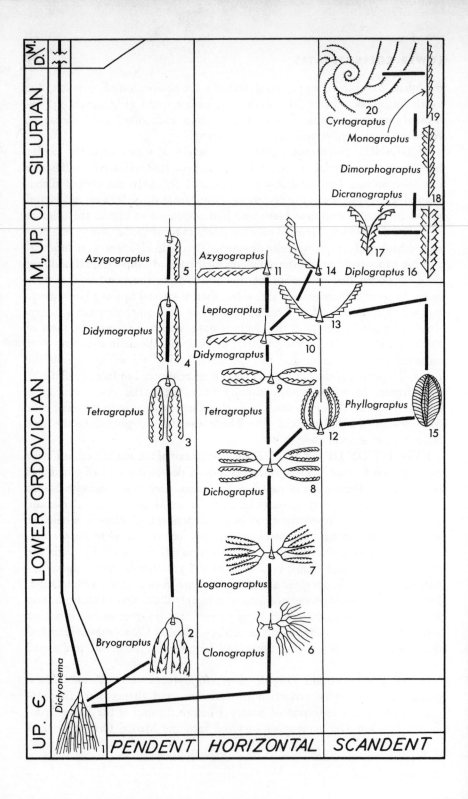

D. M.

SILURIAN

M, UP. O.

LOWER ORDOVICIAN

UP. Є

Cyrtograptus
20
Monograptus
Dimorphograptus
19
Dicranograptus
18

Azygograptus 5
Azygograptus 11
14
Diplograptus 16
17

Didymograptus 4
Leptograptus
Didymograptus 10
13

Tetragraptus 3
Tetragraptus
9
Phyllograptus
12
15

Dichograptus 8

Loganograptus 7

Bryograptus 2
Clonograptus 6

Dictyonema 1

PENDENT   HORIZONTAL   SCANDENT

gave rise to the one-stiped Genus, *Azygograptus,* before the pendent strain of graptoloids became extinct.

While the pendent strain was undergoing its modifications, the horizontal strain (Fig. 4.7.6–11) developed along a parallel course by reduction in the number of stipes. The classic series in this strain commences with *Clonograptus* and progresses through a sequence of so-called dichograptids. *Loganograptus* had from 8 to 16 stipes, whereas *Dichograptus* had 8 stipes, *Tetragraptus* had 4 stipes, and *Didymograptus* had 2 stipes. Horizontal *Didymograptus* lasted into Medial Ordovician time like its counterpart in the pendent strain. Further reduction in number of stipes from *Didymograptus* led to a sicula with one ray—a feature which seems to have been produced independently by both the pendent as well as by the horizontal strain as the Genus *Azygograptus.* This being the irreducible minimum, no further reduction of stipes could take place in either strain.

Horizontal dichograptids seem to have been vigorous, however, because they produced a second offshoot which had a promising future. By becoming increasingly erect, the four stipes of *Tetragraptus* passed through a reclined stage (Fig. 4.7.12) and eventually lay back back to back along the nema in a scandent form called *Phyllograptus* (Fig. 4.7.15). But, as if *Phyllograptus* were carried along by a stream of evolution leading to ever fewer stipes, the number of rays continued to diminish and the biserial Genus, *Diplograptus,* arose.

At the same time, *Didymograptus* was evolving toward the scandent shape of *Diplograptus* through forms such as *Leptograptus* which had reclined stipes (Fig. 4.7.13). Thus, *Diplograptus* and the whole scandent strain arose from two different lineages of horizontal graptoloids, even though they are united as a single Genus, *Diplograptus,* in Figure 4.7. Surprisingly, *Azygograptus* seems to have appeared for the third time when the reclined *Leptograptus* lost one of its stipes (Fig. 4.7.14) in the Medial Ordovician.

An interesting but short-lived side shoot arose from the main body of diplograptids in Medial Ordovician time by partial reduction in number of stipes; *Dicranograptus* split down the distal portion into two uniserial branches but remained biserial and unbranched in the proximal portion, thus forming a Y-shaped stipe (Fig. 4.7.17). This variation led nowhere, possibly because it would have been lethal if carried far enough to separate a stipe from its sicula.

When the biserial scandent arrangement had been achieved by *Diplo-*

Figure 4.7 (opposite).   Evolutionary Patterns of Graptozoans.

Rhabdosomes are shown diagrammatically and not to the same enlarged scale. The geologic time divisions are not to scale, but only indicate approximate ages. Heavy lines connect successive morphologic stages and do not represent duration of any Genus. Three reclined forms straddle the boundary between the distinctly horizontal and the distinctly scandent strains.

(After Elles, 1922, and Swinnerton, 1938.)

graptus in Medial Ordovician time, a second major evolutionary trend became evident. In it the thecal shape changed from straight to either sigmoid or lobate. The stream of thecal modification is superimposed on the continuing trend for reduction in number of stipes. If all of these trends were illustrated it would be necessary to superimpose Figure 4.6.5–13 upon Figure 4.7.16, 18, 19. In simple terms the continued reduction in number of stipes led through the Early Silurian *Dimorphograptus* with its uniserial proximal portion and its biserial distal portion, to *Monograptus* with its wholly uniserial stipe. Naturally, in *Monograptus* we see the irreducible minimum of stipes and generally a late stage in thecal changes. The end of the evolutionary history was approaching.

Final modifications in the graptoloid graptolites are manifested by strange thecal patterns in *Rastrites;* by reversions to ancestral features such as the return to straight, tubular thecae in some *Monograptus;* and by the assumption of a secondarily colonial habit through production of whorls of new stipes in *Cyrtograptus.* Even then the tendency for compactness continued to be manifested, as in coiling up of some *Monograptus* into conical helicoid spirals like watch springs suspended from their inner ends. But finally, when the graptoloid graptolites flickered out in some Late Silurian sea, the ancient, unprogressive, dendroid graptolites still were present as sessile organisms on the sea floor or on floating objects. Dendroids persisted for 75 million years, however, into Early Mississippian time when their last known remains were buried in Europe and in what is known today as the Black Hills region of South Dakota.

Extinction of the graptolites cannot be assigned with certainty to any cause. The only major carnivores that could swim about in search of these planktonic creatures in Ordovician and Early Silurian times were the cephalopods, but their living descendants do not feed upon any animals resembling the graptoloids. Graptoloids may have been unusually successsful in the Ordovician more because of lack of enemies than through perfection of structure. By latest Silurian time, however, fish had evolved, and they may very well have fed upon the planktonic graptolites. Silurian fish were not heavily armored like Ordovician ostracoderms but were slender and lithe cyclostomes.

TAXONOMIC PROBLEMS OF GRAPTOZOA. Referring to Figure 4.7, the evolution of the pendent, the horizontal, and the reclined graptoloids followed the same pattern and thereby produced three kinds of *Tetragraptus,* two kinds of *Didymograptus* plus the analogous *Leptograptus,* and three kinds of *Azygograptus.* This phenomenon is a classic example of parallel descent and even of convergence. The pendent and horizontal strains which had dichograptid budding represent parallel descent, but *Leptograptus* had a different kind of budding and therefore represents convergence of shape. Naturally, the concept of *Tetragraptus, Didymo-*

graptus, and *Azygograptus* as Genera is different from the ideal concept of a group of genetically related species. These graptoloids are referred to "form Genera" because they comprise similar but more or less distantly related organisms. Likewise, the scandent strain arrived at *Diplograptus* via two routes—through *Phyllograptus* and through *Leptograptus. Diplograptus,* as used in the illustration, is a loosely constructed form Genus which is known by specialists to contain two or more genetic strains. Moreover, each of these strains led in turn to its own descendants in the form Genus, *Monograptus.*

EVOLUTION MECHANISM OF GRAPTOZOA. There was a distinct tendency for graptolites to become simpler and more compact as time passed, so this must indicate the direction of success and survival. By Darwinian concepts, creatures tend to vary in all sorts of ways, some of which happen to be in the direction of survival, but some of which, like the pendent graptoloids and *Dicranograptus,* happen to be foredoomed to failure. In the former case, for instance, progressive compactness of stipes in pendent *Tetragraptus* would have brought polyps closer face to face until they would have competed with each other. On the other hand, the trend for ascending stipes which led to reclined and scandent forms provided the polyps with improved access to food and increased freedom of operation. The ascending trend ultimately produced what seems to be the most efficient and compact structure in *Phyllograptus* and *Diplograptus.* Graptoloids raced through most of their evolution of shape in the Early Ordovician and then they expressed their evolutionary potentiality in part by thecal modification. It is necessary to say "in part" because they continued to carry on the trend for reduction in number of branches far beyond the compact forms until they became uniserial again. In a way the monograptid shape is the scandent equivalent of *Azygograptus* in other strains. A believer in orthogenesis would maintain that some hidden drive or factor caused them to continue to evolve back into less compact uniserial forms such as their ancestors had. On the other hand, a believer in orthoselection would contend that there had to be some unexplained advantage in uniserial stipes following upon the more compact biserial stipes; therefore, natural selection operated to preserve the uniserial strains. In any case, it seems that the early pendent and horizontal graptoloids survived only as long as competition was not keen or enemies were not effective.

AFFINITIES OF GRAPTOZOA. Graptolites have been referred to three different Phyla of animals. According to the oldest theory, graptolites are coelenterates. This idea is supported initially by the shapes of rhabdosomes, which resemble hydroid generations of many Hydrozoa. *Diplograptus,* for instance, resembles *Thuiaria* (Fig. 4.2.6) in general appearance. In addition, graptolites and Hydrozoa both produced polymorphic individuals with differentiation of vegetative and reproductive functions. Both groups have the same spread of adaptation, too, for both groups contain shrubby benthonic colonies as well as planktonic colonies suspended from pneumatocysts (such as the Portuguese man-of-war, Fig. 4.4.2).

The second theory was first proposed in 1872 and currently enjoys widespread popularity since its revival in 1938. According to this view, the fuselles which are known among a few Graptozoa (principally Dendroida) are also present in the Genus *Rhabdopleura*. Inasmuch as fuselles seem to be singularly unusual structures, protagonists of this theory hold that Graptozoa and *Rhabdopleura* belong to the same Phylum. *Rhabdopleura* is an aberrant and probably primitive, colonial hemichordate which inhabits Recent marine waters.

The third theory, which seems not to be defended any more, maintains that Graptozoa are related to the moss animals or Bryozoa (Chapter 7). Some colonies of the two groups are similar and the individual polyps inhabited similar tubular sheaths. There is also polymorphism among Bryozoa, but most Bryozoa contain specialized structures not seen in Graptozoa.

In this text the Graptozoa are ranked as a separate Class closely related to the Hydrozoa. Not only does *Rhabdopleura* lack polymorphism, but its fuselles are secreted as parts of a strictly external sheath, whereas fuselles and cortex of Graptozoa were covered with some additional fleshy material in life. The two kinds of fuselles are not homologous.

Class C.   Stromatoporoidea

Many paleontologists find a sort of romantic or perhaps mystic appeal in the study of groups whose relationships with living or other fossil animals either are controversial or are unknown. Stromatoporoids constitute one of these groups, which, like the receptaculitids, archaeocyathids, and graptolites already discussed, require imaginative extrapolation of Recent biologic knowledge into the unknown past if we are to understand their nature, habits, and evolutionary position. Otherwise, several groups of extinct organisms would have to be considered just like static mineralogic components of a rock.

Stromatoporoids occur as calcareous colonies divided into minute chambers which have customarily been thought of as the dwelling places of interconnected individuals such as polyps in a colonial coral. Colonies (also called **coenostea**) range in size from small lumps the size of peas to ponderous intergrowths many feet in diameter, or, together with other organisms, build reefy masses from the substance of which commercial rock quarries can be operated. Colonies seen in most outcrops range from 3 inches to perhaps 1 foot or so in diameter. Shapes tend to assume one of three fundamental patterns. The largest colonies are sheets of laminated tissue with undulatory upper surfaces, the entire colony commonly being somewhat biconvex. Margins of these colonies are often hard to define because various layers overlap one another in fortuitous fashion according to how various areas died and were overgrown by new material. The second shape is generally bulbous, ranging from little spherical or biscuit-shaped masses to large hummocky colonies about a foot high. The least common form is composed of erect or branching, heavy, stemlike expansions with circular cross sections. Com-

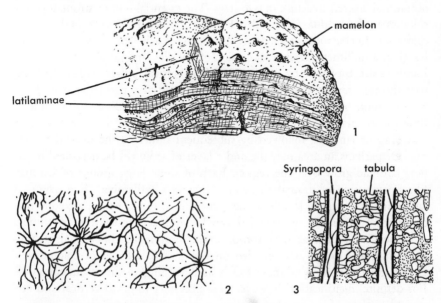

Figure 4.8.   Stromatoporoidea.
1. Schematic oblique view of an exfoliated and vertically fractured colony, 2/3X, Devonian, Nevada.   2. Astrorhizae on the surface of *Ferestromatopora larocquei*, 1X, Devonian, Ohio. 3. Vertical section of *Stromatopora* sp. surrounding two corallites of *Syringopora* sp., 12X, Devonian, Germany.
(2, 3 after Galloway, 1957.)

plete stromatoporoid colonies may weather out of impure limestone, or sheets of skeletal tissue may exfoliate from colonies where thin partitions of muddy sediment alternate with layers of organic material. Colonies in pure limestone appear only as light patches against the other limestone of the matrix and may be easily overlooked.

Surfaces of some colonies are relatively smooth except for minute pitting, but surfaces of other stromatoporoids are studded with hemispherical **mamelons** (Fig. 4.8.1) which rise 1 to 3 millimeters above the general surface. Mamelons commonly are surmounted by branching furrows which lead to a central pit, the whole radial pattern being called an **astrorhiza** in allusion to its stellate and rootlike appearance (Fig. 4.8.2). Astrorhizae communicate laterally with most of the coenosteum and also touch tips of adjacent astrorhizae. If a distinct central pit is present in an astrorhiza it represents the upper end of a vertical tube which penetrates deeply into the coenosteum. These tubes may be partitioned by a few horizontal plates, the **tabulae** (Fig. 4.8.3). Some specialists believe that astrorhizae mark the locations of the principal polyps which secreted the coenostea.

The most characteristic growth feature of stromatoporoids is the presence of internal layered structure in two sizes. The essential unit of stromatoporoid colonies is the **lamina** (also called **lamella**), which is a horizontal layer of calcareous fibers, rods, or plates (Fig. 4.9.2b). Each lamina is separated by less than a millimeter from a succession of parallel laminae above and below. Laminae are traversed by myriad, parallel, vertical **pillars** which generally pass through several laminae but may terminate at a particular one. Thus, a coenosteum resembles the steel framework of a building. From time to time the regular upward growth of a coenosteum may be interrupted by crowding of laminae, followed by subsequent return to the normal growth rate. Or perhaps an area may die and a layer of sediment be deposited before new laminae grow over the region. Each of these large groups of laminae, like a succession of annual rings in a tree, is a **latilamina** (Fig. 4.8.1). A latilamina is generally less than one-quarter inch thick; hence, a colony may consist of a succession of several dozen latilaminae. Under some conditions of preservation such as very complete calcification or differential etching, the latilaminae are clearly revealed on radial cross sections of colonies and enable the recognition of these fossils as belonging to the stromatoporoids. For definite identification, however, it is necessary to grind vertical and horizontal sections of a coenosteum prior to microscopic examination.

One noteworthy feature of the stromatoporoids is the tendency of some species to become intimately intergrown with the loosely bundled corallites of the colonial coral *Syringopora* (Fig. 4.8.3). This probable commensal association is known from Devonian strata in widely separated places. Before the characteristic structure of *Syringopora* had been recognized, the tubes were interpreted as giant pores characterizing a distinct Genus of stromatoporoid.

Principal variations in stromatoporoid construction are the shape and size of colonies, nature of the surface, and character of laminae and pillars. The oldest and most primitive stromatoporoids lack the well-developed laminae of later forms. Instead, Genera such as *Labechia* and *Aulacera* are packed with cystose structures in irregular rows (Fig. 4.9.5, 6). *Aulacera* also has an axial canal which contains even larger cysts than are present in the marginal zone. Such primitive forms, generally classed as stromatoporoids, tend to be dendritic in growth habit. The eleven known Genera comprise a special Family, the Beatriciidae, and are largely confined to Ordovician strata.

The several Families of true stromatoporoids (sometimes known in classifications as the "*Stromatoporoidea vera*") seemingly arose from the Beatriciidae by progressive perfecting of horizontal rows of cysts which became the laminae. *Clathrodictyon* (Fig. 4.9.1) represents an early stage in the series in which laminae are more distinct than are the pillars. *Actinostroma* (Fig. 4.9.2) represents an advanced stage of stromatoporoid development in which

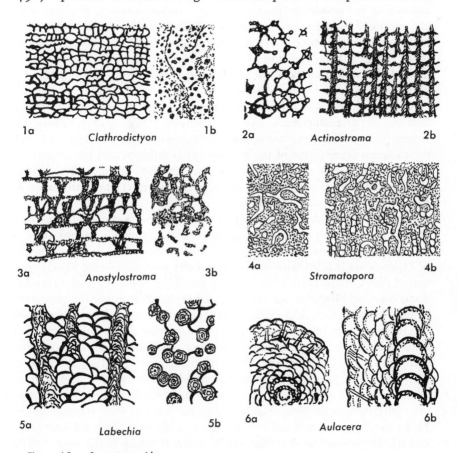

Figure 4.9. Stromatoporoidea.
1a, 1b. Vertical and transverse sections of *Clathrodictyon vesiculosum*, 11X, Silurian, Ohio. 2a, 2b. Transverse and vertical sections of *Actinostroma clathratum*, 11X, Devonian, Germany. Distinct pillars and laminae. 3a, 3b. Vertical and transverse sections of *Anostylostroma hamiltonense*, 9X, Devonian, Michigan. 4a, 4b, Transverse and vertical sections of Stromatopora concentrica, 10X, Devonian, Germany. 5a, 5b. Vertical and transverse sections of *Labechia conferta*, 11X, Silurian, England. 6a, 6b. Cross section and longitudinal section of *Aulacera plummeri*, 2X, Ordovician, Indiana.
(After Galloway, 1957.)

pillars are more prominent than the laminae are. In *Anostylostroma* the chambers are secondarily subdivided by **dissepiments** into smaller chambers (Fig. 4.9.3). *Stromatopora* itself is not constructed of as distinctive laminae and pillars as are some other Genera. It does contain many tabulate vertical tubules, however (Fig. 4.9.4). About 22 Genera of true stromatoporoids have been recognized.

BIOLOGIC AFFINITIES. Four different theories have been proposed concerning the taxonomic position of the Stromatoporoidea. Students who are impressed by the layered nature of the chambered coenostea see a similarity between stromatoporoids and the general group of larger Foraminiferida (Fig. 2.18). Although it is true that various orbitoids consist of multiple layers of chambers, they have solid walls instead of the mesh and pillar construction of stromatoporoids.

A second theory is based upon the presence of pillars and loose meshlike laminae in stromatoporoids like *Actinostroma* (Fig. 4.9.2a). These do suggest the spicular structure of some hexactinellid sponges (Fig. 3.6), but the chemical composition of the two groups is different and the hexactinellids retain rather precise triaxon symmetry of their spicules. Those who believe that the stromatoporoids are sponges interpret the astrorhizae as part of the canal system for circulation of water.

The third and oldest theory is that stromatoporoids are related to Hydrozoa in some respect. Similarity between the chitinous incrustation of *Hydractinia* and most stromatoporoids is impressive, although colonial tissue of *Hydractinia* is filled with ramifying tubules instead of being loosely connected fibers. Astrorhizae resemble very much the hydrorhizae of many hydroid colonies. Moreover, astrorhizid tubes are tabulate as are the gonopores of the hydrocoralline, *Millepora*. In life the fleshy tissue of stromatoporoids seems almost certainly to have formed a mantle over the upper surface of some colonies—a feature observed in some Hydrozoa. Moreover, a thin, incrusting, laminated organism called *Gypsina plana* (Fig. 4.3.2) has long been known to resemble the stromatoporoids *Clathrodictyon* and *Actinostroma* closely in gross aspect and in some microscopic details. *Gypsina* was originally thought to be a colonial foraminifer but is now referred to the Hydrocorallida by some authorities such as Galloway (personal communication). In view of these factors, the hydrozoan theory is the most widely held as to the affinities of stromatoporoids.

Those who support the fourth and last theory suppose that stromatoporoids constitute a group sufficiently distinct to warrant separate recognition. The massive skeletal build-ups, mixtures of features enumerated above which are reminiscent both of sponges and of hydrozoans, and the absence of any feature generally accepted as being diagnostic of one of those groups, support this fourth theory. In this book therefore, the stromatoporoids are placed in a Class near the Hydrozoa but as distinct from hydrozoans as that Class is from Scyphozoa (jellyfish) or Anthozoa (corals).

GEOLOGIC DISTRIBUTION. Stromatoporoids are known questionably from Cambrian and definitely from Middle Ordovician strata. The beatricoid type is rather generally characteristic of Ordovician strata, even though a few true stromatoporoids also occur there.

The great flare of stromatoporoids took place in the Silurian and Devonian Periods. At that time they were so abundant that the majority of carbonate rocks of that age are apt to contain colonies of stromatoporoids. Devonian strata seem to be even more replete with stromatoporoid remains than are Silurian strata. Colonies are so common that many so-called limestone strata actually consist almost entirely of stromatoporoids. At the end of Devonian time the true stromatoporoids suddenly and unaccountably became extinct. Important occurrences are known in many parts of North America and other countries; however, very little work has been done in recent years on American species until Galloway and St. Jean restudied the group.

Appendix to the Stromatoporoidea: Sphaeractinioids

During the Permian a group of stromatoporoidlike organisms appeared which have been placed by some students in the Stromatoporoidea and by other students in a separate taxon equal in rank to the Stromatoporoidea. These organisms differ from typical stromatoporoids in their microstructure and in their skeletal construction, which consists of concentric layers and radiating rows of rods. It is probable that the sphaeractinioids arose from some ancestor near *Stromatopora*. Before their extinction in the Cretaceous, six Families of sphaeractinioids had appeared. The best known of these is represented by the Genus *Milleporidium* from the Jurassic of eastern Europe and the Near East (Fig. 4.10.1).

Incertae Sedis

The Genus *Amphipora* usually is placed in or near the Stromatoporoidea in classifications. *Amphipora* is a dendroid form about half the diameter of a pencil and an inch or so in length (Fig. 4.10.2, 3). It may or may not have an axial canal like *Aulacera,* and its vaguely laminar outer tissue is reminiscent of the true stromatoporoids. Fragments of *Amphipora* are packed together in many Devonian outcrops in California, Nevada, and Utah, where, for lack of other distinctive features, their presence has caused geologists to refer to the sediments as spaghetti rock.

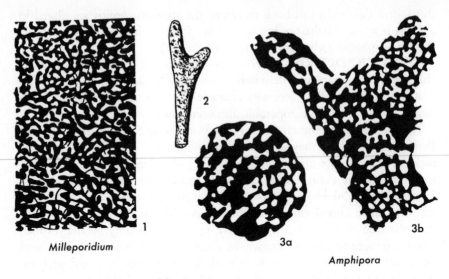

Milleporidium

3a

Amphipora

Figure 4.10.   Stromatoporoidlike Organisms.
   1. Section of a colony of *Milleporidium remesi*, 10X, Jurassic, Czechoslovakia.   2. Fragment of a colony of *Amphipora* sp., 2X, Devonian, Nevada.   3a, 3b, Transverse and longitudinal sections of *Amphipora ramosa*, 8X, Devonian, Australia.
   (1 after Hudson, 1956. 3 after Ripper, 1937.)

Class D.   Scyphozoa

Scyphozoa are the jellyfish, whose medusoid bodies consist largely of mesogloea. They differ from medusae of Hydrozoa in lacking a velum. They also have four radially disposed pouchlike depressions on the lower or concave surface, instead of being smooth as are the hydroid medusae. Adult medusae reproduce sexually to form a planula larva, and this develops into a small, sessile, inverted larva which resembles a simple four-rayed polyp, but which buds off new miniature medusae one at a time by transverse fission from the upper region (Fig. 4.11.2). These little medusae grow into adult jellyfish to complete the cycle.

Jellyfish inhabit water at various depths and can swim about by contracting their umbrella-shaped bodies. Although most are concavo-convex, they also may be cubical, helmet-shaped, constricted at a deep groove about the middle, or even flat. As in the other typical coelenterate groups, they bear stinging cells.

Even though skeletal elements are unknown in Recent jellyfish, a few impressions in ancient sediments have been referred to this group. The oldest possible representative is *Camptostroma* from the Early Cambrian of Pennsylvania. Numerous supposed internal molds of jellyfish (*Brooksella*) have

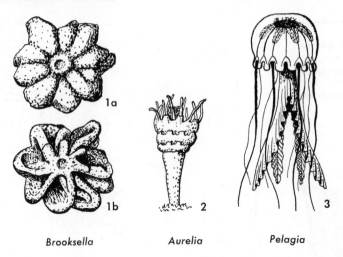

Figure 4.11.   Scyphozoa.
1a, 1b. External and internal surfaces of *Brooksella alternata*, 2/3X, Cambrian, Alabama.
2. A strobila larva of *Aurelia flavidula*, 10X, Recent.   3. *Pelagia cyanella*, 1/3X, Recent.
(1a after Walcott, 1898. 2, 3, after L. Agassiz, 1860.)

been collected from higher Cambrian strata in the Coosa Valley of Alabama (Fig. 4.11.1). Several different forms have been collected from upper Jurassic lithographic limestone at the famous Solenhofen quarries in Germany.

Appendix to the Scyphozoa: Conularioids

Few other organisms have been referred to so many diverse groups as have the conularioids. They are almost completely unlike any living creatures except that they have a simple tetramerous symmetry reminiscent of coelenterates.

These fossils consist of a very thin chitinous membrane with some admixture of phosphatic material. Undistorted specimens are invariably hollow four-sided pyramids which generally range in length from about an inch to several inches (Fig. 4.12.1b). Being hollow and thin, these pyramids commonly have been crumpled or occur completely flattened on bedding planes. Most conularioids are square in cross section, but some are elongate rectangles. Such evidence as has been forthcoming indicates that in life they were attached to some object, commonly another conularian, by their pointed tips. The large open end, which thus was free, could be closed by flaps of the membrane which folded over it with neat creases.

The most conspicuous surficial feature on each face is a system of sharp, closely spaced parallel ridges or rows of granules with intervening grooves

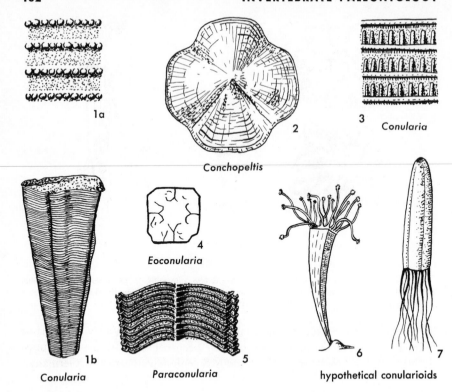

Figure 4.12.   Conularioids.
1. *Conularia undulata*, Devonian, New York. 1a, portion of surface, 12X. 1b, side view showing grooved interfacial angles, 2/3X.   2. *Conchopeltis alternata*, 1/2X, Ordovician, New York,
Minnesota.   3. Portion of the surface of *Conularia continens*, about 10X, Devonian, New
York.   4. Cross section of *Eoconularia loculata* showing septalike partitions, 7X, Silurian,
Germany.   5. Portion of *Paraconularia missouriensis* with a prominent midline and two distinct
interfacial angles, 2/3X, Mississippian, midcontinent.   6. Reconstruction of a conularioid attached
to the substratum by its apex, 1/3X.   7. Reconstruction of a conularioid in the free-living state,
with the broken apex sealed off by a diaphragm, 1/4X.
(1, 3 after Hall, 1879. 2 after Knight, 1937. 4 after Sinclair, 1944. 5 after Keyes, 1894b.
6, 7 after Kiderlen, 1937.)

about 1 millimeter apart (Fig. 4.12.1a, 3, 5). Ridges on one half of each face
are aligned with grooves on the opposite half, and the position of this alternation marks the location of the **midline.** Moreover, the midline may be
accentuated by a groove or ridge. In a few forms each transversely striated
half of a face may be divided into halves again by another but weaker **lateral
line. Interfacial angles** at the corners of the pyramids are typically grooved
and may consist of thicker periderm than do the faces themselves. Upon
close examination of the interfacial grooves it may be seen that transverse
ornamentation of adjacent faces may continue across the groove, or be in

alternation as at the midline, or even be interlocked in some intricate fashion. Great dependence in classification is placed upon features associated with the interfacial angle.

Under magnification the transverse ornamentation of the faces displays additional interesting detail (Fig. 4.12.1a, 3). Forms with linear ridges tend to bear nodose or vertically striated grooves. Where oblique ridges of variable size and altitude are present instead of striae they may appear to be caused by wrinkling of smooth periderm in the grooves during burial. If transverse rows of granules take the place of ridges, then grooves are generally striate instead of nodose. Some conularioids are even smooth, and in others the vertical ornamentation submerges the transverse pattern.

Specialists recognize a score of Genera, of which *Conularia* is the most common and representative form (Fig. 4.12.1b). It ranges through every Period in the Paleozoic Era and has produced some valuable guide fossils, in all of which the transverse ornamentation crosses the interfacial groove. *Paraconularia,* on the other hand, is a Silurian to Mississippian form in which transverse ornamentation is interrupted at the interfacial groove (Fig. 4.12.5).

AFFINITIES OF CONULARIOIDS. For many years the conularioids were assigned by different authors to the worms or gastropods (pteropods), but since Kiderlen's studies in 1937 opinion has grown that these odd structures are thin membranous cuticles secreted on the outer surface of jellyfish. External expression of tetrameral symmetry is enhanced by study of *Eoconularia,* in which four Y-shaped septa extend in from the periderm at the positions of the midline (Fig. 4.12.4). A seemingly identical arrangement exists in the soft tissue of a living jellyfish (*Craterolophus*). Moreover, various conularioids are known to develop longitudinal ridges on the inner surface in opposition to their lateral lines as well as the midlines. These ridges can be homologous either with traces of contractile muscles or with bases of attachment of tentacles in jellyfish. Perhaps the most convincing evidence is seen in a specimen of *Conchopeltis* from the Ordovician which has been figured by Moore and Harrington (1956, p. F32) and in which traces of many tentacles are preserved. *Conchopeltis* is, perversely, the most aberrant of all conularioids (if, indeed, it is a conularioid), being nearly flat (Fig. 14.12.2).

The final evidence in support of the scyphozoan affinities of the conularioids comes from the habit of these creatures. Ruedemann and others have found conularioids attached by basal discs on their slender pointed tips; therefore, at least some were sessile (Fig. 4.12.6). Others, though, had rounded apical portions and show no sign of attachment. Still others contain an oblique diaphragm near the apex and seem to have used it to seal off the extreme apical portion when the creature broke loose from its place of attachment and became free-living (Fig. 4.12.7). This history is compatible with what we know of the true Scyphozoa and their sessile actinula larvae.

As matters stand now, considerable circumstantial evidence supports assignment of the conularioids to the Scyphozoa. On the other hand, it is still possible that the conularioids may represent a separate group of animals of unknown affinities.

QUESTIONS

1. Why might problematic organisms comprising the graptolites, stromatoporoids, and conularioids all be classified with the lower coelenterates?
2. Give an example of an evolutionary "dead end" among graptolites. When did the trend become disadvantageous?
3. What similarities exist between compartmentation of the most advanced fusulinids and the most advanced stromatoporoids? What biologic significance is attached to the similarity and what explains the similarity?
4. Why should there be any reason to give different Linnaean names to hydroid and medusoid generations of the same species of Hydrozoan?
5. Explain the difference between dimorphic and polymorphic animals and support the distinction with examples.

BIBLIOGRAPHY

References pertaining to the Lower Coelenterata will be found with the other coelenterate references at the end of Chapter 5.

Chapter 5

HIGHER COELENTERATES (MAINLY CORALS)

PHYLUM IV.   COELENTERATA (Continued)

The higher coelenterates comprise the corals, the sea anemones, and the comb-jellyfish or ctenophores. Of these, only the corals are paleontologically important. Indeed, the corals constitute one of the major groups of fossils.

The classification of higher coelenterates presented below concludes the classification of coelenterates begun in Chapter 4 and contains detail on the Class Anthozoa. An attempt has been made to carry the following classification down to the level in each group which will enable practical recognition of units in the field. In different Subclasses this varies between Orders, Suborders, Families, and arbitrary morphologic groups.

Phylum IV. Coelenterata (Continued)
  Class E. Anthozoa
    Subclass 1. Tabulata
        Family a. Chaetetidae
        Family b. Tetradiidae
        Family c. Auloporidae
        Family d. Syringoporidae
        Family e. Halysitidae
        Family f. Favositidae
        Family g. Heliolitidae
        Family h. Calapoeciidae
    Subclass 2. Rugosa (Tetracoralla)
        Group of Columnariids
        Group of Cyathaxoniids
        Group of Zaphrenthids
        Group of Cyathophyllids
        Group of Clisiophyllids
        Group of Cystiphyllids
        Group of Porpitids
        Group of Lophophyllids
        Group of Polycoeliids

Subclass 3. Heterocoralla
Subclass 4. Octocoralla (Alcyonaria)
Subclass 5. Hexacoralla
   Order a. Zoanthida
   Order b. Corallimorphida
   Order c. Actinida
   Order d. Scleractinida
      Suborder (1). Astrocoeniina
      Suborder (2). Fungiina
      Suborder (3). Faviina
      Suborder (4). Caryophylliina
      Suborder (5). Dendrophylliina
   Order e. Antipathida
   Order f. Cerianthida
Class F. Ctenophora

Class E.   Anthozoa

The name Anthozoa was coined for corals and corallike animals because the brightly colored polyps with their extended tentacles resemble flowers, yet are animals. The confusion of early naturalists as to the plant or animal nature of these organisms is still reflected in our use of the name "sea anemones" for some of the soft-bodied polyps with numerous radiating tentacles. Moreover, corals, together with sponges, were formerly referred to as "zoophytes" meaning animal plants. All of the corals, as well as a few rather noncoralline-appearing organisms, constitute the Anthozoa.

ZOOLOGIC FEATURES. Principal features of the advance of corals over other coelenterates lie in the development of a more efficient digestive system. Primitive coelenterates have a simple baglike coelenteron whose digestive efficiency is measured by the area of the inner surface of the body wall. If the diameter of a coelenterate were doubled, then the area of the digestive surface would be increased fourfold in a spherical coelenteron and threefold in a cylindrical coelenteron. Although this means of increasing digestive surface might work for small increases in diameter it would be entirely unsatisfactory for major increases because not only would the volume of water in the coelenteron become so large as to limit the effectiveness of digestive juices, but the weight of the animal would be greater than the body wall could support. It is obvious, then, that the point of diminishing returns would soon be reached by this system of growth. The problem of digestive efficiency was solved in the Anthozoa by infolding the body wall into **mesenteries** (Fig. 5.1). These mesenteries are thin sheets of tissue which hang like drapery from the inner oral surface of a polyp to the floor of the

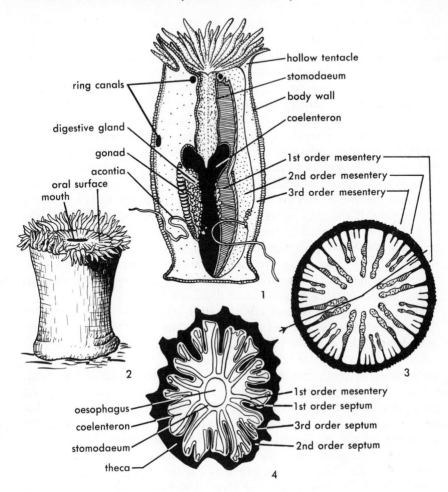

ring canals

digestive gland

gonad

acontia

oral surface
mouth

hollow tentacle
stomodaeum
body wall
coelenteron

1st order mesentery
2nd order mesentery
3rd order mesentery

1

2

3

oesophagus
coelenteron
stomodaeum
theca

1st order mesentery
1st order septum
3rd order septum
2nd order septum

4

Figure 5.1.   Morphology of Anthozoa.
  1. Schematic longitudinal section of a sea anemone, *Phellia* sp., showing internal anatomy,
about 1X, Recent.   2. Side view of a sea anemone with a slitlike mouth, 1X, Recent.   3. Schematic transverse section of *Phellia* showing three orders of mesenteries and the trace of the
longitudinal section (arrow), 1 1/3X, Recent.   4. Schematic transverse section of a young stony
coral showing relationship between soft tissue and skeleton (black), 35X, Recent.
  (1-3 after Chun, 1891. 4 after Duerden, 1902.)

coelenteron. Mesenteries normally occur in pairs. They radiate outward from
the stomodaeum, or below it they radiate from their free ends near the open
vertical axis of the coelenteron to the side walls of the coelenteron where
they merge with the body wall. Inasmuch as mesenteries may be covered
with absorptive surface on both sides, they increase the digestive efficiency
of a coral very greatly without adding anything to the size of the polyp,

and they even decrease by displacement some of the water which would otherwise dilute digestive juices. Corals emplaced their mesenteries in several patterns. Moreover, one side of each mesentery bears a thin longitudinal band of retractile muscle. **Muscle bands** of pairs of mesenteries commonly, but not in all cases, face each other (Figs. 5.1.3; 5.19.2, 3, 7). The number and patterns of mesenteries and the position of muscle bands all have come to be significant in subdividing Anthozoa into smaller taxonomic groups.

Food supply is captured by stinging tentacles on the oral surface, after which the paralyzed prey is brought into the mouth by muscular contraction of the tentacles and the oral surface. The oral opening leads into the stomodaeum, so eventually the captured crustacean, small fish, or other food enters the coelenteron and the oral opening closes by contraction of a circular muscle ring. If the prey is not dead, then additional nematocysts on the mesenteries or on threadlike **acontia** in the coelenteron finish killing it, and digestion commences. Undigested material is voided back through the stomodaeum by muscular contraction. Nutrients produced in the coelenteron diffuse into the tissues without benefit of a circulatory system, although hollow centers of tentacles assist in its distribution.

The nervous system is more effective than in primitive coelenterates, although it is still a simple net. Sexual reproduction is like that of other coelenterates, although the planula larva produces another identical coral polyp directly without recourse to alternation of generations. Sexes either are separate, or corals may be hermaphroditic. In the course of embryonic cell division, the middle layer of mesogloea which characterizes simple coelenterates may be occupied in some higher forms by cellular tissue, thus producing the three-layered condition characteristic of higher animals. Reproductive organs are located internally on the mesenteries, so sex cells or larvae must escape through the oral opening. Geographic distribution of these bottom-dwelling coralline organisms is by means of the planktonic planula larvae. Inasmuch as larval stages last from 1 to 30 days, oceanic currents of normal velocity readily can transport some species about 300 miles in one generation. This helps to explain the rapid recovery of corals upon denuded surfaces of reefs and the great geographic ranges of species. When an anthozoan polyp is at rest water enters and leaves the coelenteron freely through the oral opening. Currents of water which are set in circulation by the beating of flagella in the coelenteron and on the siphonoglyphs may transport sex cells or planula larvae out into the surrounding water.

SKELETAL FEATURES. Only those corals with solid calcareous skeletons are significant paleontologically. In its simplest form the skeleton is merely a conical cup (**theca**) which contains the soft polyp. Most corals, however, secrete radial partitions (**septa**) which lie parallel with the fleshy mesenteries and are fused to the theca (Fig. 5.1.4.). Septa serve to hold the pairs of mesenteries apart and to maintain the form of the polyp. In addition, the body wall is thrust inward as the septa grow toward the axis and therefore the digestive area within the coelenteron is increased in the same way that it was increased by development of mesenteries. Septa are inserted between pairs of mesenteries and project inward through distances proportional to the lengths of the mesenteries; hence they provide an accurate measure of this soft anatomy of the coral polyp, even in fossil forms.

As polyps grow upward they tend to seal off the earlier portions of their skeletons with horizontal plates of calcite called **tabulae.** Thus, a coral polyp only inhabits the upper portion (**calyx,** pl. **calyces**) of the skeleton.

Many corals exhibit a strong tendency toward colonial form. Each colony is a **corallum** and each individual in the corallum is a **corallite.**

CLASSIFICATION. Methods of classifying living Anthozoa are not consistent with methods applied to fossil Anthozoa. Among Recent forms the number and distribution of tentacles, kind of nematocysts, and number, symmetry, length, and microstructure of mesenteries are given prime consideration. On the other hand, all fossil and some living corals are distinguished on features such as growth habit and the sequence of appearance and the microstructure of septa.

Several satisfactory classifications of Anthozoa are available. The following arrangement is somewhat different from most recent systems because it attempts to resolve corals into a few major contrasting groups, each of which is then carried down to whatever level is generally significant to paleontologists. More definitive classifications have been proposed recently in the *Treatise on Invertebrate Paleontology,* but continued lack of agreement on number, rank, and position of taxa is a reflection of the need for additional study of Anthozoa.

SUBCLASS 1.　TABULATA

Tabulate corals consist of colonial masses of slender corallites in which septa usually are absent, but if present they are represented as vertical rows of spines. Tabulae are the only obvious morphologic features within thecae; hence the name of the Subclass. Corallites of some tabulate corals are loosely bundled together, but most polyps have grown so closely together that the corallites are prismatic. Walls of corallites may be solid but, more typically, adjacent corallites were in communication laterally in some manner. Loosely bundled corallites were variously connected by tubular processes, horizontal plates, and spongy or vesicular surrounding tissue (**coenenchyme**), but prismatic corallites communicated by means of **mural pores** which ordinarily penetrated the thecae of adjacent corallites. Mural pores have been interpreted as abortive bud bases by some paleontologists; at any rate, new corallites do seem to arise from positions of mural pores in some tabulate corals.

The colonial tendency of some tabulates progressed so far that the thecae tended to break down and calyces became interconnected. Basal and lateral portions of the massive coralla generally were enveloped in a rindlike **epitheca.**

About 100 Genera of tabulate corals are known, most of which can be assigned to one of the Families in the following key.

KEY TO COMMON FAMILIES OF TABULATA

I. Diameter of corallites generally less than 2 mm
  A. Septa lacking .... Chaetetidae
  B. Septa present .... Tetradiidae
II. Diameter of corallites more than 2 mm
  A. Coralla not massive
    1. Thecae not in contact laterally
      a. Incrusting habit .... Auloporidae
      b. Erect habit .... Syringoporidae
    2. Thecae in contact in linear series .... Halysitidae
  B. Coralla massive or with coenenchyme
    1. Corallites prismatic .... Favositidae
    2. Corallites circular
      a. Septa 12 .... Heliolitidae
      b. Septa more than 12 .... Calapoeciidae

Family a.   Chaetetidae

This Family consists of massive coralla whose very slender corallites (almost always 1 mm or less in diameter) merge laterally to form intercommunicating calyces. Tabulae are very distant. Thecae are nonperforate. Septa are absent. Colonies range from the size of biscuits to large masses a meter in diameter. Chaetetids resemble stony bryozoans so much as to cause confusion in the absence of thin sections.

The oldest coral in the world is a somewhat problematic form from the Cambrian of Montana upon which the Genus *Cambrophyllum* (Fig. 5.2.1) is based.

Lichenaria, from the lower part of the Middle Ordovician (Chazy) is one of the earliest corals. Its nonseptate corallites contain only transverse tabulae. *Lichenaria* tends to build biohermal masses in the Appalachian region and therefore is the oldest reef-making anthozoan.

Chaetetes, the type Genus of the Family, is very abundant in (and is almost restricted to) Lower Pennsylvanian strata in North America (Fig. 5.2.2, 3). It becomes a minor reef-former in the Midwest, in the Great Basin, and in the Paradox Basin. Elsewhere over the world this very simple kind of coral has been reported from Ordovician into Mesozoic and even Cenozoic rocks, but most of these non-Pennsylvanian reports need to be critically reexamined.

Family b.   Tetradiidae

Tetradiid corals have four short septalike flanges, each of which is located at the center of one of the sides of the generally square corallites. Coralla are massive heads which usually attain a diameter of 5 or 10 centimeters.

Tetradium is a common Ordovician Genus over much of the world. Its pseudosepta differentiate it readily from *Chaetetes* and the stony bryozoans (Fig. 5.2.5).

Family c.   Auloporidae

Auloporoid corals consist of low encrusting tubes which branch at frequent intervals to form a network. Septal spines and occasional tabulae are present.

Aulopora is a very simple form reported from Middle and Upper Paleozoic rocks over most of the world (Fig. 5.3.3). Its principal importance is as a probable ancestral form from which many of the erect Tabulata, such as *Syringopora,* could have arisen.

Cladochonus, from widespread Middle and Upper Paleozoic strata, produced alternating, free, conical corallites which arose from a basal attachment to some foreign object like a crinoid stem.

Family d.   Syringoporidae

Syringoporoid corals consist of loosely bundled cylindrical corallites which are joined by tubular lateral processes. These processes may be irregularly distributed, or in whorls of threes or fours. Transverse sections of corallites reveal large vesicles clustered around a central open space, but longitudinal sections show a highly diagnostic pattern in which a faintly tabulate central tube is surrounded by extremely long, nearly vertical, marginal tabulae (Fig. 5.3.2). Septal spines often can be seen in rows on the theca. Syringoporoids were modest contributors to Paleozoic bioherms and biostromes.

Syringopora is one of the most widespread Genera from Silurian to Permian, and yet it is extremely difficult to identify specifically (Fig. 5.3.1, 2). It has irregularly disposed lateral processes, whereas processes in *Hayasakaia,* from the Pennsylvanian, occur in whorls of four.

In *Eofletcheria,* from the Middle Ordovician of Quebec, Utah, and Nevada, the tubes are pipelike with a few rather transverse tabulae and no septa (Fig. 5.2.4). Corallites are loosely bundled with lateral processes as in *Syringopora. Eofletcheria* may be ancestral to the other Syringoporidae.

Family e.   Halysitidae

One manifestation of the trend toward increasing compactness of coralla is exemplified by the "chain corals," in which corallites are arranged in

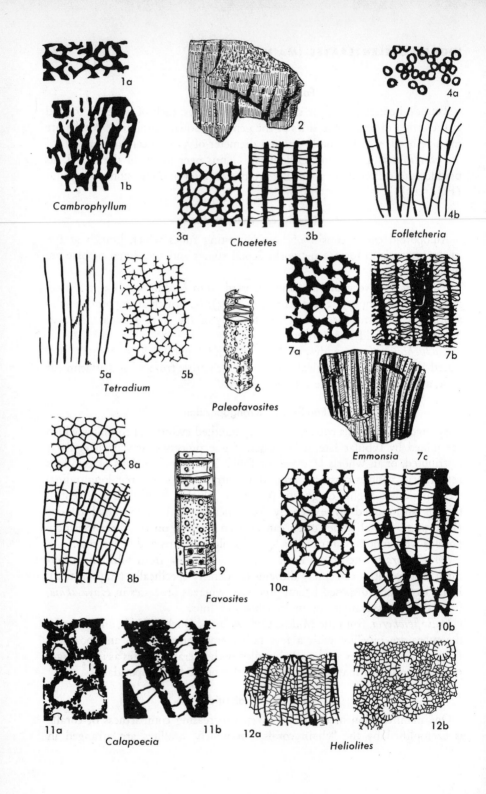

1a

1b

Cambrophyllum

2

3a

Chaetetes

3b

4a

4b

Eofletcheria

5a

5b

Tetradium

6

Paleofavosites

7a

7b

Emmonsia   7c

8a

8b

Favosites

9

10a

10b

11a

Calapoecia

11b

12a

12b

Heliolites

intersecting rows. In plan view the coralla resemble intersecting loops of
chains. In three dimensions the anastomosing rows of corallites surround
irregularly shaped vacant regions called **lacunae.** Tabulae are horizontal and
septal spines are almost unknown. Coralla usually are broad and thick, the
average large size being no more than a foot (20 to 30 cm) in diameter and
3 or 4 inches (8 or 10 cm) thick. Most colonies break up as they weather
out of the matrix.

Catenipora, the oldest and least common Genus of chain corals, is characterized by the presence of only one kind of corallite in a corallum (Fig.
5.3.4). *Catenipora* ranges from mid-Ordovician to mid-Silurian, but is rarely
encountered in other than Ordovician strata. It was never a common Genus,
except perhaps locally in Montana, Utah, and Nevada.

Halysites is the commonest Genus of chain corals (Fig. 5.3.5–7). It is
characterized by the presence of two kinds of corallites which alternate with
each other in the chainlike coralla. **Autocorallites** are the large normal corallites with elliptical cross sections. **Mesocorallites** are quadrate in cross section and are only about one-fourth as wide as the autocorallites. Mesocorallites seem to have assumed the function of providing sites from which
new branches could bud off. This seems to have been a significant advantage
because the history of chain corals reveals the ascendancy of *Halysites* and
the decline of *Catenipora. Halysites* is a world-wide index of Silurian time,
although a few Ordovician and Early Devonian occurrences have been
reported.

Family f.   Favositidae

Favositids are the most diverse of all the tabulate corals. Except among
the earliest and most primitive forms, the corallites are prismatic, and the
coralla are massive and strongly constructed. Shapes of coralla vary from

---

Figure 5.2 (*opposite*). Tabulata.
1a, 1b. Transverse and longitudinal sections of *Cambrophyllum problematicum,* the oldest
coral, 5X, Cambrian, Montana.   2. Corallum of *Chaetetes* sp., 2/3X, Pennsylvanian, widespread.
3a, 3b. Transverse and longitudinal sections of *Chaetetes eximius,* 10X, Pennsylvanian, midcontinent.   4a, 4b. Transverse and longitudinal sections of *Eofletcheria* sp., 2X, Ordovician,
Nevada and Utah.   5a, 5b. Longitudinal and transverse sections of *Tetradium fibratum,* 1 1/3X,
Ordovician, Kentucky, Ohio, Tennessee.   6. Cut-away section of a corallite of *Paleofavosites
aspera,* 5X, Ordovician, Manitoba.   7a, 7b, 7c. Transverse section and longitudinal section with
squamulae (2X) and side view (2/3X) of *Emmonsia emmonsi,* Devonian, central and eastern
United States, Ontario.   8a, 8b. Transverse and longitudinal sections of *Favosites turbinatus,* 2X,
Devonian, central and eastern United States, Ontario.   9. Cut-away section of a corallite of
Favosites gothlandicus, 5X, Silurian, Canada.   10a, 10b. Transverse and longitudinal sections
of *Favosites alpenensis* with prominent septal spines, 2X, Devonian, Michigan.   11a, 11b. Transverse and longitudinal sections of *Calapoecia canadensis,* 3X, Ordovician, Ontario.   12a,
12b. Longitudinal and transverse sections of *Heliolites interstrictus* showing coenenchyme between
corallites, 3 1/2X, Silurian, Newfoundland.
(1 after Fritz and Howell, 1955. 3 after Moore and Jeffords, 1944. 4 after Duncan, 1956.
5, 11 after Bassler, 1950. 6, 9 after Lambe, 1899. 7a, 7b, 8 after Stewart, 1938. 10 after Swann,
1947. 12 after Shrock and Twenhofel, 1939.)

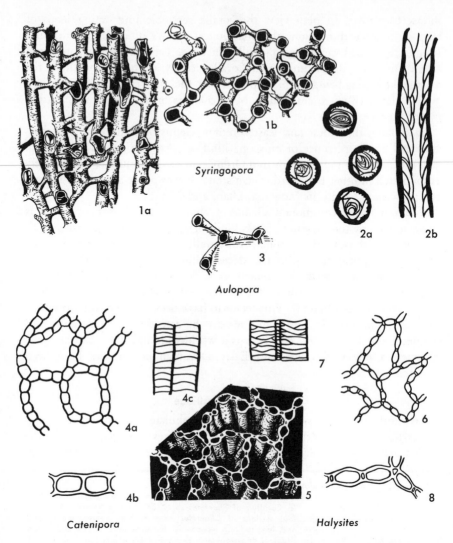

Syringopora

Aulopora

Catenipora

Halysites

Figure 5.3. Tabulata.

1a, 1b. Side and upper surface of a colony of *Syringopora* sp., 1X, Silurian, Nevada. 2a, 2b. Transverse and longitudinal sections of *Syringopora aculeata*, 4X, Mississippian, western United States. 3. *Aulopora elleri*, 1 1/3X, Devonian, New York. 4. *Catenipora gracilis*, Ordovician, western United States, Wisconsin, Manitoba. 4a, transverse section, 1 1/3X. 4b, 4c, transverse and longitudinal sections, 3X. 5. Part of a corallum of *Halysites labyrinthica*, 1X, Silurian, widespread. 6-8. *Halysites* sp., Silurian, world-wide. 6, transverse section showing large autocorallites and small mesocorallites, 1 1/3X. 7, 8, longitudinal and transverse sections, 4X.

(2 after Easton and Gutschick, 1953. 3 after Fenton, 1937. 4, 6-8 after Duncan, 1956. 5 after Buehler, 1955.)

broad expansions to small spherical, large domelike, or erect branching growths. The compact colonies are usually less than 1 foot (30 cm) in diameter, and branches of the arborescent forms are generally less than 2 inches (5 cm) in diameter. As found in the field, however, favositid corals are commonly so intergrown with other tabulates and with stromatoporoids that it may be difficult to detect the margins of individual colonies.

Septa are represented in many species by longitudinal rows of very short spines. Tabulae are horizontal and usually extend completely across the corallites. A distinctive character of all favositids is the presence of **mural pores,** which are partial or complete perforations of the walls between adjacent corallites. Mural pores are important in identification of various favositids because the number and distribution of mural pores vary among different species. Mural pores may be centered on the prism faces of the corallites or crowded near the edges, and they may be in straight lines or in obliquely offset pairs. Fortunately, when a favositid is broken, the fracture planes usually pass along the prismatic faces of corallites, whereupon mural pores can be studied readily with a hand lens. For careful work, however, it is necessary to prepare transverse and longitudinal sections of a few corallites. Favositids are known from the Ordovician to the Permian, but they are particularly abundant in Silurian and Devonian strata.

The oldest favositid is *Paleofavosites* from the Ordovician (Fig. 5.2.6). In this Genus the mural pores are on the angles between faces of the prisms.

Favosites, the typical Genus, ranged between Late Ordovician and Early Mississippian but is tremendously important in Silurian and Devonian strata (Fig. 5.2.8–10).

Emmonsia is a Devonian Genus in which many tabulae do not extend completely across the corallites (Fig. 5.2.7). Actually, *Emmonsia* contains special, thick, shelflike flanges (**squamulae**) around the inner margins of the corallite which resemble tabulae, but against which irregular tabulae abut. Squamulae are modifications of septa.

Family g.   Heliolitidae

The circular corallites of the heliolitids are surrounded by a vesicular or tubular coenenchyme. Twelve spinose septa are present, and tabulae are horizontal.

Heliolites, from the Silurian and Devonian, is the classic example of the group (Fig. 5.2.12). It resembles the Recent octocoral, *Heliopora,* so much that several paleontologists have considered *Heliolites* to be an ancient ancestor of that group, in spite of the fact that the Octocoralla all have eightfold symmetry and normally have spicular or gorgonine skeletons. *Heliolites* has also been referred to various other coralline groups or separated as a distinct Order.

Family h. Calapoeciidae

Among the coenenchymal tabulates, the calapoeciids are characterized by the presence of 12 septa and a coenenchyme consisting of tabular and septal extensions which intersect in spaces between neighboring thecae. Mural pores lie in horizontal rows.

Calapoecia is from the Ordovician and Silurian, as are the other members of the Family (Fig. 5.2.11).

GEOLOGIC HISTORY OF THE TABULATA. To the Tabulata belongs the distinction of being the oldest unquestioned corals. Bursts of colonial forms appeared among tetradiids, calapoeciids, auloporids, and possibly chaetetids in earliest Medial Ordovician (Chazy) time in North America. Almost immediately reef-making tendencies became evident among the tabulates. Halysitids, heliolitids, and syringoporids appeared by the end of the Medial Ordovician and the remaining major Family, the Favositidae, was introduced in Late Ordovician time.

Silurian tabulates are principally represented by the favositids and halysitids. By that time most of the Ordovician groups either had declined considerably or had become extinct. During Devonian time the favositids maintained their dominant position, but syringoporids were increasingly important. Finally, the syringoporids acquired and maintained dominance in the Late Paleozoic, except for the one flare of chaetetids in Early Pennsylvanian time, and except for an occasional abundance of slender-branched favositids.

During their history the tabulates were important contributors to the stratigraphic record, but they are notable for their reef-building capacity only during parts of the Silurian, Devonian and Early Pennsylvanian. Almost from their inception they were overshadowed by the next group to be considered—the Rugosa.

SUBCLASS 2. RUGOSA (TETRACORALLA)

When Anthozoa first began to build skeletons in mid-Ordovician time, the Rugosa were on hand to engage in this early explosive development among sessile organisms. Similar colonial bursts by hexacorals in the Mesozoic and Cenozoic Eras were to produce spectacular reefs whose dimensions exceed those of Paleozoic reefs. Even so, the Paleozoic corals still were sufficiently adaptive and variable to anticipate almost every structural modification followed by their later remote cousins. In fact, the structural diversity and rapidity of evolution among rugose corals have been matched by only a few other groups of animals. When any group of organisms is able to occupy a hitherto vacant space particularly suited to it in the economy of nature it is said that a **biologic niche** is being filled. Under these circumstances almost every variation in the group is successful, and we see remarkable increase in numbers and in diversity of individuals. This was the case with the Rugosa as their vigor was expressed in myriad ways during a period of about 400 million years, only to end with their sudden and inexplicable decline and extinction at the end of the Permian.

Rugose corals were generally common in the calcareous sediments of Paleozoic epeiric seas. If a coral weathers out of an outcrop so cleanly that the external shape and the details within the concave calyx can be seen, then the specimen usually is readily identifiable. But commonly the calyx is obscured with matrix and the specimens must be sawn or ground in half transversely and lengthwise in order to establish clearly the nature of internal features. The nuisance of having to make these minor lapidary preparations is more than offset by the increased usefulness of the material. Inasmuch as most corals are composed of solid tissue and are very strongly constructed, they not only resist alteration by secondary geologic agents better than many other fossils do, but they may survive intense diastrophic forces. Thus, they may even be specifically identifiable when collected from hydrothermal alteration zones bordering intrusive igneous rocks or from breccia in shatter zones of faults.

EXTERNAL FEATURES. Simple rugose corals typically are curved cones which resemble horns (that is, they are **ceratoid** in shape); hence they are also called horn corals. Most of the simple rugose corals are about ½ inch (12 mm) in diameter and 1.5 inches (35 mm) long. The largest seem to have been about 5 inches (8 cm) in diameter and possibly 2 feet (60 cm) long. Inasmuch as simple corals were generally attached to the substratum by the tip (**apex**), they were delicately and precariously balanced. An oblique and minute scar of attachment truncates the apex of many corals. Some corals propped themselves up by building a **talon** out from one side of their apical region to the substratum, and other corals accomplished the same end by secreting a series of slender **rootlets** like guy wires. There is strong evidence that many polyps preferred a particular orientation with respect to direction of current flow. For instance, if they accidentally tipped over, they changed their direction of growth in order to resume the original orientation, and they even sent out new rootlets to support the new position. Examples of these contorted or **geniculate** corals are commonly encountered among different Families (Fig. 5.9.4c).

Many corals continued to maintain their conical form as they grew upward, but eventually their diameter seems to have passed an optimum size, perhaps by enlarging the coelenteron too much and inhibiting the digestive efficiency of the polyp. In any case, it is common for corals to change their outlines from conical to nearly **cylindrical** at maturity. Alterations of this kind can be stated in terms of how many degrees of arc are included within the **apical angle.** As opposed to the normal elongate form, some corals fail to grow vertically much above the substratum and therefore become **discoidal** through lateral growth. These are the button corals (Fig. 5.13) which seemed to prefer a muddy bottom into which their large area and small mass kept them from sinking.

Cross sections of simple rugose corals normally are circular, but two significant modifications are recognized. Corals in which the theca is compressed from the sides become wedge-shaped (**cuneate**) (Fig. 5.8.2). They seem to be adapted by streamlining to an erect habit in oceanic currents. On the other hand, some simple rugose corals are notably flattened on only one side and resemble a Persian slipper with the apex representing the turned-up toe. These **calceolid** or slipper corals seem to have been adapted to a recumbent habit (Fig. 5.8.4). Some of them were provided with a movable cover (**operculum**) which could be swung across the calyx like a lid.

Colonial form was achieved by **lateral budding** from the sides of parent corallites (Fig. 5.10.2c), or by **calical budding** (Fig. 5.4.2). Because the death of the parent was commonly caused by growth of the daughter polyp(s), calical budding of this type sometimes is called **parricidal budding. Rejuvenescence** is a special kind of calical budding found in both simple and compound corals in which growth of a calyx alternately is sharply constricted or vigorously expanded (Fig. 5.4.1). Colonial growth progressed in a succession of stages starting with loosely branched forms (Fig. 5.4.3–7). **Phaceloid** coralla developed when essentially parallel corallites became grouped in bundles. Corallites of phaceloid coralla may not touch each other, or they may be closely packed, but in any case they retain their circular cross sections. Continuation of the trend toward ever more economical packing patterns naturally led to corallites in the form of hexagonal prisms, which are said to be **cerioid.** At this stage it is possible for an epitheca to enclose the entire lower and lateral sides of the coralla. By continuation of the main trend, however, the two thecae of adjacent corallites may fuse into one common theca. Still later this common theca may break down and allow tissue of one corallite to touch tissue of surrounding corallites in what is known as **astreoid** corallites. Or an intervening zone of vesicular material may separate whorls of septa in **aphroid** corallites. In the most elaborate stage (**thamnastraeoid**) the septa of one corallite become confluent with the septa of another corallite and resemble diagrams of lines of force round magnetic poles. Most of these coralla resemble living brain corals and are usually less than 1 foot (30 cm) in diameter.

It is convenient for purposes of reference and illustration to divide the calyx of a rugose coral into four **quadrants** (Fig. 5.5.1). The principal septum, which generally lies in a depression **(fossula)**, is the **cardinal septum**. In this text the cardinal position is oriented downward in illustrations of calyces or of cross sections. On the opposite side of the calyx from the cardinal septum is the generally long **counter septum**. On either side of the calyx are the two long **alar septa**, on the counter side of each of which is an extra wide space called the **alar pseudofossula**. Accordingly, the right and left cardinal quadrants extend from the cardinal septum up past the alar septa, and the right and left counter quadrants extend from the alar pseudofossulae to the counter septum.

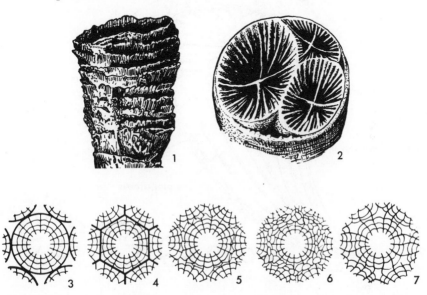

Figure 5.4.   Increase of Coralla.
1. Side view of a simple coral with numerous stages of rejuvenation, 2/3X.   2. Calical view of a simple coral with three calicular buds, 4X.   3-7. Schematic transverse sections of coralla showing progressively more compact colonial growth. 3, phaceloid. 4, cerioid. 5, astreoid. 6, aphroid. 7, thamnastraeoid.
(1 after Keyes, 1894a. 2 after Milne-Edwards and Haime, 1851. 3-7 after Easton, 1944b).

Growth of the counter quadrants usually is faster than growth of the cardinal quadrants in most simple conical corals; hence the calyx is curved toward the cardinal side, which then can be said to be the concave side when viewed from an alar position. When the cardinal septum is on the convex side of a curved coral this rather uncommon feature is assigned particular taxonomic importance. Different calceolid corals, for instance, have either the cardinal septum or the counter septum on the flattened convex side. The direction of growth was probably controlled in large part by efforts of the polyp to face into the predominant current, for it would then avail itself of the most food and the most effective sediment-dispersing action of the water. Differential growth of one quadrant over another results in increased number of septa, or **acceleration** of that quadrant.

The solid external theca around each corallite is characteristically indented by longitudinal **septal grooves** which lie along the traces of the septa, and by **interseptal ridges** which denote the positions of spaces **(loculi)** be-

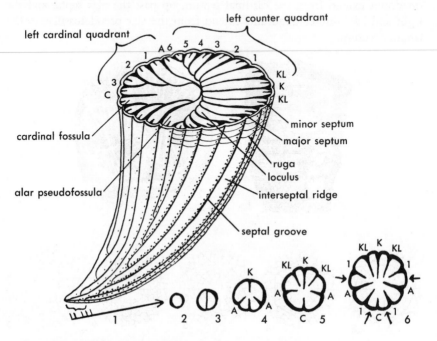

Figure 5.5　Septal Insertion in Rugose Corals.
1. Schematic oblique side view of a simple rugose coral with the septa shown in transverse section just beneath the calyx, enlarged.　2-6. Successive transverse section near the apex, much enlarged.
Abbreviations for protosepta are as follows: C—cardinal; A—alar; K—counter; KL—counter-lateral. Arrows in 6 indicate the four positions at which new septa are inserted. Numbers indicate the order of insertion of later major septa.

tween septa (Fig. 5.5.1). In only one or two instances have rugose corals been discovered in which septa are in line with external ridges in the manner which is characteristic of Hexacoralla; therefore, the nature of the external longitudinal ridges can be used to differentiate the two great groups of rugose corals and hexacorals in almost every instance. Moreover, the characteristic patterns of the septal grooves enable one to ascertain details of septal development without recourse to prepared lapidary cross sections.

In addition to longitudinal ornamentation, the thecae of most rugose corals are also marked by concentric wrinkles or **rugae,** whence came the name of the Subclass. Concentric ornaments finer than rugae are called **growth lines.**

INTERNAL STRUCTURES. Septa are the first internal structures to develop and are the most obvious features in any calyx; hence their nature is a matter of considerable importance in classification. Septa in transverse section may be straight, wavy, or zigzag. Normally they are thin, but they may be **dilated** (Fig. 5.9.4a, 5) by stereoplasm (secondary skeletal secretion) until they bridge across the intervening loculus, or they may be thickened at their inner ends to form club-shaped (**rhopaloid**) septa (Fig. 5.14.1). Two general kinds of septa can be distinguished. **Major septa** extend inward the farthest and may fuse at the axis of the coral, whereas **minor septa** alternate with the major septa and are generally confined to the outer region of a coral (Fig. 5.5.1). Minor septa may be so short as to be merely **spines** on the inner side of the theca, or they may be long and lean against the adjacent major septum on the counter side as **contratingent** minor septa (Fig. 5.8.8). Septa may be **perforate** and appear in transverse section as a line of discontinuous segments. **Carinate** septa develop sloping parallel keels or flanges on their sides which show up as spines in transverse sections (Fig. 5.10).

Two principal kinds of septal patterns are recognized, depending upon whether the septa seem to withdraw from the axial region or from the periphery. The first case is typified by the Genus *Amplexus*. Amplexoid septa extend out near the axis of the corallite along the upper surface of each newly secreted convex tabula, but instead of growing up through successive tabulae as a continuous partition in the normal fashion, amplexoid septa continue to grow vertically only near their outer edges; therefore they extend radially only as low ridges upon the upper surfaces of the tabulae. In this way they seem to retreat from the axis so that they are present in the center of any section whose plane passes just above a tabula, but are only present in the periphery of sections passing just beneath the next higher tabula (Fig. 5.8.5, 6). Moreover, there is a tendency for septa of amplexoid corals to withdraw farther from the axis in successive growth stages. **Amplexoid retreat,** therefore, refers to progressive withdrawal of septa from the axis of a rugose coral.

On the other hand, Genera such as *Lonsdaleia* acquire a marginal zone of blisterlike vesicles as growth progresses. Therefore septa which originally may have touched the theca in early growth stages are separated from the theca more and more by the vesicles. American Genera such as *Blothrophyllum* and *Caninophyllum* (Fig. 5.9.3a, 5) whose septa withdraw from the outer margin are said to undergo **lonsdaleoid retreat.**

In view of the persistent tendency of polyps to abandon early portions of their corallites and to change from conical to cylindrical, there must have been significant advantages in not becoming too long or too large. It is probable that the trend toward restriction of size is a manifestation of nicely adjusted relationships among digestive ability, food-gathering ability, and size. Efficiency of anthozoan digestive apparatus was achieved by mesenteric and septal infolding of the body wall, but the efficiency was somewhat nullified by continuous growth in length accompanied by increased volume due to flaring of the theca in conical shapes. The problem of how to retain an efficient body size was partially solved by construction of tabulae underneath polyps as they moved up in the theca. Tabulae generally are convex upward with almost flat centers and down-turned margins. They may be far apart or so close together that they resemble an inverted stack of cereal bowls, in which case a transverse plane would intersect margins of several tabulae. **Complete tabulae** extend across the entire central area (Fig. 5.8.6b) but **incomplete tabulae** are interrupted in the axial region where tabulae interlock and overlap (Fig. 5.9.4b).

Continued growth and persistent flaring in some conical corals still were great enough to disrupt the bodily efficiency, even if tabulae were present; therefore additional modifications became possible in order to perfect the construction of the organism. A large food-gathering surface is advantageous to corals, so the most successful strains seem to have been those which preserved this feature but limited digestive volume. Increased efficiency of packing of corallites and elimination of thecae in astraeoid and aphroid coralla would assist in extending the food-gathering surface in colonial forms. In addition, however, restriction of digestive volume, both in simple and in compound corals, arose by development of a cushion of frothy vesicles, the **dissepiments,** around the sides and base of a polyp (Fig. 5.9.3b). Each dissepiment was secreted between septa with its long dimension inclined obliquely downward and its convex surface facing inward. The simplest dissepiments are **concentric** or **angular** (Fig. 5.9.1). More complex ones called **herringbone dissepiments** overlap alternately (Fig. 5.9.4a). **Lonsdaleoid dissepiments** are large vesicles which invariably occur in the marginal zone and occupy as much space as three or four of the other dissepiments (Fig. 5.9.3a, 5). Orderly changes in dissepimental patterns can be detected both in growth stages and in placement in corals. The oldest kind are concentric, and these merge gradually upward into angular dissepiments. Still later, about the time that minor septa begin to appear, the margin is occupied with herringbone dissepiments and the angular and concentric types are crowded into zones closer to the axis. In the latest growth stages the margin may be occupied by lonsdaleoid dissepiments and the herringbone and other types are centrally located between the septa. Thus, the successive zones of dissepiments outward from the center of a coral record the history of dissepimental development (Fig. 5.9.5).

It is apparent that advanced rugose corals have an axial region of tabulae (tabularium) and a marginal region of dissepiments (**dissepimentarium**) (Fig. 5.9.3b, 4b). As growth progresses and flaring continues, the dissepimentarium tends to increase in width, thus continually restricting the tabularium to nearly the same space or to only a slightly increased area. Some dissepimentaria are zoned vertically with normal- and small-sized vesicles like growth rings in a tree. If, as some people think, these rings are also annular, then coral skeletons may provide their own age-determining devices. In summation, the corals are highly efficient organisms because their ingenious compartmentation increases their food-gathering capacity but restricts their bodily volume.

Another trend which may have served to decrease bodily volume in the rugose corals is the development of an axial structure (**columella**) of some sort. The simplest columella is a plate or rod which extends from an early stage up into the calyx where it protrudes as a shaft. This **palicolumella** is almost invariably attached to the counter septum and is sometimes in contact with other major septa (Fig. 5.14.2c, 2d). An axial vortex or **streptocolumella** is a conical mound consisting of the inner ends of long major septa twisted like a pinwheel (Fig. 5.8.12a). Other columellae are merely chaotic spongy secretions which accumulate in the axial region (Fig. 5.8.10). The most complicated columellae of all start with a median plate and reinforce it with short septalike **lamellae** which radiate from the axis and line up with many major septa. Between the lamellae are convex dissepimentlike **tabellae.** Transverse sections of the entire structure, when containing all of these parts, are strikingly like a spider web; hence these structures are called **arachnoid** columellae (Fig. 5.11.3c). Even if a special columella is not present the tabulae may be arched convex upward or may even rise to a crest to form tent-shaped structures. All of these axial protuberances reflect a diverse series of modifications which, by their presence in corals of many ages, seem to indicate that an upward indentation in the base of a polyp provided some selective advantage, probably by restricting the volume of the coelenteron again.

ONTOGENY. Corals are admirably suited to studies of growth stages because even the early morphologic features are preserved at their tips. Among higher groups, only the cephalopods, gastropods, and pelecypods retain a record of their growth attached to the mature skeleton. On the other hand, arthropods cast off successive skeletons by molting, brachiopods undergo metamorphosis of important internal features, and echinoderms and vertebrates expand the actual skeletons.

In the earliest stage, at the very tip of a specimen, only a vacant theca is present, but soon thereafter a single axial plate crosses the central space and divides it into equal right and left halves (Fig. 5.5.2, 3). Next the pair of alar septa is inserted on the cardinal side, and at the same time the axial plate divides into two segments which now can be called the cardinal and counter septa (Fig. 5.5.4). In a later stage the alar septa move laterally toward the counter side, and a new pair of septa is inserted on the counter side (Fig. 5.5.5). These **counter-lateral septa** bracket the counter septum. This is the final embryonic stage and is one through which all rugose corals are thought to pass. Its most important features are the presence of the six so-called **protosepta** and a marked bilateral symmetry from the earliest septate stage. In later growth stages the septa are inserted only at four points—on either side of the cardinal septum and on the counter side of each alar septum (Fig. 5.5.6). This is why the Subclass is also called the Tetracoralla. As new major septa are inserted, those already introduced grow straight up. But because the coral is conical, they seem to move away from the cardinal or alar septa; therefore space is created for new septa to be introduced in the same four places. Finally, when all major septa are in place at maturity, one complete cycle of short minor septa is inserted almost simultaneously in all quadrants; each minor septum is inserted in the loculus between two major septa. Third-order septa have been observed in a few rugose corals.

Ontogenetic studies of rugose corals have provided one of the most convincing demonstrations of the Theory of Recapitulation yet set forth. The late English paleontologist, R. G. Carruthers, described a suite of closely related rugose corals which were distributed in about half a dozen zones through a succession of 4000 feet of Carboniferous sediments. In the oldest of these corals, *Zaphrentites delanouei,* the cardinal fossula expands near the center and becomes keyhole-shaped, the cardinal septum is long, and the septal plan is strongly bilaterally symmetrical (Fig. 5.6.1, 2). In the next zone up-section, few specimens of *Z. delanouei* are present, but its descendant, *Z. parallela,* is the common form. Juvenile stages of *Z. parallela* (Fig. 5.6.3) resemble the adult stages of *Z. delanouei* (Fig. 5.6.2), but *Z. parallela* progresses into a condition in its adulthood in which the cardinal fossula becomes parallel-sided, the cardinal septum becomes shortened, and the pinnate septal pattern bordering the cardinal fossula gives way to a somewhat radial septal plan (Fig. 5.6.4). At a still higher zone, *Z. constricta* becomes the common form but *Z. parallela* is less common and *Z. delanouei* is absent. In mature stages of *Z. constricta* the cardinal fossula is narrower at its inner end than at its outer end and the septal plan is more nearly radial (Fig. 5.6.6),

Figure 5.6 (opposite).   Evolution of *Zaphrentites delanouei.*
Transverse sections of adult and juvenile corals are shown in two columns on the left. On the right is a schematic stratigraphic section 5600 feet (1530 m) thick, with collecting localities indicated by black dots. Known ranges and relative importance of each species are indicated by heavy lines in the center. The range indicated for *Z. disjuncta* is mostly a composite of three species enclosed by the bracket. Successive growth stages and successive species are numbered in the order they appeared.
(After Carruthers, 1910.)

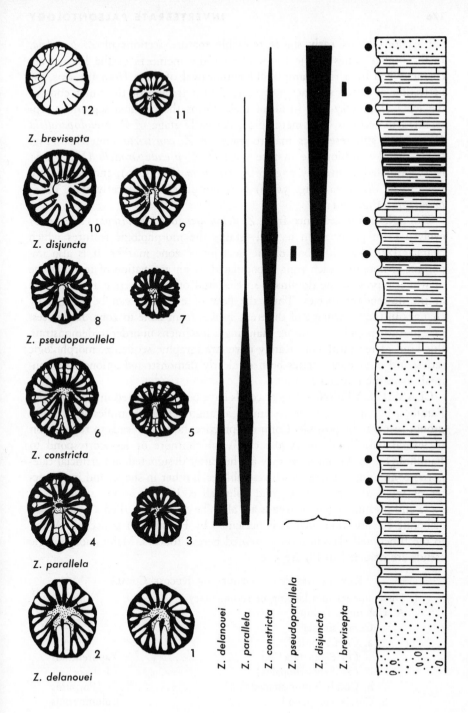

Z. brevisepta

Z. disjuncta

Z. pseudoparallela

Z. constricta

Z. parallela

Z. delanouei

Z. delanouei

Z. parallela

Z. constricta

Z. pseudoparallela

Z. disjuncta

Z. brevisepta

but sections of its early stages resemble mature sections of *Z. parallela*. In the higher zones of the Carboniferous the members of the lineage are characterized by a rapid amplexoid withdrawal of septa from the axis, the perfection of radial symmetry of septa, and a freeing of the inner ends of the septa (Fig. 5.6.7–12). In all of these forms the cardinal septum is represented in sections by a mere spine. An early stage of *Z. pseudoparallela* (Fig. 5.6.7) still resembles mature stages of *Z. constricta* somewhat (Fig. 5.6.6). In like fashion the mature stage of *Z. pseudoparallela* (Fig. 5.6.8) is recapitulated in an early stage of *Z. disjuncta* (Fig. 5.6.9), and the mature stage of *Z. disjuncta* (Fig. 5.6.10) is recapitulated in an early stage of *Z. brevisepta* (Fig. 5.6.11).

Throughout the sequence from *Z. delanouei* to *Z. brevisepta* each newly evolved form preserves in its early stages the morphologic features which characterized the adulthood of the next lower zone marker. It is also important to note that each zone is populated by an association of forms, some of which represent the dominant species, and others represent the ancestral or the descendant species. Thus, the flow of evolution can be gauged by changes in the percentage of different species from zone to zone. It is necessary to study populations rather than single specimens in order to demonstrate this kind of recapitulation. Rarely have stratigraphic sequence, morphologic series, and ontogenetic series been so clearly demonstrated among fossil animals as in the foregoing case.

CLASSIFICATION. Rugose corals have been segregated into 30 or more Families, but no very clear system of arranging these Families into larger groups seems to be possible. Common practice, however, leads to recognition of several basic kinds of rugose corals which more or less correspond to Families. These "Groups," as they are hereafter designated, are artificial categories containing Genera which resemble each other in shape, and in character of septa, dissepimentaria, and columellae. If microscopic structure of septa and presumed genetic trends are all to be considered, then a much more elaborate classification such as is presented by Hill (1956) is needed. A key to the functional classification presented herein follows. Major morphologic trends are depicted in Figure 5.16.

Key to Artificial Groups of Rugose Corals

I. Dissepimentarium lacking or rudimentary
    A. Columella lacking
        1. Corals simple
            a. Corals conical
                (1) Septa tapering .... Zaphrenthids
                (2) Septa rhopaloid .... Polycoeliids
            b. Corals button-shaped .... Porpitids
        2. Corals compound .... Columnariids

  B. Columella present
    1. Minor septa contratingent .... Cyathaxoniids
    2. Minor septa not contratingent .... Lophophyllids
 II. Dissepimentarium broad
  A. Columella lacking
    1. Tabularium lacking .... Cystiphyllids
    2. Tabularium present .... Cyathophyllids
  B. Columella present .... Clisiophyllids

Columnariids. The columnariid corals are all compound coralla with small phaceloid or cerioid corallites. Septa may be in two orders. Dissepiments are absent in early forms.

Favistella (which is widely cited in American literature as *Columnaria*) is one of the commonest Ordovician corals. It is cerioid and the septa are about 12 in number. Coralla generally are less than 10 centimeters in diameter (Fig. 5.7.1).

Cyathaxoniids. Cyathaxoniid corals are simple and usually are curved cones. Most major septa reach the columella, which consists only of an axial rod. Minor septa are contratingent. Tabulae are present but dissepiments are not.

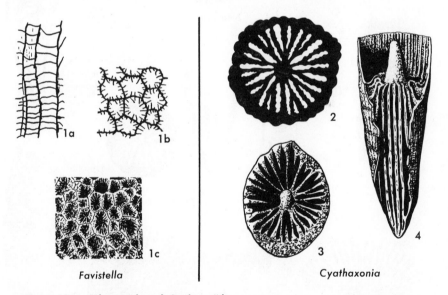

Favistella   *Cyathaxonia*

Figure 5.7. Columnariids and Cyathaxoniids.
 1a, 1b. Longitudinal and transverse sections (3 1/3X) and portion of the surface (1X) of *Favistella alveolata*, Ordovician, central and eastern United States. 2. Transverse section of *Cyathaxonia tantilla*, 5X, Mississipian, midcontinent. 3. Calyx of *Cyathaxonia venusta*, 6X, Mississippian, Indiana. 4. Cut-away side view of *Cyathaxonia dalmani*, 2X, Silurian, Sweden.
 (1a, 1b after Bassler, 1950. 2 after Easton, 1944b. 3 after Easton, 1951. 4 after Milne-Edwards and Haime, 1851.)

Cyathaxonia, the typical Genus, is characteristic of Mississippian strata over most of the world. Its carinate contratingent septa, in company with a columella and prominently ribbed exterior surface, enable ready identification (Fig. 5.7.2–4).

Zaphrenthids.   The simple, conical, zaphrenthid corals consist basically of

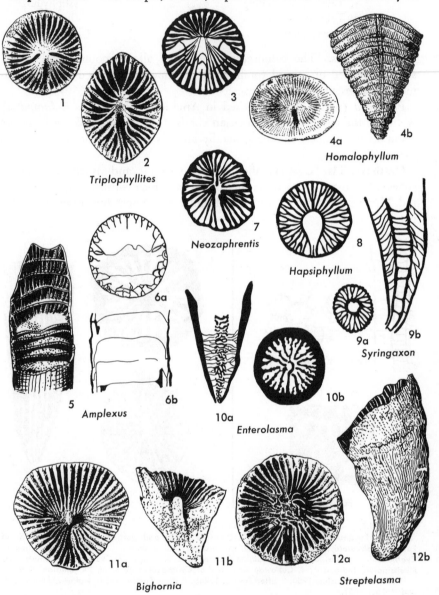

1
2
Triplophyllites
3
4a
4b
Homalophyllum
6a
7
Neozaphrentis
8
Hapsiphyllum
5
6b
Amplexus
9a
9b
Syringaxon
10a
10b
Enterolasma
11a
11b
Bighornia
12a
12b
Streptelasma

a theca, septa, and tabulae, thus comprising a sort of generalized stem group upon which later modifications could be impressed. No doubt many different genetic groups evolved from a zaphrenthid stage.

Zaphrenthis itself is a Devonian form with carinate septa, but myriad noncarinate forms in Middle and Upper Paleozoic strata have been referred to this Genus (although the name commonly has been misspelled *Zaphrentis.*)

Streptelasma, from the Ordovician, is the first simple abundant rugose coral Genus. Its streptocolumella is characteristic (Fig. 5.8.12).

Neozaphrentis (Mississippian), *Triplophyllites* (Mississippian to Permian), *Amplexus* (Devonian to Permian), and *Hapsiphyllum* (Mississippian to Permian) are representative Genera, most of which reveal a prominent cardinal fossula and two alar pseudofossulae in each calyx (Fig. 5.8.1–3, 5–8). Various strains of zaphrenthid corals became characterized by new kinds of columellae. The oldest of these axial structures were the palicolumellae in *Bighornia* (Fig. 5.8.11) and the streptocolumellae in *Streptelasma* (Fig. 5.8.12). In the Silurian, the axial region of *Syringaxon* was raised in the form of a tabulate tube (Fig. 5.8.9), and in the Devonian *Enterolasma* had a sclerocolumella (Fig. 5.8.10). The Mississippian *Neozaphrentis* (Fig. 5.8.7) did not have a true columella, but the axial tip of the counter septum projected far up into the calyx.

Cyathophyllids. Cyathophyllid corals represent a modification of the zaphrenthid form in which the tabularium is surrounded with a dissepimentarium. Both simple and compound cyathophyllid corals are known.

Aulacophyllum is a primitive Devonian cyathophyllid coral with a narrow dissepimentarium (Fig. 5.9.2). *Bethanyphyllum* is typical of a host of Devonian corals with wide dissepimentaria, concentric dissepiments, and thin major septa (Fig. 5.9.1). Corals of this sort usually have been referred to the form Genus *Cyathophyllum. Caninia,* the most common Carbonif-

---

Figure 5.8 (opposite).   Zaphrenthids.
1. Calyx of *Triplophyllites spinulosus,* 1X, Mississippian, midcontinent.   2. Calyx of *Triplophyllites lanceolatus,* 2X, Mississippian, Indiana, Kentucky, Tennessee, Alabama.   3. Transverse section of *Triplophyllites dalei,* 1X, Mississippian, midcontinent.   4a, 4b. Calyx and flattened cardinal side of *Homalophyllum ungulum,* 1X, Devonian, Kentucky, Indiana, Ontario.   5. Cut-away section of *Amplexus bicostatus,* 1X, Mississippian, Missouri.   6a, 6b. Transverse and longitudinal sections of *Amplexus rockfordensis,* 1X, Mississippian, Indiana, Illinois.   7. Transverse section of *Neozaphrentis tenella,* 3X, Mississippian, Missouri.   8. Transverse section of *Hapsiphyllum californe* with contratringent minor septa, 3X, Mississippian, Indiana, Illinois, Alabama.   9a, 9b. Transverse and longitudinal sections of *Syringaxon acuminatum,* 4X, Silurian, Tennessee. 10a, 10b. Longitudinal and transverse sections of *Enterolasma strictum,* 2X, Devonian, New York. 11a, 11b. Calyx and broken longitudinal surface of *Bighornia parva,* 2X, Ordovician, Wyoming. 12a, 12b. Calyx and side view of *Streptelasma rusticum,* 1X, Ordovician, east-central United States.

(1, 3, 7, 8 after Grove, 1935. 2 after Easton, 1951. 4a, 9, 10 after Stumm, 1949. 4b after Hall, 1883. 5 after Miller, 1892. 6 after Easton, 1944b. 11 after Duncan, 1957. 12 after Bassler, 1932.)

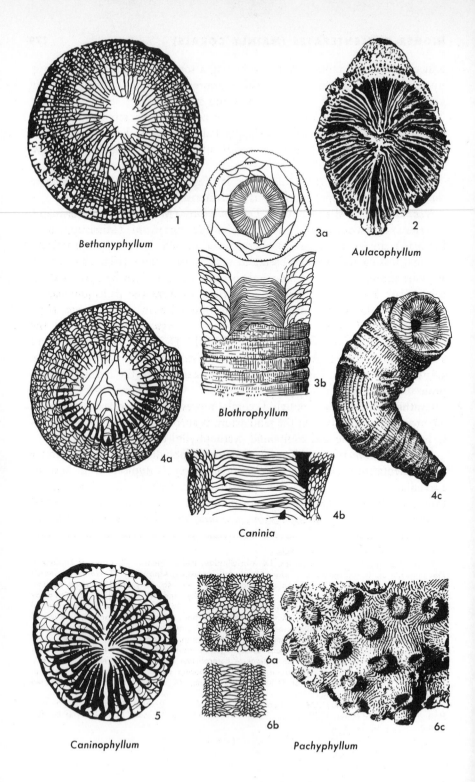

Bethanyphyllum

3a

Aulacophyllum

3b

Blothrophyllum

4a

4b

Caninia

4c

5

Caninophyllum

6a

6b

6c

Pachyphyllum

erous Genus, has prominent herringbone dissepiments, and the major septa in the cardinal quadrants are dilated (Fig. 5.9.4). In other Carboniferous Genera such as *Caninophyllum* (Fig. 5.9.5), some of the dissepiments are lonsdaleoid and all of the major septa are dilated. A separate lineage in which lonsdaleoid dissepiments are dominant is exemplified by *Blothrophyllum* (Fig. 5.9.3.) from the Devonian. Another common Genus, notable for its trend toward aphroid corallites, is *Pachyphyllum* from the Devonian (Fig. 5.9.6).

A separate group of cyathophyllid corals is characterized by the presence of carinae on the septa (Fig. 5.10). *Heliophyllum* is a common simple Genus, whereas *Eridophyllum* is loosely phaceloid and *Hexagonaria* is cerioid. All of these are common in the Devonian.

Clisiophyllids.   Addition of an axial complex to the cyathophyllid plan produces the clisiophyllids. In some clisiophyllid forms a reversal of the direction of evolution is demonstrable in which the axial structure is progressively lost. In their most complex condition the columellae consist of an axial plate, lamellae, and tabellae, but one or another of these three may dominate the structure in different Genera. Very commonly modifications of the dissepimentaria lead concurrently to development of a lonsdaleoid outer zone.

Clisiophyllum, from the Carboniferous of Europe, is the type example of the group, but numerous similar Genera occur in the Upper Paleozoic rocks of many lands. In North America *Lithostrotionella* is an advanced colonial form with lonsdaleoid dissepiments (Fig. 5.11.3). It occurs in Mississippian to Permian strata. Over much of the Midwest and Cordilleran regions from Canada to Mexico it is a characteristic Early and Middle Mississippian Genus. True *Lithostrotion* is only locally common in North America (Fig. 5.11.2).

Simple clisiophyllids are typified by *Neokoninckophyllum* from the Lower Pennsylvanian. Its columellae are dominated by tabellae and a few lamellae (Fig. 5.11.1).

Cystiphyllids.   Once the trend toward dissepiments was started it progressed to such extravagant development of this one feature that other internal structures were obliterated, leaving only dissepiments. Simple cystiphyllids seem to be short-lived offshoots of the cyathophyllids.

Figure 5.9 (opposite). Cyathophyllids.
1. Transverse section of *Bethanyphyllum robustum*, 1X, Devonian, New York, Ohio, Kentucky (typical "*Cyathophyllum*"). 2. Calyx of *Aulacophyllum sulcatum*, 1X, Devonian, Kentucky, Ohio. 3a, 3b. Transverse and longitudinal sections of *Blothrophyllum decorticum*, 1X, Devonian, Kentucky, Michigan, Ontario.   4a, 4b, 4c. Transverse and longitudinal sections (1 1/3X) and side view (2/3X) of *Caninia torquia*, Pennsylvanian, midcontinent and western United States. 5. Transverse section of *Caninophyllum incrassatum*, 1 2/3X Mississippian, western United States. 6a, 6b, 6c. Transverse and longitudinal sections (1 1/3X) and portion of the surface (1X) of *Pachyphyllum woodmani*, Devonian, Iowa and western United States.
(1, 2 after Stewart, 1938. 3 after Lambe, 1901. 4a, 4b after Easton, 1944a. 4c after Keyes, 1894a. 5 after Easton and Gutschick, 1953. 6a, 6b after Stumm, 1949. 6c after Fenton and Fenton, 1924.)

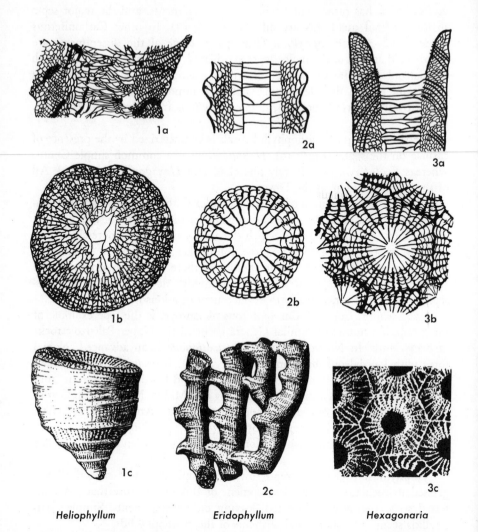

Heliophyllum   Eridophyllum   Hexagonaria

Figure 5.10.   Cyathophyllids.

1a, 1b, 1c. Longitudinal and transverse sections (1 1/3X) and side view (1X) of *Heliophyllum halli*, Devonian, New York.   2a, 2b, 2c. Longitudinal and transverse sections (3 1/3X) and side view of several corallites (2/3X) of *Eridophyllum seriale*, Devonian, Ohio.   3a, 3b. Longitudinal and transverse sections of *Hexagonaria percarinata*, the "Petosky Stone", 3 1/3X, Devonian, Michigan.   4. Portion of the surface of *Hexagonaria cedarensis*, 2X, Devonian, Iowa.

(1a, 1b after Fenton and Fenton, 1937. 1c, 2c after Milne-Edwards and Haime, 1851. 2a, 2b after Stumm, 1949. 3a, 3b after Sloss, 1939. 4 after Stainbrook, 1940.)

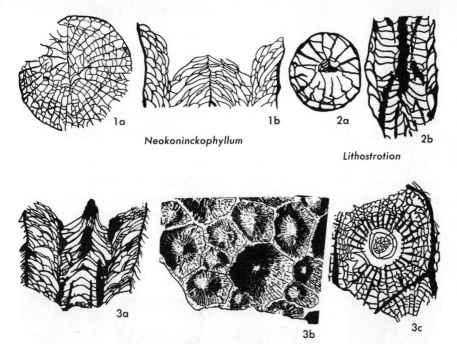

Neokoninckophyllum

Lithostrotion

Lithostrotionella

Figure 5.11.   Clisiophyllids.
1a, 1b, Transverse and longitudinal sections of *Neokoninckophyllum simplex,* 2X, Pennsylvanian, Oklahoma.   2a, 2b. Transverse and longitudinal sections of corallites of *Lithostrotion* [*Siphonodendron*] *genevievensis,* 5X, Mississippian, east central and possibly western United States. 3. *Lithostrotionella castelnaui,* Mississippian, widespread.   3a, 3c. Longitudinal and transverse sections, 1 1/3X.   3b, surface, 1X.
    (1 after Moore and Jeffords, 1945. 2 after Easton, 1957. 3b, 3c after Hayasaka, 1936.)

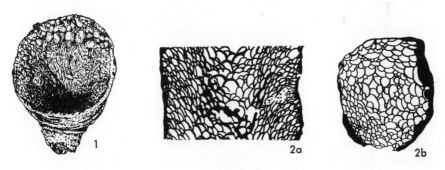

Cystiphylloides

Figure 5.12.   Cystiphyllids.
    1. Calyx of *Cystiphylloides sulcatus,* 2/3X, Devonian, Ohio. 2a, 2b. Transverse and longitudinal sections of *Cystiphylloides americanus,* 2X, Devonian, central and eastern United States and Canada.
    (1 after Stewart, 1938. 2 after Fenton and Fenton, 1937.)

Cystiphylloides from the Devonian is a fine example of the cystiphyllid trend. Some species retain relics of septa in the axis of the calyx (Fig. 5.12.1) or there are septal spines attached to some dissepiments (Fig. 5.12.2b).

Porpitids. Button corals seem to be offshoots of the simple zaphrenthids which failed to grow upward but spread out horizontally. They were particularly well adapted for life on soft bottom sediments. Most of the porpitid corals consist of little more than a solid base with ridgelike septa extending over its surface.

Porpites is a Silurian form. *Hadrophyllum* (Devonian) is probably the most common Genus in North America, although other forms are known into Pennsylvanian time (Fig. 5.13). The group seems to be decidedly polyphyletic; that is, corals with the same appearance were derived from several genetic strains.

Xenocyathellus   Porpites   Hadrophyllum

Figure 5.13. Porpitids.
1. Calyx of *Xenocyathellus thedfordensis*, 2X, Devonian, Ontario. 2. Side view of *Porpites porpita*, 1 1/2X, Silurian, Sweden. 3a, 3b. Side view and calyx of *Hadrophyllum orbignyi*, 1 1/2X, Devonian, Kentucky and Indiana.
(After Bassler, 1937.)

Lophophyllids. Lophophyllids resemble simple cyathaxonids in having a palicolumella, but they retain the septal pattern of zaphrenthids instead of having contratingent minor septa. Commonly the axial ends of septa are swollen (rhopaloid). Septa are rarely carinate.

Lophophyllidium is a very common Pennsylvanian and Permian Genus over most of the world and is especially abundant in Pennsylvanian strata in the midcontinent (Fig. 5.14.2). *Sochkineophyllum,* from Upper Paleozoic rocks of the northern hemisphere, resembles some of the next group of corals (polycoeliids) in possessing septa of different lengths (Fig. 5.14.1).

Polycoeliids. Polycoeliids are simple corals without columellae, but their major septa are generally rhopaloid. Striking bilateral symmetry is attained in those forms in which a few major septa are more rhopaloid than the remainder are.

Tachylasma and *Plerophyllum* are excellent examples of polycoeliids from

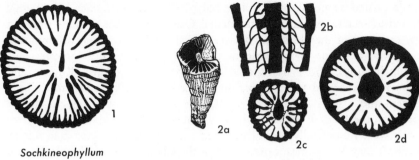

Sochkineophyllum

Lophophyllidium

Figure 5.14. Lophophyllids.
1. Transverse section of *Sochkineophyllum mirabile*, 2X, Permian, Kansas. 2. *Lophophyllidium proliferum*, Pennsylvanian, midcontinent. 2a, side view of a corallite with a broken rim of the calyx, 1X. 2b, longitudinal section, 3X. 2c, 2d, transverse sections in early and late maturity, 3X. (1 after Moore and Jeffords, 1941. 2b-2d after Jeffords, 1942.)

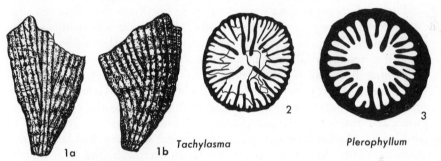

Tachylasma

Plerophyllum

Figure 5.15. Polycoeliids.
1a, 1b. Cardinal and left alar sides of *Tachylasma* sp. showing prominent septal grooves, 3X, Permian, China. 2. Transverse section of *Tachylasma elongatum* showing several orders of septa, 2X, Permian, China. 3. Transverse section of *Plerophyllum australe*, 3X, Permian, Australia.
(After Grabau, 1928.)

the Permian System of the Old World (Fig. 5.15). Although really distinctive polycoeliids are lacking in North America, the group is cited herein because the polycoeliids were the last Rugosa to evolve before the extinction of the Subclass. Moreover, some authorities have suggested that the septal patterns of the polycoeliids are transitional between patterns of corals in typical tetracorals and typical hexacorals.

GEOLOGIC HISTORY OF THE RUGOSA. Although the Tabulata are the oldest undoubted corals, they had hardly become established before the Rugosa appeared. Some paleontologists think that rugose corals must have evolved from colonial ancestors, whereas other writers think that rugose corals existed as nonskeletal simple polyps like sea anemones before they started to secrete exoskeletons in Medial Ordovician (late Chazy) time. In any case, two of the oldest Rugosa are referable to the colonial columnariid, *Favistella,* and one is referable to the simple zaphrenthid, *Streptelasma.* Okulitch (1936, 1938) has shown how greatly the corals (Rugosa and Tabulata) expanded from Chazy into succeeding Black River time. The 7 Genera and 9 species of Chazy corals were succeeded by 8 Genera and 21 species in the Black River, but Okulitch thought it probable that Black River corals were numerically several hundred times more abundant than Chazy corals. It may be significant that 7 or 8 of the Chazy corals were colonial and 16 of the Black River corals were colonial. Although the Rugosa gained only a little against the numerical dominance of Tabulata, the trend toward dominance of the Rugosa continued in succeeding Paleozoic Periods. In summary, it appears that in the Medial Ordovician the corals began to secrete skeletons in North America and then spread to Europe and the rest of the world, beginning in the Late Ordovician.

Although Silurian Rugosa were much more important than were those of the Ordovician, most of the Silurian coral faunas were still dominated by the Tabulata. Dissepimentaria were commonly introduced and odd columellae such as spongy axial structures were secreted.

Devonian time was the culmination of rugose corals in diversity and numbers. Stumm (1949) recognized 16 Families and 127 Genera. Of these Families, 6 are referable to the zapthrenthid group, 7 to the cyathophyllid group, and one each to the porpitid, columnariid, and cystiphyllid groups as used herein. Obviously, corals with dissepimental structures had become the dominant form. As for characterizing Devonian corals, the large simple zaphrenthids and simple or compound cyathophyllids are generally abundant, in addition to which cystiphyllids are common. On the other hand, columellate types are almost unknown.

Late Paleozoic rugose corals are characterized by dissepiments and, in addition, complicated axial structures. It is common to observe the trend toward lonsdaleoid dissepimentaria operating in conjunction with clisiophyllid axial modifications. Lophophyllids appeared in Mississippian time and became very important by Pennsylvanian time. Most tabulate corals had vanished by the Carboniferous.

Clisiophyllids continued to be the dominant corals until Late Permian time and were associated with a fair number of cyathophyllids and lophophyllids, as well as by increasing numbers of the polycoeliids. Although the polycoeliid vigor persisted, the other groups began to die out. Extinction of the Rugosa took place near the end of the Permian when the polycoeliids vanished.

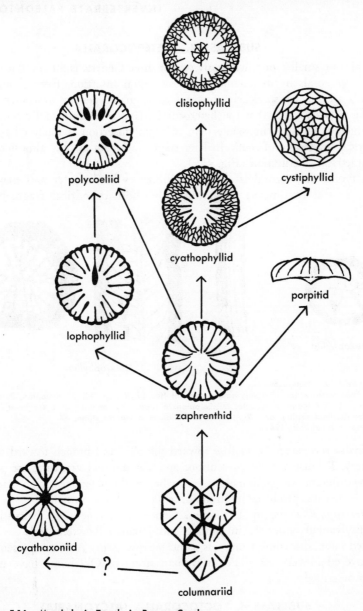

Figure 5.16. Morphologic Trends in Rugose Corals.
Probable morphologic trends are indicated by arrows connecting schematic cross sections of the nine groups of Rugosa recognized herein. In general the stratigraphic distribution is also indicated by the arrows, although many instances of parallelism and homoeomorphy are known.

SUBCLASS 3. HETEROCORALLA

This one small group, with only two or three Genera, is differentiated from all other corals by its peculiar order of septal insertion. Even though the details are not yet so clearly apparent as to enable general agreement, paleontologists do agree that the heterocorals have a fundamentally tetrameral symmetry. Thus, a rugoselike plan of septal insertion is modified by symmetrical branching of septa. In later stages the septa assume almost radially symmetrical distribution (Fig. 5.17).

A typical heterocoral is about 5 millimeters in diameter and may have been several centimeters long, but only short cylindrical fragments are

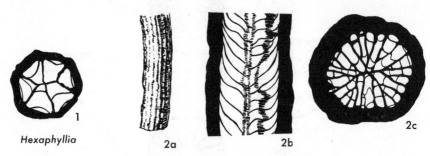

Hexaphyllia

2a

2b

Heterophyllia

Figure 5.17. Heterocoralla.
1. Transverse section of a very young stage of *Hexaphyllia* sp., 8X, Mississippian, Europe and Japan. 2. *Heterophyllia reducta*, Mississippian, Europe. 2a, exterior of a fragment, 1 1/2X. 2b, longitudinal section, 6X. 2c, transverse section of a mature stage, 4X.
(After Schindewolf, 1941.)

normally recovered. Septa fuse toward the axis and branch toward the periphery. Tabulae are also present but no other internal structures are present. Some difference of opinion exists as to whether the outer sheath is a true theca or whether it is produced by fusion of septa, or tabulae, or both.

Heterophyllia, the most common Genus, occurs near the Mississippian-Pennsylvanian boundary in Europe and Japan. All heterocorals so far reported have also come from this same narrow zone. A few representatives discovered in very Early Pennsylvanian strata of Oklahoma have not yet been described.

SUBCLASS 4. OCTOCORALLA (ALCYONARIA)

Although octocorals are important constituents of Recent coral faunas, the entire Subclass is insignificant paleontologically. The group is characterized by having eight mesenteries which differ from those of all other Anthozoa in having their muscle bands all facing the side of the oesophagus where the single siphonoglyph is located (Fig. 5.18.2). Dimorphism of polyps is the rule in this Subclass. The regular feeding polyps have a single circle of tentacles, but polyps with only one tentacle maintain a current of water through canals in the **coenenchyme** or sheet of fleshy tissue in which both kinds of polyps are inserted. Neither kind of polyp is reflected in the skeleton, unless it be merely as depressions. Calcareous septa are not present. All living octocorals are compound, the polyps forming sheaths of tissue which enclose axial skeletal parts of some sort. Wandlike shafts, branching structures, and fan-shaped expansions are the commonest shapes. Some octocorals have no skeletons at all. If skeletons are present they consist of a horny substance, **gorgonin;** or of calcareous spicules enclosed in a matrix of gorgonin; or of calcareous fibers; or of spicules cemented together with calcium carbonate. When spicular octocorals die, the spicules are freed by decomposition of the fleshy material and the gorgonin within about three days and are added to the accumulating sediments. Octocoral spicules are very common in Recent marine sediments and have been reported from Mesozoic strata, but their occurrence in the fossil state is much less common than one would expect. Spicules range from less than 0.1 to 1 millimeter in length, but the average length is in the middle of this size range. Most spicules are stubby with irregular warty excrescences or with rudely arranged spinose rays (Fig. 5.18.7-10). In spite of great diversity of form, octocoralline spicules have not been of much assistance in determination of species or of Genera.

Recent octocorals are mostly classified by reference to fleshy or horny material not normally fossilized. Even if an axis were preserved as a fossil, it might be of dubious value because the shapes and features of polyps are not reflected thereon. Living octocorals can be classified into several Orders, one of which is represented by the red, yellow, and purple "sea-fans" or gorgonid corals (*Gorgonia*) which are familiar to travelers along western Atlantic shores (Fig. 5.18.4). Another Order is characterized by the "sea pens" such as *Pennatula* (Fig. 5.8.11), which grow erect from the sea floor and maintain their position because their quill-like shafts are embedded in the sediments. *Tubipora* is a red colonial coral with many cylindrical corallites (Fig. 5.18.6). Horizontal plates of skeletal material surround the corallites at successive planes very much as floors encompass supporting steel work in a building. The precious coral, *Corallium* (Fig. 5.18.1), is composed of red calcareous branches which are fancied for jewelry and for their supposed mystical properties by people in most lands. *Corallium* is the first Genus of corals known to science. Lastly, the spectacular "blue coral," *Heliopora* (Fig. 5.18.3), lives near the shores of southeast Asia.

Octocoralla have been reported from rocks as old as Jurassic. *Corallium,* for instance, has been recorded from Cretaceous strata, and several Tertiary octocorals are on record. Unfortunately, neither spicules nor axes of most forms provide material for confident identification.

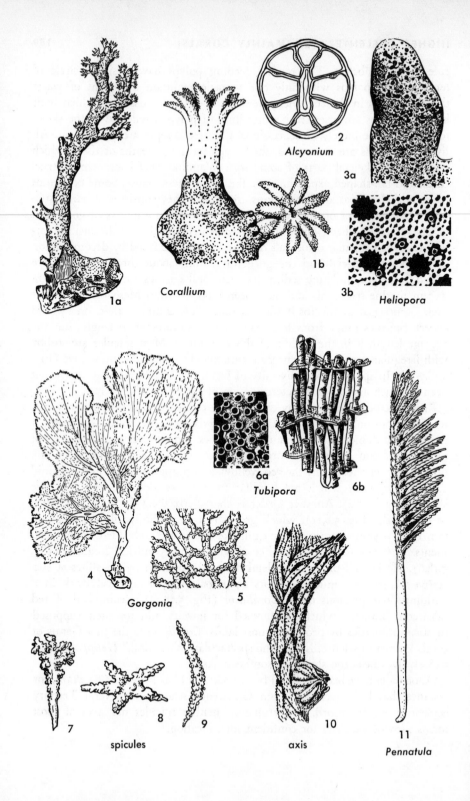

1a

Corallium

1b

2

Alcyonium

3a

3b

Heliopora

4

Gorgonia

5

6a

Tubipora

6b

7

8

9

spicules

10

axis

11

Pennatula

Even though skeletons of octocorals may consist mostly of gorgonin, the spicules embedded in the coenenchyme may provide significant amounts of sediment on the sea floor. The sea-fans or gorgoniids, which live off the coast of Florida, are important sources of calcium carbonate even though spicules only comprise from 20 to 36 per cent of the volume of the skeletons. It has been calculated that gorgoniids are capable of adding a ton of limestone to each acre of sea floor annually around the Tortugas Islands.

SUBCLASS 5. HEXACORALLA

The Hexacoralla as used herein constitute a loosely construed assemblage of corals which have six primary pairs of mesenteries. It is recognized that corals with significantly different microstructure of mesenteries are arbitrarily lumped together in the Hexacoralla, but such recognizable differences in their soft parts are rarely discernible in their hard parts. Moreover, few of the groups are found fossil, and there is not yet concordance of opinion as to the taxonomic value of these mesenteric features in any case. Those hexacorals without skeletons comprise the sea anemones, whereas those with skeletons are the stony corals or Scleractinida. Naturally, only the Scleractinida are important paleontologically.

Order a.   Zoanthida

Zoanthid corals are differentiated from the other sea anemones because the zoanthids add new mesenteries at only two places on the ventral side after the first six pairs of mesenteries appear (Fig. 5.19.7). The distinct bilateral symmetry and the pattern of mesenteries suggest that the zoanthids and the rugose corals may be interrelated. According to this view, zoanthids lost two places of mesenteric insertion when they arose from the rugose corals. Zoanthids are thought by some students to be very primitive hexacorals, or even to bear the same relationship to the tetracorals that the soft-bodied sea anemones bear to the stony corals. About half a dozen Recent Genera have been described. Fossils are not known.

Figure 5.18 (opposite). Octocoralla.
1a, 1b. Portion of a colony (3/4X) and two extended polyps (10X) of *Corallium rubrum*, Recent, Mediterranean. 2. Transverse section showing position of the radiating mesenteries and the muscle bands (hachured) in *Alcyonium* sp., enlarged, Recent. 3a, 3b. Branch of a corallum (1X) and portion of the surface (6X) of *Heliopora cerulea* with large autopores, small siphonopores, and six circular tubes secreted by a parasitic worm, *Leucodora*, Recent. 4. A sea-fan, *Gorgonia flabellum*, about 1/7X, Recent. 5. Portion of the corallum of a sea-fan, 1 1/3X, Recent. 6a, 6b. Surface and side view of *Tubipora* sp., 1X, Recent. 7-9. Alcyonarian spicules, about 75X, Recent. 10. Part of the axis of an alcyonarian showing position of the spicules, 15X, Recent. 11. A sea pen, *Pennatula aculeata*, 2/3X, Recent.
(1 after Milne-Edwards, 1857. 2 after Hertwig and Hertwig, 1879. 3, 6 after Vaughan, 1919b. 4 after Hargitt and Rogers, 1902. 7-10 after Thomson and Henderson, 1906. 11 after Verrill, 1883.)

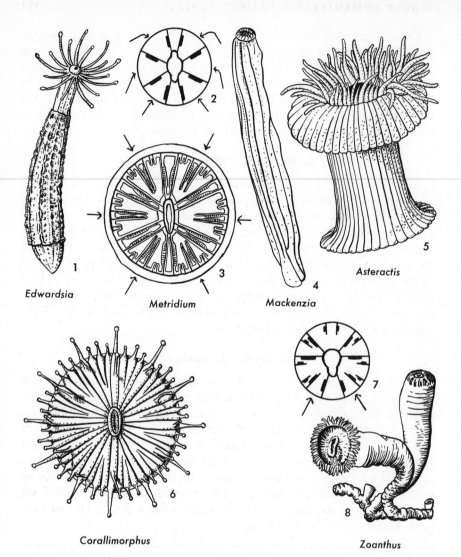

Edwardsia

Metridium

Mackenzia

Asteractis

Corallimorphus

Zoanthus

Figure 5.19. Actinida, Corallimorphida, and Zoanthida.
1. Side view of *Edwardsia* sp., 4X, Recent. 2. Schematic transverse section of *Edwardsia* sp. showing eight mesenteries and position of muscle bands, enlarged, Recent. 3. Schematic transverse section of a common sea anemone, *Metridium* sp., slightly enlarged, Recent. 4. *Mackenzia costalis*, 1X, Cambrian, British Columbia. 5. *Asteractis expansa*, 1X, Recent. 6. Oral surface of *Corallimorphus profundus*, 1X, Recent. 7. Schematic transverse section of *Zoanthus* sp. showing mesenteries and muscle bands, enlarged, Recent. 8. Portion of a colony of *Zoanthus* sp. showing expanded and retracted tentacles, much enlarged, Recent.
Arrows on 2, 3, and 7 indicate the positions at which new mesenteries are added.
(1, 8 after Andres, 1884. 2, 3, 7 after McMurrich, 1891. 4 after Walcott, 1911. 5 after Duerden, 1902b. 6 after Moseley, 1877.)

Order b.   Corallimorphida

This group of very rare sea anemones differs from the other sea anemones in having two cycles of abundant tentacles (Fig. 5.19.6). The numerous mesenteries are symmetrically placed on a hexamerous pattern as in the Actinida below. About ten Genera have been described, but no fossils have been reported.

Order c.   Actinida

Actinians are familiarly known as "sea anemones" in allusion to their colorful tentacles and oral surfaces. Insertion of mesenteries follows a perfectly hexamerous pattern (Fig. 5.19.2, 3). Although they have no skeletons, they have been reported doubtfully as far back as Middle Cambrian; *Mackenzia,* from the famous Burgess shale of Canada, may be the oldest anthozoan in the world (Fig. 5.19.4). About 700 species of living actinians have been described, some of which live in Arctic waters. Some, such as *Edwardsia,* burrow in sediment, but most of the actinians such as *Metridium* and *Asteractis* (Fig. 5.19.3, 5) incrust rocks. It is convenient to think of actinians as being common corals without skeletons but standing otherwise in close relationship with the Scleractinida. *Edwardsia,* for instance, has only eight mesenteries (Fig. 5.19.2) and these resemble a stage in the ontogeny of stony corals which is referred to hereafter (Fig. 5.20.4). Among living sea anemones, *Metridium* characterizes a group with several cycles of mesenteries.

Order d.   Scleractinida

Polyps of living scleractinian corals not only occupy the calyces but extend out over the rim and down the flanks as a thin fleshy **edge zone.** The vertical **costae,** which are the external continuation of the septa, are secreted from the edge zone. If the growth habit is colonial, the edge zones of adjacent polyps fuse and produce a thick, fleshy **coenosarc.** In that case the space between corallites often is filled with vesicular skeletal tissue (**coenosteum**) which is secreted by the coenosarc. As growth progresses, polyps move upward in the calyces and close off abandoned areas by secreting dissepiments and tabulae. An axial structure built by some polyps is a **columella.**

Simple corals not only branch to form increasingly compact coralla such as were produced by the rugose corals (Fig. 5.4.3-7), but also develop other intricate interrelationships of polyps. For instance, calyces may become very elongate but pleated back and forth like folds of drapery. Or the same pattern may be formed when adjacent polyps are intergrown in curving rows. Both of these conditions are said to be **meandroid,** in allusion to the resemblance to meanders of old-age streams (Figs. 5.23.1, 5.24.2). In common parlance, coralla of this type are called brain corals.

INSERTION OF MESENTERIES AND SEPTA. A brief investigation of the growth stages through which scleractinians pass as they attain their characteristic patterns of mesenteries and septa reveals their true symmetry and the differences between stony corals and sea anemones on the one hand and the tetracorals on the other. Even before the planula larva attaches itself to the substratum it starts to assume the shape of a tiny polyp by acquiring mesenteries. The first pair of mesenteries appears on what we may call the ventral side (Fig. 5.20.1) and the second pair appears soon after on

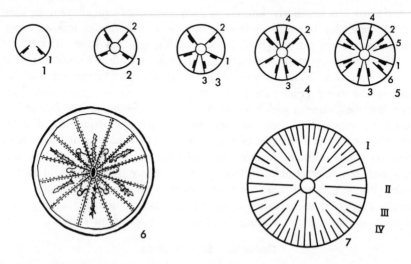

Figure 5.20. Insertion of Mesenteries and Septa.
  1-5. Schematic plan views of successive growth stages of a stony coral showing the mesenteries and muscle bands, enlarged. Arabic numerals identify the order of insertion. 6. Transparent view down into a polyp of *Siderastrea radians* at a stage when the first six septa have been secreted. Tentacles encircle the mouth and zooxanthellae (dots) surround the mouth and lie alongside the upper edges of the twelve mesenteries, 20X, Recent. 7. Schematic diagram of a stony coral showing four orders of septa which are indicated by Roman numerals.
  (1-5, 7 mostly after Duerden, 1900. 6 after Duerden, 1904.)

the dorsal side (Fig. 5.20.2). Pairs three and four then appear in succession (Fig. 5.20.3, 4). Because they define the dorsoventral plane, which is also the direction of elongation of the slitlike mouth, they are called the **directive mesenteries.** So far all of the mesenteries have reached the stomodaeum. These first eight mesenteries simulate the number, position, and microstructure of those in *Edwardsia* (Fig. 5.19.2); therefore they are referred to as **edwardsian mesenteries** and are looked upon as a link between the actinians and the scleractinians. The Scleractinida, however, continue to add cycles of mesenteries beyond the original. Thus, pairs five and six appear simultaneously, but are shorter than the others (Fig. 5.20.5). With the completion of the first 12 mesenteries there is a pause in growth before any new mesenteries are added. At this growth stage the larva has become attached to the substratum, a functional mouth opening is present, and muscle bands have appeared on the mesenteries. It is worth noting that the muscle bands on the directive mesenteries face away from each other, thus imparting a distinct bilateral symmetry to the otherwise radial pattern of mesenteric position.

Development of the skeleton commences with the secretion of a calcareous **basal disc** and a **theca**. The first septa appear all together in a group of 6, one lying in the space between each of the 6 pairs of mesenteries (Fig. 5.20.6). These 6 are the **protosepta** of a stony coral. Septa fuse with and grow upward from the basal disc, whereas the theca keeps pace by growing upward and fusing with the outer ends of the septa. As growth progresses, new pairs of mesenteries and then their corresponding new septa are inserted in simultaneous **cycles** between the first 6 septa (Fig. 5.20.6). In this way the second cycle contains 6 septa, the third sycle contains twelve septa, and each successive cycle doubles the number of septa in the previous cycle until a hundred or more septa have been inserted. Inasmuch as septa of each successive cycle ideally extend a little less far from the theca than do those of the previous cycle, the number of cycles of septa in living corals usually can be ascertained by studying the calyx.

It is important to note that septa are inserted in scleractinians at six places. Hexacorals and tetracorals both pass through a stage in which there are six major septa, but tetracorals only insert new septa at four points. Many students have hoped to find transitional stages between hexacorals and tetracorals, but the search so far has been singularly free from convincing results.

On the other hand, there is a little evidence that stony hexacorals may have evolved from sea anemones, which seem to be soft-bodied hexacorals. In the first place, the actinian *Edwardsia* has eight mesenteries in its adult stage, and these mesenteries resemble the edwardsian mesenteries of the stony corals in position and structure. Inasmuch as the edwardsian mesenteries characterize early ontogenetic stages of stony corals, it would appear from application of the principle of recapitulation that the actinians might have been potential ancestors of the scleractinians. Of course, *Edwardsia* could hardly be expected to be represented in the sedimentary record because it is soft-bodied, so it cannot be proved to have lived prior to any of the scleractinians. Nevertheless, the actinians are possibly known from very ancient rocks because *Mackenzia,* from the Middle Cambrian, seems to be an actinian. One might say, therefore, that the actinian group could be represented by a succession from *Mackenzia* to *Edwardsia* and that the scleractinians might have evolved from this lineage after the tetracorals became extinct at the end of the Permian Period. The *Mackenzia-Edwardsia* hypothesis has been supported in America chiefly by P. E. Raymond.

SEPTA. Skeletal material is secreted by specialized cells (**calicoblasts**), forming a layer where the surface of the ectoderm touches the skeleton. Each calicoblast secretes a minute bundle of crystals of aragonite (called a **sclerodermite**) which radiate from a **center of crystallization.** Sclerodermites tend to line up in vertical rods, each of which is a **trabecula** (Fig. 5.21.2). When trabeculae consist of one string of sclerodermites they are **simple,** but **compound** trabeculae consist of bundles of six or eight rods rather closely grown together. In septa the trabeculae grow upward in sprays (**fan systems**) which curve away in the plane of the septum to the right and left from the axis of divergence. One septum may consist of one or of several fan systems, and the axes of divergence of the systems may be vertical, oblique, or hori-

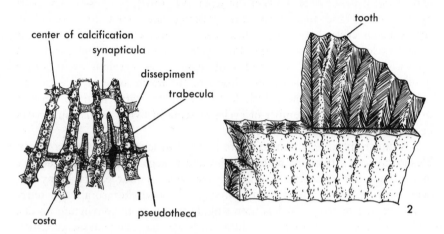

Figure 5.21. Septal Structure in Stony Corals.
1. Hypothetical transverse section, 10X. 2. Diagrammatic cut-away section showing different appearances of simple trabeculae, greatly enlarged.
(1 after Vaughan, 1900. 2 after Ogilvie, 1896.)

zontal. If the various trabeculae are solidly filled in with calcareous matrix the septa are **laminar,** but if septa are perforated by spaces between trabeculae they are **fenestrate.** In some forms adjacent septa are joined by stumpy trabecular crossbars (**synapticulae**) at right angles to the septal planes (Fig. 5.21.1). Free edges of septa may be **smooth** or minutely toothed (**dentate**).

CLASSIFICATION. Classification of Scleractinida depends in part upon soft structures of polyps; hence, it is not always decisively applicable to fossil material. Septal structure and arrangement are of prime importance, whereas colonial form and development of coenosteal features are of secondary importance. Stratigraphic distribution of septal structures among the Scleractinida is shown in Figure 5.27. Few clear-cut trends carry through the Order except for the ascendancy of the nonreef habit of growth. Primitive isolated trabeculae tend to become associated in increasingly compact linear or bundled patterns. Perforate septa probably are primitive, but the progressive trend toward laminar septa is reversed in some cases which return to secretion of fenestrate septa. Contrasting septal trends lead to more compact septa in some groups but to more porous septa in others. In fact, the end product of septal reduction is attained when only spines remain. A trend toward more numerous synapticulae is well known in two Suborders. Finally, columellae are produced in several groups.

Key to Suborders of Scleractinida

I. Septa with up to 8 trabeculae .... Astrocoeniina
II. Septa with more than 8 trabeculae
    A. Synapticulae present
        1. Septa fenestrate (at least in young stages) ....Fungiina
        2. Septa laminar .... Dendrophylliina
    B. Synapticulae absent (or very rare)
        1. Margins of septa dentate .... Faviina
        2. Margins of septa smooth .... Caryophylliina

SUBORDER (1). ASTROCOENIINA

Astrocoeniids are almost invariably colonial corals whose small polyps (about 1 to 3 mm in diameter) rarely have more than 12 tentacles. Septa in primitive forms are represented only by spines, but most Families have laminar septa which usually consist of no more than 8 simple trabeculae. Septal margins are commonly dentate.

This Suborder is one of the oldest groups of hexacorals, being first represented in Medial Triassic strata. A living representative, *Acropora,* is one of the most ubiquitous and successful of all reef corals. *Acropora* originated during the Eocene, as did *Pocillopora,* another equally common Recent reef coral (Fig. 5.22).

SUBORDER (2). FUNGIINA

Fungiid corals are characterized by the presence of more than eight trabeculae in a septum and by the occurrence of synapticulae between septa. Growth habits vary from simple to colonial. Septa of all forms are fenestrate in early stages but may become laminar as growth continues. Septal margins are always dentate.

Fungiid corals share with astrocoeniids the distinction of being the oldest hexacorals, dating back to the mid-Triassic. The Suborder soon divided into numerous subsidiary groups and had its greatest diversity in Late Cretaceous time. It was important in Tertiary time and is represented in Recent seas by a large number of familiar forms. *Agaricia,* from Recent seas in the West Indies, goes back to the Miocene. *Fungia* is the familiar, flat, solitary coral

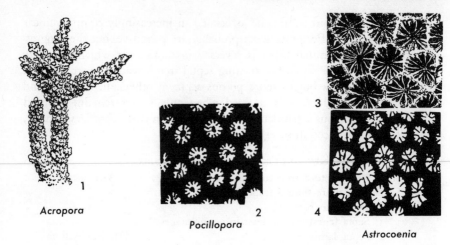

Acropora

Pocillopora

Astrocoenia

Figure 5.22. Astrocoeniina.
1. Branch of a corallum of *Acropora muricata*, 1/2X, Recent.   2. Transverse section of *Pocillopora eydouxi*, 8X, Recent.   3. Surface of *Astrocoenia guadalupae*, 5X, Cretaceous, Texas. 4. Transverse section of *Astrocoenia* sp., 3X, Triassic, California.
(1 after Vaughan, 1902. 2 after Vaughan and Wells, 1943. 3 after Wells, 1933. 4 after Smith, 1927.)

from the Indo-Pacific region which gets its name because its calyx resembles the filaments on the under side of the cap of a mushroom. *Fungia* is known from the Miocene. One of the most common reef corals in the world is *Porites,* which represents a lineage dating back to the Cretaceous, although the actual Genus is only known from Eocene and later times (Fig. 5.23).

SUBORDER (3). FAVIINA

Among corals with many trabeculae to a septum, the faviids are distinguished by having dentate septal margins, and there are almost no synapticulae. Dissepiments are common and septa are typically laminar. Solitary and colonial growth forms occur.

Montlivaltia is a solitary coral which flourished from Medial Triassic through the Cretaceous. In Recent seas the brain coral, *Favia,* is of world-wide distribution; moreover, it has survived from the Cretaceous. *Astrhelia, Septastrea,* and *Oculina* are well-known fossil corals in the Tertiary of the Atlantic Coastal Plain (Fig. 5.24).

SUBORDER (4). CARYOPHYLLIINA

Septa of this Suborder are invariably laminar with smooth margins. Synapticulae are not present. Although polyps of early forms were surrounded by a theca, later forms developed an edge zone and secreted skeletal structures on the exterior of the theca.

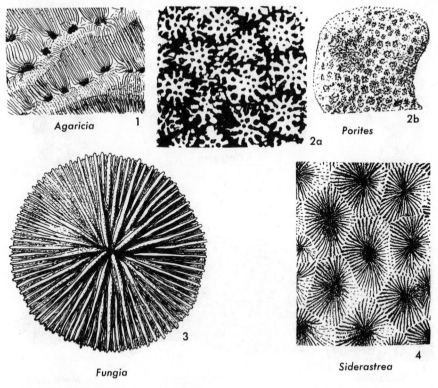

Figure 5.23. Fungiina.
1. Portion of the surface of *Agaricia* sp., enlarged, Recent. 2a, 2b. Portion of the surface (8X) and portion of a corallum (1X) of *Porites porites*, Recent. 3. Calyx of *Fungia patella*, 1X, Recent. 4. Portion of the surface of *Siderastrea siderea*, 3X, Recent.
(1, 2, 4 after Vaughan, 1902. 3 after Vaughan, 1919b.)

Caryophylliids are noteworthy because the first nonreef stony corals originated in this Suborder in Early Jurassic time. Reef corals also arose within the caryophyllids, but only incidentally. *Turbinolia* is a handsome columellate form from the Early Tertiary with prominent costae and with perforations, pits, or secondary costae in intercostal grooves. *Flabellum* is a fan-shaped solitary coral with a wrinkled epitheca; it ranges from Eocene to Recent. *Trochocyathus* was an Eocene button coral whose shape was convergent with that of the porpitid corals of the Paleozoic. *Parasmilia* is common in the Cretaceous of the Gulf Coastal Plain (Fig. 5.25).

SUBORDER (5). DENDROPHYLLIINA

Dendrophylliids resemble caryophylliids in having laminar septa with smooth edges, but dendrophylliids have many synapticulae. Moreover, even

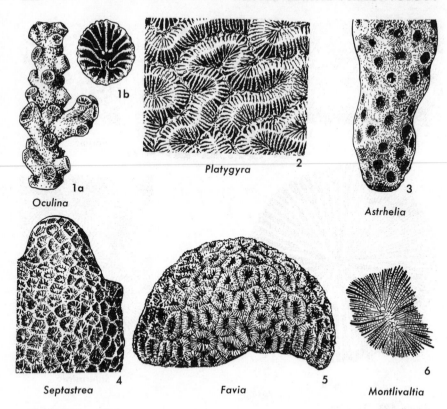

Figure 5.24. Faviina.
1a, 1b. Corallum (1X) and calyx (3X) of *Oculina mississippiensis*, Oligocene, Mississippi. 2. Portion of the surface of *Platygyra viridis* with meandriform valleys, about 1X, Recent. 3. Portion of a corallum of *Astrhelia palmata*, 1X, Miocene, Maryland. 4. Portion of a corallum of *Septastrea subramosa*, 1X, Miocene, Maryland. 5. Corallum of *Favia fragum*, 1X, Recent. 6. Transverse section of *Montlivaltia norica*, 2/3X, Triassic, Oregon, Alaska, Austria.
(1 after Vaughan, 1900. 2 after Vaughan, 1902. 3, 4 after Vaughan in Clarke, *et al.*, 1904. 5 after Vaughan and Wells, 1943. 6 after Smith, 1927.)

a porous outer wall of structures resembling synapticulae may occur. Instead of remaining rather straight, the septa in many dendrophylliids fuse into branching groups in what is called the **Pourtalès plan** of septal insertion. According to the Pourtalès plan septa higher than the third cycle may be inserted out of sequence and may become longer than septa of an earlier cycle (Fig. 5.26.2a). Most of the dendrophylliids are nonreef corals.

The dendrophylliids are the latest offshoot of the Scleractinida, having not appeared until Medial Cretaceous. *Endopachys* (Fig. 5.26.2) is a well-known solitary Eocene Genus in the United States and it is still living in Indo-Pacific waters. *Turbinaria* (Fig. 5.26.1) is a colonial columellate reef coral which ranges from Oligocene to Recent.

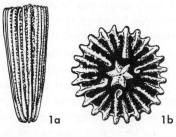

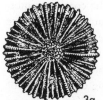

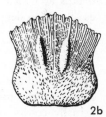

Turbinolia

Flabellum

Trochocyathus

Parasmilia

Figure 5.25. Caryophylliina.
1a, 1b. Side view (5X) and calyx (12X) of *Turbinolia pharetra*, Eocene, Gulf Coastal Plain.
2. *Flabellum cuneiforme*, 1X, Eocene and Oligocene, Gulf Coastal Plain. 3a, 3b. Calyx and side
view of *Trochocyathus lunulitiformis*, 3X, Eocene, Gulf Coastal Plain. 4a, 4b. Transverse section
and side view of *Parasmilia austinensis*, 1X, Cretaceous, Texas.
(1-3 after Vaughan, 1902. 4 after Winton, 1925.)

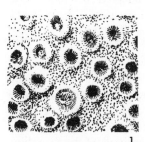

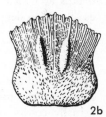

Turbinaria

Endopachys

Figure 5.26. Dendrophylliina.
1. Portion of the surface of *Turbinaria peltata*, 1X, Recent. 2a, 2b. Septal plan in calyx,
and side view of *Endopachys maclurii*, 1X, Eocene, Alabama.
(1 after Vaughan and Wells, 1943. 2 after Vaughan, 1900.)

ECOLOGY OF CORALS. Recent stony corals can be divided into two groups, the **reef corals** and the **nonreef corals,** which are also known respectively as the hermatypic and ahermatypic corals. Reef corals mostly live in water less than 150 feet (46 m) deep, in which the temperature ranges between 77 and 84 degrees Fahrenheit (25 and 29° C). Turbulent water at such shallow depths maintains a supply of nutrients and keeps sediment washed away from the polyps. Reef corals are characterized by the presence of **zooxanthellae,** which are one-celled plants (brown algae) embedded in the outer parts of their endodermal layer—that is, near the interior of the body wall of the polyp. The evidence is conclusive that these algae manufacture oxygen in the presence of sunlight and that the coral benefits thereby. Inasmuch as the algae may obtain their carbon dioxide from the coral, an interdependence amounting to symbiosis is indicated. Unfortunately, the presence of zooxanthellae is not reflected in skeletal structures; hence fossil corals may not be positively recognized as reef corals unless they can be assigned on morphologic grounds to some living species whose physiology and growth habits are known. Moreover, definite nonreef corals growing off the coast of Norway form large patches and mounds in water as deep as 8660 feet (2900 m) and at temperatures as low as 39 degrees Fahrenheit (4° C). It has been estimated that a Recent reef such as grows today in the West Indies would require between 1000 and 6000 years to obtain a thickness of 150 feet (50 m).

Nonreef corals, on the other hand, can live in water much deeper than that inhabited by reef corals. In fact, a nonreef coral has been dredged from over 19,000 feet (5870 m), although most live between 550 and 1600 feet just beyond the outer edge of the continental shelf. Inasmuch as light does not penetrate that deep into sea water, zooxanthellae are absent. At the greater depths at which they live, nonreef corals must be adapted to temperatures as low as 36 degrees Fahrenheit (2.4° C), but in their normal depth range the temperature varies between 40 and 50 degrees Fahrenheit (4.5° and 10° C).

Recent coral reefs are not typical of coral growths in the past. Intergrown build-ups as large as the Great Barrier Reef east of Australia are unknown in the fossil record. Moreover, many tropical "coral reefs" of today actually consist of more than 50 per cent (some as high as 80 per cent) of calcareous red algae such as *Lithothamnium* and *Halimeda*. It is also true that ancient reefs commonly (or even mostly) consisted of less coralline material than of other material. For instance, many Paleozoic reefs were composed largely of tabulate corals and stromatoporoids, or even of crinoids or brachiopods. For this reason it has seemed desirable for a word to be coined which has neither the connotation of corals nor of rocks and shoals such as mariners have in mind when they speak of reefs. The term **bioherm** has achieved wide acceptance by geologists for build-ups of any kind of organic skeletal material. In addition, the companion term, **biostrome,** refers to stratified deposits of fossils or fossil debris which do not stand in any appreciable relief above the general surface of deposition.

Silurian reefs were the first to be recognized in North America, where they are known to extend across the present Great Lakes region from Ontario to Iowa, with principal development in Indiana, Wisconsin, and Illinois. When oil was discovered in a bioherm (Marine Pool) in Illinois in 1943 a sudden economic impetus was given to the search for bioherms. Accordingly, much attention is now being given to ecology of reef-making organisms in the expectation that they will aid in the discovery of more oil pools in other bioherms.

Rugosa and Tabulata, in company with bryozoans, stromatoporoids, and algae, were very abundant in the Devonian and commonly constructed biostromes as at Falls of the Ohio near Louisville, Kentucky. Bioherms are less common than are biostromes in the Devonian, but they have been sought assiduously since the discovery of oil in an Upper Devonian "reef" at Leduc in Canada. Since that discovery in 1947 the Leduc reef trend has been extended a distance of 160 miles in central Alberta, and three other reef areas also have been discovered in Alberta. All together, 72 per cent of the oil produced in Alberta in 1955 came from these Devonian bioherms.

Biostromes are abundant in Upper Paleozoic strata but bioherms comparable with those of the Silurian and Devonian are unknown. Reef limestones such as occur, for instance, in England contain a small minority of coelenterates. This is also true in North America where the impressive barrier reefs of the Permian of Texas are notable for the scarcity of corals.

Three facies of Upper Paleozoic coral faunas have been distinguished. The *Cyathaxonia* fauna is analogous to the deep-water and cold-water fauna of Recent simple corals; the compound corals of the Upper Paleozoic are analogous to Recent shallow-water reef corals; and the cyathophylliid-clisiophyllid association is of intermediate type. The difference between deep-water and reef corals also has been recognized among the Ordovician Anthozoa.

GEOLOGIC HISTORY OF THE SCLERACTINIDA. After the extinction of the Rugosa at the end of the Permian, there was an interval barren of corals in the Early Triassic. Then the astrocoeniids and fungiids arose in Medial Triassic time from ancestors as yet undiscovered. The fungiid stem proved to be the more vigorous of the two, for new groups arose from it very quickly. Faviids arose in Late Triassic time, and these seem in turn to have produced the caryophylliids by Early Jurassic. Medial Triassic corals were the reef coral type, but only patches and banks are known instead of definite reefs. By Late Triassic small reefs were being built, some of which are located in California and Oregon. It was not until Medial Jurassic, how-

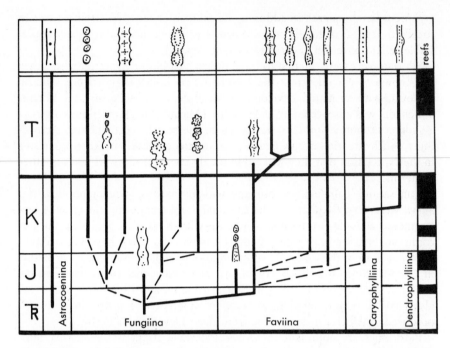

Figure 5.27. Septal Structure of Scleractinida.
Stratigraphic distribution and probable evolution of septal structure is shown for the Suborders of Scleractinida. Centers of trabeculae are shown as dots in schematic transverse sections of septa. Times of significant reef growths are indicated in the right-hand column. (After Vaughan and Wells, 1943, and Wells, 1956.)

ever, that corals engaged in their first great flare, but even this flare did not culminate in a development of extensive reefs until Late Jurassic. At that time the Tethyan geosyncline lying along the south side of the Eurasian continent was the site of major coralline evolution, migration, and reef building.

Succeeding geologic series record a seesaw history of reef construction and abandonment, with peaks of extensive reefy development in latest Early Cretaceous and Late Cretaceous, but with sparse reefs in mid-Cretaceous and Early Tertiary times. Texas and Mexico were sites of Early Cretaceous reef coral accumulations in this hemisphere.

The use of corals in paleogeographic studies is particularly well shown with respect to the connection of the Atlantic and Pacific Oceans across Mexico and Central America during the Tertiary. In Late Eocene time the reef corals reached a peak of development in the Caribbean region where important build-ups have been located in Florida, Georgia, and Mississippi, as well as in the West Indies and northern South America. The same species of Eocene corals are present in strata on both coasts of Nicaragua; hence the Pacific and Atlantic Oceans were connected at that time. Fringing reefs were widespread in Florida and Alabama during the Oligocene; in fact one formation in Alabama used to be called the "coral limestone." Farther south, at the latitude of the present Isthmus of Panama, the Atlantic and Pacific Oceans must have been confluent during the Oligocene because the same coral faunas occur in deposits on both sides of that region. During the Miocene the reef corals decreased in importance in the Caribbean and a more modern coral fauna began to appear. Meanwhile, the oceanic portal between the Atlantic and Pacific at Panama was closed, but a minor portal existed in Nicaragua.

Pliocene corals are rather distinct on opposite sides of Central America, except for one singular discrepancy; the Pliocene coral fauna near Salton Sea in southern California seems to be very similar to related species in Florida and the West Indies. Two theories have been proposed to account for this similarity. According to one, the corals are similar because there was another portal across Mexico in Pliocene time through which Atlantic faunas migrated into a local embayment in California. The second theory is supported by those who point out the lack of any direct evidence of this theoretical portal. These paleontologists suggest that the two faunas had a common origin in pre-Pliocene time and evolved by parallel descent while they were confined to different oceans. The question is still not resolved to everybody's satisfaction. Reef-building corals underwent a great expansion in the Pleistocene waters of the Caribbean; moreover, they continue to inhabit the same region today.

Paleontologic studies reveal how the corals became divided into two great faunal realms. Between the Medial Triassic and the Medial Miocene, the stony corals constituted a cosmopolitan fauna which spread into all the oceans. By Late Miocene time the Tethyan migration route in Eurasia was closed by uplift, and Central America had become an intermittent barrier; hence, the two great reef coral faunas of the Caribbean and the Indo-Pacific which we recognize today probably arose through evolution along separate courses as a result of isolation. The few Mediterranean reef corals which were isolated in western Europe became extinct in the Late Tertiary; hence the remaining reef corals of the Atlantic Ocean can be referred to as "Caribbean" because they are restricted to that western Atlantic area. Recent corals can be divided into a prolific and vigorous Indo-Pacific reef coral fauna of over 500 species and a meager Caribbean fauna of fewer than 40 species. During its history the reef coral belt tended to shift southward. In the Triassic Period the belt extended from 10 degrees south latitude to 60 degrees north latitude. It was slightly narrower but more distinctly northern during the Jurassic. In Cretaceous time the margins of the belt varied between

50 and 54 degrees north latitude on the one side, and from the Equator to 37 degrees south latitude on the other. Today the reef corals extend from 35 degrees north latitude to 32 degrees south latitude, but are largely confined to oceanic islands, areas of slow rate of sedimentation, and eastern shores of continents against which warm tropical waters consistently flow.

Contrasted with the history of reef corals is that of the nonreef corals. They originated in latest Early Jurassic as caryophyliids and immediately began to increase in importance. During Medial and Late Cretaceous time they dominated most depth zones occupied by coral faunas in Texas and many other places. When European reef corals became extinct in the Late Tertiary, the nonreef counterparts persisted there. Living nonreef corals which inhabit the greatest depths have the greatest geographic range. Thus, cosmopolitan distribution is attained by most corals if they live in 1500 feet (500 m) of water.

Order e.   Antipathida

Antipathids are colonial corals which resemble the Octocoralla in growth habit and in the presence of a central axis composed of gorgonin, but the antipathids are characterized by having thorny spines on the axis and by generally having six mesenteries (but never eight). Moreover, there is considerable variation in the patterns of mesenteries and in the location of muscle fibers on mesenteries. In fact, there is as much variation within this group as there is among other Orders of Scleractinida (Fig. 5.28,3a, 3b). Although mesenteries of most hexacorals are paired, those of the antipathids are single. Antipathida sometimes are called "black corals" or "thorn corals." They are found in Recent seas from low tide down to almost 12,000 feet (4000 m). One Miocene record is known.

Order f.   Cerianthida

Cerianthids are slender solitary polyps with many tentacles. They burrow in soft marine sediment and lack hard parts, so they have not been reported as fossils. Mesenteries of cerianthids are unpaired, as in the case of the Antipathida. Moreover, the mesenteric pattern throughout life is distinctly bilateral (Fig. 5.28,4,5) and recalls the septal plan in the Rugosa.

Class F.   Ctenophora

Ctenophores are the "comb-jellyfish," characterized by the presence of an elongate to spherical body on which eight bands of cilia run from pole to pole. At each pole is a long tentacle. At first glance ctenophores rather resemble gooseberries in both size and appearance (Fig. 5.28,1). The Ctenophora can be differentiated from all other coelenterates because they lack

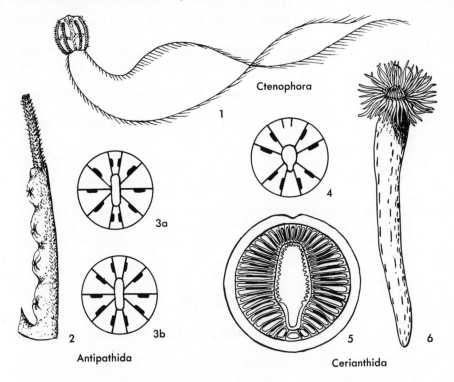

Figure 5.28. Antipathida, Cerianthida, and Ctenophora.
1. *Pleurobrachia rhododactyla*, 2/3X, Recent. 2. Fragment of a branch of *Antipathes subpinnata* with contracted polyps covering the spinose black axis, 10X, Recent. 3a, 3b. Schematic transverse sections of polyps of two Genera of Antipathida showing variation in position of muscle bands on the ten mesenteries, enlarged. 4, 5. Schematic transverse sections of an early stage and an adult stage of polyps of *Cerianthus*, enlarged. Recent. 6. Side view of *Cerianthus americanus*, 1/2X, Recent.
(1 after L. Agassiz, 1860. 2, 3 after Pax, 1940. 4 after McMurrich, 1891. 5 after Chun, 1891, and Hertwig and Hertwig, 1879. 6 after McMurrich, 1890.)

stinging cells. For this reason some authors raise the group to the rank of Phylum or Subphylum, as opposed to the so-called Cnidaria or coelenterates with nematocysts. No fossils are known.

QUESTIONS

1. How can tetracorals and hexacorals be differentiated by external and internal features?
2. Why is it difficult to be sure whether a fossil coral belongs to the reef corals or to the nonreef corals?
3. What features make the preservation of Octocoralla unlikely?

4. How might the Scleractinida or stony corals have arisen from some other Orders?
5. Why did the Rugosa and the Scleractinida pass through the same morphologic stages when they assumed colonial growth habits? What evolutionary terms describe the situation?
6. What purpose might have been served by columellae? In what ways were columellae constructed?
7. Which features of corals either inhibit or enhance their usefulness in geologic work?
8. Why are Tabulata all compound?
9. How could a previously undescribed species be assigned its proper place in a lineage such as that of *Zaphrentites delanouei* and have stratigraphic significance?
10. Paleontologists disagree about the stratigraphic ranges of chaetetids and tetradiids but are confident that they know the ranges of clisiophyllids and faviids. What principle is involved in establishing a particular degree of confidence in a range?

BIBLIOGRAPHY

Agassiz, A., 1865, North American Acalephae: Mem. Mus. Comp. Zool. (Harvard), ill. cat., no. 2.

Agassiz, L., 1860, 1862, Contributions to the natural history of the United States of America, vols. 3, 4.

Andres, A., 1884, Die Actinien: Fauna und Flora des Golfes von Neapel, Mon. 9.

Bassler, R. S., 1932, The stratigraphy of the Central Basin of Tennessee: Tennessee Div. Geol., Bull. 38.

———, 1937, The Paleozoic rugose coral Family Palaeocyclidae: Jour. Paleont., v. 11, no. 3, pp. 189–201.

———, 1950, Faunal lists and descriptions of Paleozoic corals: Geol. Soc. America, Mem. 44.

Bohlin, B., 1950, The affinities of the graptolites: Bull. Geol. Inst., Univ. Upsala (Sweden), v. 34, pp. 107–113.

Buehler, E. J., 1955, The morphology and taxonomy of the Halysitidae: Peabody Mus. Nat. Hist. (Yale), Bull. 8.

Bulman, O. M. B., 1934, Programme-evolution in the graptolites: Cambridge Phil. Soc., Biol. Revs., v. 8, no. 3, pp. 311–334.

———, 1954, Graptolithina: Bull. Mus. Comp. Zool. (Harvard), v. 112, no. 3, pp. 201–215.

———, 1955, Graptolithina *in* Treatise on invertebrate paleontology, pt. V.

Carruthers, R. G., 1910, On the evolution of *Zaphrentis delanouei* in Lower Carboniferous times: Geol. Soc. London Quart. Jour., v. 66, pp. 523–538.

Cary, L. R., 1918, The Gorgonaceae as a factor in the formation of coral reefs: Carnegie Inst. Washington Pub. 213, Dept. Mar. Biol., v. 9, pp. 343–362.

Chun, C., 1891, Coelenterata: Bronns Klassen und Ordnungen des Tierreichs, v. 2, pt. 2, pp. 49–144.

Clark, W. B., *et al.*, 1904, Miocene: Maryland Geol. Survey.

Cumings, E. R., and Shrock, R. R., Niagaran coral reefs of Indiana and adjacent states and their stratigraphic relations: Geol. Soc. America Bull., v. 39, no. 2, pp. 579–619.

Decker, C. E., 1952, A new hydrozoan from the Devonian of Michigan: Jour. Paleont., v. 26, no. 4, pp. 656–677.

———, 1956, Place of graptolites in Animal Kingdom: Bull. Amer. Assoc. Petroleum Geologists, v. 40, no. 7, pp. 1699–1704.

———, and Gold, I. B., 1957, Bithecae, Gonothecae and Nematothecae on Graptoloidea: Jour. Paleont., v. 31, no. 6, pp. 1145–1158.

Downing, J. A., and Cooke, D. Y., 1955, Distribution of reefs of Woodbend group in Alberta, Canada: Bull. Amer. Assoc. Petroleum Geologists, v. 39, no. 2, pp. 189–206.

Duerden, J. E., 1900, Order of appearance of the mesenteries and septa in the Madreporaria: Johns Hopkins Univ. Circ., v. 19, no. 146, pp. 47–53.

———, 1902a, Relationships of the Rugosa (Tetracoralla) to the living Zoantheae: Johns Hopkins Univ. Circ., v. 21, no. 155, pp. 19–25.

———, 1902b, Report on the actinians of Porto Rico: Bull. U. S. Fish Comm., v. 20, pt. 2, pp. 323–374.

———, 1902c, West Indian Madreporarian corals: Mem. Nat. Acad. Sci., v. 8, Mem. 7, pp. 399–648.

———, 1904, The coral Siderastrea radians and its postlarval development: Carnegie Inst. Washington Pub. 20.

———, 1905, Recent results on the morphology and development of coral polyps: Smithsonian Misc. Coll., v. 47, pp. 93–111.

Duncan, H., 1956, Ordovician and Silurian coral faunas of western United States: U. S. Geol. Survey, Bull. 1021-F.

———, 1957, *Bighornia,* A new Ordovician coral Genus: Jour. Paleont., v. 31, no. 3, pp. 607–615.

Easton, W. H., 1944a, Revision of Campophyllum in North America: Jour. Paleont., v. 18, no. 2, pp. 119–132.

———, 1944b, Corals from the Chouteau and related formations of the Mississippi Valley region: Illinois Geol. Survey, Rept. Inv. 97.

———, 1951, Mississippian cuneate corals: Jour. Paleont., v. 25, no. 3, pp. 380–404.

———, 1957, On the tetracoral *Lithostrotion harmodites* Milne-Edwards and Haime: Jour. Paleont., v. 31, no. 3, pp. 616–622.

———, and Gutschick, R. C., 1953, Corals from the Redwall limestone (Mississippian) of Arizona: Bull. Southern California Acad. Sci., v. 52, pt. 1, pp. 1-27.

Elles, G. L., 1922, The graptolite faunas of the British Isles. A study in evolution: Proc. Geologists' Assoc., v. 33, pp. 168–200.

———, 1940, Graptogonophores: Geol. Mag., v. 77, no. 4, pp. 283–288.

Fenton, C. L., and Fenton, M. A., 1924, The stratigraphy and fauna of the Hackberry stage of the Upper Devonian: Univ. Michigan, Contr. Mus. Geol., v. 1.

———, 1937, Heliophyllum and "Cystiphyllum," corals of Hall's "Illustrations of Devonian corals": Carnegie Mus. Annals, v. 26, pp. 207–250.

Fenton, M. A., 1937, Species of Aulopora from the Traverse and Hamilton groups: Amer. Midland Naturalist, v. 18, no. 1, pp. 115–119.

Fritz, M. A., and Howell, B. F., 1955, An Upper Cambrian coral from Montana: Jour. Paleont., v. 29, no. 1, pp. 181-183.

Galloway, J. J., 1957, Structure and classification of the Stromatoporoidea: Bull. Amer. Paleont., v. 37, no. 164, pp. 345–480.

Grabau, A. W., 1928, Palaeozoic corals of China. Part I. Tetraseptata: Palaeont. Sinica, ser. B., v. 2, fasc. 2.

Grove, B. H., 1935, Studies in Paleozoic corals, III: Amer. Midland Naturalist, v. 16, no. 3, pp. 337–378.

Hall, J., 1879, Natural history of New York: Palaeontology, v. 5, pt. 2, pls.

———, 1883, Van Cleve's fossil corals: Indiana Dept. Geol. Nat. Hist., 12th Ann. Rept., Paleontology, pp. 239–318.

Hargitt, C. W., and Rogers, C. G., 1902, The Alcyonaria of Porto Rico: Bull. U. S. Fish. Comm., v. 20, pp. 267–287.

Hayasaka, I., 1936, On some North American species of Lithostrotionella: Mem. Fac. Sci. Agr., Taihoku Imp. Univ., v. 13, no. 5, pp. 47–73.

Hertwig, O., and Hertwig, R., 1879, Die Actinien: Jenaische Zeitschr. Naturwiss., v. 13, pp. 457–640.

Hickson, S. J., 1934, On Gypsina plana, and on the systematic position of the stromatoporoids: Quart. Jour. Micro. Sci., v. 76, pt. 3, pp. 433–480.

Hill, D., 1935, British terminology for rugose corals: Geol. Mag., v. 72, pp. 481–519.

Hill, D., 1948, The distribution and sequence of Carboniferous coral faunas: Geol. Mag., v. 85, no. 3, pp. 121–148.

———, 1952, The Ordovician corals: Proc. Roy. Soc. Queensland, v. 62, no. 1, pp. 1–27. (Preprinted, 1951.)

———, 1956, Rugosa in Treatise on invertebrate paleontology, pt. F, pp. F233–F324.

Hudson, R. G. S., 1941, On the Carboniferous corals, etc.: Proc. Yorkshire Geol. Soc., v. 24, pp. 290–311.

———, 1956, Tethyan Jurassic hydroids of the Family Milleporidiidae: Jour. Paleont., v. 30, no. 3, pp. 714-730.

Hyman, L. H., 1931, Taxonomic studies on the Hydras of North America, III: Trans. Amer. Micro. Soc., v. 50, no. 1, pp. 20–29.

Jeffords, R. M., 1942, Lophophyllid corals from Lower Pennsylvanian rocks of Kansas and Oklahoma: Kansas Geol. Survey, Bull. 41, pp. 185–260.

Keyes, C. R., 1894a, Paleontology of Missouri, pt. 1: Missouri Geol. Survey, v. 4.

———, 1894b, Paleontology of Missouri, pt. 2: Missouri Geol. Survey, v. 5.

Kiderlen, H., 1937, Die Conularien, Über Bau und Leben der ersten Scyphozoa: Neues Jahrb. fur Mineralogie, Geologie, Palaeontologie, Beil.-Band 77, Abt. B, pp. 113–169.

Knight, J. B., 1937, Conchopeltis Walcott, an Ordovician Genus of the Conulariida: Jour. Paleont., v. 11, no. 3, pp. 186–188.

Kozlowski, R., 1947, Les Affinités des Graptolithes: Cambridge Phil. Soc., Biol. Revs., v. 22, no. 2, pp. 93–108.

Krempf, A., 1919a, Sur un Stade Primitif, Essentiel, non Encore Reconnu dans le Développement des Anthozoaires: Acad. Sci. (Paris) Comptes rendus, v. 169, pp. 39–42.

———, 1919b, Développement des Ebausches Musculaires chez la Larve d'un Anthozoaire (*Pocillopora cespitosa* Dana) au Stade Primitif de la Symétrie Tétraradiaire: Acad. Sci. (Paris) Comptes rendus, v. 169, pp. 929–932.

———, 1920, Sur les Principales Modalités du Développement et des Relations de l'Orthosepte et du Sterigmatosepte dans l'ensemble du Groupe des Anthozoaires: Acad. Sci. (Paris) Comptes rendus, v. 170, pp. 131–138.

Lacaze–Duthiers, H., 1873, Développement des Coralliaires: Arch. Zool. Exp. Gen., v. 2, pp. 269–348.

Lambe, L. M., 1899, A revision of the Genera and species of Canadian Palaeozoic corals: Geol. Survey Canada, Contr. Can. Palaeont., v. 4, pt. 1.

———, 1901, A revision of the Genera and species of Canadian Paleozoic corals: Geol. Survey Canada, Contr. Can. Palaeont., v. 4, pt. 2, pp. 97–197.

Lang, W. D., 1917, Homoeomorphy in fossil corals: Proc. Geologists' Assoc., v. 28, pp. 85–94.

———, 1923, Trends in British Carboniferous corals: Proc. Geologists' Assoc., v. 34, pp. 120–136.

Lecompte, M., 1956, Stromatoporoidea *in* Treatise on invertebrate paleontology, pt. F, pp. F107–F144.

McMurrich, J. P., 1890, The structure of *Cerianthus americanus*: Jour. Morph., v. 4, pp. 131–150.

———, 1891, The phylogeny of the Actinozoa: Jour. Morph., v. 5, pp. 125–164.

Miller, S. A., 1892, Palaeontology: Indiana Dept. Geol. Nat. Res., 17th Ann. Rept., pp. 611–705.

Milne-Edwards, H., 1857, Histoire Naturelle des Coralliaires ou Polypes Proprement Dits: Paris, atlas.

———, and Haime, J., 1851, Monographie des Polypiers Fossiles des Terrains Palaeozoiques: Arch. Mus. Hist. Nat. (Paris), v. 5, pp. 1–502.

Moore, R. C., and Harrington, H. J., 1956, Scyphozoa *and* Conulata *in* Treatise on invertebrate paleontology, pt. F, pp. F27–F38, F54–F66.

———, and Jeffords, R. M., 1941, New Permian corals from Kansas, Oklahoma, and Texas: Kansas Geol. Survey, Bull. 38, pp. 65–120.

———, and Jeffords, R. M., 1944, Description of Lower Pennsylvanian corals from Texas and adjacent states: Univ. Texas Pub. 4401, pp. 77–208.

Moseley, H. N., 1877, On new forms of Actiniaria dredged in the deep sea, etc.: Trans. Linnean Soc. London, Zoology, ser. 2, v. 1, pp. 295–305.

———, 1879, On the Structure of the Stylasteridae, a Family of the hydroid stony corals: Phil. Trans. Roy. Soc. London, v. 169, pt. 2, pp. 425–503.

Nutting, C. C., 1901, The hydroids of the Woods Hole region: Bull. U. S. Fish Comm., v. 19, pp. 325–386.

Ogilvie, M. M., 1896, Microscopic and systematic study of madreporarian types of corals: Phil. Trans. Roy. Soc. London, ser. B, v. 187, pp. 83–345.

Okulitch, V. J., 1936, Some Chazyan corals: Trans. Roy. Soc. Canada, ser. 3, v. 30, sec. IV, pp. 59–74.

———, 1938, Evolutionary trends of some Ordovician corals: Trans. Roy. Soc. Canada, ser. 3, v. 33, sec. IV, pp. 67–80.

Parks, W. A., 1935, Systematic position of the stromatoporoids: Jour. Paleont., v. 9, no. 1, pp. 18–29.

Pax, F., 1940, Anthozoa oder Korallentiere: Bronns Klassen und Ordnungen des Tierreichs, v. 2, pt. 2, book 3, sec. 7, pp. 177–336.

Payne, F., 1924, A study of the fresh-water medusa, *Craspedacusta ryderi*: Jour. Morph., v. 38, no. 3, pp. 387–430.

Raymond, P. E., 1924, The oldest coral reef: Vermont Geol. Survey, 14th Rept. State Geologist (1923–1924), pp. 72–76.

Ripper, E. A., 1937, A note on the occurrence of Amphipora ramosa (Phillips) in western Australia: Jour. Roy. Soc. Western Australia, v. 23, pp. 37–41.

Ruedemann, R., 1947, Graptolites of North America: Geol. Soc. America, Mem. 19.

Schindewolf, O. H., 1941, Zur Kenntnis der Heterophylliden, einer eigentumlichen palaeozoischen Korallengruppe: Palaont. Zeitschr., Band 22, pp. 213–306.

Shrock, R. R., and Twenhofel, W. H., 1939, Silurian fossils from northern Newfoundland: Jour. Paleont., v. 13, no. 3, pp. 241–266.

Sinclair, G. W., 1944, Notes on the Genera *Archaeoconularia* and *Eoconularia*: Trans. Roy. Soc. Canada, ser. 3, v. 38, sec. IV, pp. 87–95.

Sloss, L. L., 1939, Devonian rugose corals from the Traverse beds of Michigan: Jour. Paleont., v. 13, no. 1, pp. 52–73.

Smith, J. P., 1927, Upper Triassic marine invertebrate faunas of North America: U. S. Geol. Survey Prof. Paper 141.

Stainbrook, M. A., 1940, *Prismatophyllum* in the Cedar Valley beds of Iowa: Jour. Paleont., v. 14, no. 3, pp. 270–284.

Stewart, G. A., 1938, Middle Devonian corals of Ohio: Geol. Soc. America Spec. Paper 8.

Stumm, E. C., 1949, Revision of the Families and Genera of the Devonian tetracorals: Geol. Soc. America, Mem. 40.

Swann, D. H., 1947, The *Favosites alpenensis* lineage in the Middle Devonian Traverse group of Michigan: Univ. Michigan Pubs., Contr. Mus. Paleont., v. 6, no. 9, pp. 235–318.

Swinnerton, H. H., 1938, Development and evolution: British Assoc. Adv. Sci., Rept. Ann Meeting (Cambridge), pp. 57–84.

Teichert, C., 1958, Cold- and deep-water coral banks: Bull. Amer. Assoc. Petroleum Geologists, v. 42, no. 5, pp. 1064–1082.

Thomson, J. A., and Henderson, W. D., 1906, An account of the alcyonarians, etc.: Indian Museum, Calcutta.

Twitchell, G. B., 1929, The structure and relationships of the true stromatoporoids: Amer. Midland Naturalist, v. 11, pp. 270–307.

Vaughan, T. W., 1900, The Eocene and Lower Oligocene coral faunas of the United States, etc.: U. S. Geol. Survey, Mon. 39.

————, 1902, The stony corals of the Porto Rican waters: Bull. U. S. Fish. Comm., v. 20, pt. 2, pp. 289–320.

————, 1915, The geologic significance of the growth-rate of the Floridan and Bahaman shoal-water corals: Jour. Washington Acad. Sci., v. 5, no. 17, pp. 591–600.

————, 1919a, Fossil corals from Central America, Cuba, and Porto Rico, with an account of the American Tertiary, Pleistocene, and Recent coral reefs: U. S. Nat. Mus., Bull. 103 (especially pp. 189–226).

————, 1919b, Corals and the formation of coral reefs: Smithsonian Inst., Ann. Rept. for 1917, pp. 189–276.

————, and Wells, J. W., 1943, Revision of the Suborders, Families, and Genera of the Scleractinia: Geol. Soc. America Spec. Paper 44.

Verrill, A. E., 1883, Report on the Anthozoa, etc.: Bull. Mus. Comp. Zool. (Harvard), v. 11, pp. 1–72.

Walcott, C. D., 1898, Fossil Medusae: U. S. Geol. Survey, Mon. 30.

————, 1911, Middle Cambrian holothurians and Medusae: Smithsonian Misc. Coll., v. 57, no. 3, pp. 41–68.

Wells, J. W., 1933, Corals of the Cretaceous of the Atlantic and Gulf Coastal Plains and western interior of the United States: Bull. Amer. Paleont., v. 18, no. 67.

Winton, W. M., 1925, The geology of Denton County: Univ. Texas Bull., 2544.

Chapter 6

WORANDCONODONTS

In old classifications it was customary to relegate all wormlike creatures to a catch-all Phylum, Vermes, in which several important Classes were recognized. If it were not for their zoologic importance, the various kinds of worms could still be relegated to one group insofar as their paleontologic status is concerned, for only one group has left a significant fossil record. Recent zoological works subdivide the erstwhile Vermes into several Phyla, of which the four Phyla outlined hereafter represent important advances in the evolution of bodily form and differentiation of organs.

PHYLUM V. PLATYHELMINTHES

Bodily organization of flatworms is significantly more advanced than that of Coelenterata. Not only is symmetry of flatworms distinctly bilateral, so that the terms left and right are manifestly applicable, but the terms anterior and posterior can be applied to animals for the first time at this rank. Even dorsal and ventral attain their customary meanings for the first time among Platyhelminthes. Moreover, the bodies of flatworms (and of animals in subsequent Phyla) are composed of three cellular layers, of which the **mesoderm** not only replaced the mesogloea of lower animals, but became volumetrically dominant over the ectoderm and endoderm.

Reproduction may be simply sexual or may become very complicated among parasitic worms if life cycles necessitate migration among hosts. Digestion in flatworms is in a much branched but blind set of tubules connected with a ventral mouth; thus, digestive efficiency among flatworms is assured by a still different technique than was utilized by either the sponges or coelenterates. The nervous system is centered in an anterior concentration of nerve cells, the **ganglion** (pl. **ganglia**), from which two nerve cords lead posteriorly. A special excretory system of branching tubes is commonly present.

Flatworms (Fig. 6.1) are best known to mankind because of two formid-

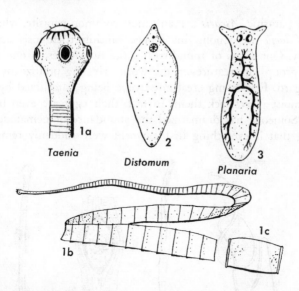

Figure 6.1. Recent Platyhelminthes.
  1. *Taenia* sp., the tapeworm. 1a, head with suckers and hooks, greatly enlarged. 1b, portion of an adult with some of the approximately 850 segments, 2/3X. 1c, a single ripe segment detached from the body, 2/3X. 2. Ventral view of *Distomum hepaticum*, the liver fluke, 2/3X.
3. Dorsal and somewhat transparent view of a free-living flatworm, *Planaria* sp., magnified.
  (Composite figures from various sources.)

able parasites, the liver fluke, *Distomum,* and the tapeworm, *Taenia.* Other flatworms inhabit marine or fresh water (*Planaria*). No direct evidence of fossil platyhelminths is known because the worms have no hard parts and do not affect the hard parts of parasitized hosts. Possibly some vague trails or burrows may have been made by flatworms.

PHYLUM VI. NEMATHELMINTHES

Most members of this Phylum are elongate and are circular in cross section; hence their common name of threadworms or roundworms. Their principal advances over the Platyhelminthes were the development of a digestive system with an anal opening and the development of a body cavity or **coelome** between the viscera and the body wall. This region in platyhelminths is filled with cellular tissue, the parenchyma, but nemathelminths and all higher animals have a coelome. Embryologists have discovered that two entirely different kinds of coelomic cavities are present among different nemathelminths, depending upon how the embryonic walls are infolded.

Of the various sorts of Nemathelminthes (Fig. 6.2), some are fresh water and some are marine like *Sagitta,* the arrowworm; but the better-known examples are parasitic. *Ascaris* is man's most common parasite, whereas *Trichina* and *Filaria* are among his worst, causing trichinosis and filariasis, respectively. One Class of roundworms, the nematodes, is one of the most abundant groups of creatures in the world, rivaling protozoans and insects in this regard. Few living creatures escape being parasitized by nematodes and few moist places lack them. In fact, their eggs are even blown about by wind. Someone has dramatized the abundance of nematode worms by suggesting that if everything in the world were suddenly removed except

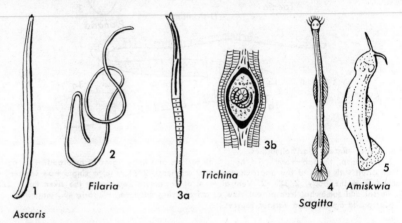

Figure 6.2.   Nemathelminthes.
1. *Ascaris* sp., the roundworm which parasitizes man, about 1/3X, Recent.   2. *Filaria* sp., the cause of filariasis, greatly enlarged, Recent.   3. *Trichina* sp., the cause of trichinosis, Recent. 3a, side view, about 50X.   3b, worm enclosed in calcareous cyst (black) between muscle fibers (cross-hatched), much enlarged.   4. *Sagitta* sp., the free-living marine arrowworm, 3X, Recent. 5. *Amiskwia sagittiformis*, 2X, Cambrian, British Columbia.
(Mostly diagrammatic after various sources.)

the nematodes, the form of almost everything would still be recognizable from the distribution of the nematodes!

Yet none of the nemathelminths occurs in the fossil state, except *Amiskwia*, a supposed arrowworm from the famous Burgess shale (Middle Cambrian) of Canada, which is probably correctly assigned here.

PHYLUM VII. TROCHELMINTHES

Most of the Trochelminthes are very tiny fresh-water worms, but a few are marine and fewer still are parasitic. A typical form is globular or pear-shaped with a stalk either equipped with movable grappling devices or merely cemented to the substratum (Fig. 6.3.1, 2). In many forms the body is encased in a transparent sheath, the **lorica**. When the anterior end of the body extends out of the lorica a ring of cilia beat in rhythmic fashion and simulate the spinning of a wheel—hence the common name rotifer or wheel animal-cule. Rotifers compare in size and appearance with ciliate protozoans such as *Vorticella*—a remarkable case of convergence which caused confusion even to serious students of biology in former years before the cell theory was well understood.

The most important feature of rotifers is the typical **trochophore** larval stage (Fig. 6.3.5) which closely resembles the adult rotifer, *Trochosphaera*. Trochophore larvae are globular and bear a double band of cilia around the equatorial area and a ciliated tuft at the apical plate on the upper end. A simple digestive track is present. Trochophore larval stages are present

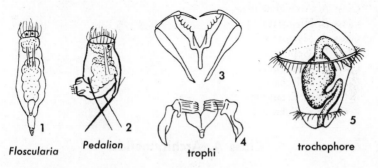

| Floscularia | Pedalion | trophi | trochophore |

Figure 6.3. Recent Trochelminthes and Trochophore Larva.
1. A sedentary rotifer, *Floscularia* sp., enlarged. 2. *Pedalion* sp., a rotifer which leaps on the tips of the long spines, enlarged. 3, 4. Two sets of chewing organs in rotifers, much enlarged. 5. Side view of a trochophore larva of an annelid worm which resembles some mature Trochelminthes.
(1-4 after Hudson, 1884. 5 after Balfour, 1880.)

in most higher invertebrates, and in some protochordates; hence many zoologists believe that advanced forms such as these were derived from crea-tures at the trochelminth level of organization.

No fossils are known, but microscopic chitinous teeth in the **mastax** or gastric mill could be fossilized (Fig. 6.3.3, 4).

PHYLUM VIII. ANNELIDA

The Annelida are so much more advanced than the other Phyla of worms that most biologists rank them above the molluscs and just below the arthropods. They are discussed at this place in this text merely as a matter of convenience.

The Annelida, or annelid worms as they are commonly called, differ from other worms in being divided by transverse walls or diaphragms into segments (**somites** or **metameres**). A blood vascular system is normally present, and the nervous system is definitely ventral. Certain vital organs such as excretory and nervous apparatus are duplicated repeatedly in a row of similar somites. Outwardly projecting lobes (**parapodia**) of the body wall on each segment serve as limbs for locomotion. Parapodia of some annelid worms are equipped with chitinous bristles (**setae**) and many of these same worms bear chitinous jaws and teeth which provide the principal source of all fossilized worm remains. A trochophore larva may be present.

In the following simplified classification many minor zoologic differences have been eliminated.

> Phylum VIII. Annelida
>   Class A. Archiannelida
>   Class B. Hirudinea
>   Class C. Myzostoma
>   Class D. Gephyrea
>   Class E. Oligochaeta
>   Class F. Polychaeta
>   Order 1. Errantida
>   Order 2. Tubicolida

Class A. Archiannelida

This Class is composed of annelids with rudimentary segmentation, a primitive nervous system, and no parapodia. *Polygordius* is a living representative, but no fossil forms are known.

Class B. Hirudinea

These, the leeches, are characterized by *Hirudo* with its sucking discs (Fig. 6.4.1). Each true segment seems to be subdivided externally into additional rings but these are not correlated with internal diaphragms. In addition to the common land leeches, there are many marine leeches. One

---

Figure 6.4 (*opposite*).   Annelida.

1. Schematic ventral view of *Hirudo medicinalis*, the common leech, 2/3X, Recent.   2. Ventral view of *Myzostoma* sp. showing proboscis, branched stomach, five pairs of suckers, and five pairs of parapodia with setae, 4X, Recent.   3. Dorsal view of *Hesperonoë adventor* showing chitinous scales, 2/3X, Recent.   4. Ring of anal spines of a gephyrean worm, *Urechis caupo*, 2/3X, Recent.   5. *Goldfingia hespera*, a gephyrean worm, Recent.   5a, side view, 2/3X.   5b, hook from anterior end, 1000X.   6. *Dendrostomum pyroides*, a gephyrean worm, Recent.   6a, side view, 2/3X.   6b, hook from anterior end, 35X.   7. Borings of *Scolithus linearis* in sandstone, 2/3X, Cambrian, world-wide.   8. Probable myzostome worm infestation in a series of crinoid columnals, 2/3X, Permian, Nevada.   9. *Wiwaxia corrugata*, a scale-bearing annelid, 1X, Cambrian, British Columbia.   10. *Ottoia prolifica*, a gephyrean worm, 1X, Cambrian, British Columbia.   11. *Listriolobus pelodes*, a gephyrean worm with a long proboscis, 1X, Recent.

(1 after various authors. 2 after Fauvel, 1927. 3, 4, 11 after Fisher, 1946. 5, 6 after Fisher, 1952. 9, 10 after Walcott, 1911.)

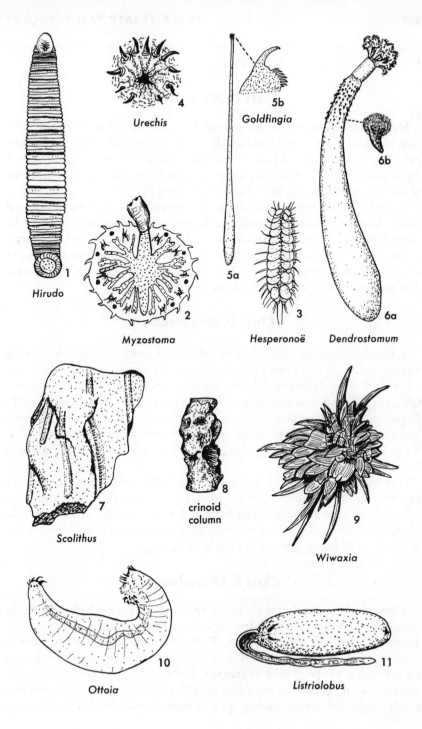

1 Hirudo

2 Myzostoma

4 Urechis

3 Hesperonoë

5a
5b Goldfingia

6b
6a Dendrostomum

7 Scolithus

8 crinoid column

9 Wiwaxia

10 Ottoia

11 Listriolobus

of the latter group, *Lecthaylus,* adopted a colonial habit. It has been reported from mid-Silurian strata near Chicago.

Class C. Myzostoma

Myzostome worms are minute discoidal creatures which parasitize crinoids and starfish. They have sucking discs reminiscent of those in leeches; parenchyma (instead of a coelome) reminiscent of flatworms; and they lack the segmentation of Annelida, although possessing the setae characteristic of some members in this latter Phylum (Fig. 6.4.2).

Myzostomes parasitize crinoids at the articular facets between dermal plates. After they infest the ectoderm between columnals, for instance, the crinoid secretes calcium carbonate to seal off the parasite and ultimately causes fusion of the column. Evidence of myzostome parasitism (Fig. 6.4.8) can be seen on Carboniferous and Jurassic crinoids as well as on Recent ones. The worms themselves have not been fossilized.

Class D. Gephyrea

A loosely construed assemblage of cylindrical, marine, mostly burrowing worms makes up this Class (Fig. 6.4.3-7, 9-11). Some have a few setae and others lack them. Segmentation has not been observed in adults, but various features of the soft anatomy seem to many zoologists to warrant referring the Gephyrea to the Annelida. Other specialists want to raise some or all members to the rank of Phylum. Some gephyreans such as *Dendrostomum* (Fig. 6.4.6) have an oral ring of tentacles, and others such as *Urechis* (Fig. 6.4.4) have a proboscis.

Direct fossil evidence of Gephyrea is lacking unless some carbonized impressions of wormlike creatures from the Burgess shale (Middle Cambrian) have been referred here properly. Various borings in sand may be made by these worms, as, for instance, *Scolithus* borings from Lower Cambrian strata of many parts of the world (Fig. 6.4.7).

Class E. Oligochaeta

Those elongate annelids with sparse setae and no parapodia belong to the Oligochaeta. Although many fresh-water forms are known, the classic example is *Lumbricus,* the earthworm. Terrestrial annelids commonly occur in great numbers in the soil, which they industriously ingest and then deposit on the surface of the ground as **castings** after they have removed the organic matter from it. Thus, they constitute an active geologic agent insofar as they modify sediments chemically. In spite of their abundance they have left no fossil remains or burrows capable of being identified other than in the most general terms.

Class F. Polychaeta

Members of this largely marine group of annelids have abundant setae. Polychaete worms generally fall into two groups according to their habits —the wanderers and the sedentary forms.

Order 1. Errantida

Most of these polychaete worms crawl about or are excellent swimmers; hence the name of the Order. Segmentation is obvious and is enhanced by the presence of paired, uniramous, or biramous parapodia on each somite. Each parapodium has one or more kinds of setae in tufts (Fig. 6.5, 1a, 2). The

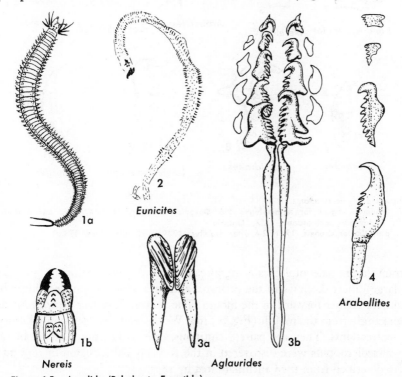

Figure 6.5. Annelida (Polychaeta Errantida).
1. *Nereis* sp., a common marine annelid, Recent. 1a, dorsal view, 2/3X. 1b, head region with large protruding teeth and tiny surficial denticles, 3X. 2. Impression of *Eunicites* sp. with lateral setae and teeth, 2/3X, Jurassic (Solenhofen), Germany. 3. *Aglaurides* sp., which preys upon coral reefs, Recent. 3a, ventral mandibles, 30X. 3b, maxillary teeth and long carriers, 30X. 4. Four maxillary teeth of *Arabellites alfredensis* with a short carrier at the base of the series as in 3b, 8X, Devonian, New York.
(1 after Ehlers, 1864-1868. 2 after Ehlers, 1868. 3 after Hartman, 1954. 4 after Eller, 1934.)

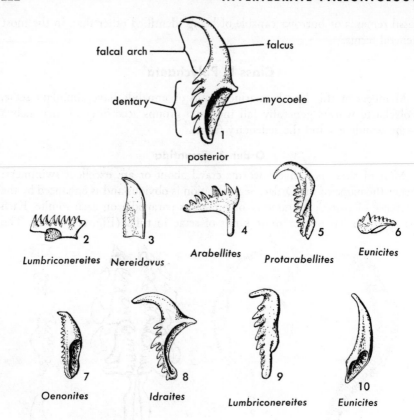

Figure 6.6. Scolecodonts.
1. Schematic figure for terminology. 2-6. Devonian scolecodonts, 30X, Ohio and Ontario.
7-10. Ordovician scolecodonts, 15X, Ontario.
(1 partly after Croneis, 1941. 2-6 after Stauffer, 1939. 7-10 after Eller, 1943.)

Errantida are paleontologically significant, however, because of the presence
of large pincerlike jaws in the pharynx and of a series of smaller chitinous
denticles farther forward in the mouth. The pincers, however, may protrude
menacingly from the mouth (Fig. 6.5.1b). Worm teeth are commonly known
as **scolecodonts.** They are paired, chitinous, dull to lustrous, and jet black.
Fossil scolecodonts were discovered in the Russian Baltic region in 1856 and
were described from the Cincinnati area by 1877.

The principal tooth unit in a typical Recent association of scolecodonts
is a pincer (Fig. 6.6.1). It is attached by a hollow base from which a pointed
prong (**falcus**) curves forward. Where the flat inner face of the base presses
against the companion element of a pair, a number of cusps form the **dentary.**
Muscles which move scolecodonts are attached to depressed areas on the

sides called **myocoeles.** Most of the small scolecodonts lack the falcus and consist of the dentary alone (Fig. 6.6.2, 4, 6, 7), and some elements are merely simple thornlike spines. The distribution of all of these maxillae is shown by comparative illustrations of Recent *Arabella* and fossil *Arabellites* (Fig. 6.5.3b, 4).

Names of scolecodonts have mostly been coined according to a time-honored paleontologic formula, one which was first applied to scoleco-donts by Ehlers in 1869. The suffix *-ites* (from the Greek *lithos,* stone) is added to the root of the generic name of a Recent annelid in order to coin the name of a fossil scolecodont which resembles the Recent form. Thus we find *Arabellites* was named for *Arabella* (Recent) as noted above, and *Eunicites* was named for the Recent *Eunicea.*[1]

Genera and species are recognized by variations in shape, size, number of teeth in the dentary, and curvature of the falcus. Unfortunately, jaws of Recent annelid worms are known to be highly variable; hence, too many species presumably have been erected for fossil forms. Moreover, another peculiarly paleontologic problem is exemplified by the scolecodonts; namely, that several diverse skeletal elements are present in the same individual but become so scattered after death that it is impossible to decide which ones belong together. Accordingly, so-called paleontologic "species" of scolecodonts admittedly are highly artificial instead of being genetic. Each maxilla of a worm would normally be placed in a different species by a paleontologist, and different major kinds of maxillae may be classified as different Genera, yet it is obvious that the specimens might have come from the pharynx of one and the same individual worm. These kinds of artificial Genera and species are functionally necessary, even though they violate the rules established for Linnaean nomenclature. Nor is it a problem peculiar to scolecodonts, for students of such diverse creatures as trilobites and dinosaurs are vexed by the same difficulty. It is only very rarely that specimens of worms are found such as one from the Solenhofen lithographic limestone (Jurassic), which retain the scolecodonts in natural position on the bodily outline (Fig. 6.5.2). A few articulated scolecodonts also have been found without the outline of the worm body being preserved.

Living annelid worms with jaws inhabit very shallow water near shore, on either sandy, muddy, or rocky bottoms. A few secrete tubes and some burrow into sediment, shells, or rock. A similar ecologic distribution is indi-cated for fossil scolecodonts, for many of these much-abraded and broken fossil teeth occur in well-sorted sandstone, indicating extensive reworking. They may be abundant in particular zones or on bedding planes where they

---

[1] In this same fashion, *-ites* has been used to denote many other fossil Genera, some of which are of dubious complimentary value, as in the case of *Maclurites,* which is a gastropod named for Maclure (therefore, "Maclure's stone").

have been concentrated by currents as natural placer deposits of fossil debris. Inasmuch as scolecodonts consist of chitin, they can be recovered as insoluble residues from limestone after acidation with dilute hydrochloric acid, or even from quartzose sandstones after treatment with hydrofluoric acid. Specimens are picked and mounted on slides under a binocular microscope in the same fashion as foraminifers are. Scolecodonts range in age from Cambrian to Recent, but most faunas have been described from strata ranging in age from Ordovician to Devonian.

Order 2. Tubicolida

To this Order belong the sedentary marine annelids which encase themselves in a membranous, calcareous, or agglutinated tube of foreign particles. A species can be very adaptable and build tubes out of mineral grains in one place and diatom tests at another place, thus presenting very different appearances (Fig. 6.7.5).

Serpula is probably the best known of the tubiculous annelids. Members of this "form Genus" build rather smooth calcareous tubes which tend to grow in closely appressed clusters and even to form colonies of considerable size (Fig. 6.7.4). Tubes of this kind may occur as far back as mid-Paleozoic. By the Jurassic the serpuloid worms were minor reef-makers, and they created notable biostromes in the Cretaceous of Germany (for example, the Serpulitenkalk). Large masses of so-called *Serpula* colonies in the Miocene and Pleistocene of the Pacific Coast are really referable to the serpulid Genus *Dodecaceria* (Fig. 6.7.7). Perhaps the best-known serpulid growth in Recent seas is the so-called *Serpula* atolls of Bermuda.

One of the most common and widespread Genera of serpulid worms is *Spirorbis* (Fig. 6.7.1, 2). It forms coiled tubes 1 to 3 millimeters in diameter which resemble tiny gastropods cemented to some suitable substratum by their apices. *Spirorbis* incrusts rocks, shells, seaweed, and any relatively solid object in the oceans. From the apertures of living examples a tentacle-bearing body can be extended. When the animal retracts into the tube, it can close the aperture with an operculum or lid; moreover, because the same operculum is hollow it may also serve as a brood chamber in which young are sheltered. Zoologists sometimes define Subgenera of *Spirorbis* upon the number of thoracic segments which are present, the nature of the operculum, the location of the brood region, and the direction of coiling. It is a peculiarity of living species of *Spirorbis* that the Antarctic forms are coiled counterclockwise, the Arctic forms are coiled clockwise, and the geographically intermediate forms display one or the other method of coiling. *Spirorbis* occurs in rocks as old as Ordovician. Fossil forms are differentiated according to size and ornamentation, but these criteria are generally inadequate for recognition of living species; therefore it is probable that Genera and species of fossil *Spirorbis* are really form Genera and highly artificial species.

Trumpet-shaped tubes with ornamentation which have been reported from Paleozoic strata are generally referred to *Cornulites,* whereas rather highly ornamented tubes from Cretaceous to Recent strata seem to be referable to *Hamulus* (Fig. 6.7. 8, 9). A similar Recent form with a straight but relatively unornamented tube is *Pomatoceras* (Fig. 6.7.3).

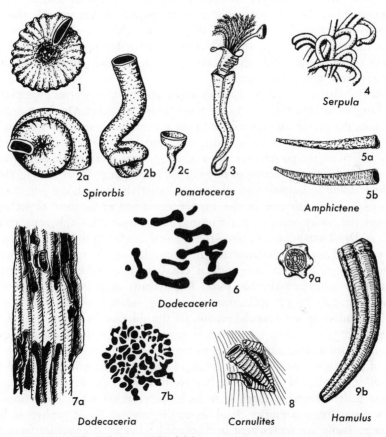

Figure 6.7. Annelida (Polychaeta Tubicolida).
1. *Spirorbis* sp., 10X, Mississippian, Indiana. 2. *Spirorbis spirillum,* about 10X, Recent. 2a, closely coiled tube. 2b, elongate tube. 2c, operculum. 3. Schematic view of *Pomatoceras* sp. showing tube, tentacles, and tack-shaped operculum, slightly enlarged. 4. *Serpula pervermiformis,* 1X, Cretaceous, Tennessee. 5. *Amphictene auricoma,* 2/X, Recent. 5a, tube composed of sand grains. 5b, tube composed of fragmentary sponge spicules. 6. Dumbbell-shaped perforations of *Dodecaceria* sp. in the surface of a scallop shell, 4X, Recent. 7. *Dodecaceria fistulicola,* 1X, Recent. 7a, longitudinal view of a broken colony. 7b, transverse section of part of a colony showing cross sections of tubes in solid black. 8. Three tubes of *Cornulites flexuosus* attached to a brachiopod shell, 1 1/2X, Ordovician, Indiana. 9. *Hamulus onyx,* 3X, Cretaceous, Tennessee. 9a, aperture with operculum in place. 9b, side view of tube.
(2, 3 after McIntosh, 1923. 4 after Wade, 1926. 5 after McIntosh, 1894.)

Some difference of opinion exists about the proper taxonomic assignment of serpuloid tubes such as *Tubelelloides* (commonly called *Serpulites*) from Lower Paleozoic rocks. Some authorities wish to link these smooth, conical, slightly contorted tubes with the annelid worms, but other specialists wish to ally them with the conularioids under the Scyphozoa (Chapter 4).

GEOLOGIC WORK OF WORMS. Worms of several Phyla are so common locally on sea floors that their combined volume exceeds that of all other material present. Most of these worms either live attached to the substratum, or they occupy themselves by plowing through the thin surficial veneer of sediments while they scavenge upon the rich supply of organic debris. A few worms swim about.

The Polychaeta seem to be the most important group of worms geologically speaking, or at least their works are most readily apparent. On the constructive side, the polychaetes contribute to the accumulating sediments by building their external tubes, as has been described heretofore. In contrast with these activities, the polychaetes also engage in some more subtle but equally important destructive activities of geologic importance. Chief among these is their ability to burrow into all sorts of materials; indeed, the polychaetes probably are as effective in the marine environment as their oligochaete cousins, the earthworms, are in the terrestrial environment. Gephyrean worms such as *Dendrostomum* and *Urechis* are fine examples of these burrowers, or lobworms. They are characterized in particular by their ability to pump water through a special longitudinal canal in their bodies and to eject it posteriorly with considerable force. Gephyreans construct U-shaped burrows (Fig. 6.8) in soft sediments which they excavate with a proboscis or with thornlike spines near the mouth, on the sides, or in a ring around the anus. Once a burrow is completed, it may be lined with mucus and then inhabited for a long time by one worm. Sand and fecal pellets are swept out of the burrow by the strong stream of water and accumulate around the posterior opening of the burrow like ejecta around the vent of a volcano. These little submarine cones seem to be in eruption when the stream of dirty water forms a murky cloud above the burrow. Fossil gephyrean burrows probably are represented by U-shaped tubes of *Arenicolites* from the Paleozoic. Straight, vertical, sand-filled tubes of *Scolithus* have world-wide distribution in rocks of Early Cambrian age. *Scolithus* tubes may have been formed by some other kind of burrower than a worm because no trace of actual bodily substance has ever been found in these burrows. In fact, no setae of gephyreans have been reported fossil, although one would suppose they should be encountered inasmuch as scolecodonts are fossilized.

A second destructive activity of worms causes the disintegration of shells and other calcareous material. Numerous polychaetes burrow within and through the hard shell of molluscs and the calcareous skeletons of corals, for instance. If burrows reach the inside of the shell and begin to irritate the flesh of a clam, the infested animal covers the inner openings of the burrows with extra layers of calcareous material which usually present a warty appearance. After the death of a mollusc, however, the burrowing continues unchecked until the shell is riddled with galleries. In addition to burrowing in skeletal substances, worms also attack wood; lithified, fine-grained, clastic rocks; and limestone. Openings of worm burrows commonly have a dumbbell-shaped outline at the surface of a shell (Fig. 6.7.6). On the other hand, openings of galleries made by boring sponges with which they might be

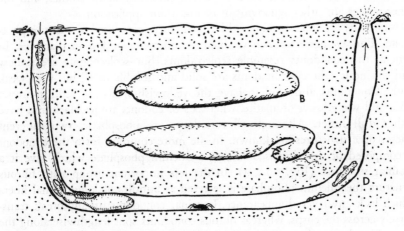

Figure 6.8. Burrow of Gephyrean Worm.
The U-shaped tube, about 2 feet between openings, is dug by *Urechis caupo*, lying at the lower left bend (A). The worm sets up currents of water shown by arrows. The two inserts indicate an individual resting (B) and digging with the anal setae (C). Food is ensnared in a tube of mucus which lines the left shaft of the burrow. Burrows of this species customarily are inhabited by one or two small fish (D), a crab (E), and the scale-bearing annelid worm *Hesperonoë* (F). The whole association is an excellent example of commensalism.
(After Fisher, 1946.)

confused are tiny circular holes. Incidentally, both kinds of organisms are apt to occur together, as on many oyster shells.

Many chaetopod worms are parasitic, although their works may not be apparent in fossils. Starfish and ophiuroids, for instance, usually are infested with chaetopods as internal parasites. External parasitism of discs and arms of crinoids may be evident in some dislocation of skeletal plates of the host.

Appendix to the Worms—Phylum Chordata: Group Conodontophoridia

Conodonts are probably the most perplexing fossils with which paleontologists have dealt. At this time, 100 years after their discovery, the most qualified specialists have not agreed as to what function these fossils served in life or even as to whether they belonged to invertebrates or vertebrates. Nevertheless, conodonts have become important economically and rank with ostracodes as the most valuable Early and mid-Paleozoic microscopic guide fossils. Their importance in Late Paleozoic strata is superseded by fusulinids, but both groups are valuable because they typify generally different biofacies. Conodonts seem to be characteristic of shallow marine waters and to be particularly abundant in argillaceous sediments.

The 1500 species of conodonts have been grouped into 132 Genera, of which about 80 names are used at present in stratigraphic studies, and the other names are either synonyms or of uncertain application.

Conodonts are microscopic toothlike structures composed of calcium phosphate. The average specimen is about 1 millimeter or less in diameter. In general the conodonts resemble scolecodonts, but scolecodonts are hollow and chitinous, whereas conodonts are solid and soluble in all but very weak acids. Conodonts also tend to have the yellowish-brown or reddish-brown color and waxy luster of apatite, whereas scolecodonts are jet black and have rather dull luster. Although all conodonts are phosphatic, two different microscopic structures are known. In the more common form the conodont is composed of superimposed layers of calcium phosphate which give it a **laminar** structure (Fig. 6.9.3, 4). In the less important group with **fibrous** structure the calcium phosphate is secreted as bundles of longitudinal fibers which lack any layered appearance. Laminar conodonts usually break transversely across the cusps, whereas fibrous conodonts split lengthwise along the cusps. Simple conodonts such as *Distacodus* are cones (Fig. 6.10.1, 2). Among the more complicated elongate shapes, *Prioniodus* exemplifies one group which has a large cusp at one end of a single row of smaller cusps (Fig. 6.10.3, 4). *Prioniodina* typifies another elongate type in which small cusps are located both in front of and behind a large central or subcentral cusp (Fig. 6.10.5-10). Both the prioniodid and the prioniodinid shapes are constructed upon bases formed as rodlike **bars** or as platelike **blades**. Bars and blades intergrade. Conodonts with lateral rows of cusps alongside the median

Figure 6.9 (*opposite*). Morphology of Conodonts.

1a, 1b. Lateral and oral views of a platform type of conodont, with terminology, much enlarged. 2. Lateral view of a prioniodid conodont, with terminology, much enlarged. 3. Longitudinal thin section of a distacodid conodont, *Oistodus* sp., showing distinct pulp cavity (black) near base, and uniaxial lamellar structure in the upper half, 70X. 4. Longitudinal thin section of the blade of a platform conodont, *Gnathodus* sp., showing distinct polyaxial lamellar structure characteristic of most conodonts, 100X. 5. Conodont assemblage consisting of eight *Hindeodella*, 35X, Pennsylvanian, Illinois. 6. Conodont assemblage consisting of four *Hindeodella* and one *Prioniodus* to the right, surmounted by a *Prioniodella*, 35X, Pennsylvanian, Illinois. 7. Conodont assemblage consisting of five *Hindeodella* and one *Prioniodus* to the right, 35X, Pennsylvanian, Illinois. 8. One band of radular teeth of a gastropod, much enlarged, Recent.

(1, 2 after Rhodes and Dineley, 1957. 3, 4 after Hass, 1941. 5-7 after Scott, 1934. 8 after Woodward, 1880.)

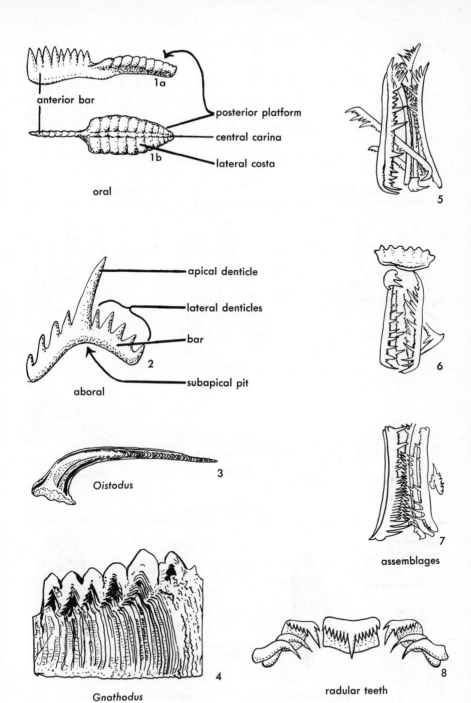

1a

anterior bar

posterior platform

central carina

lateral costa

1b

oral

apical denticle

lateral denticles

bar

subapical pit

2

aboral

Oistodus

3

Gnathodus

4

5

6

7

assemblages

8

radular teeth

1a

1b

1c

2a 2b

Oistodus

Distacodus

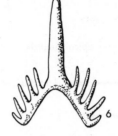

3

Prioniodus

4

Ligonodina

DISTACODID

PRIONIODID

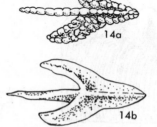

5

Bryantodus

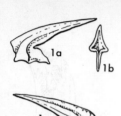

6

Hibbardella

7

Lonchodina

8

Prioniodina

9

Hindeodella

10

Palmatodella

PRIONIODINID

11a 11b

Panderodella

13

Polylophodonta

14a

14b

Ancyrodella

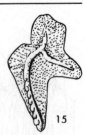

15

Palmatolepis

12a 12b

Polygnathus

POLYGNATHID

row constitute the **platform** type, such as *Polygnathus;* it resembles a shoe sole with a pavement of nodular cusps for cleats (Fig. 6.10.11-15).

Terminology for orientation of conodonts is based upon the assumption that they are teeth; therefore the cuspate surface is said to be oral; as opposed to the basal or aboral side. Cusps generally curve or slant posteriorly, and the wide parts of platform types are said to be anterior. Conodonts can be matched in bilateral pairs, left and right.

The evolution of conodonts principally involves variation in the number of cusps and increase in the strength of the main framework. Individual cusps may increase or decrease in prominence, and they may coalesce into transverse ridges. Even though the number and prominence of cusps may diminish, the total cuspate area consistently increases.

In presenting the evolutionary patterns of conodonts graphically (Fig. 6.11) it is assumed that the fibrous and laminar groups evolved from the same ancestral form. Actually, both groups appeared at the same time in the Early Ordovician. Cones were the first shapes in both groups, and these were soon followed by bars and blades, after which the platform types appeared. Fibrous and laminar groups evolved at different rates, however, for the fibrous group gave rise to its platform stage and became extinct before the laminar group produced any platforms. Nevertheless, the over-all pattern of conodont evolution is one of parallel descent, in which natural selection favored the multicuspate forms and particularly those with the most solid construction. Much more is known about the laminar forms than about the fibrous forms, which may explain why it is possible to show additional detail in the evolutionary pattern of the former group. The platform or polygnathid group of laminar conodonts seems to have arisen from two sources within the prioniodinid strain—the bars and the blades (Fig. 6.12). In both cases subsidiary flanges appeared along the sides of the main skeletal frame and became cuspate. While the flanges were increasing in width, the cusps along the main frame decreased in height and number. Eventually, the flanges became the dominant part of each unit and the shape is distinctly of the platform type. In some forms at a very advanced stage, the cusps on the flanges were replaced with low transverse ridges, or the cusps gave way to concentric ridges in the fashion that *Polygnathus* (Fig. 6.10.12) gave rise to *Polylophodonta* (Fig. 6.10.13). It is strange how the evolution of polygnathid conodont teeth resembles the change in surface of teeth from mastodon to elephant.

The actual rise of platform shapes from prioniodinids is shown in Figure

---

Figure 6.10 (opposite). Conodonts.
The four main shapes of conodonts are represented by typical Genera. Ranges cover most of the Paleozoic. Most figures are about 10X.
(1-12, 14, 15 after Ulrich and Bassler, 1926. 13 after Branson and Mehl, 1933.)

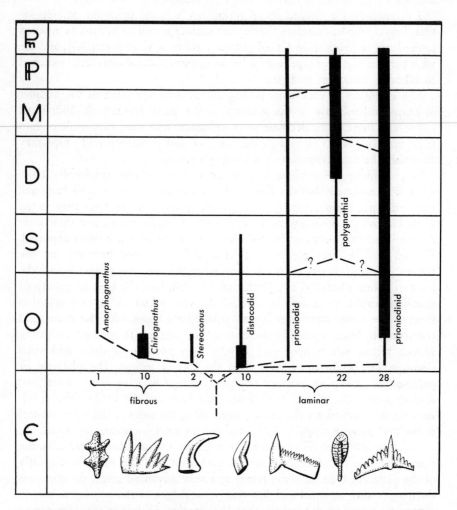

Figure 6.11. Evolution and Geologic Ranges of Conodonts.
Parallel descent of fibrous and laminar conodonts is illustrated. Probable evolution of fibrous conodonts is illustrated by three Genera. Probable evolution of laminar conodonts is illustrated by four main shapes, which correspond roughly to Families. The polygnathid or platform type arose by iterative evolution from bars and blades in the prioniodinid line.
(Based on data from Ellison, 1940.)

6.12. *Spathognathodus* (Fig. 6.12.1) is a blade-shaped prioniodinid with a slightly expanded base. It seems to have given rise to *Gnathodus* (Fig. 6.12.2) through a series of intermediate types which bridge the gap between prioniodinid and platform groups. The rise of platform shape from a bar is even more extreme, for *Prioniodina* (Fig. 6.12.3) has no basal expansion. Species of *Prioniodina* usually have several denticles in the posterior limb, but the illustrated form has lost all but three. Loss of the remaining three posterior denticles and creation of two lateral flanges gave rise to *Gondolella*. Transitional stages (Fig. 6.12.4) do not have denticles on the flanges, but advanced stages (Fig. 6.12.5) are typical platform types with cusps or ridges. Inas-

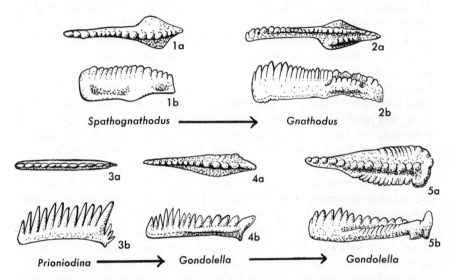

Figure 6.12. Parallel Evolution of Platform Conodonts.

1a, 1b. Oral and lateral views of *Spathognathodus commutatus*, 35X, Mississippian, Oklahoma. 2a, 2b. Oral and lateral views of *Gnathodus roundyi*, 20X, Pennsylvanian, Missouri, Kansas, Texas. 3a, 3b. Oral and lateral views of *Prioniodina camerata*, 35X, Pennsylvanian, midcontinent. 4a, 4b. Oral and lateral views of *Gondolella symmetrica*, 30X, Pennsylvanian, midcontinent. 5a, 5b. Oral and lateral views of *Gondolella neolobata*, 30X, Pennsylvanian, midcontinent.

(1 after Branson and Mehl, 1941. 2, 3b, 4, 5 after Ellison, 1941.)

much as the prioniodinids gave rise to platform types through two independent strains, they exemplify compound iterative evolution (page 41).

Classifications of conodonts are based upon their microscopic structure and their complexity and symmetry of cusp development. Some specialists characterize the laminar conodonts further by the presence of a pit on the aboral side, but no pit is present on the fibrous conodonts. Platform types in particular can be differentiated according to whether the scar of attachment is large or small.

TAXONOMIC PROBLEMS. Conodonts usually occur singly or as ill-sorted heaps in the center of a discolored area such as might represent a coprolitic mass. There is no indication of what they came from or with what they may have been associated in life. As long as one conodont was assumed to be characteristic of one species of animal, there were no problems with names. Paleontologists gradually began to realize, however, that several kinds of conodonts might have been incorporated within one animal, just as one shark can have several different kinds of teeth. It was observed from time to time that several species of conodonts occurred close to each other on a bedding plane as though they might represent a natural but somewhat disassociated death assemblage. In fact, some conodonts in assemblages (Fig. 6.9.5-7) seem to be distributed in symmetrical fashion such that they seem not to have been disturbed much after the death of the animal that bore them. For instance, single patches of *Polygnathus, Bryantodus,* and *Hindeodella* are known to be associated in the ratio of 1:1:4 in one Pennsylvanian formation. Moreover, when many single specimens representing the same three Genera are counted in the same formation, the same ratio is preserved. It is very probable, therefore, that these three types of conodonts were present in one living animal. Recognition of conodont assemblages made it obvious that different so-called species, Genera, and even Families were supposed to be present in the same living animal. Inasmuch as the rule of priority in nomenclature requires that a species have only one name, it follows that numerous synonyms should be dropped among names of conodonts if the rule is to be applied. Incidentally, the same problem arises with regard to names of scolecodonts. In both cases it is extremely desirable that some name be available for those isolated conodonts or solecodonts which have never been relegated to an assemblage. Two solutions to the nomenclatorial problem have been proposed. One group of specialists wishes to continue to name conodonts as before and to ignore the taxonomic problem raised by the rather rare assemblages. Another group of specialists proposes that insoluble problems of this sort be removed from the rules of Linnaean nomenclature. Two names would still be used, but the names would be referred to some artificial system of classification.

ZOOLOGIC AFFINITIES. The discoverer of conodonts thought that they were teeth of fish, but no other remains of fish have been found in rocks as old as those which contain conodonts; therefore paleontologists have been prone to speculate upon what other groups the fossils might represent. In the ensuing 100 years, conodonts have been referred to polychaete and gephyrean worms, to cyclostome and myxine fishes, to selachians and elasmobranchs, to gastropods and cephalopods, and to arachnids and crustaceans. Three of these theories contain much of the evidence which bears upon all of the other theories.

In general appearance conodonts resemble jaws (scolecodonts) of annelid worms and toothlike parts of the mastax of trochelminthid worms, but differ chemically; conodonts are phosphatic but worm jaws are chitinous. Oriented associations of conodonts indicate that they are paired organs arranged in linear series and consisting of different shapes. This arrangement simulates the distribution of maxillae in many polychaete worms and seems at first glance to support the interpretation of conodonts as chewing devices. Moreover, it is possible that traces of carbonaceous films near conodonts may represent the carbonized flesh of a soft-bodied creature with parapodia. On the other hand, it is hard to see how delicately constructed objects such as conodonts could be used as chewing devices without suffering serious breakage and abrasion of cusps. Some abraded specimens, particularly platform types, have been reported, but most specimens seem to have been relatively intact when buried.

So-called teeth on the rasps (radulae) of various molluscs such as gastropods are similar to conodonts (Fig. 6.9.8), but radular teeth are always chitinous instead of phosphatic.

The preponderance of evidence is accumulating in favor of the theory that the conodonts are referable to the vertebrates. Phosphatic composition itself is suggestive of vertebrate origin because of its common occurrence in vertebrate skeletons; it is not confined to that Phylum, however. More convincing evidence comes from the common association of conodonts with phosphatic jaw material and even bony substance adhering to the teeth.

The toothlike appearance has suggested that these objects may be teeth of fish or of some more primitive vertebrate. It has also been suggested that they may have been dermal denticles or even gill rakers of some chordate. In any of these cases the evidence of wear and breakage should be widespread. The fact is, however, that conodonts are singularly free from imperfections until they are exposed as fossils in their sedimentary matrix. Moreover, cases are known in which a cusp was broken off in life and then the fracture was healed over with more calcium phosphate without loss of the broken tip. It therefore appears to be very likely that conodonts were completely buried in the flesh of the creature that bore them. This contention is supported further by the presence of concentric layers in the group with laminar structure, which must have been secreted by successive additions from surrounding tissue. Possibly conodonts served as spicular skeletons.

If none of the foregoing explanations is adequate, then conodonts may represent an extinct group of creatures which had no close relatives, living or fossil. Unfortunately, this kind of an explanation is beyond proof. Instead, it seems probable that conodonts were internal spicular skeletons of a wormlike chordate and served a function as yet unknown. Inasmuch as conodonts cannot be referred to any one taxonomic section of the known Chordata, they are treated herein as a Group of unknown rank.

GEOLOGIC OCCURRENCE. Conodonts appeared suddenly and in

great numbers in the Early Ordovician, at which time the simple cones were the dominant shape. Bars and blades became the most common shapes from Medial Ordovician through the Silurian, but platforms are the most valuable conodonts from the Devonian into the Permian. When conodonts were first reported from post-Paleozoic rocks they were suspected of being reworked Paleozoic specimens, but the continued discovery of conodonts in Triassic rocks of many regions supports their actual Triassic range. Fibrous conodonts are restricted to the Ordovician, but laminar conodonts range from Ordovician to Permian.

Specimens occur most abundantly in argillaceous sediments such as clay shales and black fissile shales, but they may also be abundant in limestone and sandstone. The solvent power of ground water is sufficient to dissolve carbonates and to cause the disassociation of argillaceous rocks, yet not to corrode conodonts. As a result of the relatively low solubility of calcium phosphate, conodonts may accumulate as a lag deposit in soil and then be transported to another site of deposition. This process is generally referred to in paleontology as **reworking,** no matter what size of fossil is affected. If reworked specimens are added to new faunas characteristic of a higher stratigraphic unit, the resulting compound fauna is called a **stratigraphic admixture.** In other cases the reworked specimens sift into solution channels or into cracks in older sediments and give the appearance of occurring too low in the standard faunal zonation. At Chicago, for instance, Late Devonian conodonts occur in narrow solution cracks in Silurian dolomite. This is a **stratigraphic leak.** Use of conodonts in zonation requires unusual perspicacity on the part of a paleontologist lest he be deceived by reworking or delude himself into explaining truly unusual populations as being due to leaks or admixtures.

QUESTIONS

1. What are some constructive and some destructive functions of worms?
2. Why are polychaetes more important than other worms are in geology?
3. What philosophy of classification (Chapter 1) is reflected in the subdivision of the Polychaeta?
4. How can scolecodonts and conodonts be differentiated?
5. What problems affect the proper taxonomic assignment of the conodonts?
6. What qualities of conodonts limit their usefulness in correlations?

BIBLIOGRAPHY

Balfour, F. M., 1880, Larval forms: their nature, origin, and affinities: Quart. Jour. Micro. Sci., n. ser., v. 20, pp. 381–407.

Branson, E. B., and Mehl, M. G., 1933, Conodonts from the Grassy Creek shale óf Missouri: Univ. Missouri Studies, v. 8, no. 3, pp. 171–259.

——, and Mehl, M. G., 1940, The recognition and interpretation of mixed conodont faunas: Bull. Denison Univ., v. 35, pp. 195–209.

——, and Mehl, M. G., 1941, New and little known Carboniferous conodont Genera: Jour. Paleont., v. 15, no. 2, pp. 97–106.

Caullery, M., and Mesnil, F., 1897, Études sur la Morphologie Comparée et la Phylogénie des Espèces chez les Spirorbes: Bull. Sci. France Belgique (Bull. Biol. Sci.) v. 30, pp. 185–233.

Croneis, C., 1941, Micropaleontology—past and future: Bull. Amer. Assoc. Petroleum Geologists, v. 25, no. 7, pp. 1208–1255.

Dubois, E. P., 1943, Evidence on the nature of conodonts: Jour. Paleont., v. 17, no. 2, pp. 155–159.

Ehlers, E., 1864–1868, Die Borstenwürmer (Annelida Chaetopoda) nach systematischen und anatomischen Untersuchungen. Leipzig.

——, 1868, Ueber eine fossile Eunicee aus Solenhofen (*Eunicites avitus*), nebst Bemerkungen über fossile Würmer überhaupt: Zeitschr. Wiss Zool., v. 18, pt. 3, pp. 421–443.

Eller, E. R., 1934, Annelid jaws from the Upper Devonian of New York: Carnegie Mus. (Pittsburgh), Annals, v. 22, pp. 303–316.

——, 1943, Scolecodonts from the Erindale, Upper Ordovician, at Streetsville, Ontario: Carnegie Mus. (Pittsburgh), Annals, v. 29, pp. 241–262.

Ellison, S. P., 1941, Revision of the Pennsylvanian conodonts: Jour. Paleont., v. 15, no. 2, pp. 107–143.

——, 1946, Conodonts as Paleozoic guide fossils: Bull. Amer. Assoc. Petroleum Geologists, v. 30, no. 1, pp. 93–110.

Etheridge, R., 1880, A contribution to the study of the British Carboniferous tubicolar Annelida: Geol. Mag., dec. 2, v. 7, pp. 258–266, etc.

Fauvel, P. 1927, Polychètes Sédentaires: Faune de France, Off. Cent. Faunistique, no. 16.

Fisher, W. K., 1946, Echiuroid worms of the North Pacific Ocean: Proc. U. S. Nat. Mus., v. 96, pp. 215–292.

——, 1952, The sipunculid worms of California and Baja California: Proc. U. S. Nat. Mus., v. 102, pp. 371–450.

Hartman, O., 1954, Marine annelids from the northern Marshall Islands: U. S. Geol. Survey Prof. Paper 260-Q, pp. 619–644.

Hass, W. H., 1941, Morphology of conodonts: Jour. Paleont., v. 15, no. 1, pp. 71–81.

Hudson, C. T., 1884, An attempt to reclassify the rotifers: Quart. Jour. Micro. Sci., n. ser., v. 24, pp. 335–356.

Ireland, H. A., 1958, Microfauna of Wenlockian and Ludlovian Silurian beds in western England: Geol. Soc. America Bull., v. 69, no. 12, pt. 2, p. 1592.

James, J. F., 1892, Studies in problematic organisms—the Genus *Scolithus*: Geol. Soc. America Bull., v. 3, pp. 32–44.

Korringa, P., 1951, The shell of Ostrea edulis as a habitat: Arch. Néerlandaises Zool., v. 10, pp. 32–152 (especially pp. 52–54, 91–101).

McIntosh, W. C., 1894, On certain homes or tubes formed by annelids: Annals Mag. Nat. Hist., ser. 6, v. 13, pp. 1–18.

————, 1923, A monograph of the British marine annelids: Ray Society (London), v. 4, pt. 1, pp. 251–538.

Reish, D. J., 1952, Discussion of the colonial tube-building polychaetous annelid *Dodecaceria fistulicola* Ehlers: Bull. Southern California Acad. Sci., v. 51, pt. 3, pp. 103–107.

Rhodes, F. H. T., and Dineley, D. L., 1957, Devonian conodont faunas from southwest England: Jour. Paleont., v. 31, no. 2, pp. 353–369.

————, and Wingard, P., 1957, Chemical composition, microstructure, and affinities of the Neurodontiformes: Jour. Paleont., v. 31, no. 2, pp. 448–454.

Scott, H. W., 1934, The zoological relationships of the conodonts: Jour. Paleont., v. 8, no. 4, pp. 448–455.

Stauffer, C. R., 1939, Middle Devonian Polychaeta from the Lake Erie district: Jour. Paleont., v. 13, no. 5, pp. 500–511.

Ulrich, E. O., and Bassler, R. S., 1926, A classification of the toothlike fossils, conodonts, with descriptions of American Devonian and Mississippian species: Proc. U. S. Nat. Mus., v. 68, pp. 1–63.

Wade, B., 1921, The fossil annelid Genus *Hamulus* Morton, an operculate Serpula: Proc. U. S. Nat. Mus., v. 59, pp. 41–46.

————, 1926, The fauna of the Ripley formation on Coon Creek, Tennessee: U. S. Geol. Survey Prof. Paper 137.

Walcott, C. D., 1911, Middle Cambrian annelids: Smithsonian Misc. Coll., v. 57, no. 5, pp. 109–144.

Chapter 7

BRYOZOANS AND PHORONIDS

PHYLUM IX. BRYOZOA

The name Bryozoa, which means "moss animals," was coined in allusion to the growth habit of a few common forms which resemble the true mosses or Bryophyta. The majority of living bryozoans and the important stony bryozoans of the Paleozoic, however, are not mossy in appearance. Some of these latter creatures are and were incrusting. Others constructed erect bushy colonies. The arborescent forms seem to have occupied the same biologic niche that hydrozoans, such as *Millepora,* and staghorn corals, such as *Acropora,* occupy today. Although Bryozoa abound in shallow water, they also live in marine water as deep as 18,000 feet (about 6000 m) below sea level.

Recent bryozoan colonies tend to assume one of two growth habits, whether the environment is fresh or salt water. In one case the individual animals (**zooids**), about 1 millimeter in diameter, build a lacy, calcareous, pavement-like colony (**zoarium**) which incrusts some hard surface over an area up to 5 centimeters in diameter. Each zooid consists of a fleshy **polypide** which occupies one chamber or **zooecium** in the colony. Zoaria of this sort commonly incrust the more rugged seaweeds found along all shores and also constitute a major element of the fauna which fouls the bottoms of ships. So effective is the reproduction of these animals that locally they are able to cover almost every shell or rock on the sea floor. They are major economic pests in the oyster industry because they prevent the new oyster spat from finding a place to settle down.

Growth among other Recent bryozoans typically assumes a shrubby habit, in which zoaria are generally a few centimeters tall. Zooecia in these forms are noncalcareous; therefore the skeletal tissue is flexible, and the zoaria are soft and spongy. As a matter of fact, it is not easy at first glance to tell the differences among the gelatinous zoaria of some Bryozoa, the hydroid generations of some Hydrozoa, and the soft bodies of some Demospongea. Among the foregoing groups, the Hydrozoa and Bryozoa are so similar in

239

general appearance that they were formerly grouped together with some other animals as the "zoophytes."

Among simply constructed Recent Bryozoa, the polypide is surrounded by a thin transparent zooecium secreted by the ectoderm (Fig. 7.1.1a, 1b, 8). The fleshy polypide can project from the aperture of the zooecium when in feeding position or it can be retracted within the zooecium to a position of safety by retractor muscles around the aperture. The digestive system is a simple U-shaped tube suspended within the body cavity. The mouth occupies the central position within the aperture and is surrounded by a ring of hollow tentacles attached to a fleshy ridge (**lophophore**). The anal opening is either on the oral surface just outside the lophophore (the **ectoproct** condition, Figs. 7.1.1, 6, 7), or it may be within the tentacular ring almost in contact with the mouth (the **entoproct** condition, Fig. 7.1.5). Food consists of microorganisms which are swept down to the mouth by cilia on the tentacles. When the extruded portion of the polypide is retracted into the zooecium, the digestive system is pulled farther back into the body cavity by special muscles attached to the floor of the zooecium. Respiration is effected by the tentacles. No circulatory system is present, but the body cavity contains a colorless fluid in which corpuscles are suspended. If a nervous system is present, it consists of a single ganglion near the mouth and a short nerve cord running alongside the digestive track.

Both sexes are contained in one zooid, and fertilization of eggs takes place within the body cavity. Fertilization leads to development of a modified trochophore larva which escapes from the body cavity in one of three ways. Some leave through a special opening in the body wall and others congregate in a special chamber, the **ooecium** or **ovicell** (Fig. 7.14), before entering the water. The third group is freed only when the parent body disintegrates entirely in a special **metamorphosis**. Larvae are free-living only for a few hours, after which they settle down on the substratum. From this time onward, Bryozoa develop along two lines so different that some zoologists divide them into two different Phyla. So-called cyphonautes larvae of ecto-

---

Figure 7.1 (*opposite*). Morphology and Development of Recent Bryozoa.

1a, 1b. Schematic diagrams of an ectoproctan with lophophore extended and retracted, enlarged. 2a, 2b. Side and plan views of a statoblast, enlarged. 3a, 3b. Oblique and end views of a cyphonautes larva of *Membranipora* sp., enlarged. 4. Side view of an avicularium showing jaws and muscles, greatly enlarged. 5. Polypides of the entoproctan, *Pedicellina cernua*, 10X. 6. *Beania mirabilis*, a gymnolaemate ectoproctan, enlarged. 7. *Plumatella* sp., a phylactolaemate ectoproctan with a distinct epistome above the mouth, enlarged. 8. Part of a colony of *Scrupocellaria scruposa*, 45X. Extended and retracted polypides at A and B. Empty zooecium at C. Incompletely degenerated and encysted polypide with brown body at D. Brown body only at E. 9. Nearly completely degenerated polypide in which tentacles adhere to brown body, greatly enlarged. 10. Successive budding from paired ancestrulae (A), enlarged. 11. Successive budding from a single ancestrula (A), enlarged. 12. Simultaneous budding from single ancestrula (A), enlarged.

(1, 4-6, 9 after Hincks, 1880. 2 after Simpson, 1895. 3, 7 after Marcus, 1940. 8 after Claparède, 1871. 10 after Waters, 1926. 11, 12 after Stach, 1938.)

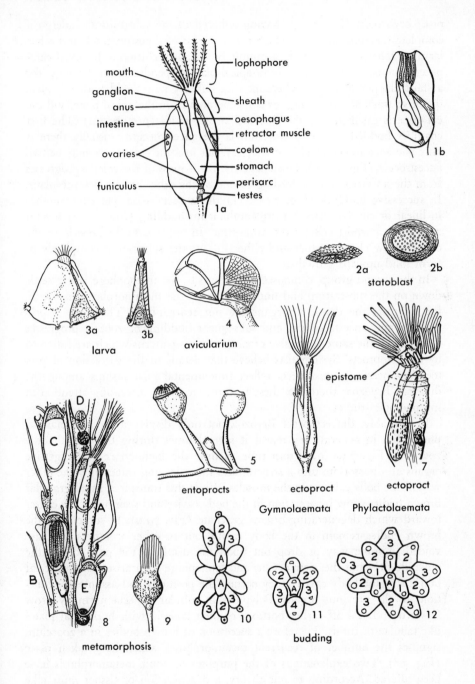

mouth

ganglion

anus

intestine

ovaries

funiculus

lophophore

sheath

oesophagus

retractor muscle

coelome

stomach

perisarc

testes

1a

1b

2a

2b statoblast

3a   3b

larva

4

avicularium

epistome

5

entoprocts

6

ectoproct

Gymnolaemata

7

ectoproct

Phylactolaemata

8

9

10   11   12

metamorphosis

budding

proct bryozoans (Fig. 7.1.3), having adhered to the substratum, undergo a complete metamorphosis in which every vestige of digestive track and other larval organs is lost and only a minute bell-shaped, chitinous, bivalved carapace remains, in which there is an **apical plate** suspended from the apex like a short clapper in a bell. Thereupon an entirely new zooid with complete digestive track and other organs is regenerated from the apical plate, and the carapace is calcified into the first saclike zooecium (**protoecium**). The first chamber budded off the protoecium is the **ancestroecium;** usually there is only one ancestroecium (Fig. 7.1.11, 12), but in some cases there may be two ancestroecia (Fig. 7.1.10). Growth of the main mass of the colony progresses from the ancestroecium according to one or the other of two definite plans. In **successive budding** (Fig. 7.1.10, 11) the zooecia arise one after another in linear or curved series, but in **simultaneous budding** (Fig. 7.1.12) several zooecia in a whorl arise at the same time. In either case the zooecia in the colony grow close together and either incrust the substratum completely or form solid upward growths.

In the second group, composed of entoprocts, the trochophore larvae settle down on the substratum and undergo only partial metamorphosis in which, for instance, the digestive organs are not reorganized. There are a protoecium and ancestroecium, and subsequent budding of zooecia progresses along much the same successive or simultaneous patterns which are followed by the ectoprocts. Systematists believe that details in the succession of protoecium-ancestroecium-zooecia reflect fundamental relationships among the different Bryozoa; therefore, these features are given increasing attention in morphologic studies.

Remarkably, the ectoproct Bryozoa not only display a larval metamorphosis, but in general they repeat it several times during the growth of a zoarium (Fig. 7.1.8, 9). From time to time the lophophore and digestive organs all disassociate into a structureless mass, leaving intact only the outer wall of the body cavity and the muscles. While this transpires, small granular **brown bodies** grow by accretion in the body cavity and seem to be the center toward which degenerating organs gravitate (Fig. 7.1.9). In some cases the brown bodies remain in the body cavity, but in other instances they are voided in some way or drop out upon the death of the polypide. If the polypide does not die, new organs and lophophore then arise from a special bud inside the body cavity; they occupy the positions and assume the functions of the previous organs. Polypides in tubular zooecia normally grow forward and seal off earlier portions of their zooecia with horizontal plates like tabulae in corals. Therefore a succession of brown bodies in a zooecium signifies the number of recurrent metamorphoses which have taken place (Fig. 7.8). Two explanations of the purposes of adult metamorphosis have been offered. According to one theory, a degeneration of tissues must take place in order to allow larvae to escape from the body cavity. Proponents of the other theory maintain that the absence of excretory organs among the ectoprocts necessitates some other way of disposing of nitrogenous waste; brown bodies, being highly nitrogenous, may represent a method of dealing with physiologic problems which are solved in other animals by the functioning of nephridia or of kidneys.

Defensive or cleansing mechanisms consist of whiplike rods (**vibracula**) and of tiny jaws (**avicularia**), which bear a singular resemblance to the heads of birds (Fig. 7.1.4). The tiny jaws snap this way and that with vigor and may succeed in grasping some tiny foreign object which is then moved off the surface of the zoarium. Avicularia and vibracula are equally interesting zoologically, for they are both the outwardly extended parts of highly modified zooecia. The little zooecium to which an avicularium is attached, for instance, is an **aviculoecium** (Fig. 7.16.9). Except for highly specialized larval stages of insects, the differentiation of zooecia among Bryozoa represents the last attempt at functional dimorphism by animals. This excludes sexual dimorphism, of course, which is the rule among higher animals and is a different kind of dimorphism than that illustrated by Bryozoa.

CLASSIFICATION. As is commonly the case for other groups of animals, classifications of Bryozoa by paleontologists and zoologists are based upon different criteria. It is widely recognized that endoprocts and ectoprocts are notably different, but the criteria upon which the difference is based are not recognizable in skeletal construction. Moreover, some fossil Bryozoa differ from Recent species in habit and in zooecial details. Under these circumstances the currently accepted classifications are hybrid things in which some basic assumptions of relationships are not capable of proof.

Until a few years ago the three groups of invertebrate creatures with a lophophore were grouped together as the Phylum Molluscoidea. Of these, the bivalved brachiopods are, as the word Molluscoidea implies, "mollusclike," but phoronids are wormlike, and bryozoans are mosslike. It is interesting, however, that some Bryozoa have a bivalved larval stage, even though some authorities relegate this stage to a position of small or of no evolutionary importance because it seems to arise late in the development of the group. Not only is the old Phylum Molluscoidea now split into three Phyla (of which Phylum Bryozoa is one), but more recent zoologic taxonomists recognize Phylum Endoprocta and Phylum Ectoprocta. The intermediate three-part solution is followed herein, with all bryozoanlike creatures placed in the same Phylum; and the phoronids and brachiopods are placed in separate Phyla.

Incidentally, the word Polyzoa was proposed one year before the word Bryozoa as the name of this Phylum. In British and continental literature

Polyzoa ordinarily is used, whereas in America Bryozoa is preferred. Priority does not govern taxonomic status of names higher than Genera so nationalistic opinions may influence the choice of names for the higher taxa.

KEY TO MAJOR TAXA OF BRYOZOA

I. Anal opening within the lophophore .... Class Entoprocta
II. Anal opening outside of the lophophore .... Class Ectoprocta
    A. Mouth with hood (epistome) .... Subclass Phylactolaemata
    B. Mouth without hood .... Subclass Gymnolaemata
       1. Colonies typically thin and incrusting
          a. Apertures comb-bearing .... Order Ctenostomida
          b. Apertures round
             (1) Zooecia tubular .... Group 1 Cyclostomida[a]
             (2) Zooecia boxlike .... Order Cheilostomida
       2. Colonies typically erect
          a. Colonies lacy .... Order Cryptostomida
          b. Colonies stony
             (1) Walls minutely porous........ Group 2 Cyclostomida[a]
             (2) Walls solid .... Order Trepostomida

[a] Notice that two different groups can be distinguished within the Order Cyclostomida when general external features are considered. The two groups intergrade, however, and therefore have not been deemed worthy of erecting special taxa for their reception.

Class A.   Entoprocta

The entoprocts are characterized not only by having the anal opening surrounded by a circular lophophore, but their tentacles cannot be retracted into the zooecium (Fig. 7.1.5). Although the digestive apparatus resembles that of other Bryozoa, it is suspended in a gelatinous parenchyme-filled body cavity instead of in a fluid-filled body cavity. Moreover, a very primitive excretory system is present which consists of a pair of tubules with flickering cilia forming "flame cells," as in the Platyhelminthes. Entoprocts are small unimportant inhabitants of fresh water and salt water. Although most of them are colonial, the only noncolonial bryozoan known belongs here. Only about 40 species are known and none has been reported fossil.

Class B.   Ectoprocta

The ectoprocts are large Bryozoa in which the anal opening is outside of the lophophore and the tentacles are retractile. They lack an excretory system. The body cavity is filled with fluid. Ectoprocts are the most common bryozoans and to them most of the general descriptive material applies. It is customary to divide them into two groups according to whether the mouth is covered by a little fleshy hood (**epistome**) or is devoid of this structure.

SUBCLASS 1. PHYLACTOLAEMATA

In this group there is an epistome, and the lophophore is ovate or horse-shoe-shaped (Fig. 7.1.7). They engage in a remarkable kind of reproduction, however, in which a minute, discoidal, chitinous, resting stage (**statoblast,** Fig. 7.1.2) is formed; this appears to be capable of fossilization. During drought or at the approach of cold weather these statoblasts form on the muscle which retracts the digestive tract. After death of the polypide, the statoblasts are released, even being transported by wind. When normal aqueous conditions prevail again, the statoblasts rupture and produce new colonies. Because of their ease of transportation, these Bryozoa become a twentieth-century nuisance by clogging up air-conditioning systems and cooling towers with their gelatinous colonies. Heretofore, they had also been identified as the inhabitants of systems carrying unfiltered water in some European cities. All of the 40 known species inhabit fresh water and none has been reported fossil.

SUBCLASS 2. GYMNOLAEMATA

This group lacks the epistome, and the lophophore is circular. More important, the members normally have calcareous skeletons, so almost all of the known fossil forms are referred here, even though in them the nature of the lophophore and the character of the mouth region are absolutely unknown.

Order a. Cyclostomida

As the name implies, these Bryozoa have a circular aperture. In addition, the zooecia tend to be tubular, with porous calcareous walls, but without transverse partitions or an operculum. Avicularia and vibracula are absent. It has become increasingly evident that environmental differences control the shape of zoaria so much that identification is very doubtful if based on simple zooecial features alone. Colonies of a species grown in quiet water are long and slender, whereas colonies of the same species grown in rough water are short and broad. Accordingly, present practice is to rely almost exclusively on characters of the ovicells for definitive recognition of species and Genera, both of the thin incrusting forms and of the erect but delicately constructed colonies. Most of these lacy and delicate cyclostomes (Fig. 7.2.1, 4, 5, 6) are post-Paleozoic, but they are known in strata as old as the Ordovician through *Stomatopora* (Fig. 7.2.2, 3). They comprise the Group 1 cyclostomes indicated in the key above. Possibly they might be referred to as "stomatoporoid cyclostomes."

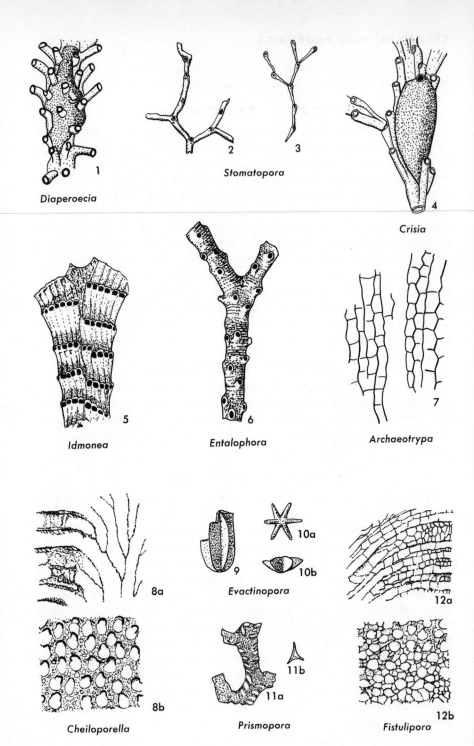

Diaperoecia

Stomatopora

Crisia

Idmonea

Entalophora

Archaeotrypa

Cheiloporella

Evactinopora

Prismopora

Fistulipora

The so-called Group 2 cyclostomes indicated in the key are composed of husky calcareous zoaria (Fig. 7.3.6, 7, 8) which resemble the massive stony bryozoans (Order Trepostomida) so closely in external appearance that they can be told apart only by study of thin sections. Walls of these stony cyclostomes are minutely porous, whereas those of trepostomes are solid and are modified by special structures described hereafter in this chapter. Nevertheless, structure of the stony cyclostomes is convergent with that of the Trepostomida by having small accessory zooecia (mesopores), a thickly constructed outer zone, and either smooth depressions or tiny nodules on the surface (Fig. 7.3). A calcareous hood (**lunarium**) may overhang the aperture in some forms (Fig. 7.3.3). In transverse sections of zooecia the traces of the lunaria may be represented in the walls by moon-shaped figures (Fig. 7.3.1, 2). Lunaria are as diagnostic of Cyclostomida as are their perforate walls.

Possibly the oldest bryozoan yet discovered is a stony cyclostome, *Archaeotrypa,* from Upper Cambrian strata of Alberta (Fig. 7.2.7). One of the commonest of all Paleozoic bryozoans is *Fistulipora*. Different species are incrusting, massive, or arborescent. *Fistulipora* is particularly noteworthy for the **coenosteum** of vesicular chambers which fill the broad spaces between zooecia (Figs. 7.2.12 and 7.3.5). So singular is this kind of structure among bryozoans that it commonly is referred to as **fistuliporoid structure** in order to distinguish it from the very similar coenostea of corals. Among some unusually shaped zoaria, *Evactinopora* (Mississippian) is star-shaped (Fig. 7.2.9, 10), and *Prismopora* (Devonian to Permian) is prismatic with a triangular cross section (Fig. 7.2.11).

Group 2 cyclostomes might be called "fistuliporoid cyclostomes" or "lunarioid cyclostomes" in order to differentiate them from the Group 1 or stomatoporoid cyclostomes.

Order b. Ctenostomida

Ctenostomes, or "comb-mouths," get their name from an operculum of tiny spines or setae which can cover the aperture in some forms. In others, the aperture is closed by wrinkles in the tentacle sheath as the tentacles are with-

---

Figure 7.2 (*opposite*). Cyclostomida.
1. *Diaperoecia floridana* with stippled ovicell, 15X, Recent. 2. *Stomatopora granulata*, 15X, Recent. 3. *Stomatopora delicatula*, 8X, Ordovician, Ohio. 4. *Crisia pugeti* with stippled ovicell, 15X, Recent. 5. *Idmonea magna*, 8X, Eocene, Georgia. 6. *Entalophora proboscidea*, 8X, Eocene and Oligocene, Alabama and North Carolina. 7. Vertical section of a colony of *Archaeotrypa prima*, the oldest bryozoan, 8X, Cambrian, Alberta. 8a, 8b. Longitudinal and tangential sections of *Cheiloporella flabellata*, 12X, Ordovician, Ohio. 9. Side view of *Evactinopora radiata*, 2/3X, Mississippian, Kentucky. 10a, 10b. Plan and side views of *Evactinopora sexradiata*, 2/3X, Mississippian, Iowa. 11a, 11b. Side view and cross section of *Prismopora trifolia*, 2/3X, Mississippian, Iowa. 12a, 12b. Longitudinal and tangential sections of *Fistulipora spinulifera*, 12X, Devonian, Michigan.
(1, 2, 4 after Osburn, 1953. 3 after Bassler, 1906. 5, 6 after Canu and Bassler, 1920. 7 after Fritz, 1947. 8-12 after Ulrich, 1890.)

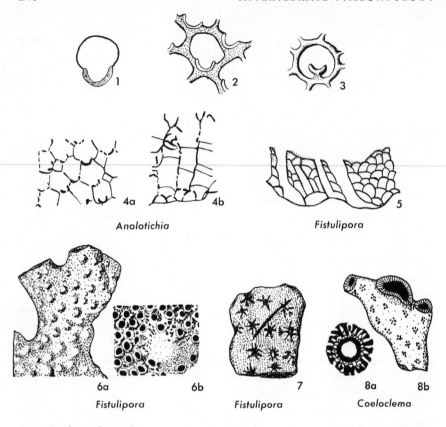

Anolotichia   Fistulipora

6a   6b   7   8a   8b

Fistulipora   Fistulipora   Coeloclema

Figure 7.3. Cyclostomida.
  1, 2. Tangential sections of zooecia with lunaria, 25X. 3. Surface view of *Buskopora* sp.
with a lunarium overhanging a zooecium, about 25X. 4a, 4b. Tangential and longitudinal
sections of *Anolotichia spinulifera*, showing lunaria, porous walls, and diaphragms, 15X,
Ordovician, Oklahoma. 5. Longitudinal section of *Fistulipora crustula* showing fistuliporoid
structure, 14X, Silurian, New York. 6. *Fistulipora monticulata*, Devonian, Iowa. 6a, portion of
a zoarium, 1X. 6b, detail of a smooth-surfaced node, 8X. 7. Surface of *Fistulipora astrica*
with smooth star-shaped depressions, 1X, Devonian, Iowa. 8. *Coeloclema concentricum*, 1X,
Ordovician, Ohio. 8a, transverse section with hollow axis and thick inner epitheca. 8b,
surface of a branch.
  (1-3, 6-8 after Ulrich, 1890. 4 after Loeblich, 1942. 5 after Bassler, 1906b.)

drawn (Fig. 7.4.1). Avicularia, vibracula, and ooecia are absent. This group
is almost entirely marine. Inasmuch as the zooecia are typically chitinous,
only a few calcified members are known. Instead, the former positions of the
chitinous sheaths are commonly indicated by delicate indentations where
the colony has dissolved the incrusted surface of calcareous materials. Indeed,
the oldest ctenostomes, such as *Vinella* (Ordovician), are represented by such
shallow excavations (Fig. 7.4.4a). In most of the early species the growth pat-

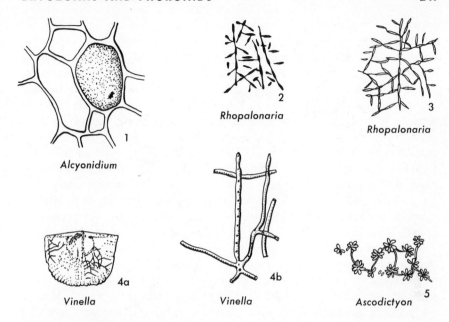

Figure 7.4. Ctenostomida.
1. Portion of a zoarium of *Alcyonidium polyoum* with detail of one zooecium, about 15X, Recent. 2. Excavations made by *Rhopalonaria attenuata*, 6X, Silurian, New York. 3. *Rhopalonaria, tenuis,* 6X, Devonian, Ontario. 4. *Vinella repens,* Ordovician, Minnesota. 4a, excavations on the inner surface of a brachiopod shell, 2/3X. 4b, portion of zoarium, 12X. 5. *Ascodictyon floreale,* 6X, Devonian, Michigan.
(1 after Osburn, 1953. 2-5 after Ulrich and Bassler, 1905.)

tern is netlike, with tubular stolons and transverse branches. Erect tubular zooecia are encountered in Mesozoic or Cenozoic rocks on rare occasions, and this growth habit is common in Recent seas. Although the Ctenostomida range from Early Ordovician to Recent, they are never important. *Alcyonidium* is a well-known Recent Genus.

Order c.   Trepostomida

Of all the Orders of Bryozoa, the Trepostomida are the most important rock-makers. These are commonly referred to as the stony bryozoans, although it will be remembered that some of the Cyclostomida also merit this name. Zoaria consist of a multitude of slender tubular zooecia packed tightly together into rocklike masses. No soft parts have ever been described for members of this Paleozoic Order; hence, their systematic position in the Phylum is only inferred.

The simplest growth form of stony bryozoans is as thin incrustations on some hard object such as the skeleton of a coral, brachiopod, or another bryo-zoan, or as incrustations on a rock. Zooecia in these thin expansions are tubular or prismatic and rise to meet the surface at about a right angle, instead of being pavements of boxlike zooecia as in most other incrusting bryozoans. By continued upward growth the **incrusted** form gives rise to hemispherical, or tabular, **massive** zoaria which vary in size from mounds the size of bonbons (Fig. 7.5.3) to great slabs several centimeters thick and almost a meter in diameter. Other bryozoans grow upward more than laterally and produce erect, branching, or anastomosing shrubbery with stems about as thick as pencils and with colonies as much as a meter in height. This is the **ramose** habit (Fig. 7.5.1, 2, 8a, 9a). Or the upward growth may be in the form of a flat, or contorted, fan-shaped zoarium as large as the palm of one's hand, but only a few millimeters thick. These are the **frondose** zoaria (Fig. 7.5.5). They may consist of two sheets of tissue backed up as a **bifoliate** zoarium or they may be **unilamellar.** As has been pointed out previously, growth habit alone is not sufficient for differentiation of bryozoan groups.

Surfaces of trepostomes ordinarily provide meager information for use in their identification. In exceptionally clean material it is seen that two sizes of apertures are present. The smaller apertures denote the location of **mesopores** or slender tubules packed in among the zooecia (Fig. 7.5.9b). Most of the zooecial apertures are round, although polygonal apertures are also known. *Rhombotrypa* (Ordovician) is almost unique in having variously oriented patches of quadrate apertures (Fig. 7.5.6). Some species bear minute granules on the walls between zooecial apertures. Surfaces of many trepostomes are evenly textured and regular, whereas others bear unusually smooth-floored areas (**maculae,** Fig. 7.5.9b) or low mounds (**monticules,** Fig. 7.5.7). Both of these irregularities represent clusters of mesopores. Maculae and monticules occur at relatively constant intervals, such as two or three in 1 centimeter, and are of some taxonomic value. For instance, *Hallopora* is characterized by abundant, ridgelike, or nodose monticules (Fig. 7.5.1, 2), whereas *Constellaria* is strikingly studded with star-shaped maculae (Fig. 7.5.4).

In spite of variability in shape and surficial characters, it is necessary to study the internal skeletal anatomy of stony bryozoans in order to be confident of identifications. Many years ago, when only external features were considered, there was great confusion as to whether *Monticulipora* belonged with the Bryozoa or with the tabulate corals such as *Chaetetes* and *Tetradium*. Colonies of all of these Genera consist of slender tabulate tubules. When the use of thin sections became general, about 1890, the key to careful discrimination of species was at hand. The "Monticuliporoid Controversy" was irrefutably solved in 1912 when the presence of protoecia and ancestroecia was demonstrated in thin sections of *Monticulipora*. Now it is customary for authors to illustrate internal anatomy of trepostomes as seen in thin sections and even to omit illustrations of external features.

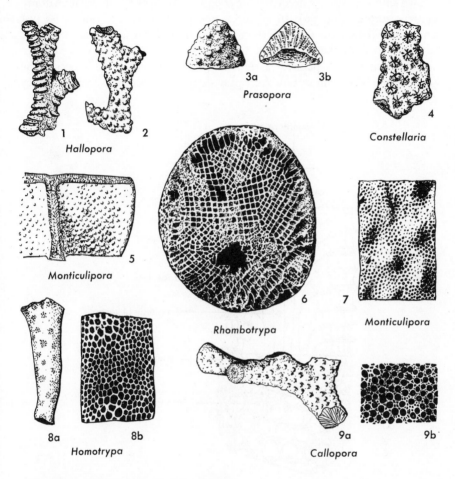

Hallopora

Prasopora
3a   3b

Constellaria
4

Monticulipora
5

Rhombotrypa
6

Monticulipora
7

Homotrypa
8a   8b

Callopora
9a   9b

Figure 7.5. External Features of Trepostomida.
1. *Hallopora rugosa*, 1X, Ordovician, Indiana. 2. *Hallopora ramosa*, 1X, Ordovician, Indiana and Ohio. 3a, 3b. Side view and broken transverse section of a zoarium of *Prasopora conoidea*, 1X, Ordovician, Minnesota. 4. Surface of *Constellaria constellata* with raised stellate maculae, 1X, Ordovician, Indiana, Ohio, Kentucky. 5. Surface of a frond of *Monticulipora mammulata*, 1X, Ordovician, Indiana and Ohio. 6. Tip of a branch of *Rhombotrypa quadrata*, 6X, Ordovician, east-central United States. 7. Details of monticules on *Monticulipora mammulata*, 6X, Ordovician, Indiana and Ohio. 8. *Homotrypa minnesotensis*, Ordovician, Minnesota. 8a, portion of a ramose branch with clusters of large zooecia but no monticules, 1X. 8b, detail of surface, 6X. 9. *Callopora subnodosa*, Ordovician, Ohio. 9a, branch with monticules, 1X. 9b, clusters of mesopores on two monticules, 8X.
(1, 2, 4, 5, 7 after Cumings, 1908. 3, 8 after Ulrich, 1895. 6 after Bassler, 1932. 9 after Ulrich, 1890.)

Two thin sections are necessary for adequate study of the internal anatomy of trepostomes (Fig. 7.6). In all cases, one plane of section must pass just under and parallel to the surface of the zoarium. This **tangential section** is intended to show the microscopic features of zooecial walls as viewed transversely; that is, in a plane at a right angle to the axis of the zooecia. The plane of the other thin section must pass along the axes of the zooecia as they

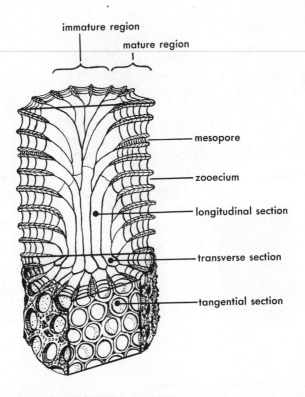

Figure 7.6.   Orientation of Thin Section of Stony Bryozoa.
Cut-away diagram of a trepostome bryozoan showing the appearance of zooecia and meso-pores in longitudinal, transverse, and tangential sections.

rise through the zoarium to form a **longitudinal section** of the zooecia. In incrusting and massive forms this plane will be located vertically at right angles to the surface. In ramose zoaria the plane must include the axis of a stem, and therefore is axial and radial, as well as longitudinal. A well-oriented longitudinal section reveals how the zooecia rise almost vertically from the axial region and then curve outward rather abruptly to meet the surface at an acute angle or at a right angle. In frondose zoaria the plane of section must lie normal to the surfaces and parallel to the direction of growth; this means

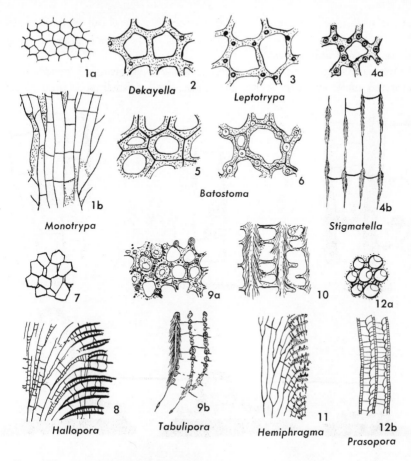

Figure 7.7.   Internal Morphology of Trepostomida.

1a, 1b. Tangential and longitudinal sections of *Monotrypa cumulata,* a very simple form with only diaphragms, 6X, Ordovician, Minnesota.   2. Tangential section of *Dekayella praenuntia* showing amalgamate wall with sparse acanthopores, 35X, Ordovician, Minnesota.   3. Tangential section of *Leptotrypa discoidea* showing amalgamate walls with numerous acanthopores, 35X, Ordovician, Indiana. 4a, 4b. Tangential and longitudinal sections of *Stigmatella spinosa* showing amalgamate walls and zones of acanthopores, 35X, Ordovician, Indiana.   5. Tangential section of *Batostoma decipiens* showing integrate walls without acanthopores, 35X, Ordovician, Minnesota.   6. Tangential section of *Batostoma winchelli* showing integrate walls with acanthopores, 35X, Ordovician, Minnesota.   7, 8. Tangential and longitudinal sections of *Hallopora ramosa* showing mesopores and mature region, 12X, Ordovician, east-central states.   9a, 9b. Tangential and longitudinal sections of *Tabulipora carbonaria* showing perforate diaphragms, acanthopores, and moniliform (beaded) walls, 12X, Pennsylvanian, widespread.   10. Longitudinal section showing hemiphragms in *Hemiphragma ottawaense,* 25X, Ordovician, Minnesota. 11. Longitudinal section of *Hemiphragma irrasum* showing complete diaphragms in immature region and hemiphragms in mature region, 6X, Ordovician, Minnesota. 12a, 12b. Tangential and longitudinal sections of *Prasopora simulatrix* showing cystiphragms, 12X, Ordovician, Minnesota.

(1, 2, 5, 6, 10, 11 after Ulrich, 1895. 3, 4, 8 after Cumings, 1908. 9 after Ulrich, 1890.)

that the section will be vertical near the center of a frond but inclined somewhat if taken near the side of a zoarium because the zooecia grow in spray
fashion upward and outward.

Once the thin sections are prepared, a whole new group of morphologic
features is made available. In the first place, the longitudinal sections reveal

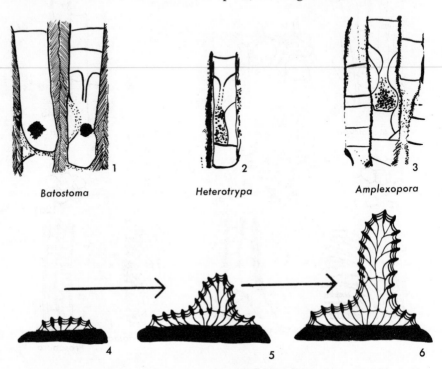

Batostoma   *Heterotrypa*   *Amplexopora*

Figure 7.8.   Brown Bodies and Regeneration.
1. Longitudinal section of two zooecia of *Batostoma variabile* showing brown bodies and
remnants of one cystlike chamber, 45X, Ordovician, Indiana. 2. Longitudinal section of *Heterotrypa subramosa* with a cluster of brown bodies in a cystose chamber, 45X, Ordovician, Indiana.
3. Longitudinal section of *Amplexopora pustulosa* with small brown bodies in a distinct cystose
chamber, 45X, Ordovician, Indiana. 4-6. Schematic drawings to illustrate the Paradox of the
Trepostomes. 4, incrusting stage before any metamorphosis. 5, beginning of ramose habit
after one metamorphosis. 6, later ramose shape after two metamorphoses. All enlarged about
5X.
(1-3 after Cumings and Galloway, 1915.)

two distinct zones in trepostomes (and in some Cyclostomida), the outer one
of which forms a sort of coarsely constructed rind, the **mature region,**
and the inner or earlier one of which is the delicately constructed **immature
region** (Fig 7.6). Zooecial walls in the immature region are thin and commonly are wrinkled, whereas they are very thick and straighter in the mature
zone. Beaded walls are said to be **moniliform** (Fig. 7.7.9b). Cutting across

zooecia at right angles are thin plates, the **diaphragms,** which are exactly analogous to tabulae in corals. Diaphragms are closer together in mature regions than in immature regions. Diaphragms may be uninterrupted plates (**complete**), or they may extend only halfway across a zooecium (**hemiphragms,** Fig. 7.7.10, 11), or they may be **perforate** (Fig. 7.7.9a). Special cystose structures (**cystiphragms,** Fig. 7.7.12b), analogous to dissepiments in corals, may lie in a vertical series along one side of the inside of zooecia of some Genera. Cystiphragms are concentrated almost exclusively in the mature region of some bryozoans but occupy both regions in other Genera. Mesopores, as seen in longitudinal section, are slender tubes only about one-fourth as wide as zooecia and are present only in the mature region (Fig. 7.7.8, 12b). They are filled with closely packed diaphragms. Walls of zooecia in the mature region may contain minute longitudinal tubules called **acanthopores** which open at the surface at the spines or granules on zooecial walls (Fig. 7.7.3, 4, 6, 9). In life they also may have supported avicularia or vibracula, but their function is actually problematical because no living bryozoans and no fossil bryozoans other than the trepostomes have acanthopores.

Tangential sections, by being just beneath the surface, reveal the microscopic features of the mature region. These sections are particularly useful for determining diameters of zooecia, mesopores, and acanthopores; for determining wall thicknesses; for detecting perforate diaphragms; and for determining which acanthopores lie wholly within the zooecial walls and which bulge out into zooecial chambers. Moreover, tangential sections reveal whether walls of adjacent zooecia are separate and meet at a median line (**integrate walls,** Fig. 7.7.5, 6) or are fused into a common wall (**amalgamate walls,** Fig. 7.7.2, 3, 4a).

From the foregoing description of longitudinal sections it is apparent that the mature region is much more complicated than is the immature region. Stony bryozoans seem to grow forward by adding new material to the surface and by sealing off inner regions with diaphragms, very much as corals do (Fig. 7.8.4-6). In this way the tip end of a ramose branch is always formed by the mature region, and the surficial rind of a massive form always comprises mature region. How then is it possible for the thin-walled and simple features of the immature region to arise if they once were part of the mature region but now are sealed off from the polypide by diaphragms? This is the "Paradox of the Trepostomes." Obviously, trepostomes found some way to alter the construction of the inner recesses of a zoarium by resorbing some skeletal tissues. The best suggestion as to how this alteration was accomplished involves the phenomenon of adult metamorphosis, which has been observed among Recent Bryozoa. In this instance a polypide would undergo its periodic degeneration, in which not only much of the fleshy tissue, but, in the case of the Trepostomida, some or most of the structures of the mature re-

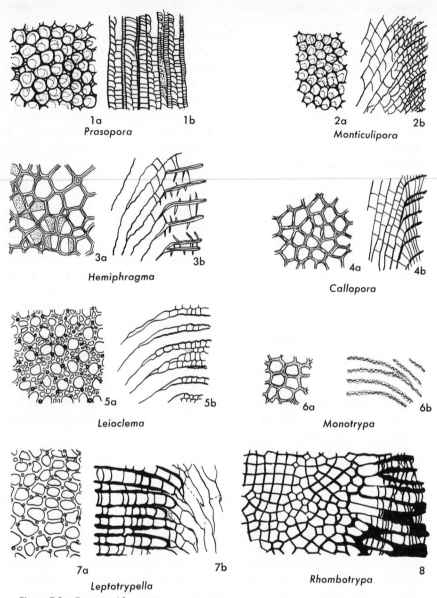

1a **1b**
Prasopora

2a **2b**
Monticulipora

3a **3b**
Hemiphragma

4a **4b**
Callopora

5a **5b**
Leioclema

6a **6b**
Monotrypa

7a **7b**
Leptotrypella

8
Rhombotrypa

Figure 7.9. Trepostomida.

1-7 are tangential and longitudinal sections. 1. *Prasopora simulatrix*, 12X, Ordovician, Minnesota. 2. *Monticulipora arborea*, 12X, Ordovician, Kentucky. 3. *Hemiphragma whitfieldi*, 14X, Ordovician, Ohio. 4. *Callopora multitabulata*, 14X, Ordovician, Kentucky. 5. *Leioclema monroei*, 14X, Devonian, New York. 6. *Monotrypa benjamini*, 8X, Silurian, New York. 7. *Leptotrypella aequabilis*, 14X, Devonian, Michigan. 8. Transverse section of *Rhombotrypa quadrata*, 12X, Ordovician, east-central states.

1, 2 after Ulrich, 1895. 3, 4 after Bassler, 1906a. 5 after Ulrich and Bassler, 1905. 6 after Bassler, 1906b. 7 after Duncan, 1939. 8 after Cumings, 1908.)

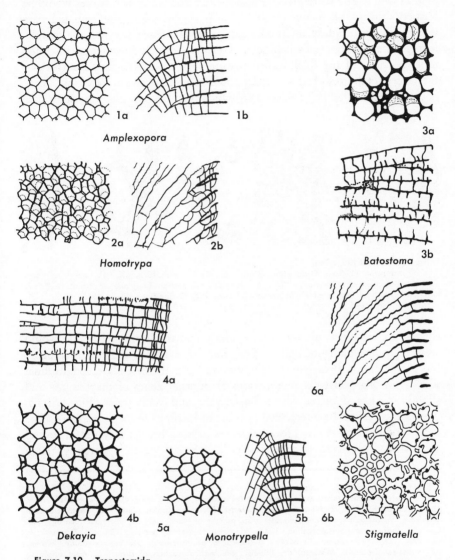

1a **1b**

Amplexopora

2a **2b**

Homotrypa

3a

3b

Batostoma

4a

6a

4b **5a** **5b** **6b**

Dekayia *Monotrypella* *Stigmatella*

Figure 7.10. Trepostomida.
All figures are longitudinal and transverse sections. 1. *Amplexopora pustulosa*, 12X,
Ordovician, Ohio. 2. *Homotrypa flabellaris*, 12X, Ordovician, Illinois. 3. *Batostoma imperfecta*,
Ordovician, Illinois. 4. *Dekayia subfrondosa*, 12X, Ordovician, Indiana. 5. *Monotrypella
aequalis*, 12X, Ordovician, Indiana. 6. *Stigmatella crenulata*, 14X, Ordovician, Indiana.
(1-3 after Ulrich, 1890. 4-6 after Cumings, 1908.)

gion as well would be resorbed. Presumably a zone of brown bodies would be formed during the metamorphosis. Upon regeneration, the new polypide would advance slightly in its zooecium and lay down the normal complement of new diaphragms behind it. During these readjustments either the inner portions of the thick-walled mature region were slightly resorbed, or they were totally resorbed and redeposited in more outward locations. There does not seem to be any evidence on which method prevailed. In either case

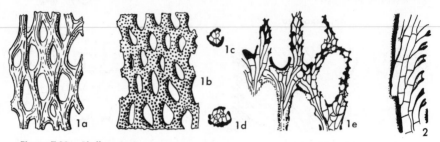

Figure 7.11. Phylloporina.
1. *Phylloporina sublaxa*, Ordovician, Minnesota. 1a, reverse face, 6X. 1b, apertural face, 6X. 1c, 1d, transverse sections, 12X. 1e, longitudinal section in plane of frond, 12X. 2. Radial longitudinal section of *Phylloporina corticosa*, 12X, Ordovician, Minnesota.
(After Ulrich, 1895.)

the mature region would advance regularly and the immature region would seem to follow along behind it. Two lines of evidence indicate that metamorphosis did take place in the Trepostomida. In the first place, longitudinal sections of zoaria usually retain traces of internal zones of diaphragms and slightly thickened places where diaphragms and walls meet (Fig. 7.8.4-6). These features can be interpreted as relics of incomplete metamorphosis. The most conclusive evidence, however, seems to have been discovered in several species of Ordovician trepostomes (Fig. 7.8.1-3) which apparently retain

---

Figure 7.12 (*opposite*). Cryptostomida.
1. *Fenestella rudis;* Mississippian, east-central states. 1a, 1b, reverse and apertural faces, 6X. 1c, branch, 12X. 2. *Pinnaretepora conferta*, 6X, Mississippian, Iowa. 3. *Septopora subquadrans*, Mississippian, east-central states. 3a, portion of frond, 1X. 3b, apertural face of frond, 5X. 3c, shallow tangential section, 12X. 3d, deep tangential section, 12X. 4. *Taeniodictya subrecta*, 12X, Mississippian, Kentucky. 5. *Polypora nodocarinata*, 6X, Pennsylvanian, Illinois. 6. *Hemitrypa proutana*, Mississippian, Illinois. 6a, vertical section of branch at right angle to frond, 12X. 6b, surface with superimposed network on left, 6X. 7. *Rhombopora lepidodendroides*, Pennsylvanian, widespread. 7a, 7b, transverse and longitudinal sections, 8X. 7c, portion of surface, 6X. 7d, fragment of branch, 4X. 8. Transverse section of calcareous support of *Lyropora ranoscula* with embedded frond, 2/3X, Mississippian, Kentucky. 9. Side view of *Lyropora quincuncialis* with remnant of frond, 2/3X, Mississippian, Illinois. 10. *Worthenopora spinosa*, 6X, Mississippian, Illinois. 11a, 11b. Longitudinal section and side view of an axis of *Archimedes invaginatus*, 2/3X, Mississippian, Illinois. 12. Two spirals arising from the edge of a flat frond of *Archimedes distans*, 2/3X, Mississippian, Illinois. The right spiral twists counterclockwise and the left, clockwise. 13. Cut-away schematic diagram of *Archimedes*, 1X.
(1-6, 8-12 after Ulrich, 1890. 7 after Condra, 1903.)

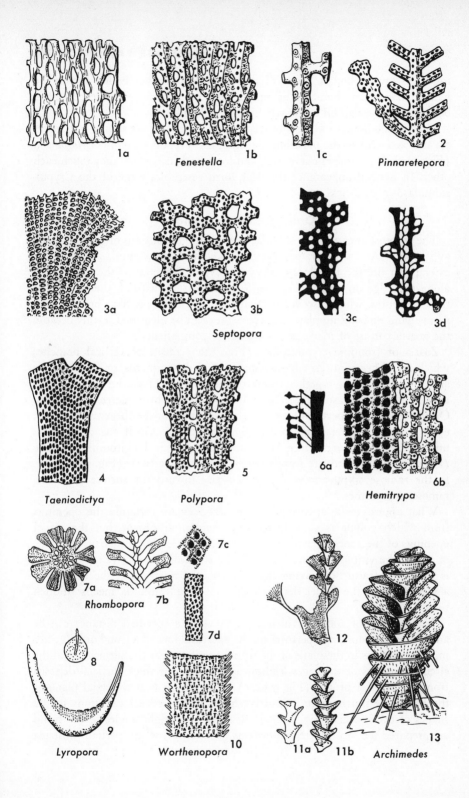

1a

Fenestella 1b

1c

Pinnaretepora 2

3a

Septopora 3b

3c

3d

Taeniodictya 4

Polypora 5

Hemitrypa 6a 6b

Rhombopora 7a 7b 7c 7d

Lyropora 8 9

Worthenopora 10

11a 11b *Archimedes* 12 13

fossilized brown bodies. Some of these supposed brown bodies merely lie within abandoned chambers of zooecia, but others seem definitely to have been specially sealed off or encysted by the polypide.

Some of the familiar Genera of trepostome bryozoans are shown in Figures 7.9 and 7.10. One of the most interesting of the Trepostomida is *Phylloporina* (Fig. 7.11). Its branches curve back and forth and fuse where they touch each other. In general appearance this lacy form resembles some of the Crypto-stomida discussed next.

Order d.   Cryptostomida

The cryptostomes are almost all lacy, erect, thin expansions of great delicacy and beauty. A few are rather ramose, like the Trepostomida. All are cal-careous. In life the frondose erect zoaria were cemented to the substratum along the edge on which they were balanced. It is natural, therefore, that these creatures, when discovered in the rocks, usually occur as broken frag-ments lying on bedding planes. Even so, they can be identified readily because the zoaria consist of identically constructed components.

Zoaria of frondose cryptostomes (Fig. 7.12) consist of vertical **branches** which are either connected by crossbars called **dissepiments**, or the branches are sinuous and fuse together where they converge. Thus, the branches and dissepiments frame small windows (**fenestrules**) which pierce the fronds. On the obverse or **apertural face** of a zoarium the branches bear two to about eight rows of zooecial apertures (Fig. 7.12.1b, 3b, 5). If the zoarium is unilamellar, the **reverse face** lacks apertures but is longitudinally striate (Fig. 7.12.1a). In bifoliate fronds both faces bear apertures (Fig. 7.13.3a, 7). In the ramose cryptostomes the zooecia rise toward the surface as in the ramose trepostomes.

What appear to be apertures on the branches are certainly the openings from which polypides gained access to their environment, but the actual openings of the zooecial chambers are at the lower end of a tube or **vestibule**, of which the visible aperture is merely the surficial opening (Fig. 7.13.6). It is from this feature of having the true zooecial aperture at the bottom of a vestibule that the Order derives its name; Cryptostomida means "hidden mouth."

The number of zooecia which are present in a specified distance can be ascertained by counting apertures on the apertural face of a frond or by grind-ing thin sections in the plane of the frond. Sections near the surface reveal the circular outlines of the tubes leading up through the thick surficial deposits from the zooecia proper (Fig. 7.12.3c). Sections cut near the axial plane of the frond are much more instructive because they reveal variations in the shapes of the zooecia (Fig. 7.12.3d). If sections at right angles to the frond are prepared the incomplete diaphragms (**hemisepta**) which partially obstruct the passage between the zooecia and the surface can be seen (Fig. 7.13.6-8).

The origin of the Cryptostomida is somewhat controversial. Some authorities think that the Cryptostomida were derived from the Cyclostomida, but other specialists are impressed with the similarity between the anastomosing

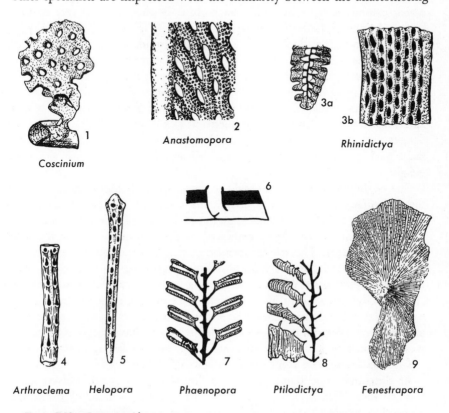

Figure 7.13. Cryptostomida.
1. Frond of *Coscinium latum*, 2/3X, Mississippian, Illinois. 2. Apertural face of *Anastomopora cinctuta* with thickened margin, 4X, Devonian, New York. 3a, 3b. Transverse section of bifoliate frond and surface of *Rhinidictya neglecta*, 12X, Ordovician, Kentucky. 4. *Arthroclema striatum*, 8X, Ordovician, Minnesota. 5. *Helopora harrisi*, 12X, Ordovician, Ohio. 6. Schematic vertical section through a zooecium of a fenestellid bryozoan showing thickening around the vestibule and the superior and inferior hemisepta, about 20X. 7. Vertical section of *Phaenopora lindstromi* with two hemisepta, 15X, Silurian, Sweden. 8. Vertical section of *Ptilodictya magnifica* with several hemisepta, 15X, Ordovician, Ohio. 9. Basal view of a frond of *Fenestrapora occidentalis*, 2/3X, Devonian, Iowa.
(1, 6-9 after Ulrich, 1890. 2 after Simpson, 1895. 3-5 after Ulrich, 1895.)

trepostome, *Phylloporina* (Fig. 7.11), and the cryptostome, *Anastomopora* (Fig. 7.13.2). The most characteristic of all of the cryptostomes is *Fenestella*, which ranges from Ordovician to Permian and is one of the commonest Paleozoic fossils. From it arose numerous fenestellid variations, such as increasing the number of rows of apertures on a branch or extending apertures continuously along both the branches and the dissepiments. Thus, the entire frame surrounding each fenestrule in *Septopora* is covered with apertures (Fig. 7.12.3b). Another trend led to increased height of the ridge or **carina** which extends lengthwise along the midline of the apertural face of each branch. In unspecialized forms the carina is low (Fig. 7.12.1c), but it may become high enough to double the thickness of a frond. In even more elaborate forms such as *Hemitrypa* (Fig. 7.12.6) the carinae are not only high, but they have produced flanges along their sides. These flanges extend across the intervening space between carinae and fuse with their opposite number on the adjoining carina. The whole meshwork thus formed produces a false apertural face lying above the true apertural face. Presumably the carinae and flanges protected the fleshy tentacles, but the addition of skeletal material must have taxed the strength of the delicate fronds to support the extra weight.

One of the most peculiar animals known to paleontologists is the cryptostome *Archimedes*. Members of this Genus consist of a calcareous axial support which is coiled in a helicoid spiral and a fenestellid frond which is enrolled so that its lower edge is embraced by the crests of ridges on the solid axis (Fig. 7.12.13). The whole assemblage was balanced on its tip, but was kept erect by an elaborate system of oblique props like guy wires; the props traversed several layers of fronds in passing from the axis to the substratum. As normally preserved in Mississippian strata in several of the middle and eastern states, the delicate fronds have been broken away and only the solid axes remain (Fig. 7.12.11). *Archimedes* seems to have migrated into the western states by Pennsylvanian time. Moreover, the last representatives of the Genus are known from the Permian of Russia.

At the same time that *Archimedes* flourished, *Lyropora* evolved along similar lines (Fig. 7.12.8, 9). In that Genus a flat, fenestellid frond was suspended between the arms of a U-shaped support like an ancient lyre.

Among ramose cryptostomes, *Rhombopora* is the best-known Genus (Fig. 7.12.7). It is especially abundant in Pennsylvanian strata but ranges from Devonian to Permian.

All Cryptostomida were marine.

Order e.   Cheilostomida

As the frondose Cryptostomida were the most delicate of all Paleozoic Bryozoa, so the Cheilostomida were in post-Paleozoic times. If ever the word beautiful were applicable to fossils, it should be applied to these elegantly contrived creatures. The Order consists mostly of incrusting zoaria, although a few erect fronds and even rather solid ramose growths are known. Typically, a colony consists of a one-layered pavement of zooids in which the zooecia occur more or less side by side like bricks in sidewalk, except that among cheilostomes the outlines usually are ovate or casket-shaped instead of being rectangular. The only exposed surface, which is called the **frontal wall,** generally bears a wonderful variety of spines, pores, granules, pits, and lacy fretwork which delight the eye and facilitate identification of many species. Apertures are modified into a considerable diversity of ovate, quad-

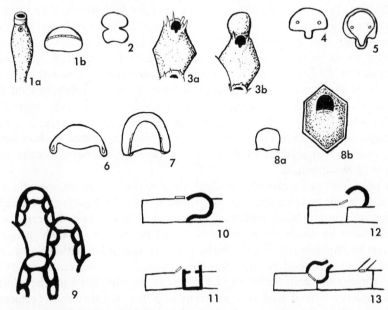

Figure 7.14. Morphology of Cheilostomida.
1-5 are ascophorans; 6-8 are anascans. All illustrations enlarged. 1a, 1b. Zooecium with distinct ascopore, but an operculum resembling anascans. 2. Operculum with indentations on side for cardelles. 3a, 3b. Zooecia without and with ovicells. 4, 5. Typical ascophoran opercula. 6, 7. Typical anascan opercula. 8a, 8b. Operculum and frontal wall with aperture it closed. 9. Dietellae. 10-13. Different positions of ovicells (heavy lines) on zooecial walls (thin lines). Opercula are indicated by tiny open rectangles.
(After Canu and Bassler, 1920.)

rate, trilobate, lunate, elongate, and keyhole-shaped outlines. Of particular significance is the presence of a movable **operculum** or lip which can close the aperture (Fig. 7.14.10-13); indeed, the name of the order means "lip mouth."

Zooecia which are specially modified for reproductive purposes are called **ooecia** or **ovicells** (Fig. 7.14.10-13). They usually are bulbous swellings of notably different shape than the zooecia of feeding zooids. Larvae escape from ovicells through an aperture which commonly is connected with or adjacent to the zooecial aperture. Ovicells currently are assigned paramount importance in identification of cheilostomes; in fact, some specialists categorically question the identification of any species for which ovicells are as yet unknown. Ornamentation of ovicells, and size, shape, and location between, or above, or indenting zooecia are all important.

Recent cheilostomes also are characterized uniquely by the presence of avicularia and vibracula. These singular structures are not found fossil but their locations on zooecia may be indicated by special perforations or scars. In spite of the remarkable self-sufficiency of individual zooids, they seem to cooperate to some degree, such as nourishing nonfeeding zooids and coordinating movements of vibracula. The only communication among adjacent zooecia seems to be by microscopic fibers which pass through tiny holes (**septula**) in the lateral walls. For reasons not clear, cheilostomes restrict the volume of the zooecia by building up a layer of vesicles (**dietellae**) on the lateral walls analogous to dissepiments in corals and to cystiphragms in trepostomes (Fig. 7.14.9). As a result of all these internal complications, students of cheilostomes are coming to rely more and more on horizontal and vertical thin sections to show wall structure, profiles of ovicells, and nature of the apertures.

A polypide can be extruded through the aperture when the operculum is open, or it can be retracted and then sealed within the zooecium by closing of the operculum. Much importance is attached to the two different *basic* mechanisms by which the polypide is moved in and out. In both instances it must be remembered that the fleshy parts are suspended within fluids confined within the zooecium; therefore the technique of movement must utilize the property of incompressibility of fluids. In the simplest case the central region of the frontal wall is a chitinous and flexible membrane (**ectocyst**) which can be pulled down a short distance into the zooecial chamber by a set of muscles, thereby compressing the fluid in the zooecium and forcing the polypide out of the aperture (Fig. 7.15.1c, 1d). When the muscles relax the frontal wall springs back to its normal position by its natural resiliency, and the polypide is forced back into the zooecium by the higher external water pressure (Fig. 7.15.1a, 1b). The action of retractor muscles attached to the base of the polypide is coordinated with action of muscles attached to the ectocyst. Naturally, the ectocyst is not preserved fossil; hence bryozoans with this kind of structure are unusually lacy in appearance (Fig. 7.18.1, 2.) A slightly different variation of the foregoing operation is provided by Bryozoa in which there is a perforated skeletal platform (**cryptocyst**) beneath the ectocyst. Action is the same as in the forms with only an ectocyst, except that muscles pass through the holes in the cryptocyst (Fig. 7.15.2). Yet another variation is seen in forms in which there is a perforated skeletal roof (**pleurocyst**) above the ectocyst (Fig. 7.15.4). In this arrangement the pores in the pleurocyst allow water to force the ectocyst down when retractor muscles contract.

In the second *basic* method of operation the entire zooecium is calcareous and imperforate; hence the frontal wall is rigid (Fig. 7.15.3). Fluid pressure increases within the zooecia of primitive members of this group when a special bag or **compensating sac** (also called the **ascus**) expands. The ascus

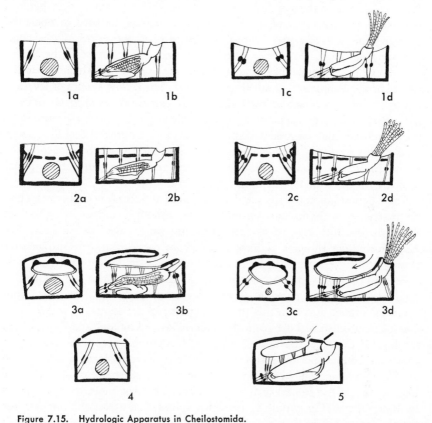

1a   1b   1c   1d

2a   2b   2c   2d

3a   3b   3c   3d

4   5

Figure 7.15. Hydrologic Apparatus in Cheilostomida.
1, 2, 4 are anascans; 3, 5 are ascophorans. All illustrations enlarged. Skeletal material is indicated by heavy lines. Contraction of muscle strands is indicated by bunching of central area. 1. Operation with ectocyst. 1a, 1b, transverse and longitudinal cross sections with retracted polypide. 1c, 1d, transverse and longitudinal sections with extended polypide. 2. Operation of zooecium with cryptocyst below ectocyst. 2a, 2b, retracted. 2c, 2d, extended. 3. Operation of a simple ascophoran, as in 1 and 2. 4. Transverse section of an anascan with a pleurocyst, but which would have functioned as in 1. 5. Longitudinal section of an advanced ascophoran with a retracted polypide, with an ascopore. Operation would have been as in 3.
(Mostly after Harmer, 1902.)

lies alongside the digestive track and opens to the outside of the zooecium through a special orifice that indents the posterior side of the aperture. If muscles inserted between the elastic base of the compensating sac and the rigid zooecial walls contract, the sac expands and forces the polypide out of the aperture (Fig. 7.15.3c, 3d). At the same time water from outside is sucked into the orifice of the compensating sac and enables it to expand.

Conversely, contraction of the compensating sac and simultaneous expulsion of its contents reduces fluid pressure within the zooecium, and the polypide is forced back to its retracted position by water from the outside (Fig. 7.15.3a, 3b). Naturally, the operculum opens and closes in conformity with the different positions of the polypide, but the hydrologic system is so ingenious that while the anterior end of the operculum swings outward to open the aperture, the posterior part swings inward to open the orifice of the compensating sac. Opercula of these cheilostomes reflect the nature of the hydrologic apparatus because they bear a tonguelike appendage which closes the mouth of the compensating sac (Fig. 7.14.4, 5). The seesaw system of leverage has as its fulcrum a pair of toothlike spines (**cardelles**) on opposite sides of the aperture. If large cardelles articulate with the operculum the outline of the operculum may be indented into the shape of a numeral 8 (Fig. 7.14.2). In the most advanced cheilostomes with compensating sacs the mouth of the sac has migrated back out of the zooecial aperture and opens through a special **ascopore** on the frontal wall (Figs. 7.14.1a and 7.15.5).

The Cheilostomida usually are divided into two Suborders depending upon the nature of the hydrologic system. Those without a compensating sac are the Anascina, and those with a compensating sac are the Ascophorina. The Ascophorina are thought to have arisen from the Anascina by progressive closing off of the ectocyst by one of the skeletal layers shown in Figure 7.15.

Perhaps the best-known sequence of modifications by which some Anascina produced some Ascophorina is the development of a pleurocyst from apertural spines. Stages in this morphologic series are shown in Figure 7.16. The Genera illustrated are from the Cretaceous of England and Europe, but the figured examples are not all in strict stratigraphic sequence and do not constitute an evolutionary series as shown. The ancestral form is represented by *Membranipora,* in which a simple ectocyst is surrounded by a ring of long spines on the frontal wall (Fig. 7.16.7). The first modification appears in *Myagropora* (Fig. 7.16.1, 8) in which spines arch across the ectocyst but remain unfused. The first fusion of the tips of spines characterizes the Genus *Anaptopora* (Fig. 7.16.2), in which an **apertural bar** is formed by cohesion of the first set of spines posterior to the aperture. Inasmuch as apertural spines are slightly offset on opposite sides of the frontal wall, they do not meet symmetrically across the ectocyst. As a result of this, the apertural bar in primitive Genera is asymmetrical, but it becomes symmetrical in advanced Genera. Successive rows of spines rapidly become fused into **costae** which meet along the midline in *Thoracopora* (Fig. 7.16.3). At this stage one can say that the spines have been transformed into a pleurocyst. Moreover, the aperture begins to show a waistlike constriction which presumably signifies that a compensating sac was present. Solidification of the pleurocyst came about through two processes. Some Genera such as *Calpidopora* (Fig. 7.16.4)

increased the number of costae and the strength of each costa, whereas
Genera such as *Andriopora* (Fig. 7.16.5) are characterized by the presence
of lateral processes which bridge the space between adjacent costae. The

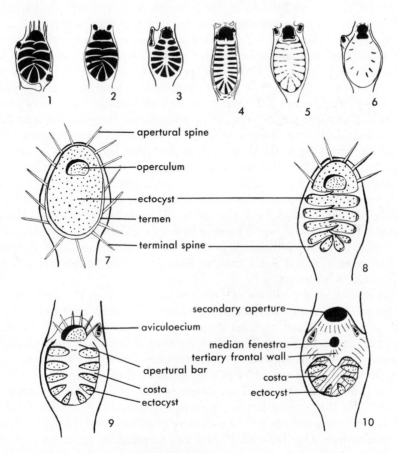

Figure 7.16.   Modifications of Frontal Walls.
1-6. Morphologic series showing development of a solid frontal wall from spines, enlarged.
7. Schematic diagram of *Membranipora* sp. with the ectocyst stippled, enlarged.   8. Schematic
diagram of *Myagropora* sp., enlarged.   9. Schematic diagram of a so-called cribrimorph
cheilostome (one with prominent costae), enlarged.   10. Schematic diagram of a so-called
steganomorph cheilostome (one with a secondary roof), enlarged.
(1-6 from Lang, 1921, 1922. Reproduced by permission of the Trustees of the British Museum.
7-10 after Lang, 1921-1922.)

pleurocyst has become a solid plate without perforations in *Tricolpopora*
(Fig. 7.16.6); hence there is no question that this form must have had a com-
pensating sac. Moreover, the aperture is distinctly ascophorine in outline.
   Evolution of the so-called cribrimorph group of cheilostomatous bryozoans

has been studied in great detail by Lang (1919, 1921-1922).[1] He recognized ten Families of cribrimorphs, each of which he concluded arose independently from an ancestor resembling *Membranipora* (Fig. 7.16.7) and then evolved by parallel descent with the other nine Families. As an example, the patterns and changes within the Pelmatoporidae are shown in Figure 7.17.

The frontal wall of the Pelmatoporidae consists of arched hollow costae which meet and fuse along the midline of the frontal wall; but the tips of the costae bend up to form low spines (**pelmae**) which resemble hobnails on the frontal wall. The aperture of an unspecialized form bears four spines on its distal margin and is flanked on its proximal margin by a heavy apertural bar. Large primary avivuloecia are conspicuous alongside the aperture. The principal adaptive problem involves the addition of increasing amounts of calcium carbonate to the skeleton until the spaces between the costae are filled and the frontal wall becomes essentially solid; apertural spines are then entombed; and the lateral walls between zooecia are thickened and covered with a secondary deposit. If the apertural spines are lost, the position of the middle pair is occupied by a pair of small secondary aviculoecia. Minor changes concern rather general increase in size (not shown); general increase in number of costae; and change in the shape of the aperture from elongate to transverse. Colonial habit changes from incrusting to erect and from unilaminar to bilaminar.

The main line of evolution of *Pelmatopora* passes from *P. calceata* to *P. damicornis* by changing the habit from incrusting, through erect and unilaminar, to erect and bilaminar. Sizes of zooecia increase, but they are all depicted the same size in Figure 7.17 for greatest clarity. Zooecia lose their elliptical shape and become parallel-sided. Costae increase in number. Primary pelmae migrate laterally and secondary or even tertiary pelmae occupy the midline of the fused costae. Apertural spines are present up through the stage of *P. pero*, but that species has no secondary aviculoecia. *P. brydonei* bears one pair of spines and one pair of secondary aviculoecia and thereby occupies an intermediate stage between *P. pero* and members of the series from *P. marsupitum* through *P. damicornis* which have no spines, but whose secondary aviculoecia become increasingly prominent.

A second trend originated with *P. calceata* and terminated with *P. simplex*.

---

[1] Professor H. Dighton Thomas of the British Museum has been good enough to inform me that some work which he and Dr. G. P. Larwood have been completing has led them to differ in some respects from Lang's analysis of the cribrimorph bryozoans which has been largely followed in this text.

Figure 7.17 (opposite). Evolution of Some Cheilostomida.
Decurtaria, Pelmatopora, and *Tricephalophora* are abbreviated D., P., and T., respectively. Four standard stage names of the Cretaceous are given along the left margin.
(Mostly from Lang, 1921-1922. Reproduced by permission of the Trustees of the British Museum.)

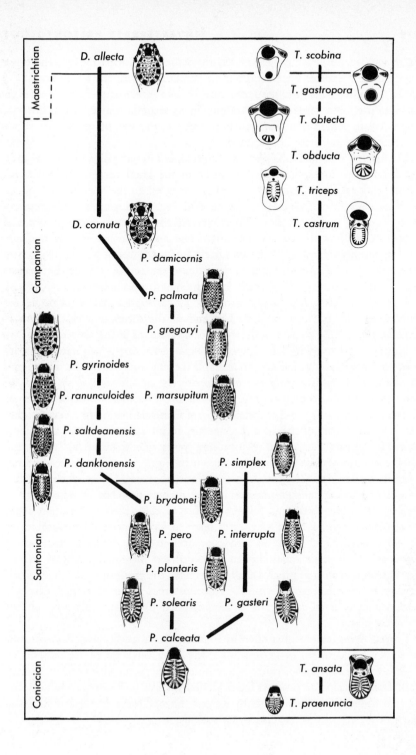

Maastrichtian

D. allecta

T. scobina

T. gastropora

T. obtecta

T. obducta

T. triceps

T. castrum

Campanian

D. cornuta

P. damicornis

P. palmata

P. gregoryi

P. gyrinoides

P. ranunculoides   *P. marsupitum*

P. saltdeanensis

P. danktonensis

P. simplex

P. brydonei

Santonian

P. pero   *P. interrupta*

P. plantaris

P. solearis   *P. gasteri*

P. calceata

Coniacian

T. ansata

T. praenuncia

In this strain the principal characteristic is the small aperture, but the other morphologic features were modified in parallelism with the main strain.

On the other hand, the sequence from *P. danktonensis* to *P. gyrinoides* resembles the main line in the devolopment of secondary aviculoecia, but it is regressive in some other respects. For instance, the size of zooecia decreases and the number of costae decreases.

Decurtaria is a late offshoot of *Pelmatopora* which illustrates the characteristic reduction in number of costae in the latest forms. Moreover, the second pair of secondary aviculoecia has appeared on the aperture.

While species of *Pelmatopora* were evolving, species of *Tricephalophora* went through their evolution. Their characteristic feature is the presence of a tertiary wall which covers the costae like an apron, except for a single perforation, the fenestra. In the two early forms the apron had hardly begun to appear and there is no fenestra. In *T. castrum* and *T. triceps* the tertiary wall covers about half of the costae and the fenestra occupies its normal median position. From *T. obducta* through *T. gastropora* the fenestra shifted proximally and became smaller. The end of the series was reached in *T. scobina,* in which only one of the aviculoecia remains at the aperture.

Figure 7.17 exemplifies how morphologic series can be arranged in conformity with stratigraphic occurrence and thereby lend support to interpretation of the group as a truly evolutionary series. In addition, the illustration conveys an idea of the actual rate of evolution. That portion of the geologic column presented by the European stages of Coniacian through Maastrichtian corresponds to part of the Late Cretaceous, an interval of perhaps 25 million years. It appears that about 1½ million years would be required for the stabilization of each named species shown in Figure 7.17. The total duration of each species is not indicated on that figure, however. Most of the modifications of cheilostomes emphasize a fundamental problem of bryozoans as well as of most other creatures—to dispose of calcareous material in some constructive way. Many invertebrates seem to have entombed themselves in excessive deposits of calcium carbonate and to have evolved very slowly thereafter. Few other invertebrates have utilized increased amounts of calcium carbonate with as much versatility as have the cheilostomes. The general change of chemical composition of cheilostomes from chitinous through chitino-calcareous to calcareous is accompanied by remarkable adaptability and creativity.

Typical Anascina are illustrated in Figure 7.18.1-4, and typical Ascophorina are shown in Figure 7.18.5-12. It is not always easy to recognize the ascopore of these latter cheilostomes because it resembles other perforations on the frontal wall. The Anascina are known from Medial Jurassic to Recent, and the Ascophorina range from Cretaceous to Recent. Except for a few inhabitants of brackish water, all Cheilostomida are marine.

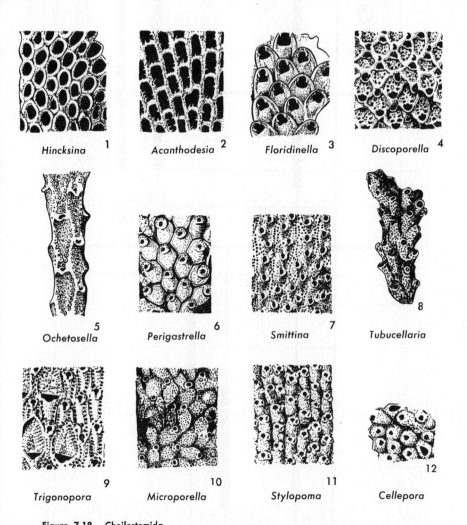

Figure 7.18. Cheilostomida.

1-4 Anascina.   5-12 Ascophorina.   1. *Hincksina jacksonica,* 14X, Eocene, Georgia.   2. *Acanthodesia oblongula,* 14X, Miocene, Maryland.   3. *Floridinella vicksburgica,* 16X, Oligocene, Alabama.   4. *Discoporella umbellata,* 16X, Miocene, Santo Domingo. The ancestrular region is in the center.   5. *Ochetosella jacksonica,* 14X, Eocene, North Carolina.   6. *Perigastrella plana,* 14X, Oligocene, Alabama.   7. *Smittina trispinosa,* 14X, Miocene, North Carolina.   8. *Tubucellaria punctulata,* 8X, Pleistocene, California.   9. *Trigonopora colligata* with simple zooecia and elaborate ovicells, 14X, Miocene, Santo Domingo.   10. *Microporella ciliata* with tiny ascopores and distinct aviculoecia, 14X, Pleistocene, California.   11. *Stylopoma spongites* with ascopore in base of aperture, 14X, Pliocene, Florida.   12. *Cellepora maculata,* 12X, Miocene, Maryland.

(1, 3, 5 after Canu and Bassler, 1920. 2, 4, 7-12 after Canu and Bassler, 1923.)

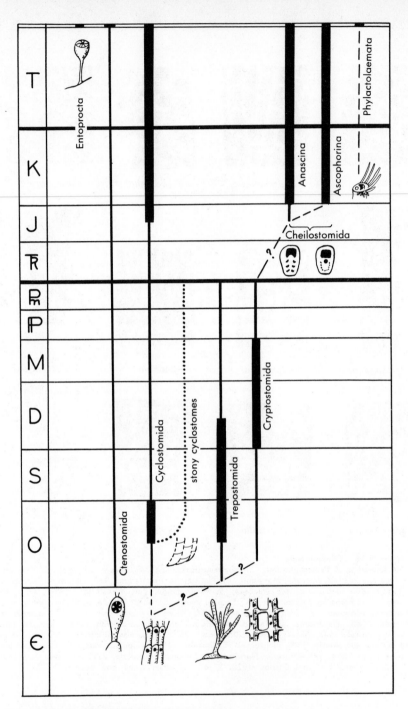

Figure 7.19. Geologic Distribution of Bryozoa.

Cheilostomida are thought by some authorities to have evolved from the Cryptostomida. Their zoaria are similarly constructed and some cheilostomes have a tubular extension to the aperture which resembles the vestibules of cryptostomes. On the other hand, cheilostomes may have sprung from a strain of chitinous cyclostomes and only appeared in the Jurassic when sufficient calcification had taken place to enable them to be preserved.

GEOLOGIC DISTRIBUTION OF BRYOZOA. Bryozoa are exceedingly rare prior to the Middle Ordovician, although they have been found in Upper Cambrian sediments. They must have had an even more ancient history than that, however, because the several Orders are well differentiated at their first appearances. By the Late Ordovician the Bryozoa were very abundant, as in the vicinity of Cincinnati, Ohio, where their study in this country was first most seriously undertaken. There the trepostomes and stony cyclostomes are so common that they spew down the slopes of almost every exposed hillside and are among the most conspicuous fossils. During the Silurian the Trepostomida were joined by increasing numbers of Cryptostomida, as is shown in the well-known biostromes at Clinton, New York. Another flare of Bryozoa took place locally in the Devonian when both the trepostomes and the cryptostomes shared dominance. Devonian faunas of bryozoans are transitional between older and younger Paleozoic forms. Thereafter, calcareous Paleozoic rocks are strewn mostly with fenestellids but with only a few trepostomes. The Pitkin limestone (Mississippian) of Arkansas and Oklahoma, for instance, was originally named the Archimedal Limestone. After the extinction of the Trepostomida and Cryptostomida at the end of the Permian there was a dearth of Bryozoa until the Cyclostomida reappeared in the Middle Jurassic. They continued to be important into the Recent, but were always overshadowed by the lacy Cheilostomida, even in Recent seas. Tertiary cheilostomes are very unevenly distributed, there being many in sediments of the Atlantic Coastal Plain but essentially none in contemporaneous deposits on the Pacific Coast. In England, the name of the Coralline Crag formation (Pliocene) was derived from the great abundance of Cheilostomida which it contains.

PHYLUM X. PHORONIDA

The phoronids (Fig. 7.20) constitute a small group of wormlike animals which lie on the ocean floor, surround themselves with tubular skeletons of sand grains, or inhabit burrows. When arenaceous tubes are built, a phoronid demonstrates remarkable selectivity in choice of clear grains of silica and rarely utilizes a dark mineral grain. The grains are cemented upon an inner chitinous sheath. No hard organic skeleton is present; hence these animals are unknown as fossils unless their burrows or tubes have been preserved. It is probably impossible to tell the difference between phoronid burrows and the burrows of some worms; therefore, sediment-filled fossil burrows, such as have been called *Scolithus,* have been referred to both kinds of animals by different authorities.

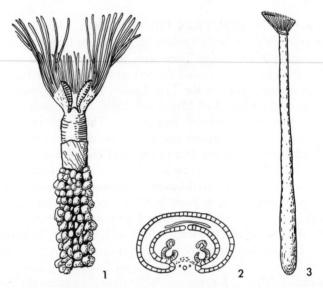

Figure 7.20. Recent Phoronids.
1. Branchial end of *Phoronis architecta.* with sand removed from part of the chitinlike tube, about 20X. 2. Schematic transverse section of the lophophore of *P. architecta,* about 100X. The slitlike mouth is at the upper end and the anal opening flanked by two nephridial openings is near the bottom of the figure. 3. Side view of *P. architecta* removed from its tube, 3X.
(1, 2 after Andrews, 1890. 3 after Brooks and Cowles, 1905.)

A phoronid has a pencil-shaped slender body a few centimeters (generally less than about 15 cm) long and about 5 millimeters in diameter. The oral end bears a spirally enrolled set of tentacles which are attached to a lophophore. The digestive system is organized somewhat as in Bryozoa and in some tubiculous annelids, in that it is U-shaped and the anal opening is on the oral end but outside of the lophophore. Phoronids are generally grouped near the Bryozoa because of these and lesser similarities with that group.

QUESTIONS

1. What feature may explain most readily the lack of fossil material which would clarify the problem of the origin of the Orders of Bryozoa?

2. What other groups, studied so far, construct tubular skeletons? How readily identified are these kinds of creatures?
3. If, as has been claimed, Families of Bryozoa should be defined on the basis of larval stages, then what attitude should a paleontologist have on the problem of their classification?
4. What relationship is there between brown bodies and the Paradox of the Trepostomida?
5. How have the Cheilostomida made effective use of calcium carbonate?
6. Where would you put the break between the Anascina and the Ascophorina with reference to soft anatomy? Skeletal features only?
7. What might acanthopores and mesopores have represented in the living trepostomes?
8. Why might species of Bryozoa make good index fossils?
9. Why might *Archimedes* seem to migrate westward, in view of general circulation of oceanic waters in this hemisphere?
10. How might Cryptostomida have evolved from Cyclostomida? From Trepostomida?

BIBLIOGRAPHY

Andrews, E. A., 1890, On a new American species of the remarkable animal Phoronis: Annals Mag. Nat. Hist., ser. 6, v. 5, pp. 445–449.

Bassler, R. S., 1906a, A study of the James types of Ordovician and Silurian Bryozoa: Proc. U. S. Nat. Mus., v. 30, pp. 1–66.

———, 1906b, The bryozoan fauna of the Rochester shale: U. S. Geol. Survey, Bull. 292.

———, 1932, The stratigraphy of the Central Basin of Tennessee: Tennessee Div. Geol., Bull. 38.

———, 1953, Bryozoa *in* Treatise on invertebrate paleontology, pt. G.

Boardman, R. S., 1954, Morphologic variation and mode of growth of Devonian trepostomatous Bryozoa: Science, v. 120, no. 3112, p. 322.

Brooks, W. K., and Cowles, R. P., 1905, Phoronis architecta: its life history, anatomy, and breeding habits: Nat. Acad. Sci., v. 10, mem. 4, pp. 71–148.

Brydone, R. M., 1913, 1917, Notes on new or imperfectly known Chalk Polyzoa: Geol. Mag.; dec. 5, v. 10, pp. 436-438; dec. 6, vol. 4, pp. 492-496.

Canu, F., 1920, Bryozoaires Crétacés des Pyrénées: Bull. Soc. Géol. France, ser. 4, v. 19, pp. 186–211.

———, and Bassler, R. S., 1920, North American Early Tertiary Bryozoa: U. S. Nat. Mus., Bull. 106 (especially pp. 41–72).

———, and Bassler, R. S., 1923, North American Later Tertiary and Quaternary Bryozoa: U. S. Nat. Mus., Bull. 125.

Claparède, E., 1871, Beiträge zur Anatomie und Entwicklungsgeschichte der Seebryozoen: Zeitschr. Wiss. Zool. v. 21, pp. 137–174.

Clark, D. L., 1959, Conodonts from the Triassic of Nevada and Utah: Jour. Paleont., v. 33, no. 2, pp. 305–312.

Condra, G. E., 1903, The Coal Measure Bryozoa of Nebraska: Nebraska Geol. Survey, v. 2, pt. 1.

Cumings, E. R., 1908, The stratigraphy and paleontology of the Cincinnati Series of Indiana: Indiana Dept. Geol. Nat. Res., 32nd Ann. Rept., pp. 605–1189.

———, and Galloway, J. J., 1915, Studies of the morphology and histology of the Trepostomata or Monticuliporoids: Geol. Soc. America Bull., v. 26, no. 3, pp. 349–374.

Davenport, C. B., 1891, Observations on budding in Paludicella and some other Bryozoa: Bull. Mus. Comp. Zool. (Harvard), v. 22, no. 1, pp. 1–114.

Duncan, H., 1939, Trepostomatous Bryozoa from the Traverse group of Michigan: Univ. Michigan, Contr. Mus. Paleont., v. 5, pp. 171–269.

Fenton, M. A., and Fenton, C. L., 1934, *Scolithus* as a fossil phoronid: Pan-Amer. Geologist, v. 61, pp. 341–348.

Fritz, M. A., 1947, Cambrian Bryozoa: Jour. Paleont., v. 21, no. 5, pp. 434–435.

Gregory, J. W., 1896, Catalogue of the fossil Bryozoa. The Jurassic Bryozoa: London, British Mus. (Nat. Hist.), pp. 3–35.

———, 1909, Catalogue of the Fossil Bryozoa. The Cretaceous Bryozoa: London, British Mus. (Nat. Hist.), v. 2, pp. xiv–xlviii.

Harmer, S. F., 1901, On the structure and classification of the cheilostomatous Polyzoa: Proc. Cambridge Phil. Soc., v. 11, pt. 1, pp. 11–17.

———, 1902, On the morphology of the Cheilostomata: Quart. Jour. Micro. Sci., n. ser., v. 46, no. 182, pp. 263–350.

———, 1930, Polyzoa: Proc. Linnaean Soc. London, sess. 141, pp. 69–118.

Hincks, T., 1880, A history of the British marine Polyzoa: London, John van Voorst, 2 vols.

Lang, W. D., 1919, The Pelmatoporinae, an essay on the evolution of a group of Cretaceous Polyzoa: Phil. Trans. Roy. Soc. London, ser. B, vol. 209, pp. 191–228.

———, 1921–1922, Catalogue of the fossil Bryozoa (Polyzoa). The Cretaceous Bryozoa (Polyzoa): London, British Mus. (Nat. Hist.), vols. 3, 4 (especially pages i–lxxvi).

Loeblich, A. R., 1942, Bryozoa from the Bromide formation, Oklahoma: Jour. Paleont., v. 16, no. 4, pp. 413–436.

Marcus, Ernst, 1940, Mosdyr (Bryozoa Eller Polyzoa): Danmarks Fauna, Dansk Naturhistorisk Forening, 46, Kobenhavn.

Marsson, T. F., 1887, Die Bryozoen der weissen Schreibkreide der Insel Rügen: Geol. Palaeont. Abh., v. 4, pt. 1.

Osburn, R. C., 1950–1953, Bryozoa of the Pacific Coast of America: Los Angeles, Univ. Southern California Press, Allan Hancock Pacific Expedition, v. 14, nos. 1–3. (Ctenostomida with J. D. Soule.)

Pratt, H. S., 1948, A manual of the common invertebrate animals. Philadelphia, The Blakiston Co.

Simpson, G. B., 1895, A handbook of the Genera of the North American Palaeozoic Bryozoa: New York State Mus., 48th Ann. Rept., v. 2, pp. 403–669.

Stach, L. W., 1938, Colony-formation in Smittina papillifera (MacGillivray, 1869) (Bryozoa): Proc. Zool. Soc. London, ser. B, v. 108, pp. 401–415.

Ulrich, E. O., 1890, Palaeontology of Illinois. Palaeozoic Bryozoa: Illinois Geol. Survey, v. 8, pt. 2, sec. 6, pp. 283–678.

———, 1895, On Lower Silurian Bryozoa of Minnesota: Minnesota Geol. Nat. Hist. Survey, v. 3, pt. 1, ch. 4, pp. 96–332.

———, and Bassler, R. S., 1905, A revision of the Paleozoic Bryozoa: Smithsonian Misc. Coll., v. 47, pp. 15–55.

Waters, A. W., 1926, Ancestrula of Cheilostomatous Bryozoa. Part V. *Cupularia etc.:* Annals Mag. Nat. Hist., ser. 9, v. 18, pp. 424–433.

Chapter 8

BRACHIOPODS

PHYLUM XI. BRACHIOPODA

From time to time one group or another of fossil organisms has been especially popular for paleontologic studies, but the brachiopods seem to have been more consistently studied than have any other groups. More than 1200 Genera have been recognized, of which 68 are represented by living species. Even in this time of increasing specialization their elucidation continues to occupy the talents of numerous paleontologists whose primary interest is with other Phyla. Naturally, this continued interest is merely a reflection of the value of brachiopods in applied geology as well as in purely systematic studies. In particular, brachiopods are popular in paleontology because they generally provide well-preserved fossils; they are common; many of them can be identified from their external characteristics; there is considerable diversity of form; their species have reasonably short duration in time; and they range rather widely in geographic distribution. In addition, major advances are being made in understanding the evolutionary history of brachiopods; hence, systematic studies now promise to be unusually rewarding in the way that similar studies are for cephalopods.

THE LIVING ANIMAL. Brachiopods are bivalved organisms which generally live attached to some hard object by a muscular stalk that protrudes from a hole in the posterior part of the shell. A few brachiopods are free-living, although they merely lie on the ocean floor, but others are cemented to the substratum in the fashion of oysters, and some burrow into unconsolidated sediments. Although a few Recent brachiopods such as *Lingula* can tolerate brackish water, almost all fossil brachiopods are indicative of a marine environment. Moreover, a similar ancient distribution is indicated by associations of strictly marine organisms with fossil brachiopods. Residents of North America rarely find a Recent brachiopod shell washed up on the beaches, but brachiopods abound in shallow water in the western and southern

Pacific Ocean. They are even said to be used as food in Japan. By one count, 71 per cent of the Recent brachiopods live in less than 600 feet of water, and almost all of the remainder live near the continental margins rather than in the deep sea. Dredging discovers myriad brachiopods clustered together, such as off Southern California where bushels of *Laqueus* have been recovered in water about 200 to 300 feet (60-100 m) deep. In general, the deep-water forms are thin-shelled and smooth, whereas the shallow-water forms are thick-shelled and may be ribbed.

Brachiopods are filter-feeders; that is, they circulate water between their shells and strain out the microscopic organisms. They therefore require a shell with a large volume to contain an adequate filtering device and they need some sort of musculature to open and close the two **valves** or halves of their skeleton. Brachiopods tend to be sedentary creatures because their shells must be thickest, heaviest, and most cumbersome when they live in shallow water where the greatest food supply exists. Even so, they have remained vigorous longer than have the members of most other Phyla.

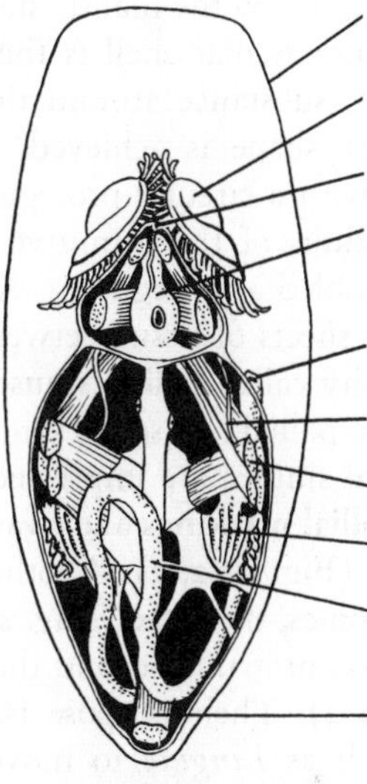

The soft parts which occupy the interior of a brachiopod shell can be divided into two portions. Some or most of the interior of the shell is occupied by a large system of fluffy tentacles which are borne on

Figure 8.1. Anatomy of a Brachiopod.
Dorsal view of *Glottidia* sp. with the dorsal shell and part of the digestive and reproductive glands removed, about 3X, Recent.
(After Morse, 1902.)

two fleshy armlike cores, the whole apparatus being called the **lophophore** or **brachia** (Figs. 8.1; 8.8). Cilia on the tentacles create currents in the water which flow toward the mouth. Moreover, respiration is carried on by the lophophore.

Behind the lophophore is the visceral mass, which is principally interesting because of its incredibly small size in proportion to the size of the entire shell. The mouth leads into a simple digestive track which has an anus in one group but which ends blindly in the other group. The anterior part of the nervous system encircles the digestive track. Some other parts serve light-sensitive functions. Excretory functions are carried on by one or two pairs of nephridia. Although a tiny heart is present, the circulatory system is rudimentary. Sexes are separate. Very early development of larvae of some Recent brachiopods is passed within the shell of the female. After leaving a brood chamber the larva passes through a trochophorelike stage and then fastens itself down on the substratum by its pedicle. The total free-living period lasts only about one day. There is then a metamorphosis of the larva in which two flaps of tissue, the mantle lobes, swing forward to enclose the main part of the animal as if in a shell. One of these mantle lobes develops into the two **mantles** which eventually secrete the shell and then persist through life as the fleshy internal lining of the shell.

Secretion of a shell by the mantle starts soon after the larva becomes sedentary. This minute circular shell is the **protegulum.** It grows by progressive addition of shell substance around the margin and over the inner surface until the mature shape is achieved. Even elongate, transverse, or conical shells start out with a circular protegulum. To many authorities this feature indicates that adults of the primitive group from which brachiopods arose must have resembled a protegulum. Although mantles are thin, they consist typically of two sheets of tissue between which are located lobate extensions of the body cavity called **pallial sinuses.** Sex glands are located in branched extensions of the pallial sinuses of some brachiopods. In those brachiopods in which the pallial sinuses are impressed into the inner surfaces of the valves, the patterns (**pallial markings** and **ovarian impressions**) they make are useful in classification (Fig. 8.2.2, 3). Another function of the mantle is to secrete tiny chitinous spines, the **setae** (sing. **seta**), which are embedded in the edge of the mantle and protrude beyond the margin of the shells of some brachiopods (Fig. 8.4.2–4). Their purpose is, at least in part, to assist inarticulate brachiopods such as *Lingula* to move and to burrow into sediment. It is true that most linguloids burrow "tail first" by means of their pedicle, but they also may burrow "head first" by a combination of sliding action of the valves and use of setae. Setae may be indicative of a relation between brachiopods and some annelid worms, because these are the only two Phyla in which setae are embedded in soft tissue.

COMPOSITION. Chemical composition of brachiopod shells varies but falls into two great groups. The most primitive shells are more chitinous and phosphatic than are the shells of advanced forms. Those with phosphatic shells, for instance, consist of 25 to 42 per cent organic substance combined in layers or in intimate mixture with mineral matter. The mineral matter alone may be composed of 75 to 92 per cent calcium phosphate and as much as 11 or 12 per cent calcium carbonate. On the other hand, those with calcareous shells contain about 5 per cent organic substance in the shells and the mineral matter is composed of about 98 per cent calcium carbonate and of only very little calcium phosphate. It is very probable that brachiopods weather out of rocks so nicely because the chitinous and phosphatic substances which may be present are less soluble in water than is calcium carbonate.

ORIENTATION. In common parlance the brachiopods are often referred to as "lamp-shells," in allusion to their resemblance to the oil lamps of antiquity with their spoutlike supports for wicks. The fact is, however, that brachiopods grow into a variety of shapes, some of which are hardly recognizable as being bivalves at all. The form for which the appellation of lamp-shell is appropriate is exemplified by Recent brachiopods such as *Terebratula,* which are ovate in outline, no matter how they are viewed. Many Paleozoic brachiopods, such as *Spirifer,* were articulated along a hinge line, the length of which is greater than is that of the anterior-posterior dimension. The classic chitino-phosphatic brachiopods, such as species of *Lingula,* are tongue-shaped or spatulate, but some of their relatives are more or less circular. Among calcareous shells, triangular, semicircular, quadrate, and V-shaped outlines are common; and bivalved shapes range from lenticular to hemispherical, spherical, cuboidal, and conical. Probably the most bizarre are *Richthofenia* and its allies in which the conical ventral valve is cemented to the substratum and guyed with oblique props like *Archimedes* and some corals. Moreover, the coralline shape of this brachiopod is enhanced by the reduction of the circular dorsal valve to the status of an inconspicuous operculum lying below septumlike spines around the aperture of the large ventral valve.

Two schools of thought exist as to how to designate the two valves of brachiopods. According to one school the large valve from which the pedicle protrudes could be called the ventral valve, whereas this is called the **pedicle valve** by other specialists. The other or dorsal valve is called the **brachial valve** by most specialists now because the lophophore or brachia is attached to it. For a time it was thought that dorsal and ventral might have been confused in the terminology of some brachiopods, but recent embryologic studies fortunately have stabilized the long-term usage. Pedicle valves are primarily characterized by the presence of the opening for the pedicle, and, otherwise, by the large size and by the rather general presence of a broad depression, the **sulcus,** which indents the anterior portion of the valve (Fig. 8.10.4a). Brachial valves are smaller than pedicle valves and bear a **fold** or raised area corresponding with the sulcus of the pedicle valve (Fig. 8.10.4a). It is customary to speak of the anterior-posterior dimension of brachiopods as the **length,** the distance in the direction of the hinge line as the **width,** and the dorsal-ventral distance through the two valves as the **thickness.** The pointed posterior extremity of a valve is the **beak.** Valves of many brachiopods are more convex for a short distance just anterior to the beak than they are in the anterior halves of the valves; that is, the radius of curvature of the surface is shorter near the beak than near the anterior edge.

This humplike raised area of indefinite extent is called the **umbo** (pl. **umbones**).

MUSCULATURE. Valves of **articulate** brachiopods interlock by teeth and sockets, whereas valves of **inarticulate** brachiopods lack teeth and sockets. The fundamental difference between inarticulate and articulate brachiopods is reflected not only in the construction of the articular devices of the shells, but also in the nature of the muscles which open and close the valves. Moreover, modification of position and size of muscles have to be coordinated with changes in proportion and function of shells in all groups; therefore systematists rely upon musculature for assistance in classifying all kinds of brachiopods. Naturally, muscles decompose upon the death of the animal, but their impressions (**muscle scars**) in the shell substance leave characteristic patterns over the areas of insertion (Fig. 8.2.1a, 1b). Musculature has been worked out for several Recent brachiopods, so it is possible to demonstrate homologies with muscle scars in ancient forms. In interpreting position of muscle scars it is necessary to relate scars to age of shells because the scars move anteriorly and inwardly during growth and leave **muscle tracks** as evidence of the history of these changes.

Inarticulate brachiopods are equipped with numerous pairs of muscles, some of which are normal to the inner surfaces of the valves and some of which are oblique (Figs. 8.1; 8.4.5). Valves are opened by contraction of muscles near the beak and relaxing muscles farther forward, which forces fleshy tissue forward and causes the valves to gape along the anterior margin. Closure is accomplished by contracting all of the muscles. In the absence of teeth and sockets, the oblique muscles serve to adjust the two valves into nicely opposed position, very much as if these muscles were the crisscrossed mooring lines between a ship and a pier. This characteristic sliding action of the valves of inarticulates also enables the creatures to shift their valves over the sea floor or to burrow into soft sediment. In general, musculature of inarticulates evolved from many to fewer pairs of muscles. Unfortunately, muscle scars are very hard to detect on inarticulate valves.

Articulate brachiopods, on the other hand, very generally have well-defined muscle scars which are useful in identification (Fig. 8.2). An articulate opens and closes the shell by movements of the brachial valve as if it were a simple lever whose fulcum is along an imaginary line connecting the two sockets. The valves are brought together by contraction of **adductor muscles,** one end of which is attached to the long arm of the lever (that is, anterior to the sockets), and the other end of which is inserted on the floor of the pedicle valve at a corresponding position anterior to the teeth. Adductor muscles are paired, so there are two adductor muscle scars in the pedicle valve. As the adductors ascend toward the brachial valve they each split into two strands;

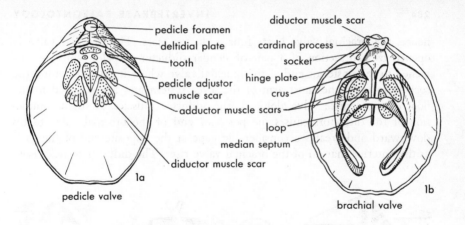

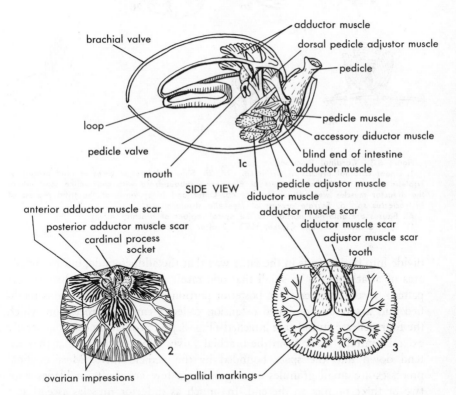

Figure 8.2. Musculature of brachiopods.

1. *Waldheimia flavescens*, IX, Recent. 1a, interior of pedicle valve. 1b, interior of brachial valve. 1c, side view obliquely up into both valves, with median septum and lophophore removed. 2. Internal mold of brachial valve of *Orthostrophia strophomenoides*, 1 1/3X, Devonian, midwestern and eastern states. 3. Schematic view of interior of pedicle valve of *Plaesiomys subquadrata*, 1 1/3X, Ordovician, widespread in United States and Canada.

(1 after Davidson, 1886. 2 after Hall and Clarke, 1892. 3 after Schuchert and Cooper, 1932.)

hence, the brachial valve bears four adductor scars. The brachial valve is opened by contraction of a pair of slender **diductor muscles** which are attached to the posterior end of the brachial valve where it extends behind the sockets to form the short arm of the lever system and are attached to the floor of the pedicle valve alongside the adductor muscles. A slight contraction of the diductors causes the posterior end of the brachial valve to tip downward and creates a considerable gape at the opposite end of the shell as the anterior margin of the brachial valve rises. The diductor muscles each

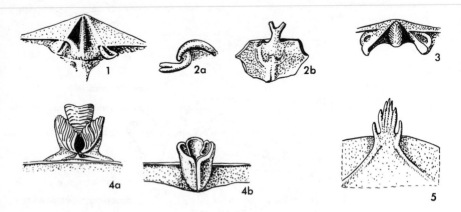

Figure 8.3. Cardinal Processes.
1. Linear cardinal process of *Orthis* sp. 2a, 2b. Side and interior views of bifid process of *Triplesia ortoni*. 3. Bulbous process of *Plaesiomys subquadrata* with chevronlike scars where the diductor muscles were attached. 4a, 4b. Outer and inner views of the trifid process of *Dictyoclostus* sp. 5. Serrate process of *Meekella striatocostata*.
All figures are enlarged portions of the apical regions of brachial valves.
(1, 2, 4, 5 after Hall and Clarke, 1892. 3 after Meek, 1873.)

divide into two strands in the same way that the adductors do, but the whole area of attachment is so small that one rarely can observe any distinct scar pattern. Instead, the extreme posterior portion of the brachial valve is modified into a specially designed extension called a **cardinal process** on which the four delicate strands are attached (Fig. 8.3). Cardinal processes generally extend ventrally away from the brachial valve, which is to say that they extend down into the space bounded by the pedicle valve. Most cardinal processes are small granules or ridges, but a few are shafts or blades with two or three prongs on the end. Inasmuch as diductor muscles ascend at a very acute angle toward the brachial valve, the cardinal process provides an inclined surface for the most advantageous attachment of the muscles and also increases the force with which the valve is opened by increasing the length of the short arm of the lever. Diductor scars on the pedicle valve are characteristically larger than are the adductors and tend to enclose the adductors. It must be emphasized that the central portion of each valve bears four prominent scars, but those in the brachial valve are all adductors, whereas two of those in the pedicle valve are adductors and two are diductors.

Those brachiopods which have a functional pedicle adjust their position upon it by two sets of muscles. The single **protractor muscle** retracts the pedicle. Its scar is located in the umbo of the pedicle valve posterior to the main muscle field. **Adjustor muscles** which occur as a dorsal pair and as a ventral pair rotate the shell about upon the pedicle. Their tiny scars are sometimes apparent behind the diductor scars on the pedicle valve and behind the outside adductor scars on the brachial valve. If **accessory diductor muscles** are present (as most commonly found in some post-Paleozoic brachiopods) their scars will be located in continuity with and just posterior to the adductor scars in the pedicle valve. No muscles such as those which perform the sliding actions of inarticulate shells are present.

CLASSIFICATION. It presumably is apparent to the reader by now that brachiopods can be divided into two very different groups on the basis of composition, articulation, and musculature. In fact, these two groups diverge so much that there is almost no reason to discuss additional morphologic features except as they apply to one or the other group. The situation is analogous to that among some Vertebrata, for there is as much difference between inarticulate and articulate brachiopods as there is between birds and mammals. Accordingly, the Phylum Brachiopoda is divided into two Classes, the Inarticulata and the Articulata.

Class A. Inarticulata
    Order 1. Atremida
    Order 2. Neotremida

Class A. Inarticulata

The Inarticulata are mostly chitino-phosphatic shells, although a few are calcareous. Their principal characteristic is the absence of teeth and sockets, as a result of which they utilize a complicated musculature for keeping the valves in precise opposition. Their soft anatomy (Fig. 8.1) is characterized by the presence of an anal opening. Embryologically they differ from articulates in producing the pedicle from a different region than do the articulates.

Shells of brachiopods with a high percentage of phosphate and chitin are formed in two ways. If the two materials are present in alternate layers (Fig. 8.6.1), the shells tend to exfoliate readily, whereas if the chitin and calcium phosphate are mixed, the shells tend to be more solid. Some shells are almost entirely chitinous and others are phosphatic.

Skeletal supports for the lophophore are absent in inarticulates, as are most other internal skeletal structures which occur so commonly among the articulates. Ornamentation commonly consists of weak concentric **growth lines.** The two Orders, Atremida and Neotremida, are differentiated on the basis of the nature of the pedicle openings.

Order 1. Atremida

This Order contains inarticulates in which the pedicle opening is shared by both valves or is a slot in the ventral valve, but never passes through a hole or pedicle foramen (Fig. 8.4). Atremida means "without hole." Early stages in the progressive incorporation of the pedicle within the lower or ventral valve, such as can be detected in Genera of Atremida, are thought to represent a major evolutionary trend among brachiopods. Ornamentation generally consists of growth lines only.

Obolus is a small circular form (Fig. 8.4.1) which epitomizes the simplest stage of brachiopod development. Some observers think that the oboloid brachiopods represent the stage represented in the protegulum of more advanced forms. Oboloid brachiopods occur in Precambrian strata as well as in Paleozoic rocks.

By far the most common atrematous brachiopods are referable to *Lingula,* a Genus of tongue-shaped or spatulate shells which is supposed to range from Ordovician (some say Cambrian) to Recent (Fig. 8.4.2-4). If this range is correct, then *Lingula* has lived longer than any other Genus of living creatures. Linguloid brachiopods are represented commonly in many parts of the geologic record. They commonly are the only fossils found in some strata. Living representatives select foul mud as sites for their burrows, and many ancient populations are found in black shales, but fossil linguloids also occur in coarse-grained sandstones. Their simple unornamented shells normally are devoid of detectable muscle scars; hence, *Lingula* and its close relatives are very difficult to identify. This abundant group is almost worthless in stratigraphic paleontology, except that they indicate a brackish or marine environment.

Trimerella is an unusual Silurian Genus with calcareous shells and a raised muscle platform in the ventral valve (Fig. 8.4.8, 9).

Order 2. Neotremida

The Neotremida are inarticulates in which the pedicle has become confined to the ventral valve, even though it may not pass through a circular pedicle opening. Neotremida are equipped with an arched cover (**homoeodeltidium**) which partly closes the pedicle opening. Neotremida are rather characteristically circular in plan view with one flat valve and one conical valve, although

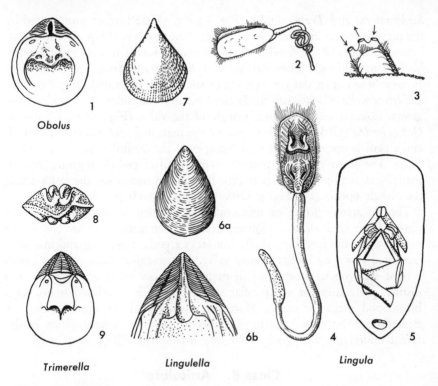

Obolus

Trimerella   Lingulella   Lingula

Figure 8.4.   Atremida.
1. Interior of pedicle valve of *Obolus celatus*, 4X, Cambrian, Russia.   2. *Lingula lepidula* with pedicle contracted, about 1X, Recent.   3. *Lingula lepidula* burrowed into sediment with currents of water (arrows) circulating through setal tubes, about 1X, Recent.   4. *Lingula anatina* with mud tube around tip of extended pedicle, setae, and disposition of viscera, 1X, Recent.   5. Musculature of *Lingula* sp., about 2X.   6. *Lingulella ampla*, Cambrian, widespread. 6a, exterior of ventral valve, 2X. 6b, interior of apex of ventral valve showing pedicle groove and some muscle scars, 4X.   7. Exterior of ventral valve of *Lingulella acuminata*, 1 1/3X, Wisconsin and Minnesota.   8. Posterior view of internal mold of *Trimerella ohioensis*, showing fingerlike projections which fit under muscle platforms, 1/3X, Silurian, Ohio.   9. Interior of pedicle valve of *Trimerella* sp. showing muscle platforms in central area, enlarged.
(1, 6, 7 after Walcott, 1912. 2-4 after Morse, 1902. 5 after Bulman, 1939. 8 after Meek, 1873. 9 after Hall and Clarke, 1892.)

in different groups either the ventral or dorsal valve may be the conical one. Their shell composition is mostly chitino-phosphatic, as in the Atremida.

Paterina is a common Cambrian Genus with concentric ornamentation and a shape resembling the protegulum stage of many branchiopods. *Paterina* has been considered by some paleontologists to be the most primitive known brachiopod.

Schizambon (Fig. 8.5.4.) resembles *Obolus* and some of the linguloids among the Atremida except that it has a very small pedicle opening.

Siphonotreta and *Trematobolos* (Fig. 8.5.2, 3, 5) are further complicated by the presence of an internal tube or sheath leading up to the pedicle foramen.

Several stages in the development of a pedicle foramen seem to be detectable in a morphologic series starting with *Schizocrania* from the Ordovician. It has a broad open slot through which the pedicle extended (Fig. 8.5.7). In *Lindstroemella* (Devonian to Pennsylvanian) the sides of the slot have grown together near the outer margin of the valve (Fig. 8.5.8). Finally, in *Orbiculoidea* (Ordovician to Permian) the marginal area has become fused, and a pedicle opening is left near the apex of the conical ventral valve (Fig. 8.5.9). The inner or apical portion of this kind of pedicle opening may be partially closed by a special plate, the **listrium,** in somewhat the fashion that the pedicle openings of higher Orders of brachiopods are closed.

The calcareous group of neotremates is typified by *Petrocrania,* which ranges from Ordovician to Permian. It is constructed more or less in the same way as the foregoing shells, but lacks a pedicle opening and instead is cemented down by its flat ventral valve. The so-called craniate brachiopods incrust solid objects contained in many Paleozoic strata and may show a distinct preference for a particular substratum such as crinoid stems, large brachiopod shells, or corals. Moreover, members of the same species can demonstrate the most remarkable ability to copy the ornamentation of different underlying surfaces in their own architecture. (Fig. 8.5.11, 12).

Class B.   Articulata

The Articulata characteristically secrete calcareous shells with teeth and sockets, and they utilize a diagnostic musculature for opening and closing the brachial valve. In soft structure they differ from inarticulates in the absence of an anus. Moreover, in their larval development they undergo a metamorphosis which is lacking among Inarticulata. The pedicle among articulates originates from the posterior segment of the larva instead of from a mantle lobe.

Articulates are differentiated among themselves on the basis of shell structure, shape, ornamentation, nature of the hinge region, and on internal features, almost all of which are not represented among Inarticulata. An especially important structure in several groups is the **brachidium,** which is a calcareous support for the lophophore.

Most of the common and paleontologically significant brachiopods are articulates.

SHELL STRUCTURE. Calcareous shells are formed in three ways, the discrimination of which is absolutely necessary for the accurate identification of most species. **Impunctate** shells consist of an outer organic layer, the

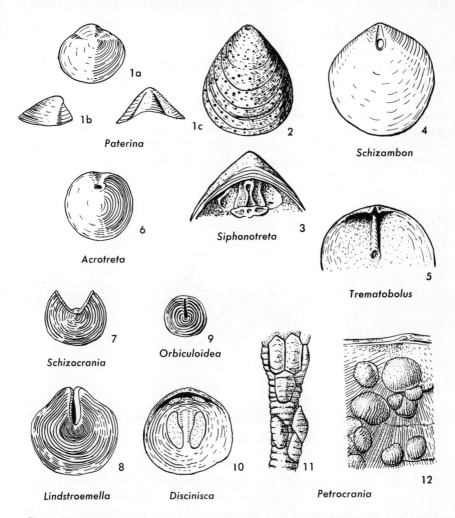

Figure 8.5. Neotremida.
1a, 1b, 1c, apical, side, and posterior views of ventral valve of *Paterina bella*, 10X, Lower Cambrian, Pennsylvania. 2, 3. Pedicle valves of *Siphonotreta* spp., Cambro-Ordovician, Russia. 2, exterior, 3X. 3, pedicle sheath and muscle scars at apex of interior of pedicle valve, about 5X. 4. Exterior of pedicle valve of *Schizambon typicalis*, 4X, Ordovician, Nevada. 5. Pedicle sheath in interior of pedicle valve of *Trematobolus insignis*, 2X, Cambrian, Nova Scotia. 6. Exterior of pedicle valve of *Acrotreta gemmula*, 8X, Cambrian, Nova Scotia. 7. Exterior of pedicle valve of *Schizocrania filosa*, 1 1/3X, Ordovician, eastern states. 8. Exterior of pedicle valve of *Lindstroemella aspidium*, 1/2X, Devonian, New York. 9. Exterior of pedicle valve of *Orbiculoidea missouriensis*, 2X, Pennsylvanian, widespread. 10. Interior of brachial valve of *Discinisca lugubris*, 1X, Miocene, Maryland. 11. Several *Petrocrania scabiosa* incrusting a crinoid column, 3X, Ordovician, Kentucky. 12. Several *Petrocrania scabiosa* incrusting *Rafinesquina alternata*, 1X, Ordovician, Kentucky.

(1-6 after Walcott, 1912. 7, 8, 11, 12 after Hall and Clarke, 1892. 9 after Dunbar and Condra, 1932. 10 after Clark et al., 1904.)

periostracum, and of two kinds of underlying calcareous layers which may be repeated in several layers. If two layers are present, the outer calcareous layer consists of laminated calcium carbonate deposited like shingles in a roof so that successive plates overlap toward the margin in the same way that shingles overlap in successive rows up the pitch of a roof. The innermost calcareous layer is shingled like the laminar layer but the plates consist of prismatic calcium carbonate. Impunctate shells are known in strata from the Cambrian to the Recent. Their basic structure is known among the inarticulates (Fig. 8.6.1) as well as among the articulates.

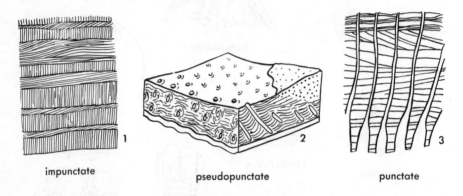

impunctate   pseudopunctate   punctate

Figure 8.6. Structure of Brachiopod Shells.
1. Transverse section of *Lingula anatina*, greatly enlarged. 2. Pseudopunctate shell with spine bases embedded in fibrous layer, and with lamellar layer at base, enlarged. 3. Punctate shell of a terebratulid brachiopod, 85X.
(1 after Hall and Clarke, 1892. 2 after Williams, 1953a. 3 after Carpenter, 1845.)

Punctate shells (Fig. 8.6.3) consist of the same layers as are present in the impunctate shells, but the shell is traversed by microscopic tubules, the **punctae** (sing. **puncta**). These are mostly the spaces occupied in life by cylindrical microscopic columns of fleshy material (the **caeca,** sing. **caecum**) extending up from the mantle; but some punctae seem to originate from the exterior and extend down into the shell; therefore they cannot have arisen from the mantle. If punctae traverse the valve completely or are of the exterior variety (**exopunctae**), they are readily visible on the surfaces of the valves. On the other hand, those caeca which traverse only the inner part of the valves produce **endopunctae** which are not visible on the surface. In this case it is necessary to dissolve or grind away a little of the surface of a shell in order to reveal punctae. Fortunately, many shells exfoliate in such a way that endopunctae are exposed when shells are cracked out of their matrix. Endopunctae are known from rocks as old as Chazy, whereas exopunctae first appear a little later in the Medial Ordovician. Punctae can be seen in many shells with a hand lens, but in others a microscope or even preparation of thin sections may be necessary in order to reveal them. Their sizes and patterns are variable, although not much use has been made of these minor differences for classification.

Pseudopunctate shells (Fig. 8.6.2) seem at first glance to be punctate, particularly if only the surface is viewed. As a matter of fact it may be necessary to prepare thin sections tangential to the surface in order to show that dots which appear to be punctae are actually solid substance instead of voids formerly occupied by caecae of the mantle. Longitudinal sections demonstrate clearly that pseudopunctae are rods embedded in the shell substance. The rods are the lower ends of minute external spines which commonly are broken off at the surface of the shell and thereby leave stumps which falsely resemble punctae. Pseudopunctae are known from the Early Ordovician to the Recent.

SHAPE. The normal or generalized shape of brachiopod shells is such that both valves are externally convex and the pedicle valve is the larger of the two. These are the **biconvex** shells (Figs. 8.12, 8.20). Modifications of shape commonly affect the brachial valve more than the normally convex pedicle valve, with the result that brachial valves may be flat in **plano-convex** shells (Fig. 8.10.2, 3) or depressed to displace some volume of the pedicle valve in **concavo-convex** shells (Fig. 8.17.2, 3). It will be noticed from the foregoing linguistic constructions that the shape of the brachial valve is stated before that of the pedicle valve in each compound term. Although the pedicle valve is usually convex, it is flat or concave in some strains which therefore have **convexo-plane** or **convexo-concave** shells respectively. Shells of other brachiopods are initially concavo-convex near the beaks but then their curvature is reversed abruptly and becomes convexo-concave in their anterior portions; these are **resupinate** in shape (Fig. 8.17.1). Shells with the foregoing shape but in which brachial and pedicle are reversed are **pseudoresupinate.** Finally, some odd shapes of conical or irregular shells are known.

Shell shape is paleontologically valuable in two ways. First, unusual shapes such as resupinate or conical are rarely encountered and thereby enable rapid recognition of a fossil. It is by recognition of the unusual or abnormal features that many excellent guide fossils are established. Moreover, the unusual species generally are more readily identified than are their more conventionally constructed relatives. Unfortunately, brachiopods are notoriously repetitious in duplicating the same shapes in unrelated strains and at various times in the geologic record; that is, they are prone to evolve in convergent patterns. Second, either the brachial or the pedicle valve may be concave;

hence two evolutionary trends are possible. Each trend consists of the same consecutive stages and culminates in the appropriate resupinate or pseudo-resupinate shape. No small genetic group goes through all of the stages between biconvex and resupinate (or pseudoresupinate), but various presumed genetic strains pass through part of the sequence in their history; and different strains may pass through the same stages at different times. Although the same sequence of changes affects creatures with different shell structure (impunctate, punctate, and pseudopunctate), it is only the pseudopunctate shells which achieve the highest degree of resupinate and pseudoresupinate modification. Convergence of shapes of brachiopods presents an intricate pattern in time and in evolution; therefore differences in shape are of importance in identifying brachiopods.

It is customary to illustrate brachiopods by orienting the posterior or the dorsal aspect toward the upper edge of the page as the case may require, even though this violates the normal rule for orienting the illustration of an animal so that the anterior is toward the top of a page.

ORNAMENTATION. Identification of brachiopods is greatly facilitated by the presence of ornamentation. Those few forms which are completely smooth are apt to be difficult to identify from external features because they are either inarticulates or are of the common lamp-shell shape. Even the latter generally bear a sulcus and fold; hence they may be said to bear ornamentation of a sort. Incidentally, the use of "ornamentation" has come to imply all sorts of surface modification rather than merely the seemingly decorative features. It is presumed that all of these features had some function during the life of the animal and that purely decorative design did not prevail. It is not known that vanity can be attributed to any invertebrate and to any but a very few vertebrates.

Ornamentation of brachiopods falls into two groups, the concentric and the radial. The simplest ornamentation consists of **growth lines,** which represent the successive increments of shell material which are added around the margins of the valves. **Lamellae** (sing. **lamella**) are overlapping concentric frills which may extend out a millimeter more or less from the shell surface. Large skirtlike lamellae are **frills** (Fig. 8.15.3). Lamellae may be frayed along the outer edge to produce **spines,** and these may be simple or may be paired like barrels of a double-barreled shotgun (Fig. 8.15.1a). All of these delicate lamellose and spinose features normally are broken off or eroded away when brachiopods become separated from their matrix. Brachiopods may also bear fine concentric ridges (**fila;** sing. **filum**) or coarse ones (**rugae;** sing. **ruga;** Fig. 8.18.14).

Radial ornamentation is more useful than is concentric ornamentation in identifying brachiopods. In a sense the fold and sulcus comprise conspicuous radial ornamentation which becomes integrated with less pronounced radial ornamentation in some forms. The finest radial ornamentation consists of raised threadlike ridges called **costella** (sing. **costellum**) which are analogous to the fila of concentric ornamentation (Fig. 8.11.3, 4). Most radial ridges which are 1 millimeter or less in height are called **costae** (sing. **costa**; Fig. 8.11.1, 2). Very coarse radial ridges are called **plicae** (sing. **plica**) because they resemble pleats of the shell substance (Fig. 8.11.6).

Special ornamentation, such as large curved spines, is present in the Late Paleozoic productids. These spines served to fasten shells to the substratum. Finally, concentric and radial ornamentation may be combined in various ways. Growth lines, for instance, cut across the radial ornamentation, but when rugae and costae of equal strength intersect in netlike patterns the shell is said to be **reticulate** (Fig. 8.18.14, 16).

CARDINAL MARGIN. The **cardinal margin** of a brachiopod is that part of the shell connected with and posterior to the imaginary **hinge line** (Fig. 8.7.4, 5). It consists of the articular regions of both valves and of the pedicle structures of the ventral valve.

The most readily visualized structures of the cardinal margins are present on **transverse** shells which articulate along straight margins, such as in *Spirifer* (Fig. 8.13.7–9) rather than on **rostrate** shells with little or no straight margin of articulation, such as in the terebratuloids (Fig. 8.20). It is very likely, however, that rostrate shells gave rise to transverse shells, if any significance is to be attached to relative time of occurrence of the two forms in supposed developmental series.

In the **pedicle valve** the hinge line coincides with the anterior edge of the **cardinal shelf,** which overhung the visceral mass somewhat in life (Fig. 8.7.2). The external surface of the cardinal shelf is the **interarea** (or the **cardinal area**). In cases in which the midregion of the cardinal shelf is indented by a triangular notch called the **delthyrium,** there are naturally two symmetrical interareas. Interareas are generally triangular because the posterior margin of the valve slopes down from the beak to meet the outer ends of the hinge margins at the **cardinal extremities.** Interareas may be flat or curved and may be parallel to the plane of commissure or inclined to it as much as, or even more than, 90 degrees. In the latter case the beak of the pedicle valve overhangs the umbo of the brachial valve. Features which make interpretation of the lamp-shell kind of brachiopods difficult are associated with having small interareas or none and consequently reduced hinge margins; also, the interareas may curve laterally as well as dorsoventrally to merge insensibly with the lateral slopes of the pedicle valve. Interareas may bear distinctive striation, or hinge margins may bear a row of small toothlike nodes in **denticulate** shells (Fig. 8.17.7, 8). Both of these modifications of the cardinal shelf facilitate identification.

Great systematic importance is attached to modifications of the delthyrium. During life it not only provided for passage of the fleshy pedicle, but it also enabled the cardinal process and the posterior tip of the brachial valve to swing ventrally when the diductor muscles contracted. Accordingly, changes in habit of attachment and in the hingeing of the two valves are reflected in the appearance of the delthyrium. Although a delthyrium may be an open perforation in a fossil specimen, it is possible that some sort of calcareous cover (**deltidium**) was present in life (Fig. 8.7.4). A deltidium may consist of a single tiny plate or of two or three plates. Apparently the two conditions are very remote genetically, because the single plate arises during embryonic stages, whereas the compound plates arise postembryonically. In the case of the single-plated deltidium (sometimes called a pseudodeltidium), the plate was located on the ventral or beak side of the pedicle; as growth of the plate progressed, the pedicle was crowded toward the base of the delthyrium (Fig. 8.7.4). At the same time the deltidium tended to fuse with the lateral margins of the delthyrium and to connect the two interareas with a flat or convex hoodlike structure. It is thought that progressive stages in the growth of deltidia have evolutionary significance in various strains of brachiopods.

In the case of deltidia consisting of more than one plate, the commonest form has two tiny plates which grow together and eventually fuse with each other as well as with the margins of the delthyrium. When they are separate they are **discrete** (Fig. 8.7.7a), whereas they are **conjunct** when they just barely meet (Fig. 8.7.7b) and are **fused** in their most advanced condition (Fig. 8.7.8). Even when they are fused their presence and number may be determined by sutures, grooves, or micro-ornamentation. Compound deltidial plates may meet and seem to crowd the pedicle away from the apex, or toward the apex, or the pedicle may be grasped on all sides in a median position in the delthyrium. If a third deltidial plate is present, it lies along the base of the delthyrium and serves as a base on which the two upper plates stand.

Very strangely, the pedicle opening in some brachiopods has migrated entirely out of the delthyrium and occupies a position entirely within the

---

Figure 8.7 (opposite). Hinge Features.
1. Oblique view into apex of pedicle valve of *Punctospirifer transversus*, 1 1/3X. 2. pedicle valve of *Crispella crispa*, 4X. 3. Apical region of pedicle valve of *Platyrachella oweni*, 2X. 4. Exterior hinge features of *Eospirifer niagarensis*, 3X. 5. Posterior view of *Rafinesquina alternata*, 3X. 6. Ontogenetic series of *Homoeospira evax* showing progressive fusion of deltidial plates and migration of pedicle foramen into beak. 6a, early stage, 7X. 6b, later stage, 3X. 6c, mature stage, 2X. 7a, 7b. Early and late stages of deltidial plates in ontogeny of *Delthyris sulcatus*, about 3X. 8. Fused deltidial plates of *Delthyris perlamellosus*, about 3X. 9. Pedicle foramen in umbo of *Dielasma bovidens*, 2X. 10. Separate deltidial plates and pedicle foramen invading the umbo of *Zygospira modesta*, about 7X. 11. Simple deltidial plate and pedicle foramen of *Triplesia ortoni*, 2X.
(1-4, 6-10 after Hall and Clarke, 1894. 5, 11 after Hall and Clarke, 1892.)

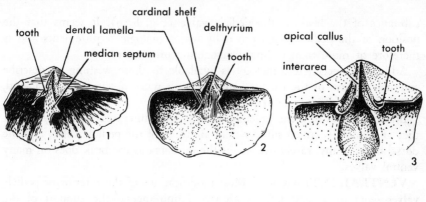

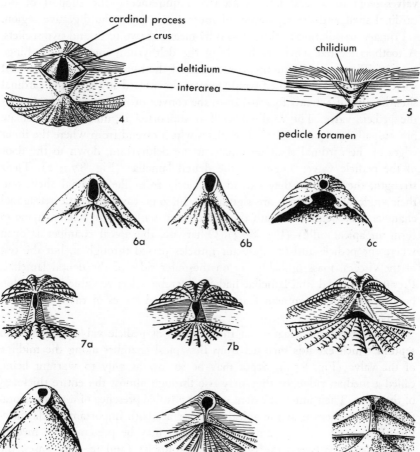

substance of the beak of the pedicle valve (Fig. 8.7.9). It seems that the position of the pedicle is governed by major biologic requirements and is therefore of more than ordinary taxonomic importance.

Additional special terminology is available to those wishing to describe external features of the cardinal margin with more precision, as in Cloud, 1942, and Schuchert and Cooper, 1931.

Brachial valves of some brachiopods also have interareas (Fig. 8.7.4), but they are generally much smaller than are those of the pedicle valve, and the dorsal beak, if any, rarely overhangs the interarea as the beak does on many ventral valves.

VENTRAL INTERIORS. Most modifications of the interior of pedicle valves seem to be associated with two requirements—the support of the cardinal shelf and the separation of musculature from the digestive region.

Primary articulation in this Class is by means of two teeth and two sockets. A tooth is located where each side of the delthyrium intersects the hinge margin (Fig. 8.7.1). Naturally, contraction of the muscles when the brachial valve was opened and closed would exert a downward strain on the cardinal shelf because it extends forward from the convex or main ventral portion of the pedicle valve. The cardinal shelf is supported in numerous articulate brachiopods by a pair of flanges or plates which extend from where the inner edges of the cardinal shelf terminate at the delthyrium, down to the floor of the pedicle valve. These are the **dental lamellae** (Fig. 8.7.1, 2). Their strength, the distance they extend anteriorly from the cardinal shelf, and their angle of divergence are significant. In some cases the little tetragonal chamber they delimit beneath the delthyrium is filled with sclerenchyme to form an **apical callus** (Fig. 8.7.3). Otherwise, the apical chamber is open where the pedicle and the diductor muscles passed through it, but the rest of the visceral mass probably lay on the outer sides of the dental lamellae. Presumably, the dental lamellae had considerable selective value in evolution because they are prominent features in advanced stages of many strains of brachiopods.

The most common feature of the interiors of pedicle valves is a **median septum** which extends forward from the apical chamber along the midline of the valve (Fig. 8.7.1). Septa may be so low as only to warrant being called a median ridge, or they may rise through almost the entire thickness of the valve. Their anterior extent and the possible presence of a tiny perforation through them near the apical chamber are both important in classification. Less commonly, a pair of lateral septa may be present. The median septum passed between the two adductor muscles (and in some cases, the diductors, too) and may have helped to keep the strands of the adductors separated when median septa were very high. Even so, the advantage of a median septum is not apparent. It may have served to strengthen the pedicle valve, like the inner keel on a ship.

Some of the most singular features of brachiopods are connected with building muscle attachments up above the floor of the pedicle valve. In the simplest condition the adductor and diductor muscles are attached a short distance anterior to the digestive region. In this position the dorsally directed strands of the muscles pass among the arms of the lophophore and partially obstruct the mouth region. Moreover, the reproductive glands and vascular sinuses detour around the areas upon which the muscles are attached. It is no wonder, then, that several strains of brachiopods evolved along lines which led to rearrangement of these conflicting structures. One solution was to raise the adductor and diductor muscles upon moundlike **platforms.** In this position there was less interference of diductors with the dorsal region of the visceral mass, but not much improvement was evident unless it enabled advantageous positioning of the diductor muscles.

The more complex but apparently most successful solution involved insertion of muscles upon a false floor raised above the inner surface of the pedicle valve. Any structure of this sort in articulates is called a **spondylium.** In its simplest form the spondylium consists of the two dental lamellae which have converged along the midline of the pedicle valve to form a V-shaped chamber, the keel of which extends out on the floor of the valve a short distance. Commonly, however, the spondylium is supported by the median septum to form a **spondylium simplex** (Fig. 8.12.3) or is supported upon a pair of septa to form a **spondylium duplex** (Fig. 8.12.1d, 4a). Spondylia apparently were advantageous because they enabled better separation of diductor muscles and digestive organs, provided freedom for continuation anteriorly of soft parts, such as generative organs, increased the strength of shells and provided support and protection for the posterior strands of the diductor muscles. The structures are present in different strains of articulates, and an analogous structure (which originates without presence of dental lamellae) is even known among some Atremida, such as the Silurian *Trimerella* (Fig. 8.4.8). The appearance of true spondylia, however, coincided with the development of complete dental lamellae in the Late Cambrian. According to one interpretation the spondylium is primarily an area of muscular implantation which arose from forward growth of the dental lamellae. According to another theory the spondylium arose primarily as a shelf over part of the viscera as the muscle tracks moved anteriorly and dorsally during enlargement of the valve and thereby overrode soft tissue, as it were. If the seemingly nonhomologous platforms of forms such as *Trimerella* are eliminated from consideration, then the two theories can be used conjointly to explain origin and function of the spondylia.

DORSAL INTERIORS. Interiors of brachial valves are modified in almost exact parallelism with those of the pedicle valves. In addition, the brachial valve is characterized by its unique supports for the lophophore just as the pedicle valve is characterized by singular modifications associated with the pedicle opening. All of the internal features in the posterior part of the brachial valve are termed the **cardinalia.**

Sockets are located near the margin of the valve (Fig. 8.8.1). That central region between sockets may be partially or completely roofed over by one or more plates which together are referred to as the **cardinal plate.** If the plates do not quite meet along the median line the plate is **divided,** and if it bears a tiny hole near the posterior edge it is **perforate** (Fig. 8.20.2a). In life the diductor muscles were attached to it or to its posterior edge at the cardinal process.

The free portions of the two brachidia are attached either to the posterior margin of the brachial valve or to the anterior edge of the cardinal plate. In the latter case their substance can be traced back into the cardinal plate in many brachiopods. The simplest forms of brachidia consist of minute spines (sometimes called **brachiophores**) to which the fleshy lophophore was attached (Fig. 8.8.5). More advanced brachidia consist of long slender supports which resemble arms reaching forth from the cardinal plate (Fig. 8.8.2). These are called **crura** (sing. **crus**). Finally, the brachidia may become very complex and either form a closed **loop** (Fig. 8.2) or coil up in helicoid spires called **spiralia** (Fig. 8.8.6–8).

It is apparent that cardinal plates may be subjected to varying strains connected with the use of sockets and the suspension of the brachidia. It is not surprising, therefore, that the cardinal plate may also be supported by a pair of **crural plates** which are analogous to the dental lamellae in the pedicle valve. Moreover, the crural plates may extend forward to form a V-shaped trough or platform called a **cruralium,** which is the analogue of the spondylium of the opposite valve. It is even used for implantation of muscles, but, of course, these are adductors in the brachial valve. Finally, a single septum may be present in the brachial valve and may even support the cruralium. If a double septum is present, it is apt to bear a special trough which resembles the cruralium, although no true cruralium is present.

CLASSIFICATION. At least three fundamental concepts are involved in various classifications of articulates—structure of the shell, kind of pedicle opening, and nature of the brachidia. To a lesser degree shell shape and some additional internal features are considered to be important. Unfortunately, these features occur in various combinations such as to make a straight-forward classification impossible. For instance, there is a fundamental difference of opinion over whether loop-bearing brachiopods gave rise to spire-bearers or vice versa. Careful investigation of the problem leads to some

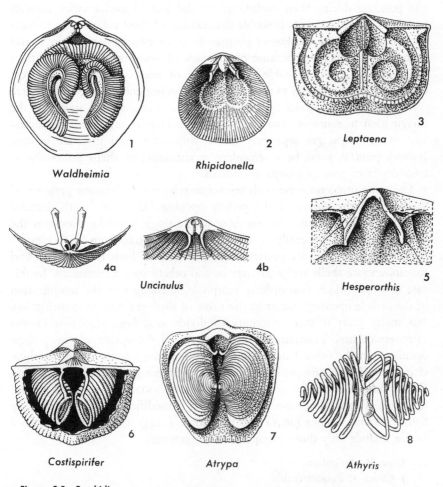

Figure 8.8 Brachidia.
1. Partial cut-away view of the lophophore inside the brachial valve of *Waldheimia* sp., 1X.
2. Short crura of *Rhipidomella thiemi*, 3X. 3. Stubby crural bases and impressions of spiral lophophore on inner surface of brachial valve of *Leptaena rhomboidalis*, 1X. 4a, 4b. Posterior and interior views of very long and elevated crura of *Uncinulus abruptus*, 2X. 5. Simple brachial plates bordering the notothyrium and continuing forward as brachiophores of *Hesperorthis tricenaria*, 4X. 6. Cut-away view of the spiriferid spiralium of *Costispirifer arenosus*, 3/4X.
7. Dorsally directed atrypid spiralium of *Atrypa reticularis*, 1X. 8. Oblique dorsal view of the athyrid spiralium of *Athyris angelica* var. *occidentalis*, 5 1/2X.
(1 after Davidson, 1886. 2, 3 after Hall and Clarke, 1892. 4, 6, 7 after Hall and Clarke, 1894. 5 after Schuchert and Cooper, 1932. 8 after Crickmay, 1957.)

major dilemmas. Were some strains of brachiopods alternately impunctate and punctate during their evolution? Or did spiralia evolve twice without genetic relationship? It is probable that neither of these solutions is acceptable. In the first case the loss of punctae from an evolutionary strain would probably be permanent because of the Law of Irreversibility of Evolution (page 42). It is not probable that punctae of brachiopods should be lost and then regained exactly as they were before an impunctate stage intervened.

Modification of spiralia follows such orderly patterns that it strains the imagination to conceive how convergence could have produced the succession of various stages separately in the impunctate and punctate groups. Instead, punctae must be a secondary modification of shells somewhat as spinosity is in various groups of animals.

The same problems arise with respect to relationship between presence of punctae and the nature of the pedicle opening. Articulates with deltidial plates are **telotrematous,** whereas those with a single hoodlike plate over the delthyrium (and generally a chilidium) are **protrematous.** All pseudopunctate brachiopods are protrematous but some of both the punctate and the impunctate shells are protrematous and others are telotrematous. In this case it is very likely that orderly morphologic changes in the modification of the pedicle opening transcend the value of shell structure in classification. For many years it was customary to divide articulates into two Orders (Protremida and Telotremida) on the basis of the nature of the pedicle opening. On the other hand, a few forms now are known which combine characters of both groups; hence, authorities do not recognize the foregoing Orders any more. Unfortunately, no substitute system has received general approval. The classification used herein is a modification of proposals by Schuchert and Cooper (1931) and by Cooper (1944). Categories recognized herein include only those groups of major interest.

> Class B. Articulata
>   Order 1. Palaeotremida
>   Order 2. Protremida-Telotremida
>   Suborder a. Orthina
>   Superfamily (1). Orthicae
>   Superfamily (2). Dalmanellicae
>   Suborder b. Pentamerina
>   Superfamily (1). Syntrophiicae
>   Superfamily (2). Pentamericae
>   Suborder c. Spiriferina
>   Superfamily (1). Spirifericae
>   Superfamily (2). Rostrospiricae
>   Superfamily (3). Punctospiricae

Suborder d. Strophomenina
  Superfamily (1). Strophomenicae
  Superfamily (2). Producticae
Suborder e. Rhynchonellina
Suborder f. Terebratulina

Contrasted with the purely biologic approach is the somewhat cruder necessity of being able to assign a shell to the lowest possible category on the basis of readily apparent features. Accordingly, the following artificial key is based upon the use of as many external features as possible; but in some cases the relative ranks of the taxa were decided upon other grounds. The key is intended to serve only for the recognition of the most common and readily identifiable articulates, such as are of general interest. A vast literature is available to those who progress far enough to discover the shortcomings of this sort of key.

KEY TO HIGHER CATEGORIES OF COMMON ARTICULATE BRACHIOPODS

I. Teeth and sockets rudimentary .... Order Palaeotremida
II. Teeth and sockets well developed
  A. Shells impunctate
    1. Mostly transverse
      a. Spiralium absent .... Superfamily Orthicae
      b. Spiralium present .... Superfamily Spirifericae
    2. Mostly rostrate
      a. Spondylium absent
        (1) Spiralium absent .... Suborder Rhynchonellina
        (2) Spiralium present .... Superfamily Rostrospiricae
      b. Spondylium present .... Suborder Pentamerina
        (1) Spondylium simplex .... Superfamily Syntrophiicae
        (2) Spondylium duplex .... Superfamily Pentamericae
  B. Shells punctate or pseudopunctate
    1. Shells pseudopunctate .... Suborder Strophomenina
      a. Not spinose .... Superfamily Strophomenicae
      b. Spinose .... Superfamily Producticae
    2. Shells punctate
      a. Mostly transverse
        (1) Costellate .... Superfamily Dalmanellicae
        (2) Costate, with spiralium ... Superfamily Punctospiricae
      b. Mostly rostrate, with loop .... Suborder Terebratulina

Order 1. Palaeotremida

This rare Order consists of brachiopods in which teeth and sockets are poorly developed, the two valves articulate imperfectly along the hinge line, and the delthyrium is rudimentary. Shells are largely calcareous, but some phosphatic material is also present. All of these features have been interpreted

as evidence that the Palaeotremida occupy an evolutionary position intermediate between the Inarticulata and the rest of the Articulata. The known
forms are all from Lower Cambrian strata.

Kutorgina is the best-known Genus. It is biconvex and has a sulcus on
the pedicle valve (Fig. 8.9.2). The interarea is poorly developed, but there
may be a sort of sheath over the pedicle in the delthyrium of some forms.
This serves the same function that a deltidium does in later forms.

Order 2. Protremida-Telotremida

Primitive Protremida had an open delthyrium, but a single plate (deltidium) covered the delthyrium in advanced forms. Moreover, the notothyrium in the latter forms was also covered by a single plate (the **chilidium**).
Most shells are transverse, with only one group (the pentameroids) being
rostrate. The most advanced brachidia seem to be brachiophores or crura.

Rustella   *Kutorgina*

Figure 8.9 Palaeotremida.
1. Exterior of pedicle valve of *Rustella edsoni*, 2/3X, Cambrian, Georgia and Vermont.
2a, 2b. Dorsal and side views of *Kutorgina cingulata*, 1X, Cambrian, eastern states and Canada.
(After Walcott, 1912.)

Telotremates, on the other hand, generally have two or three plates forming the deltidium. Shells are either transverse or rostrate. Spiralia or a loop
are normally present.

SUBORDER A.   ORTHINA

Superfamily (1).   Orthicae

These impunctate shells are almost all notably transverse (Fig. 8.10), but
the straight hinge upon which the "orthid" feature was conceived (Greek:
orthos, straight) is found in other groups of Articulata. Most characteristically the pedicle emerged freely from an unobstructed delthyrium, although
the delthyrium was roofed over in a few forms. Internally the lophophore
was attached to brachiophores. In one strain (by some separated as the
clitambonitids) a small spondylium was present (Fig. 8.10.7). Muscle scars
and the character of external ornamentation are very important in identifying orthid brachiopods. The Orthicae ranged from Cambrian into the

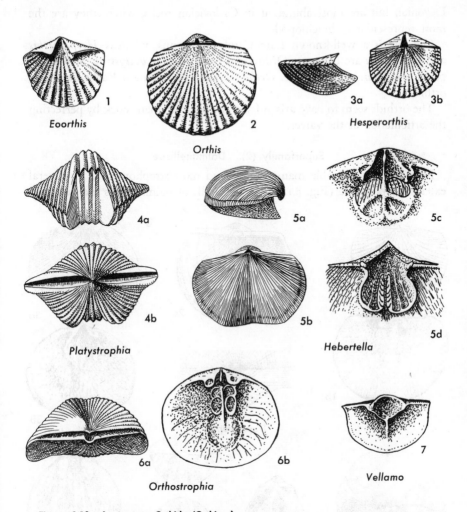

Eoorthis

Orthis

Hesperorthis

Platystrophia

Hebertella

Orthostrophia

Vellamo

Figure 8.10. Impunctate Orthids (Orthicae).
1. Interior of pedicle valve of *Eoorthis remnicha*, 3X, Cambrian, widespread. 2. Dorsal view of *Orthis michaelis*, 1 1/3X, Ordovician, Nevada. 3a, 3b. Lateral and dorsal views of *Hesperorthis tricenaria*, 1X, Ordovician, eastern states and Canada. 4a, 4b. Anterior and posterior views of *Platystrophia acutilirata*, 1X, Ordovician, midcontinent. 5a, 5b, 5c, 5d. Lateral dorsal views (2/3X), and interiors of brachial and pedicle valves (2X) of *Hebertella sinuata*, Ordovician, eastern states. 6a, 6b. Posterior view and interior of brachial valve of *Orthostrophia strophomenoides*, 1X Devonian, eastern states. 7. Interior of pedicle valve of *Vellamo trentonensis*, showing spondylium simplex, 1X, Ordovician, Ontario, Minnesota.
(1 after Walcott, 1912. 2 after Ulrich and Cooper, 1938. 3, 5c, 5d, 6 after Hall and Clarke, 1892. 4, 5a, 5b after Meek, 1873. 7 after Schuchert and Cooper, 1932.)

Devonian but are most abundant in Ordovician rocks, where they are the most representative brachiopods.

Eoorthis is a well-known Late Cambrian Genus, whereas *Hesperorthis* and *Hebertella* are common Ordovician Genera, as is *Platystrophia* with its prominent *Spirifer*-like costae. *Orthostrophia* is a common Early Devonian orthid.

The orthids seem to have arisen from the palaeotremate stock by perfecting the articulation of the valves.

Superfamily (2).   Dalmanellicae

Dalmanellids resemble many orthids and most strophomenids in general external appearance (Fig. 8.11), but the shells of dalmanellids are punctate.

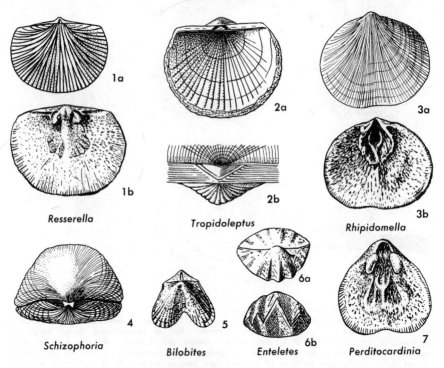

Figure 8.11.   Punctate Orthids (Dalmanellicae).
1a, 1b. Dorsal view (1 1/2X) and interior of brachial valve (2X) of *Resserella meeki*, 1X, Ordovician, east-central states. 2a, 2b. Dorsal view (1X) and hinge region (3X) of *Tropidoleptus carinatus*, Devonian, eastern states and New Mexico. 3a, 3b. Exterior and interior of pedicle valve of *Rhipidomella oweni*, 1X, Mississippian, east-central states. 4. Posterior view of *Schizophoria resupinoides*, 2/3X, Pennsylvanian, widespread. 5. Dorsal view of *Bilobites bilobus*, 3X, Silurian, widespread. 6a, 6b. Posterior and anterior views of *Enteletes hemiplicatus*, 1X, Pennsylvanian, Midwest. 7. Interior of pedicle valve of *Perditocardinia dubia*, 2X, Mississippian, Midwest.
(1, 7, after Schuchert and Cooper, 1932. 2 after Hall and Clarke, 1894. 3 after Weller, 1914. 4, 6 after Dunbar and Condra, 1932. 5 after Hall and Clarke, 1892.)

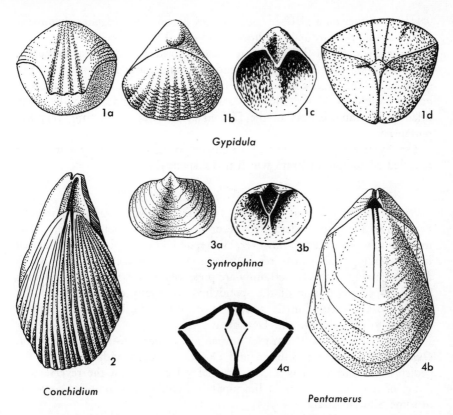

Figure 8.12. Pentamerids.
1. *Gypidula coeymansensis*, Devonian, eastern states. 1a, 1b, anterior and dorsal views, 1X. 1c, interior of pedicle valve with spondylium, 1X. 1d, posterior view of internal mold with paired median septa of brachial valve and spondylium of pedicle valve, 1 1/2X. 2. Dorsal view of internal mold of *Conchidium laqueatum*, 2/3X, Silurian, Indiana. 3a, 3b. Exterior and interior of pedicle valve of *Syntrophina calcifera*, 2X, Ordovician, Canada. 4a, 4b. Diagrammatic cross section and dorsal view of internal mold of *Pentamerus laevis*, 2/3X, Silurian, Alaska to United States.
(1 after Hall 1861. 2, 4a after Hall and Clarke, 1894. 4b after Hall and Whitfield, 1875.)

The delthyrium is usually open although it may be covered by a small deltidium. Surface ornamentation consists of fine costae.

Dalmanellids apparently arose from the orthids by becoming punctate.

SUBORDER B. PENTAMERINA

Superfamily (1). Syntrophiicae

Syntrophiid brachiopods are rostrate, biconvex, and either smooth or costate (Fig. 8.12.3). No deltidium or chilidium is present. A spondylium simplex is present in the ventral valve, but the muscle scars on the dorsal valve are neither on a platform nor are they outlined by ridgelike extensions of plates from the cardinal margin. A short cruralium is present in that valve, however. Members of this group are not easy to identify. Syntrophiids differ from rhynchonellids in having a spondylium and differ from pentameroids either in lacking muscle attachments to a cruralium or in having a ridgelike border around the dorsal muscle scars. The group originated in the Cambrian and became extinct in the Devonian, but was at no time very important.

The Syntrophiicae presumably originated from the Orthicae out of the so-called clitambonitid strain which had a spondylium.

Superfamily (2). Pentamericae

Pentamerid brachiopods are rather typically biconvex, ovate, and rostrate (Fig. 8.12). Faint to moderate costae or plicae are commonly present. The most definitive character, however, is a spondylium duplex. This internal feature would be difficult to see if it were not for the fact that many specimens belonging to this Superfamily are preserved as internal molds in which the Y-shaped impression of the spondylium is readily observable near the ventral beak. A cruralium is present in some Genera. The Superfamily is confined to the Silurian and Devonian.

Characteristic Genera from the Silurian are *Pentamerus* and *Conchidium*. *Gypidula* is a common Silurian and Devonian Genus with a fold on the pedicle valve and a sulcus on the brachial valve, which is the reverse condition of that present in most brachiopods. Pentamerids comprise coquinas in some Silurian strata.

The pentamerids evolved out of the syntrophiid brachiopods by creating the spondylium duplex, perfecting the cruralium, or enclosing muscle scars of the brachial valve with a ridge.

SUBORDER C.   SPIRIFERINA

Members of this Suborder are defined by the presence of spiralia and impunctate shells. Spiralia can be differentiated into three categories depending upon the orientation of their conical helicoid spirals and upon the course of the **primary lamellae** by which the spiralia are connected to the shell. Those in which the axes of coiling of the spiralia are arranged transversely (right and left, as it were) and the primary lamellae curve out directly from the shell are said to have **spiriferoid spiralia** (Fig. 8.8.6). On the other hand, coils which are oriented with their axes vertically are called **atrypoid spiralia** (Fig. 8.8.7). In the third group the primary lamellae start to follow the inner surface of the brachial valve as in spiriferoid and atrypoid spiralia, but then the lamellae double back on themselves to reverse their course before generating spiralia. These are the **athyroid spiralia** (Fig. 8.8.8).

Naturally, one either needs to have access to remarkably well-preserved material or needs to grind away shell substance in order to observe these important inner details.

Superfamily (1). Spirifericae

Spiriferid brachiopods are characterized by a trilogy of features in which the presence of a spiralium is augmented by an impunctate shell and a more or less transverse shape (Fig. 8.13). Interareas are normally present, as is radial ornamentation. Some sort of deltidium is generally present, although the discrete plates may fall out posthumously, whereupon the delthyrium resembles that of the orthids. Indeed, it is not easy to differentiate between some spiriferids (such as *Spirifer*) and some orthids (such as *Platystrophia*) unless one has access to internal characters.

Two Sections can be recognized, according to whether the spiralia are directed laterally or dorsally.

SECTION (a). SPIRIFEROID SPIRALIA. Within this Section one can make two or three further divisions, depending upon whether the tips of the spiralia point outward or inward, or essentially are enrolled in a plane. It may be necessary to cut a specimen in half transversely in order to determine which course the spiralia take, although in most spiriferids the spiralia point outward. Most of the common spiriferid brachiopods belong in this Section.

Eospirifer (Silurian and Devonian) is entirely covered with fine radiating ridges. Devonian spiriferids such as *Mucrospirifer, Platyrachella,* and *Costispirifer* are costate on the lateral slopes, but the fold and sulcus are either smooth or have one costa or groove. A few Upper Devonian spirifers (*Cyrtospirifer*) and all Mississippian and Pennsylvanian forms (*Spirifer*) have a costate fold and sulcus. In *Neospirifer* (mostly Pennsylvanian and Permian) the costae become increasingly coarse and are characteristically bundled together in fascicles of three to five costae. Genera in this Section range from Medial Ordovician to Triassic.

SECTION (b). ATRYPOID SPIRALIA. Primary lamellae diverge and follow along the margin of the shell before coiling dorsally. Many shells have hemispherical brachial valves and nearly flat pedicle valves. Only a few Genera belong here, but the best-known Genus, *Atrypa,* constitutes one of the most prolific elements of Devonian faunas all over the world. *Zygospira* is a well-known Ordovician Genus which probably belongs here (Fig. 8.13.1). The group ranges from Ordovician into Lower Mississippian strata.

DEVELOPMENT OF SPIRALIA. The ontogenetic series in the development of spiralia has been worked out for the very early spiriferid, *Zygospira* (Fig. 8.14). In its earliest stage the brachidium is an anteriorly

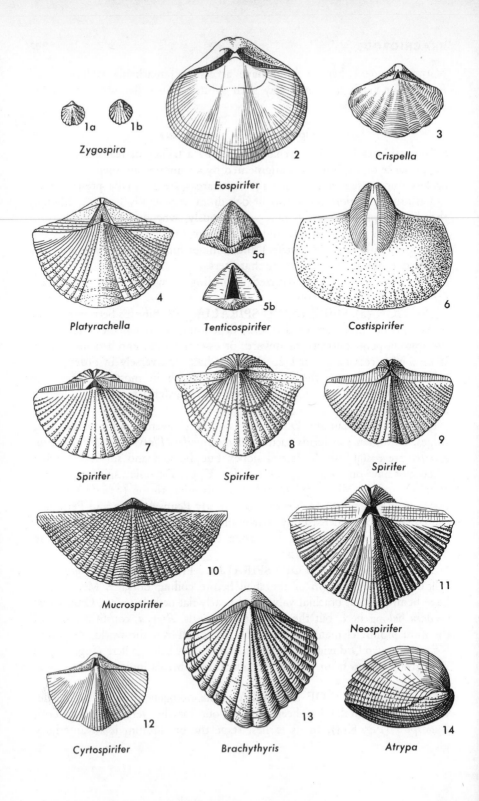

1a 1b
Zygospira

2
Eospirifer

3
Crispella

4
Platyrachella

5a
5b
Tenticospirifer

6
Costispirifer

7
Spirifer

8
Spirifer

9
Spirifer

10
Mucrospirifer

11
Neospirifer

12
Cyrtospirifer

13
Brachythyris

14
Atrypa

pointed loop. In the next stage of development, however, the anterior point of the loop is resorbed, and two armlike extensions grow forward from lateral portions of the loop. At this stage (Fig. 8.14.2) the loop is quadrate in shape and its transverse anterior bar (**jugum**) connects the two lateral arms. Indefinite forward growth of the lateral arms is not possible within the visceral cavity; hence the brachidia can grow longer only if they coil up

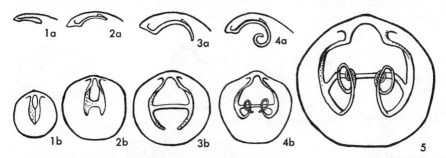

Figure 8.14. Metamorphosis and Growth of a Spiralium.
Side views of spiralia of a *Zygospira* are shown in the upper row and five plan views of brachial valves are shown in the lower row. 1. Centronelliform loop, 16X. 2. *Dielasma*-like loop, 16X. 3. Ventrally curved lamellae projecting from loop, 8X. 4. Early spiralium, 8X. 5. Mature spiralium with 2 1/4 volutions, 5X.
(After Beecher and Schuchert, 1893.)

into spiralia. Only one or two volutions are present in early stages of spiralia, but several volutions occur in adults of different species of *Zygospira* (Fig. 8.14.5). It is thought that other spiriferids could have evolved from *Zygospira* through variations in degree and orientation of spirals.

It is probable that the earliest spiriferids arose from some orthid ancestor. Presence of a loop in early stages is remarkably similar to the condition in primitive loop-bearers, but these latter all lived too late to give rise to spiriferids.

Figure 8.13 (*opposite*). Spiriferids (Spirifericae).
1a, 1b. Dorsal and ventral views of *Zygospira modesta*, 1X, Ordovician, eastern states. 2. Dorsal view of *Eospirifer radiatus*, 1X, Silurian, eastern states and Canada. 3. Dorsal view of *Crispella crispa*, 2X, Silurian, widespread. 4. Dorsal view of *Platyrachella oweni*, 1X, Devonian, Midwest. 5a, 5b. Anterior and posterior views of *Tenticospirifer cyrtiniformis*, 2X, Devonian, Iowa. 6. Internal mold of pedicle valve of *Costispirifer arenosus*, 2/3X, Devonian, widespread in United States and Canada. 7. Dorsal view of *Spirifer rockmontanus*, 1X, Pennsylvanian, widespread. 8. Dorsal view of *Spirifer increbescens*, 1X, Mississippian, widespread. 9. Dorsal view of *Spirifer centronatus*, 1X, Mississippian, western states. 10. Dorsal view of *Mucrospirifer mucronatus*, 1X, Devonian, eastern states. 11. Dorsal view of *Neospirifer triplicatus*, 1X, Pennsylvanian, western states. 12. Dorsal view of *Cyrtospirifer whitneyi*, 1X, Devonian, widespread. 13. Dorsal view of *Brachythyris subcardiiformis*, 1X, Mississippian, Midwest. 14. Side view of *Atrypa reticularis*, 1X, Silurian and Devonian, world-wide.
(1 after Meek, 1873. 2-5, 10, 12, 14 after Hall and Clarke, 1894. 7, 9, 11 after White, 1877. 8, 13 after Weller, 1914.)

Superfamily (2).   Rostrospiricae

These are rostrate shells (Fig. 8.15) with a spiralium, as the name of the Superfamily indicates. Moreover, the spiralium is of the athyroid type. In addition, the jugum bears spines or is Y-shaped instead of being a simple transverse bar.

Composita is by far the most important Genus and is one of the most abundant brachiopods of all time; species are with difficulty differentiated

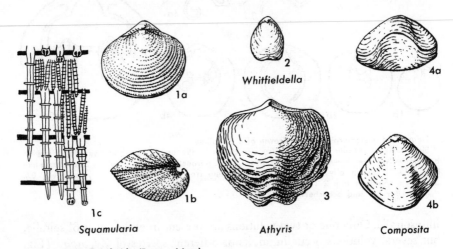

Figure 8.15. Spiriferids (Rostrospiricae).
1. *Squamularia perplexa*, Pennsylvanian, Midwest. 1a, 1b, dorsal and lateral views, 1X. 1c, details of spines, greatly enlarged.   2. Dorsal view of *Whitfieldella nitida*, 1X, Silurian, eastern states.   3. Dorsal view of *Athyris spiriferoides*, 1X, Devonian, eastern states.   4a, 4b. Anterior and dorsal views of *Composita subquadrata*, 1X, Mississippian, widespread.
(1 after Dunbar and Condra, 1932. 2 after Grabau, 1901. 3 after Hall and Clarke, 1894. 4 after Weller, 1914.)

on the bases of subtle differences in shape and character of the sulcus and fold.

Rostrospirids undoubtedly arose from the main line of spiriferid brachiopods by a slight change in the trace of the primary lamellae.

Superfamily (3).   Punctospiricae

Some punctate spiriferids (Fig. 8.16) are rostrate and others are transverse; thus, they resemble the Rostrospiricae and the Spirifericae. Surfaces are not only distinctly punctate, but wavy lamellose growth lines and minute spines are commonly present. The delthyrium is open or closed by a complicated deltidium. Representatives of the Superfamily are most important in Upper Paleozoic strata but occur as high as the Jurassic.

Cyrtina (Silurian to Mississippian), *Punctospirifer* (Mississippian to Per-

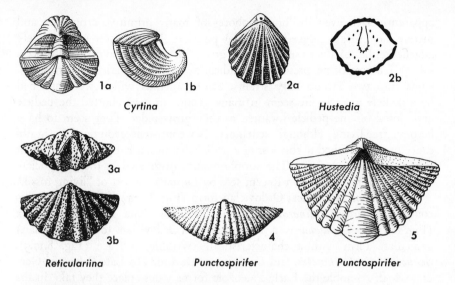

1a   1b   2a   2b

Cyrtina   Hustedia

3a

3b

Reticulariina   Punctospirifer   Punctospirifer

4   5

Figure 8.16. Spiriferids (Punctospiricae).
1a, 1b. Posterior and lateral views of *Cyrtina alpenensis*, 1X, Devonian, Michigan.   2a, 2b.
Dorsal view and transverse section of *Hustedia mormoni* showing jugum and spiralium, 2X,
Pennsylvanian and Permian, widespread.   3a, 3b. Anterior and ventral views of *Reticulariina
spinosa*, 1 1/2X, Mississippian, widespread.   4. Ventral view of *Punctospirifer transversus*, 1X,
Mississippian and Lower Pennsylvanian, widespread.   5. Dorsal view of *Punctospirifer pulcher*,
1X, Permian, western states.
   (1 after Hall and Clarke, 1894. 2 after Dunbar and Condra, 1932. 3, 4 after Weller,
1914. 5 after Meek, 1877.)

mian), *Reticulariina* (Mississippian and Pennsylvanian), and *Hustedia*
(mostly Pennsylvanian and Permian) show the diversity of form in the
group. Triassic and Jurassic Genera are not common in North America,
although they are well known in Europe.

It is probable that punctospirids arose from the impunctate spiriferids.

SUBORDER D.   STROPHOMENINA

Superfamily (1).   Strophomenicae

Strophomenid brachiopods are most readily characterized externally by
their very compressed shapes and long hinge lines (Fig. 8.17). In most cases
their pseudopunctate shell structure can be detected only in thin sections.
Most strophomenids also are characterized by details of the cardinal margin.
A chilidium and a deltidium are present and both are hood-shaped. Ornamentation typically consists of fine radial ridges. There is some evidence
from impressions on interiors of shells (Fig. 8.8.3) that a spiral lophophore
was present in life; moreover the only strophomenids which have a brachidium (*Thecospira* from the Triassic) have a spiralium. Other strophomenids

apparently lack even the brachiophores of many primitive articulates and merely have socket ridges in a similar position. The diductor muscles were attached either to a very small septate groove or to a bilobed cardinal process —both features being present and indicating a differentiation of strophomenids into two evolutionary strains. Strophomenids which were attached by a pedicle in early life seem in many groups to have aborted the pedicle and closed off the pedicle foramen as they grow older. They seem to have become free-living, although sedentary. No consistent evolutionary significance can be attached to this loss of a pedicle because it happened in different groups at different times. The strophomenids originated in the Ordovician, and they are represented in Recent seas by *Lacazella,* a sort of "living fossil."

Strophomena is a typical Ordovician form (Fig. 8.17.1), which is convexo-concave, whereas *Rafinesquina* from the same strata is concavo-convex (Fig. 8.17.2). *Leptaena* is a long-ranging (Ordovician to Mississippian) geniculate form with a characteristically wrinkled surface (Fig. 8.17.5). *Schuchertella, Orthotetes,* and *Derbyia* are Devonian or Late Paleozoic Genera, which resemble the Early Paleozoic forms whose place they take in the later faunas. The group almost became extinct at the end of the Paleozoic, but was of major importance during much of that era. Strophomenids were particularly important during the Ordovician and Silurian.

Probably the most peculiar of all strophomenids is *Scacchinella* from the Permian, which had a very elongate pedicle valve divided into chambers by a series of transverse partitions (Fig. 8.17.9). Apparently the partitions served to confine the viscera to a small region at the same time that the valve was becoming elongate for some other purpose, such as rising above the level of sedimentation.

One group of strophomenids, which is typified by *Stropheodonta* and *Douvillina* (Fig. 8.17.7, 8), is characterized by a denticulate hinge margin. These so-called stropheodontids developed teeth increasingly farther out on the hinge margin as the individuals grew up; and the several strains also show an evolutionary progression toward more and more denticulate hinge

Figure 8.17 (opposite). Strophomenids (Strophomenicae).

1a, 1b, 1c, 1d. Dorsal view, interiors of brachial and pedicle valves, and cross section of *Strophomena planumbona,* 1X, Ordovician, Midwest.   2a, 2b. Dorsal view and cross section of *Rafinesquina alternata,* 1X, Ordovician, eastern states.   3a, 3b. Dorsal view and cross section of *Sowerbyella rugosa,* 1 1/2X, Orodvician, Midwest and eastern states. 4a, 4b. Lateral and dorsal views of *Derbyia crassa,* 1X, Pennsylvanian, Midwest.   5. Exterior of pedicle valve of *Leptaena rhomboidalis,* 1X, Silurian and Devonian, world-wide.   6a, 6b. Lateral and posterior views of *Meekella striatocostata,* 1X, Pennsylvanian and Early Permian, widespread.   7. Interior of hinge region of *Stropheodonta* sp., 1 1/2X, Devonian, widespread. 8a, 8b. Interior of pedicle valve and ventral view of *Douvillina arcuata,* 1 1/2X, Devonian, Iowa. 9a, 9b. Cut-away diagram and oblique posterior view of *Scacchinella* sp., 1X, Permian, world-wide.   10. Interior of incomplete pedicle valve of *Leptodus americanus,* 2/3X, Permian, Texas.

(1, 2b, 3 after Meek, 1873. 2a, 6 after Hall and Clarke, 1892. 4 after Dunbar and Condra, 1932. 5 after Grabau, 1901. 7, 8 after Williams, 1953b. 9a after Williams, 1953a. 9b after Stehli, 1954.)

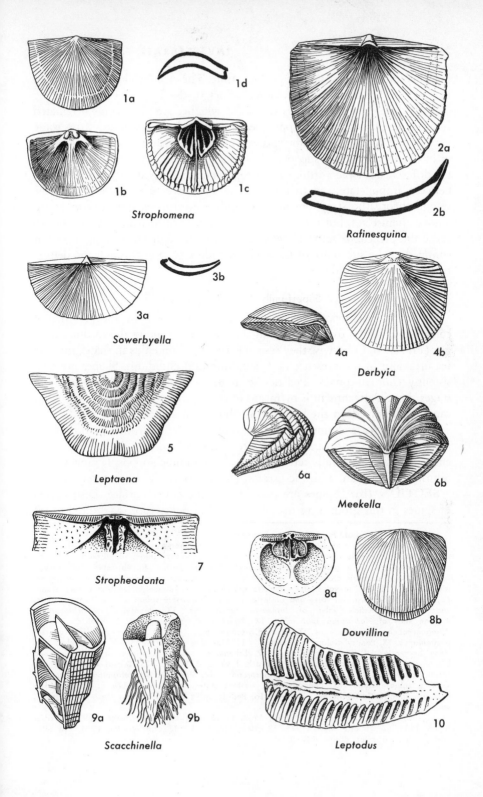

1a
1d
1b
1c
Strophomena

2a
2b
Rafinesquina

3a
3b
Sowerbyella

4a
4b
Derbyia

5
Leptaena

6a
6b
Meekella

7
Stropheodonta

8a
8b
Douvillina

9a
9b
Scacchinella

10
Leptodus

margins during the passage of geologic time. The stropheodontids originated in the Late Ordovician and became extinct in the Late Devonian.

Some difference of opinion exists as to whether strophomenids originated from some orthid, or the strophomenids and orthids descended from some very distant common ancestor and evolved along separate courses. Similarity of internal construction supports the former hypothesis, in addition to which the difference between orthids and strophomenids is essentially the difference between impunctate and pseudopunctate shell structure. According to the second theory the strophomenids not only constitute a very diverse group among themselves, but they cannot have been derived from the orthids because the pedicle of some (*Leptaena*) passed through an opening which is confined to the substance of the shell instead of passing through the delthyrium as in the orthids.

Superfamily (2). Producticae

Productid brachiopods are particularly characterized by the presence of conspicuous spines over the general shell surface or along the cardinal margin (Fig. 8.18). Otherwise they resemble the strophomenids in shape, internal features, and in the presence of a deltidium and chilidium. Shapes are consistently concavo-convex. Pedicles seem to be consistently absent in adult stages; hence, attachment is by means of the prominent spines. Two Sections can be recognized on the basis of distribution of spines.

SECTION (a). Spines are present only along the cardinal margin. *Chonetes, Mesolobus,* and *Lissochonetes* are common Genera (Fig. 8.18.1-3). The entire Section is generally referred to as chonetid brachiopods. It ranges from Silurian to Permian, with the greatest abundance in the Carboniferous.

SECTION (b). Spines are present over the entire surface. Distribution of spines in this group is of major importance; hence care is required to see

---

Figure 8.18 (*opposite*). Productids (Producticae).

1a, 1b. Pedicle valve and diagrammatic cross section of *Chonetes granulifer*, 2X, Pennslyvanian, widespread.   2. Pedicle valve of *Mesolobus mesolobus*, 2X, Pennsylvanian, widespread.   3. Pedicle valve of *Lissochonetes geinitzianus*, 2X, Pennsylvanian, Midwest.   4a, 4b. Interior of brachial valve and diagrammatic cross section of both valves of *Productus cestriensis*, 1X, Mississippian, widespread.   5. Pedicle valve of *Productella spinulicosta*, 1X, Devonian, eastern United States. 6a, 6b. Interior of brachial valve and posterior view of *Kozlowskia splendens*, 1X, Pennsylvanian, widespread.   7. Pedicle valve of *Juresania nebrascensis*, 1X, Pennsylvanian, widespread. 8. Side view of *Horridonia subhorrida*, 1X, Permian, western states.   9. Pedicle valve of *Waagenoconcha montpelierensis*, 1X, Permian, western states.   10. Pedicle valve of *Linoproductus prattenianus*, 1X, Pennsylvanian, widespread.   11. Side view of *Prorichthofenia* sp. attached to a stony bryozoan, 1X, Permian, Texas.   12. Schematic cut-away diagram of a richthofeniid brachiopod showing vesicular walls and brachial valve, 1 1/3X.   13. Dorsal view of *Echinoconchus alternatus*, 2/3X, Mississippian, widespread.   14. Side view of *Antiquatonia hermosana*, showing spinose ridge, 1X, Pennsylvanian, western states.   15. Side view of *Proboscidiella proboscidea*, 1X, Carboniferous, Europe.   16. Pedicle valve of *Dictyoclostus ivesi*, 1X, Permian, western states.

(1-3, 6a, 7 after Dunbar and Condra, 1932. 5, 15 after Hall and Clarke, 1892. 6b after Stehli, 1954. 4, 10 after Butts, 1926. 12 after Böse, 1916. 13 after Weller, 1914. 14 after Girty, 1903. 16 after White, 1877.)

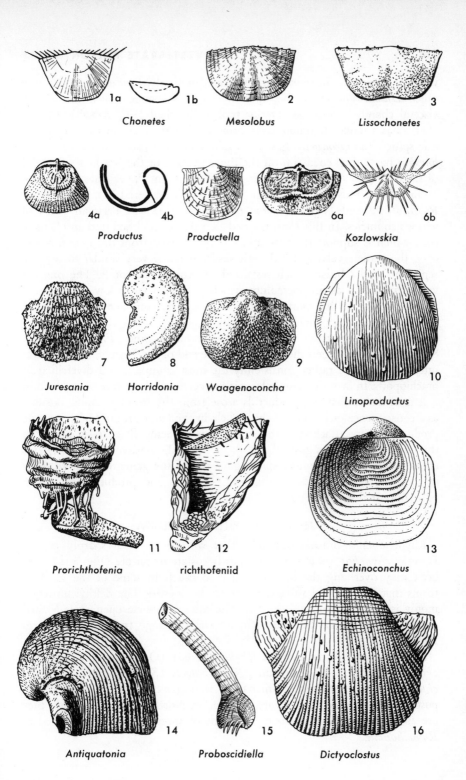

1a   1b   2   3

Chonetes   *Mesolobus*   *Lissochonetes*

4a   4b   5   6a   6b

Productus   *Productella*   *Kozlowskia*

7   8   9   10

Juresania   *Horridonia*   *Waagenoconcha*

Linoproductus

11   12   13

Prorichthofenia   *richthofeniid*   *Echinoconchus*

14   15   16

Antiquatonia   *Proboscidiella*   *Dictyoclostus*

whether they occur in rows, patches, bands, or singly. *Productus* (commonly called *Diaphragmus*) has an internal transverse flange which divides the visceral chamber from the anterior **trail** of the shell (Fig. 8.18.4b). *Dictyoclostus* has a reticulate umbo, *Echinoconchus* has parallel transverse bands of fine spines, *Linoproductus* has fine costae and coarse spine bases, and *Kozlowskia* has a thickened rim on the inner margin of the brachial valve. All of these Genera (Fig. 8.18.4, 6, 10, 13, 16) occur in Upper Paleozoic rocks.

One of the most peculiar fossil groups ever discovered is represented by *Richthofenia* and *Prorichthofenia* (Fig. 8.18.11, 12) in Permian rocks of various countries. In this form the pedicle valve is modified into an elongate cone which is supported on its tip by props derived from the spines. Moreover, the pedicle valve is filled with vesicular tissue very similar to the dissepiments and tabulae which restricted the volume of corals. The brachial valve functioned as an operculum which is located far below the aperture and is overgrown by short radiating spines. The complete brachiopod resembles a coral very much at first glance.

The oldest productids lived in Late Devonian time (*Productella*, Fig. 8.18.5) and the youngest died out before the end of the Permian. During this interval they were rather consistently the most abundant and diversified of brachiopods. In fact, the Late Paleozoic has been called the Age of Productids.

It is probable that the productids arose from the strophomenids, possibly as a consequence of the loss of the pedicle in the latter group. Many juvenile productids were attached to the substratum by being fixed to an object by the curved spines alongside the beak of the pedicle valve. Apparently this chonetidlike arrangement of spines gave rise to the generally spinose shells of the productids. Times of origin of chonetids and productids would in part support this explanation.

SUBORDER E. RHYNCHONELLINA

Rhynchonellid brachiopods are either rostrate or even sharply beaked (Greek: *rhynchos,* snout) and are mostly costate or plicate (Fig. 8.19). The beak may overhang the brachial valve so much in some of the globular forms that the brachial valve can scarcely be opened. The delthyrium commonly is closed. Crura are present. The minute pedicle opening is located almost at the tip of the beak. Rhynchonellids range from Ordovician to Recent.

Lepidocyclus (formerly called *Rhynchotrema*) (Ordovician), *Camarotoechia* (Devonian to Mississippian), *Rhynchotreta* (Silurian), and *Leiorhynchus* (Devonian to Pennsylvanian) are well-known Paleozoic Genera. No post-Paleozoic rhynchonellids are common in North America although they are abundant in Eurasia, where hundreds of species have been referred to *Rhynchonella.*

Rhynchonellids were a particularly well-adapted and successful group of brachiopods. They commonly lived in numbers such as to constitute coquinas, as in the Devonian. Although geographic distribution of simple species or Genera was apt to be restricted by bottom conditions, different members of the Suborder occupied diverse substrata. Some rhynchonellids lived on bottoms composed of rather pure lime mud or of argillaceous lime mud, whereas others lived on fragmental shell debris. Still others, such as *Leiorhynchus,* are generally found only in the carbonaceous shales of the Upper Paleozoic; they recur from time to time over a long vertical range whenever that lithology is present.

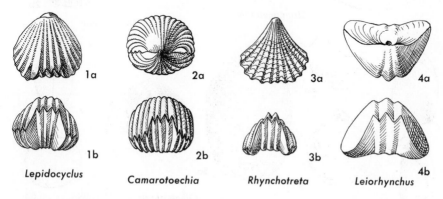

Figure 8.19. Rhynchonellids (Rhynchonellina).
1a, 1b. Dorsal and anterior views of *Lepidocyclus capax,* 1X, Ordovician, widespread in United States and Canada.   2a, 2b. Posterior and anterior views of *Camarotoechia congregata,* 1X, Devonian, eastern states.   3a, 3b. Ventral and anterior views of *Rhynchotreta americana,* 1X, Silurian, eastern United States and Canada.   4a, 4b. Posterior and anterior views of *Leiorhynchus rockymontanus,* 1X, Pennsylvanian, Midwest.
(1 after Meek, 1873. 2 after Hall and Clarke, 1894. 3 after Grabau, 1901. 4 after Dunbar and Condra, 1932.)

Rhynchonellids seem to constitute a polyphyletic group. One strain may have arisen from some syntrophiid ancestor with a simple cruralium. On the other hand, other rhynchonellids seem to have evolved along several lines from origins within the Orthicae by becoming rostrate and by losing costae. Finally, the presence of a spiral lophophore in some rhynchonellids might indicate that they had a spiriferid ancestor.

SUBORDER F. TEREBRATULINA

Terebratulid brachiopods are fundamentally characterized by the presence of a loop-shaped brachidium. Most of them are rostrate and all are punctate. Some are costate, but most are smooth. The delthyrium is closed by some more or less complicated system of plates. Naturally, intricacies of loops are rarely observable in fossil material, but shape and ornamentation enable

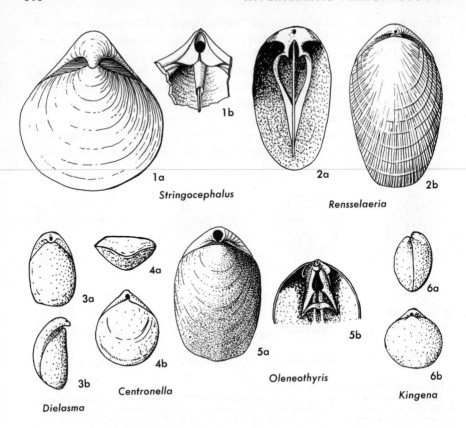

Figure 8.20. Terebratulids (Terebratulina).
1. *Stringocephalus burtoni,* Devonian, world-wide. 1a, dorsal view, 1/2X. 1b, apical interior of pedicle valve with pedicle sheath, enlarged.   2a, 2b. Interior of brachial valve and dorsal view of *Rensselaeria marylandica,* 1X, Devonian, Maryland.   3a, 3b. Dorsal and lateral views of *Dielasma bovidens,* 2/3X, Pennsylvanian, widespread.   4a, 4b. Anterior and dorsal views of *Centronella campbelli,* 2/3X, Devonian, Indiana.   5a, 5b. Dorsal and interior of brachial valve of *Oleneothyris harlani,* 1 1/2X, Eocene, New Jersey. 6a, 6b. Side and dorsal views of *Kingena wacoensis,* 1X, Cretaceous, Texas.
(1, 2b after Hall and Clarke, 1894. 2a, 4 after Cloud, 1942. 3 after Dunbar and Condra, 1932. 5 after Weller, 1907.)

recognition of some Genera. *Centronella, Stringocephalus,* and *Rensselaeria* (Devonian), *Dielasma* (Mississippian to Permian), *Kingena* (Cretaceous), and *Oleneothyris* (Eocene) are well-known Genera (Fig. 8.20). Terebratulids are known to occur abundantly in a very few localities in Triassic rocks of Nevada and Idaho and have been reported from Jurassic strata in California, British Columbia, and the northern Rocky Mountains. Some Cretaceous strata on the Gulf Coast contain abundant terebratulids.

DEVELOPMENT OF LOOPS. Great attention is paid to the configuration of the loops of the various terebratulids. In its simplest condition

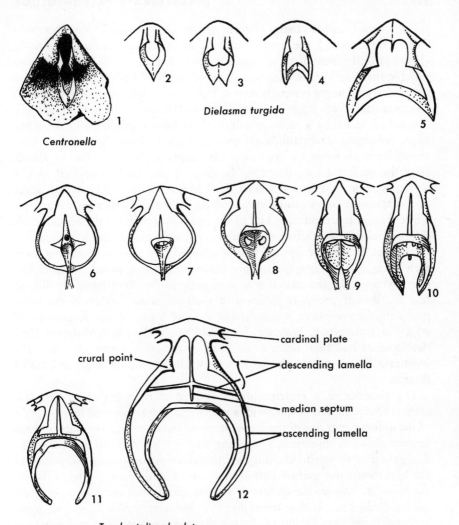

Centronella

Dielasma turgida

crural point — — cardinal plate

— descending lamella

— median septum

— ascending lamella

Terebratalia obsoleta

Figure 8.21. Growth and Metamorphosis of Loops.
1. *Centronella* sp., 4X, Devonian.   2-5. Successive stages in *Dielasma turgida*.   2, centronelliform, 8X.   3, slight resorption of centronelliform tip, 8X.   4, early dielasmoid stage, 8X. 5, advanced dielasmoid stage, 6X.   6-12. Successive stages in *Terebratalia obsoleta*.   6, descending lamellae fused to median septum bearing rudimentary loop of ascending lamellae, 15X.   7, 8, growth with partial resorption of ascending lamellae, 15X.   9, partial fusion of ascending and descending lamellae, 8X.   10, continued resorption of descending lamellae, 6X. 11, youthful loop with jugum formed from descending lamellae, 2X.   12, mature loop, 2X.
   (1 after Cloud, 1942. 2-5 after Beecher and Schuchert, 1893. 6-12 after Beecher, 1893.)

yet discovered, called **centronelliform** (from its presence in the Devonian Genus, *Centronella*) the loop is narrow, elongate, and pointed anteriorly (Fig. 8.21.1). In most of these simple terebratulids the cardinal plate is more variable than the loop is. Stages of development of the loop in *Dielasma* are illustrative of changes generally seen in Paleozoic loop-bearers (Fig. 8.21.1–5). The centronelliform stage is followed by one in which the anterior margin is resorbed and then a rather quadrate short loop is produced in the adult stage. Advanced terebratulids are thought to have been derived from centronelliform ancestors by extending the length of the loop until it almost filled the shell and then doubling the anterior arch back posteriorly as if a person were to fold back a rubber band into a V-shape. The actual stages in this transformation can be very intricate, as is shown in Figure 8.21.6–12. These figures represent only half of the story, however, for the terebratulids diverged along two different evolutionary lines between the Mesozoic and the Recent. In both groups the loop is attached to a median septum at some early stage, but in one group this connection is not broken until a late stage, whereas the connection is severed early in the other group. In Recent seas the former group is confined to southern waters, whereas the latter group inhabits northern waters. If one did not know of the developmental stages in each group, however, he would not realize how different their development had been because the loops in the adult forms are essentially identical. This is one of the most remarkable known instances of parallel descent.

The presence of a centronelliform loop in early stages of terebratulids such as *Dielasma* and of spiriferids such as *Zygospira,* followed by resorption of the anterior margins of the loops, seems to indicate a relationship between terebratulids and spiriferids. For a long time it was supposed that terebratulids gave rise to spiriferids, but two things seem to prevent acceptance of the hypothesis; the terebratulids are punctate and they are unknown before the Silurian, whereas the spiriferids are impunctate and occur as early as the Medial Ordovician. It now seems probable that terebratulids arose from some early spiriferid stem by loss of the spiralia and assumption of punctate shell structure.

GEOLOGIC DISTRIBUTION OF BRACHIOPODS. A few Atremida such as *Obolella* have been discovered in Proterozoic strata and the Atremida are common from Early Cambrian to Recent. Neotremida also range from Early Cambrian to Recent, but are of little more importance than are the Atremida. The first Articulata lived during the Early Cambrian and probably gave rise, through the Palaeotremida, to the higher groups of brachiopods. Orthids and strophomenids dominated brachiopod faunas during the Ordovician, but were assisted somewhat by the rhynchonellids and dalmanellids. During the Silurian these groups continued and most of the remaining

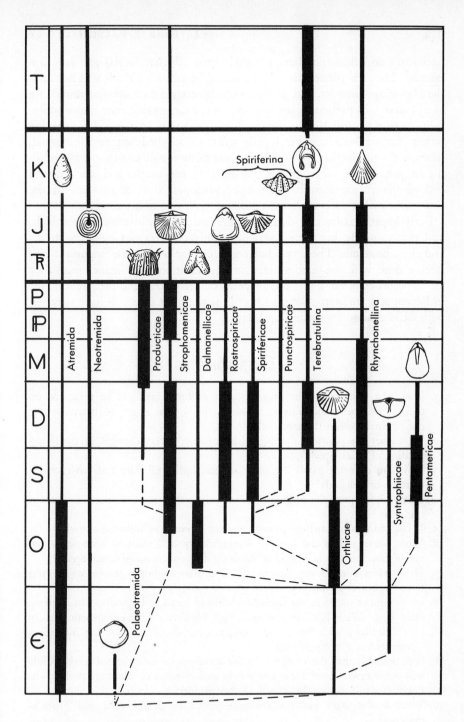

Figure 8.22. Geologic Distribution of Brachiopods.

Suborders and Superfamilies appeared; thus Silurian faunas are very important. They are particularly characterized by pentamerids. It was not until the Devonian, however, that the brachiopods reached their greatest abundance and diversity. In particular, the spiriferids exploded at that time into wonderfully numerous and diverse forms. Late Paleozoic brachiopod faunas are rather distinct because several early groups had died out or diminished, whereas the productids dominated the seas so thoroughly as almost to nullify the importance of other groups. Changes in the brachiopod stock at the end of the Paleozoic were even more profound than at the end of the Devonian, owing to cumulative effects of evolution and extinction.

Early Mesozoic brachiopod faunas contained a few spiriferids, rostrospirids, and punctospirids, but were overwhelmingly characerized by terebratulids and rhynchonellids. These two latter groups continued to be important into Recent time, with the terebratulids gaining additional dominance until they are the most common living brachiopods. Of second rank to the terebratulids in Recent seas are inarticulates such as *Lingula,* some of which have survived with little change from the Cambrian.

QUESTIONS

1. How is it possible for the growth stages of brachiopods to be preserved on the exteriors of adult valves, although the young stages of brachidia are not retained within the same valves?
2. How does the position of the pedicle foramen reflect changes in the living position of brachiopods?
3. How can different kinds of ornamentation indicate habits and environment of some brachiopods?
4. How might spondylia originate? How might they acquire selective value in evolution?
5. What changes in cardinal processes affect leverage of diductor muscles?
6. What bearing does the Law of Irreversibility of Evolution have upon the use of punctae and brachidia in devising a classification of brachiopods?
7. How widespread is metamorphosis in the invertebrate groups which you have studied thus far?
8. Knowing the stages in the metamorphoses of loops and spiralia, which group came first? What law are you applying? How can their ontogenetic history be rationalized with the known stratigraphic distribution of the Suborders Terebratulina and Spiriferina?
9. Is it probable that the northern or the southern strain of recent terebratulids was the ancestral one? How and where and in rocks of what age could additional evidence be sought regarding this problem?
10. What evolutionary patterns are exemplified by *Scacchinella* and *Prorichthofenia?*

BIBLIOGRAPHY

Arber, M. A., 1939, The nature and significance of the pedicle-foramen of *Leptaena* Dalman: Geol. Mag., v. 76, pp. 82–92.

——, 1942, The pseudodeltidium of the strophomenoid brachiopods: Geol. Mag., v. 79, pp. 179–187.

Beecher, C. E., 1893, Revision of the Families of loop-bearing brachiopods: Trans. Connecticut Acad. Sci., v. 9, pp. 376–391, 396–398.

——, 1893, The development of Terebratalia obsoleta, Dall: Trans. Connecticut Acad. Sci., v. 9, pp. 392–395, 399.

——, and Schuchert, C., 1893, Development of the brachial supports in Dielasma and Zygospira: Proc. Biol. Soc. Washington, v. 8, pp. 71–78.

Bulman, O. M. B., 1939, Muscle systems of some inarticulate brachiopods: Geol. Mag., v. 76, pp. 434–444.

Butts, C., 1926, The Paleozoic rocks: Alabama Geol. Survey, Spec. Rept. 14, pp. 40–230.

Carpenter, M. D., 1845, On the microscopic structure of shells: Rept. British Assoc. Adv. Sci., 14th Meeting (York), pp. 1–24.

Clarke, F. W., and Wheeler, W. C., 1915, The composition of brachiopod shells: Proc. Nat. Acad. Sci., v. 1, no. 5, pp. 262–266.

Cloud, P. E., 1942, Terebratuloid brachiopods of the Silurian and Devonian: Geol. Soc. America Spec. Paper 38 (especially pp. 1–41).

——, 1948, Notes on recent brachiopods: Amer. Jour. Sci., v. 246, no. 4, pp. 241–250.

Cooper, G. A., 1944, Phylum Brachiopoda *in* Index fossils of North America, New York, John Wiley & Sons, Inc., pp. 277–365.

——, and Williams, A., 1952, Significance of the stratigraphic distribution of brachiopods: Jour. Paleont., v. 26, no. 3, pp. 326–337 (especially p. 332).

Crickmay, C. H., 1957, Elucidation of some western Canada Devonian formations: Calgary, Canada, Imperial Oil Limited, 16 pp., 1 pl.

Davidson, T., 1886–1888, A monograph of Recent Brachiopoda: Trans. Linnean Soc. London, Zoology, ser. 2, v. 4.

Dunbar, C. O., and Condra, G. E., 1932, Brachiopoda of the Pennsylvanian Series in Nebraska: Nebraska Geol. Survey, Bull. 5, ser. 2.

Girty, G. H., 1903, The Carboniferous formations and faunas of Colorado: U. S. Geol. Survey Prof. Paper 16.

——, 1920, Carboniferous and Triassic faunas: U. S. Geol. Survey Prof. Paper 111, pp. 641–657.

——, 1927, Descriptions of new species of Carboniferous and Triassic fossils: U. S. Geol. Survey Prof. Paper 152, pp. 411–446.

Grabau, A. W., 1901, Guide to the geology and paleontology of Niagara Falls and vicinity: New York State Mus., Bull., v. 9, no. 45.

Hall, J., 1861, Palaeontology: New York Geol. Survey, v. 3, pt. 2.

————, and Clarke, J. M., 1892, 1894, An introduction to the study of the Genera of Palaeozoic Brachiopoda: New York Geol. Survey, v. 8, pts. 1, 2.

————, and Whitfield, R. P., 1875, Descriptions of Silurian fossils: Ohio Geol. Survey, v. 2, pt. 2, pp. 65–161.

McEwan, E. D., 1939, Convexity of articulate brachiopods as an aid in identification: Jour. Paleont., v. 13, no. 6, pp. 617–620.

Meek, F. B., 1873, Description of invertebrate fossils of the Silurian and Devonian Systems: Ohio Geol. Survey, v. 1, pt. 2, pp. 1–243.

————, 1877, Palaeontology: U. S. Geol. Expl. 40th Parallel, v. 4, pt. 1.

Morse, E. S., 1902, Observations on living Brachiopoda: Mem. Boston Soc. Nat. Hist., v. 5, pp. 313–386.

Schuchert, C., 1897, A synopsis of American fossil Brachiopoda: U. S. Geol. Survey, Bull. 87 (especially pp. 11–17, 73–119).

————, 1911, Paleogeographic and geologic significance of Recent Brachiopoda: Geol. Soc. America Bull., v. 22, pp. 258–275.

————, and Cooper, G. A., 1931, Synopsis of the brachiopod Genera of the Suborders Orthoidea and Pentameroidea, with notes on the Telotremata: Amer. Jour. Sci., ser. 5, v. 22, pp. 241–251.

————, and Cooper, G. A., 1932, Brachiopod Genera of the Suborders Orthoidea and Pentameroidea: Peabody Mus. Nat. Hist. (Yale), Mem., v. 4, pt. 1.

Stehli, G., 1954, Lower Leonardian Brachiopoda of the Sierra Diablo: Bull. Amer. Mus. Nat. Hist., v. 105, pp. 257–358.

Ulrich, E. O., and Cooper, G. A., 1938, Ozarkian and Canadian Brachiopoda: Geol. Soc. America Spec. Paper 13 (especially pp. 1–22).

Walcott, C. D., 1912, Cambrian Brachiopoda: U. S. Geol. Survey, Mon. 51.

Weller, Stuart, 1907, A report on the Cretaceous paleontology of New Jersey: New Jersey Geol. Survey, v. 4.

————, 1914, The Mississippian Brachiopoda of the Mississippi Valley Basin: Illinois Geol. Survey, Mon. 1.

White, C. A., 1877, Report upon the invertebrate fossils, etc.: U. S. Geog. Survey W. 100th Merid., v. 4, pt. 1.

Williams, A., 1953a, The Classification of the strophomenoid brachiopods: Jour. Washington Acad. Sci., v. 43, no. 1, pp. 1–13.

————, 1953b, North American and European stropheodontids: their morphology and systematics: Geol. Soc. America, Mem. 56.

CHITONS, PELECYPODS, AND SCAPHOPODS

PHYLUM XII.   MOLLUSCA

The most common molluscs are the clams and snails, but the octopods and squids also are part of the Phylum Mollusca. In addition, the uncommon "tusk-shells" and "coat-of-mail" shells belong with the Mollusca. It can be seen that some molluscs are typified by the presence of a shell, whereas others are soft-bodied. Accordingly, scientists who study shell-bearing forms may be thought of as conchologists, whereas specialists who think that molluscs are better characterized by soft parts than by skeletal structures are apt to consider themselves malacologists. The words "mollusc" and "malacology" both come from the same classical root, meaning soft, in allusion to the soft bodies of the entirely shell-less forms.

Molluscs have been economically important since before written history because they comprise some of the most abundant and easily obtainable articles of food. Various sorts of clams, oysters, marine and terrestrial snails, squids, and octopods are eaten. Molluscs also have been and are commonly used for adornment, as in the case of pearls and mother-of-pearl. Some colorful and precious molluscs, such as cowries, have even served as money. Thus, during the last century in India, about 4100 cowries could be exchanged for 1 rupee. In fact, the scientific name of one cowry, *Cypraea moneta,* was coined in allusion to the use of cowry shells for money. In North America the Indians used "tusk-shells" and snails for monetary exchange and wove wampum out of beads which they fabricated from the common clam, *Venus.* Finally, a particular snail belonging to the Genus *Purpurea* furnished the dye called Tyrrhenian purple, with which the garments of rulers were tinted in classical times.

Shell-bearing molluscs are of great importance in paleontologic work because they occur in rocks of many ages, are relatively easily identified, are widely distributed geographically, and may have short stratigraphic ranges. Some molluscs, such as the cephalopods, have been considered for many years as unusually valuable index fossils in Paleozoic and Mesozoic rocks. Pelecypods and gastropods begin to be especially important for applied paleontology in Mesozoic rocks and they are the most important of all megafossils in Cenozoic rocks. Field geologists in many lands have become expert in identification of members of these two Classes. Thus, oysters are used for zonation of Cretaceous strata on the Atlantic and Gulf Coastal Plains, and Pectens and Turritellas are of first importance in the field for subdividing the Tertiary strata of the Coast Ranges in the western United States. When the first paleontologic laboratories were established by oil companies (on the Gulf Coast) the employees drew upon the wealth of literature which had been published on conchology in order to make correlations. Shortly thereafter conchologic studies were used in California to date strata. When correlation by use of microfossils became general about 1920, conchologic studies in economic paleontology declined until now they pertain mostly to field work and are even augumented there by study of foraminifers.

Bottom-dwelling molluscs are rather sensitive to depth, temperature, and nature of sediment; therefore, they can be used in reconstructing ancient environments. Moreover, their geographic distribution may be restricted in an area of diverse sedimentation because of their preference for a particular environment. Opportunities for constructive work with molluscs are better now than ever because of the interest in ecology and because the stratigraphic distribution of megafossils can be correlated with that of microfossils.

The several groups of Mollusca are so different from one another that it is difficult to characterize the entire Phylum. Molluscs are unsegmented, are distinctly bilaterally symmetrical, and are generally enclosed within some sort of calcareous exoskeleton which is secreted by the inner fleshy lining or **mantle** (Fig. 9.1). Respiration is mostly by gills. The nervous system is concentrated at one or more interconnected centers (ganglia). Several types of light-sensitive organs are developed by molluscs, varying from a generally light-sensitive surface of the body, to rows of pigmented spots on the edge of the mantle of pelecypods, and to image-forming eyes in cephalopods and in some gastropods. Sexes generally are separate.

A trochophore larval stage is succeeded by a characteristic top-shaped **veliger** larval stage with an equatorial flange (the velum) bearing cilia (Fig. 9.14.1d). Molluscan larvae mostly are free-living for only four or five days, but the planktonic phase of some, such as the larvae of oysters, may last as long as two weeks.

Many molluscs rasp away food into small particles with a **radula**. This is an extrusible organ devised on the principle of a pulley, the surface of which is studded with orderly rows of minute chitinous teeth, each of which bears serrated rows of sharp cusps (Fig. 6.9.8). Opposable muscular systems draw

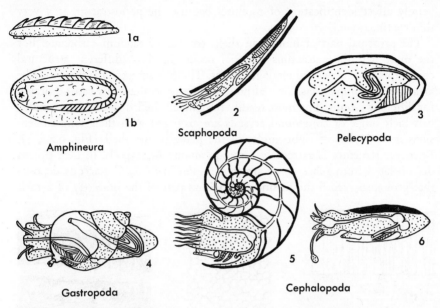

Figure 9.1. Classes of Mollusca.
Typical examples of molluscs are shown mostly in their living positions and with anterior toward the left. Shells are indicated by heavy lines when feasible; digestive tracks by an open tube; and gills by hachures. Two cephalopods are shown—nautiloid (5) and squid (6). All views are from the side except that 1b is ventral and 4 is dorsal.
(Mostly after Lang, 1896. 3 partly after Turton, 1840.)

the radula back and forth across the surface on which the mollusc is feeding. Some radulae are even capable of drilling holes through the calcareous shells of animals in order to feed upon the soft tissues inside. Radulae are not present among pelecypods, but are found in most divisions of the other major groups. Some radulae bear only a few teeth, but most radulae have several hundred and a few have tens of thousands of radular teeth.

SHELL COMPOSITION AND STRUCTURE.   Shells of molluscs can be characterized on the basis of chemical composition, arrangement of layers, and mineralogic constitution. Different groups may tend to be constructed along some plan rather typical of the group, but variation in shelly features is so extreme that valves of different kinds of pelecypods, for instance, may differ from one another as much as their shells differ from conchs of gastropods.

In general, molluscs are covered with an exterior cuticle or **periostracum** which is composed of a chitinlike organic compound called **conchiolin**. The periostracum is relatively structureless, elastic, and decomposes readily after death; hence it is rarely fossilized. Loss of the periostracum does not adversely affect identification of molluscs because the periostracum is a very thin coating.

The principal part of molluscan shells consists of calcium carbonate. For the most part the calcareous material occurs in three different structural conditions and in two mineralogic forms. The five foregoing factors may be arranged in complex fashions, although some generalizations can be drawn for different groups. The most readily recognized shell structure is **prismatic,** in which single or compound crystals are arranged with their long dimensions more or less at right angles to the plane of the shell (Fig. 9.2.1, 2). Prismatic structure is extremely common among pelecypods. In fact, prisms disassociated from *Inoceramus* are so common in many Cretaceous deposits that geologists record the prisms routinely as part of the lithology of a rock

 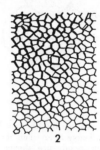 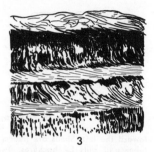

Figure 9.2. Shell Structure.
1. Vertical section through the shell of *Avicula* sp. showing the prismatic layer above the nacreous layer, 35X. 2. Tangential section of the prismatic layer of *Pinna* sp., 35X. 3. Vertical section through part of a shell of *Ostrea* sp. showing alternating foliated layers in which fibers vary from nearly horizontal to nearly vertical, 35X.
(After Bøggild, 1930.)

and interpret them as presumptive evidence of the Cretaceous age of the strata which contain them. The luster of prismatic layers is normally rather dull, or chalky.

In shells with a **foliated** structure, the calcium carbonate is arranged in thin micalike leaves which mostly are parallel to the surface but also can be oblique or irregular (Fig. 9.2.3). Shells such as those of oysters, with lamella on the surface, are foliated; but so, also, are scallop shells, in which foliation is not very distinct in fresh material. Individual foliated layers may be as much as 0.1 to 0.5 millimeter thick. The luster of foliated material is moderately bright.

Finally, shells with **nacreous** structure are characterized visually by the iridescent luster which gives this substance its common name: mother-of-pearl. Nacreous structure consists of alternating layers of calcium carbonate and organic material, each of which is only about 1 micron thick (Fig. 9.2.1).

Mineralogically, molluscan shells consist of two polymorphic forms of calcium carbonate—calcite and aragonite. These minerals can be detected with confidence only by optical or X-ray examination; hence, gross features are not of much assistance in their differentiation. Some shells are all calcitic, some are all aragonitic, and others consist of both minerals. Foliated structure is consistently calcitic, and nacreous structure is uniformly aragonitic. Prismatic structure may be either calcitic or aragonitic, although the calcitic kind predominates. Mineralogic constitution is functionally important because it affects the state of preservation of molluscs. Aragonite is slightly more soluble in ground water than calcite is; hence, aragonitic shells commonly are less well preserved than calcitic shells are. The effect of the difference in solubility is revealed most clearly in chalk deposits, such as in western Europe, where aragonitic shells are represented by molds in a matrix of calcitic chalk.

Arrangement of layers both as to structure and mineralogic form can be very simple, but it also may be so complex that small taxa of shells may some day be characterized by physical peculiarities of their minute constitution. In general, however, shells consist of two or three layers, of which the outer one is always the periostracum. The prismatic layer may or may not be present, but when it is, it generally lies just beneath the periostracum. If a third or innermost layer is present, it has either foliated or nacreous structure. In other shells, layers with prismatic structure may alternate with layers of either foliated or nacreous structure. In any case, foliated and nacreous structure never occur in the same shell. The foregoing intricacies can be simplified for some practical use because shells with largely prismatic structure or foliated structure, or with combinations of both kinds, are less soluble than are shells with largely nacreous structure. Moreover, shells with a prismatic outer layer and a nacreous inner layer commonly will have lost the inner layer by solution.

Structure and texture affect the three important groups of molluscs as follows. Pelecypods, having the most prismatic structure and the most calcitic constitution, are the best-preserved molluscs. Gastropods with very little calcitic or prismatic material tend to be rather poorly preserved. Voids left after removal of aragonitic material commonly are filled with granular calcite, some of which may grow in crystallographic continuity with the matrix; hence it may be difficult to remove gastropods from limestone. Cephalopods are subject to the same solvent effect of ground water that gastropods are because cephalopod shells also are largely aragonitic. Fortunately, loss of the shell of cephalopods enhances their value because it lays bare the patterns of the underlying sutures. In argillaceous sediments, however, such as the Pierre shale in the northwestern Great Plains, cephalopods and other molluscs tend to retain not only their shells but even relics of the iridescent sheen which they reflected in Cretaceous seas.

Some molluscs lose the tips of their shells by solution during their lifetime. It seems that damage of the periostracum by abrasion or by activity of worms or other organisms enables solution to bring about a sort of decay, called **erosion,** of the calcareous substance. Erosion particularly affects the tips of gastropods and the beaks of pelecypods. Erosion is greater in water with meager amounts of calcium salts than in lime-rich water and is greater in fresh water than in marine water.

CLASSIFICATION. It is customary to divide the Mollusca into several Classes, which can be recognized primarily by the shape of the shell, when present. Actually, however, the names of the Classes were derived from the character of the fleshy part of the body which protruded from the shell (Fig. 9.1). Thus, gastropods are "stomach-footed" and cephalopods are "head-footed."

Class A. Amphineura. Shell consisting of eight dorsal plates. These are chitons, or "coat-of-mail" shells.

Class B. Pelecypoda. Shell bivalved. Clams, oysters, pectenoids, and mussels belong to this class.

Class C. Scaphopoda. Shell tapered and tubular. The only living forms are the "tusk-shells."

Class D. Gastropoda. Shell spiral and not chambered. Snails, conchs, periwinkles, and whelks are common examples.

Class E. Cephalopoda. Shell mostly spiral and chambered, but some are straight and others lack a shell. The pearly nautilus, squids, and the octopus belong here, as do a host of extinct forms.

Class A.   Amphineura

The Amphineura are oval molluscs with a straight digestive tract, along each side of which extends a nerve cord—hence the name of the Class, which means "nerves on both sides." The most readily identifiable amphineurans are covered with a dorsal carapace which consists of a single row of eight large, overlapping, calcareous plates, the edges of which are embedded in a marginal mantle (Fig. 9.3). Some other amphineurans lack the dorsal plates but bear calcareous spicules in the soft tissue. Amphineurans grow to be more than 6 inches (15 cm) long.

Living amphineurans are generally called chitons in allusion to their being invested in a cover like a tunic (Greek: *chiton,* tunic). Each animal is able to adhere firmly to a rock or shell by powerful suction exerted by the foot. When feeding, the chiton moves only short distances from its habitual resting place and browses on the thin film of alga which coats the surface of the rock. An animal may not move from the same spot any farther than its own length during its lifetime. Plate-bearing chitons abound on rocky headlands in the intertidal zone where they are periodically exposed to the air. They also range down into deep water, but the plated forms always require a solid surface on which to attach themselves. It follows that presence of the peculiar plates generally indicates strong currents, exposed rock surfaces, and relatively shallow water in Recent seas.

Chitons range from Ordovician to Recent, but are rarely an important part of a fauna. One puzzling occurrence is their abundant representation in a diverse marine fauna in mid-Pennsylvanian black shale in Illinois (associated with the Herrin coal near Danville). Alternating widespread coal

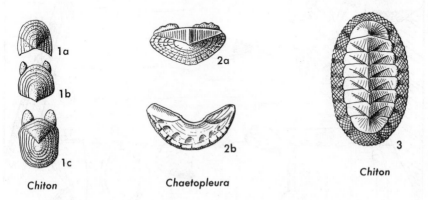

Chiton

Chaetopleura

Chiton

Figure 9.3. Chitons.
1a, 1b, 1c. Anterior, medial, and posterior plates of *Chiton carbonarius*, 1X, Pennsylvanian, Illinois.   2a, 2b. Exterior of posterior plate and interior of anterior plate of *Chaetopleura apiculata*, 3X, Miocene to Recent, Atlantic Coast.   3. Dorsal view of *Chiton squamosus* with the leathery girdle encompassing the edges of the eight plates, 1/2X, Recent.
(1 after Meek and Worthen, 1873. 2 after Clark, et al., 1904. 3 after Woodward, 1866.)

swamps, floodplains, and very shallow continental seas supposedly dominated that region during the Medial Pennsylvanian, so perhaps some Amphineura lived differently then than they do now.

Class B.   Pelecypoda

Pelecypods are bivalved molluscs which inhabit both marine and fresh water. They range in size from a few millimeters to about 2 meters in length, the largest being *Tridacna* of the South Seas. *Tridacna* is notorious for the great strength with which it can close its valves and is reputed to be feared by pearl divers lest they be caught and drowned if valves should close upon a hand or foot. Even specimens a foot long could be dangerous because the living shells are commonly embedded in coral reefs with the open portion or gape upward.

Pelecypods can be grouped into three main categories, depending upon their relationship to the substratum (Fig. 9.4). Most of them normally are **mobile,** in which case they usually plough through the surficial sediment, but a few, such as *Pecten,* can swim about for a few seconds. When partly or entirely buried, and not apt to move about much, they are **burrowing** types. Burrowing pelecypods such as *Teredo,* the shipworm, attack wood, whereas other burrowing pelecypods, such as *Pholadidea,* penetrate solid rock. Most geologists learn early in their studies of the borings of marine pelecypods

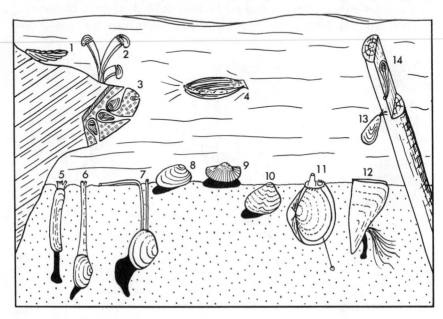

Figure 9.4. Adaptations of Marine Pelecypods.
 1, 2. *Ostrea* and *Coralliochama* cemented to substratum.   3, 14. *Zirphaea* and *Teredo* burrowing in rock and wood.   4. *Pecten* swimming.   5, 6, 7. *Solen, Mya,* and *Scrobicularia* burrowing in soft sediment.   8, 9. *Venus* and *Arca* creeping over substratum.   10. *Acila* partly buried.   11, 12. *Notocorbula* and *Atrina* partly buried but attached by byssal threads. 13. *Mytilus* attached by byssal threads.
 All forms are shown schematically and not to scale. The foot, when present, is shown in black in its extended position. Arrows in some forms indicate movement of water.
 (5-7 after Yonge, 1949. 11, 12 after Stenzel, Krause, and Twining, 1957.)

halfway up the marble columns of the Temple of Jupiter at Pozzuoli, Italy; these burrows, of course, prove a cycle of marine submergence and emergence since the temple was built in classical times. Members of the third group, the **sedentary** pelecypods, attach themselves to some hard object either during their entire life or only in youthful stages. Attachment can be through anchoring by means of one or more tough **byssal threads,** or attachment can be by cementing one valve to the substratum, as in the case of oysters.

EXTERNAL FEATURES.   The plane of symmetry in pelecypods passes anteroposteriorly as well as dorsoventrally, but the **valves** are right and left, instead of being dorsal and ventral the way they are in brachiopods. **Length** is measured anteroposteriorly; **height** is measured dorsoventrally; and **thickness** is measured from right to left through both valves. The greatest **convexity** is located with respect to imaginary vertical or horizontal **midlines.** Valves which are mirror images of each other and have the same convexity are said to be **equivalved** (Fig. 9.7.5, 7), whereas shells such as oysters, in which the two valves bear little or no resemblance to one another, are said to be **inequivalved** (Figs. 9.14; 9.18). If anterior and posterior halves of each valve are symmetrical as viewed from the side, they are **equilateral** (Fig. 9.9.7), whereas a valve with more substance on one side of the midline than on the other side is said to be **inequilateral** (Fig. 9.9.6). Pelecypods characteristically are equivalved and inequilateral, whereas brachiopods are inequivalved and equilateral.

The ventral and lateral edges of each valve below the **hinge** comprise the **margin,** the curvature of which is a characteristic feature in different groups. In some shells the anterior margin is pointed, whereas it is more broadly rounded than the posterior margin in other groups. The exterior of each valve generally culminates in a **beak** on the dorsal margin above the indefinite convex region near the beaks called the **umbo** (Fig. 9.6). If preserved, the minute, unornamented embryonic shell, the **prodissoconch** (Fig. 9.14.1c), is at the summit of each beak. Beaks generally curve up gracefully above the hinge but curve away from the plane of symmetry between the valves. If they lean across the hinge toward each other they are **orthogyre** (Fig. 9.9.7, 9), but if they curve anteriorly (the most consistent condition) they are **prosogyre** (Fig. 9.6). In a few Genera such as *Nuculana* (Fig. 9.8.5) and *Trigonia* (Fig. 9.16.1) the beaks point posteriorly and are called **opisthogyre;** these unusual shells are apt to be distinctive.

SCULPTURE.   Both radial and concentric sculpture can be present on pelecypods, but concentric sculpture is much the commoner of the two. **Growth lines, ridges,** and protruding **growth lamellae** are the principal kinds of concentric sculpture. Radial ornamentation consists of **lirae, costae,** and **plicae,** in increasing magnitude of strength. If both radial and concentric sculpture are present the intersections of two elements may be marked by **nodes.** Moreover, **spines** may project above the surface from growth lamellae or from nodes. Intersecting ridges and costae produce **cancellate** patterns. It is customary in describing ornamentation to count the total number of ribs which occur on a valve of given dimensions or to state how many ribs occur within some unit of length such as 10 centimeters measured at a given distance ventrally from the beak.

SOFT ANATOMY. The visceral mass of a pelecypod occupies about half of the interior of the valve and is located centrally; thus, the laminar gills hang down freely on both sides of the visceral mass within the branchial cavity between the visceral mass and the valves. Pelecypods are filter-feeders; hence water is circulated over the gills and elsewhere between the valves by

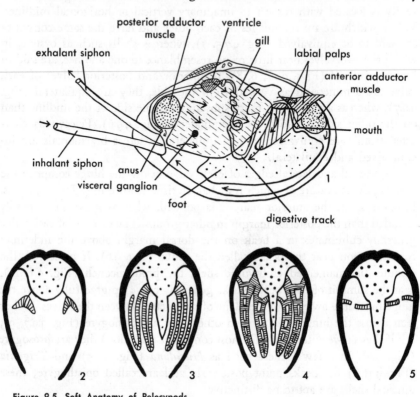

Figure 9.5. Soft Anatomy of Pelecypods.
   1. Simplified view of left valve and viscera of *Tellina tenuis* with the right valve and right mantle lobe removed. Arrows indicate the direction of flow of water.   2. Protobranchial gills. 3. Filibranchial gills.   4. Eulamellibranchial gills.   5. Septibranchial gills.
   In the schematic transverse sections of pelecypods, 2-5, shells are solid black; visceral mass and foot together are stippled; and gills are hachured.
   (1 after Yonge, 1949. 2-5 after Lang, 1896.)

action of cilia on the gills (Fig. 9.5). Microscopic food particles are washed into the mouth by ciliary action and are digested in an S-shaped digestive track. Refuse is washed away by the current of water between the valves. A definite pulsating heart connects arterial and venous circulatory systems containing colorless blood. The nervous system consists of several interconnected ganglia distributed about the body. Sexes are either separate or combined, or a creature may alternately change sex. After fertilization of the eggs a trochophore larva is formed, and this develops into a characteristic veliger larval stage. Thereupon the embryonic shell (**prodissoconch**) is secreted, after which the larva settles down on the substratum and assumes its more or less sedentary habits. Attached pelecypods either cement themselves down (Fig. 9.4.1, 2) or are anchored by tough **byssal threads** (Fig. 9.4.11–3) which they secrete.

Among attached pelecypods circulation of water between the valves is possible when the valves are opened, but in the burrowing forms it is necessary to provide some connection between the animal and open water. Accordingly, the burrowing pelecypods extend their fleshy substance posteriorly as a pair of parallel tubes, the **siphons.** Water flows in the lower or **inhalant siphon,** circulates within the branchial cavity, and then flows out through the upper or **exhalant siphon.** Thus, a buried animal may project the siphons out of the sediment into clear water or may retract the siphons by special muscles. Valves are closed by **adductor muscles.**

In general, pelecypods can be classified according to whether they have one adductor muscle like an oyster or scallop (**monomyarian**) or have two like a clam (**dimyarian**) (Figs. 9.13.1; 9.14.1a). Among dimyarian shells, those with subequal muscle scars are **isomyarian,** whereas those in which the anterior scar is much reduced in size are **anisomyarian.** It is generally believed that dimyarian shells are the generalized type and that monomyarian shells were derived from them by progressive reduction of the anterior part of the shell, including the anterior adductor muscle.

GILL STRUCTURE. Pelecypods can be grouped into four main categories which differ from one another in construction of the gills. Gills consist of sheets of fleshy tissue which hang down ventrally from the sides of the visceral mass into the two branchial cavities. In most pelecypods the gills in each chamber are W-shaped, with only the central apex of the W attached lengthwise along the roof of the branchial cavity (Fig. 9.5.3). The outer or ascending lamellae of the W are continuous with the inner or descending lamellae but are merely folded back dorsally to become free along their outer edges.

The foregoing gill structure is thought to have evolved from the simplest condition known, in which **protobranchial gills** are just a pair of tufts in each gill chamber (Fig. 9.5.2). Extension of these tufts would first produce vertical curtainlike lamallae and ultimately the standard W-shaped **filibranchial gill** (Fig. 9.5.3). Reinforcement of the W-shaped gill by transverse connections between descending and ascending lamellae would lead into the third form or **eulamellibranchial gill** (Fig. 9.5.4). Transverse connections either consist of insecure unions produced by intertwined cilia, or the connections become permanent columns of cellular tissue. In the last and most advanced condition, the gills are reduced to the condition of a transverse plate (**septibranchial gill**) which divides the branchial cavity into upper and lower portions (Fig. 9.5.5). Water is admitted into the upper or innermost chamber through perforations in the transverse plate. Recognition of these four types is of paramount importance in the study of Recent pelecypods; hence a special terminology for gill structures is widely used by specialists.

INTERNAL SKELETAL FEATURES. The most striking feature of the interior of pelecypod valves generally is the division into a concave visceral area and a flat hinge area (Fig. 9.6). The hinge area usually bears teeth and sockets and may overhang the visceral area as a shelf. The visceral area is marked by one or two adductor muscle scars, depending upon whether

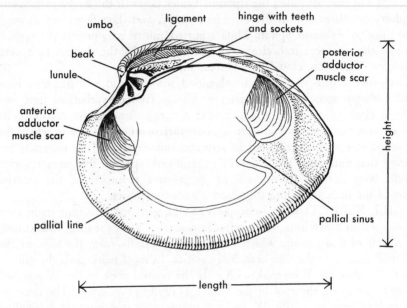

Figure 9.6. Terminology of Pelecypod Valves.
Interior of right valve of *Venus mercenaria*, 1X, Cenozoic, world-wide.

the shell is monomyarian or dimyarian. In the dimyarian type the **anterior adductor muscle scar** is a slightly depressed elliptical area just behind the anterior margin, and the **posterior adductor muscle scar** occupies the corresponding position on the opposite margin. In addition, two or three small depressions near the large scars indicate the sites of attachment of **retractor muscles** which pulled in the foot or the siphons. The number, shapes, positions, and sizes of adductor muscle scars are of considerable taxonomic value.

A narrow groove extending between the two adductor muscle scars and lying parallel to the ventral margin denotes the **pallial line.** In life the mantle hung free beyond the pallial line and only precipitated skeletal substances when it lay against the shell. In shells which had siphons during life the trace of the pallial line is indented by a minor to distinct anterior bend just below the posterior adductor muscle scar. This **pallial sinus** records the space into which the siphons could be retracted when the creature was disturbed. Inasmuch as the deepest burrowers needed the longest siphons in order to reach the surface, the depth of the pallial sinus records to a certain degree the habits of the animal. Moreover, the pallial sinus lies in the posterior part of the shell, so it can be used as an infallible guide in determining orientation of shells. Recognition of significant and unusual things such as opisthogyre beaks may be facilitated if it can be observed that the beaks point toward the end of a shell bearing a pallial sinus.

Interiors of shells rarely bear any kind of ornamentation, although scallops are an exception to this rule. Many pelecypods such as *Venus* have a row of toothlike **crenulations** just inside the margin of the shell. Crenulations help keep the valves in correct orientation by relieving the teeth of some of the strain.

DENTITION. As in the case of the brachiopods, teeth and sockets keep the two valves of pelecypods in opposition. Pelecypod dentition, however, is so wonderfully variable that it has acquired major importance in differentiation of various systematic categories of these bivalves.

The most primitive pelecypods seem to have had poorly developed teeth and sockets—indeed, the ancestral forms may not have had dentition at all. Their dental condition is called **dysodont.** Qualified authorities disagree as to the manner in which pelecypod dentition arose, but several hypotheses are based upon the idea that crenulations along the hinge, or ends of ribs extending up to the hinge, provided the indefinite beginnings of teeth and sockets. According to one hypothesis the primitive dentition (disregarding dysodont dentition) consists of a row of similar teeth and sockets extending along the hinge shelf (Fig. 9.9). This pattern is **taxodont** dentition, in which the separate teeth of most forms are oriented either at right angles or oblique to the hinge line. Authorities who believe that taxodont dentition is primitive would derive the other kinds from taxodont dentition by progressive reduction of the number of teeth in each row, bunching up of teeth under the beak, enlargement of the few remaining teeth, and reorientation of a few teeth near the margins of the hinge plate so that they become more or less parallel to the dorsal margin of the shell.

Eventually a rather radial pattern of teeth and sockets arose, which is called **heterodont** dentition (Fig. 9.6). Heterodont dentition is characterized by the presence of one **cardinal** group and two **lateral** groups of teeth. Cardinal teeth lie immediately beneath the beak; anterior and posterior lateral teeth lie on either side of the cardinals in positions described by their names. Lateral teeth generally are few in number and may even be lacking. There are three cardinal teeth in the right valve and two in the left valve in generalized heterodonts, but numerous modifications of the basic plan have been described. Several names have been proposed for special cases among variants and the same kinds of dentition have been given different names in different treatises (Neumayr, 1884; Dall, 1889). Dentition is acknowledged by all students of pelecypods to be of major importance in taxonomy; therefore specialists have even devised shorthand methods by which some different kinds of heterodont dentition can be described schematically. The two most widely used systems of **dental formulae** were devised by Steinmann and Döderlein (1888) and by Bernard and Munier-Chalmas (in Bernard, 1895), but both systems have been modified slightly by various subsequent workers. Systems of dental formulae are useful to specialists but formulae require excessive concentration on the part of less dedicated investigators. The function of dental formulae can be served best by well-chosen illustrations.

LIGAMENTS. The two valves of pelecypods are held together by continuation across the hinge of the flexible tough periostracum. Although the hinge margins of some pelecypods are straight, most dorsal lines of articulation in the group are more or less curved and the valves tend to gape slightly along the anterior and posterior parts of the hinge line when the valves open. If a thin sheet of periostracum lay across the hinge line, it would be torn when the valves opened. On the other hand, a thick sheet would keep the valves from opening; therefore, in most pelecypods the conchiolin is concentrated in a central location near the beaks as a thick but short block called the **ligament** (Fig. 9.7). The basic ligamental arrangement is analogous to that in which a circular door on a steel safe may be hung with one big hinge tangent to the edge. In most pelecypods the ligament is posterior to the beaks and is said to be an **opisthodetic** ligament (Fig. 9.7.5). Less commonly the ligament is **prosodetic;** that is, it is anterior to the beaks. In some pelecypods with nearly straight hinge lines the ligaments may occur on both sides of the beak; these are **amphidetic** ligaments (Fig. 9.7.7). Very commonly the ligament is concentrated as a thick welt in a groove (the **escutcheon**) posterior to the beaks. If an escutcheon is present, then there is likely to be a heart-shaped area (the **lunule**) devoid of ligament just anterior to the beaks. Perversely, in a few forms (nuculoids) the lunule is on the posterior side of the beaks and true orientation of the valves is very deceptive (Fig. 9.8). Fortunately, muculoids have a distinct pallial sinus and their orientation can be established beyond doubt.

Inasmuch as the opposing valves of pelecypods are held together by a ligament, changes in the habits of the creatures affect operation of the valves and nature of the ligament. In the position of rest the valves of pelecypods are slightly agape. The ligament is located along the dorsal margin in a position such that closing the valves stretches the upper part of the ligament at the same time that the lower part is being compressed. The part subjected to tension is made of tough laminar conchiolin, whereas the compressed portion has a fibrous appearance because many acicular crystals of aragonite

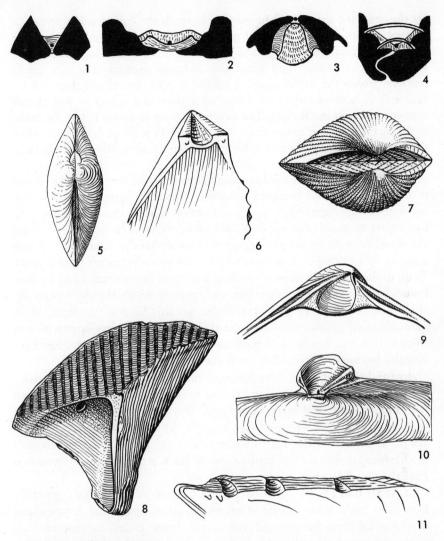

Figure 9.7. Ligamental Features.

1-4. Various types of ligaments as seen in transverse section through the hinge lines. Shells are solid black; lamellar tissue is striated horizontally; fibrous tissue is striated vertically; and the axis of rotation is indicated by a dot in each case.   5. Dorsal view of *Dosinia* sp. with lunule and escutcheon.   6. Groove for alivincular ligament in hinge of *Lima sp.*   7. Dorsal view of *Diluvarca* with amphidetic and duplivincular ligament.   8. Hinge of *Melina maxillata* with numerous groovelike resilifers, 1/3X, Miocene, Maryland.   9. Large resilifer in left valve. 10. Dorsal view of *Mya* showing large chondrophore, 1X.   11. Hinge of *Perna* sp. with three resilifers in a multivincular ligament.

(1, 3 after Newell, 1937. 2, 4, after Newell, 1942. 5, 7 after Gardner, 1926. 6 after Woodward, 1866. 8, 10 after Clark, *et al.*, 1904. 11 after Jackson, 1890.)

are disseminated through it. In many pelecypods the compressible portion is isolated as a **resilium** in a special pit, the **resilifer,** just ventral to or in line with the cardinal teeth (Fig. 9.7.8). When adductor muscles contract, the resilium is compressed; and when the adductor muscles relax, the elastic resilium pushes the valves apart. A rubber stopper would function as a resilium if it were placed in the hinge of a door and the door was closed, thus compressing the stopper. The axis of rotation of valves lies in the midst of the ligament dorsal to the teeth; hence the teeth serve as fulcra only when the ligament actually lies in the hinge line proper alongside the teeth (Fig. 9.7.1–4).

In its possible ancestral condition the ligament lay hidden within or ventral to the hinge line and occupied a resilifer; **internal ligaments** of this sort occur in young stages of pelecypods and persist in adult Pectens (Fig. 9.13.1). Ligaments of many pelecypods consist of an exposed elongate band along the dorsal edge of the hinge (Fig. 9.7.6). This **alivincular ligament** definitely seems to be a primitive stage from which some other ligaments were derived. Thus, **multivincular ligaments** consist of a series of fibrous resilia and laminar external bands along the hinge line, each pair of which thereby repeats the alivincular condition (Fig. 9.7.11). *Perna* has this kind of ligament. In its most advanced general condition, the elongate ligament develops an arcuate cross section and has been likened most appropriately to a C-spring. **Parivincular ligaments** of this kind are borne by *Cardium* and *Mytilus*.

Arca and some of its relatives develop a characteristic variety of the parivincular ligament in which sloping **cardinal areas** above the hinge are covered with fibrous layer, and successive laminar layers are inserted at intervals in grooves on the cardinal area (Fig. 9.7.4, 7). Thus, when the conchiolin is absent, as in fossil shells, the former traces of the laminar layers are visible as chevronlike slits on the cardinal areas. This arrangement constitutes a **duplivincular ligament.**

CLASSIFICATION. Systems of classification of pelecypods generally have been based upon gill structure, musculature, ligamental features, and dentition. Of these features, gill structure is almost useless for paleontologic purposes because the gills leave no impression upon the shell and there is no general correlation between structure of the gills and either the musculature or the dentition. Nevertheless, paleontologists dealing with Cenozoic molluscs sometimes use classifications based in part upon soft structure because representatives of the Families of molluscs with which they deal are mostly still living. Importance attached to gill structure is reflected in the use of "Lamellibranchia" by many systematists for the Class called "Pelecypoda" by other systematists.

Muscle scars are helpful in classification, but there is rarely enough difference in musculature of different dimyarian molluscs to divide them into groups of general utility. It is convenient, however, to separate those pelecypods with notably anisomyarian (including monomyarian) muscle scars from those with isomyarian scars.

Use of dentition for classification of pelecypods was promoted most assiduously by paleontologists because teeth and sockets are not only durable but are variable shell structures which lend themselves to evolutionary studies. In the past 50 years paleontologists and zoologists alike have carried forward studies of dentition until very elaborate terminology and dental formulae are in use.

It is apparent that classifications can and do involve different kinds of variables. For reasons of consistency, systematists try to create classifications in which changes in one structural category are reflected in changes of names at the same taxonomic level. Thus, names of Classes of Mollusca reflect the nature of the foot (hence, Pelecypoda). Systems of this sort are said to be **coordinate classifications.** On the other hand, in **noncoordinate classification** the names of creatures at the same taxonomic level are based upon different kinds of features. The Orders of Pelecypoda used herein comprise a noncoordinate classification.

KEY TO ORDERS OF PELECYPODA

I. Isomyarian
   A. Dentition taxodont .... Taxodontida
   B. Dentition heterodont .... Heterodontida
II. Anisomyarian .... Anisomyariida

The 26,000 species of pelecypods have been referred to nearly 8000 Genera. Inasmuch as Linnaeus recognized only 15 Genera of pelecypods, it is apparent that a great amount of descriptive work has been published on this group. One of the major problems encountered in identification of pelecypods is the extraordinary diversity of systems of classification. Between the levels of Order and Genus lie several intermediate taxa, the recognition of which requires more than casual interest in the Class. In short, pelecypods require more specialized study than is accorded most other groups of megafossils. Malacologists recognize the need for keys; therefore excellent outlines have been prepared for many groups of pelecypods in many regions (Keen and Frizzell, 1953). The plan used herein is to describe some common groups in each Order, without trying to take up each of the 30 or more Superfamilies which are generally recognized.

Order 1. Taxodontida

All pelecypods with taxodont dentition belong in this Order. All taxodont pelecypods are also dimyarian. Some of them have protobranch gills and others have filibranch gills (Fig. 9.5.2, 3).

Nuculoids. Nuculoid pelecypods have the usual two rows of taxodont teeth, in addition to which a distinct chondrophore lies beneath the beak and separates the two series of teeth (Fig. 9.8). More than 1000 species of nuculoid pelecypods have been described. Some specialists consider that nuculoids are the only true taxodonts.

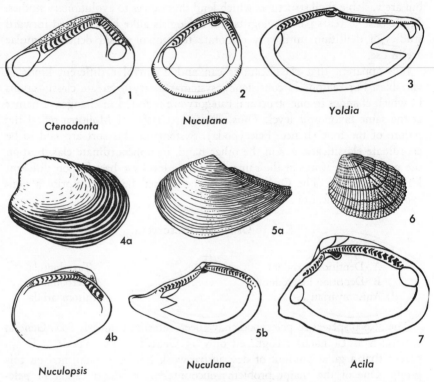

Figure 9.8. Nuculoids.
1. Interior of right valve of *Ctenodonta planodorsata*, 3X, Ordovician, Minnesota.   2. Interior of right valve of *Nuculana senaria*, 6X, Miocene, Florida.   3. Interior of right valve of *Yoldia soror*, 4X, Miocene, Florida.   4a, 4b. Exterior and interior of right valves of *Nuculopsis girtyi*, 2X, Pennsylvanian, midcontinent.   5a, 5b. Exterior and interior of left valve of *Nuculana acuta*, 5X, Miocene to Recent, Atlantic Coast.   6. Exterior of right valve of *Acila shumardi*, 2X, Oligocene, Oregon.   7. Diagrammatic view of the interior of the left valve of an *Acila*, about 4X.
(1 after Ulrich and Scofield, 1897. 2, 3, 5 after Gardner, 1926. 4 after Girty, 1915. 6, 7 after Schenck, 1936.)

Ctenodonta (Ordovician and Silurian) is the oldest of the nuculoids and is one of the oldest of the taxodonts. *Nucula* and *Nuculana* (Silurian to Recent) and *Yoldia* (Pennsylvanian to Recent) are other representative Genera. *Acila* is particularly interesting because it is a very easily recognized Genus with a significant geographic distribution. It flourished in the Indo-Pacific faunal realm from Cretaceous to Recent and tended to live in the northern hemisphere. The only times *Acila* occurred in Europe were during the Cretaceous and in the Pliocene. Students of geographic distribution have concluded that *Acila* migrated across the arctic polar region in order to occupy its isolated position in the Pliocene of the Atlantic realm.

Arcoids. Arcoid pelecypods are typically taxodont and resemble nuculoids except that arcoids do not have a chondrophore (Fig. 9.9). The presence of a duplivincular ligament is a characteristic feature of many arcoids. This is the most common and abundant group of taxodonts, with about 1300 living and fossil species known so far. The arcoids have been called the Prionodonta by some systematists.

It appears that arcoid dentition arose among arcoids from a form such as the Ordovician *Cyrtodonta* in which several long lateral teeth lay parallel to the margin of the valve (Fig. 9.9.1). From Devonian to Jurassic, arcoid dentition was characterized by that of *Parallelodon* in which the posterior part of the hinge plate bears three long teeth lying parallel to the hinge, but the short anterior teeth are inclined toward the ventral interior (Fig. 9.9.3). In *Nemodon* (Cretaceous), however, all teeth are long and are parallel to the hinge line. *Cucullaea* is typical of the group of Jurassic to Recent taxodonts in which the long dimensions of lateral teeth on both the anterior and posterior sides of the hinge are nearly parallel to the hinge line, but the central teeth lie more or less at a right angle to the hinge line (Fig. 9.9.9). In all of the foregoing taxodonts the long teeth tend to slope outward and ventrally (or to lie subparallel to the hinge line) in a fashion termed **divergent.**

A second group of arcoids is characterized by teeth which tend to slope inwardly and ventrally in a **convergent** fashion. Convergent patterns are thought to have evolved during the Mesozoic from Genera with divergent teeth such as *Parallelodon* and *Cucullaea*. In some instances teeth may be convergent at one place on a hinge plate and divergent at another, as in the possible ancestral type, *Cucullaea*. Or the teeth may be chevron-shaped as in the Cretaceous to Recent Genus, *Glycymeris* (Fig. 9.9.7a, 8). Size and number of teeth are also significant because there is a general tendency for the number of teeth to increase as the size of individual teeth decreases. *Arca,* the typical Genus (Fig. 9.9.6), has been subdivided into several Genera and Subgenera, some of which may extend back from the Recent to the Triassic. Thus, *Barbatia* (Fig. 9.9.4) is a well-known Cenozoic Genus with much finer external sculpture than is present in *Arca*. In summation, almost all of the older arcoids had divergent teeth, but so many strains evolved from divergent to convergent that almost all arcoid pelecypods living today have convergent teeth. Modern arcoids developed explosively since the Cretaceous and have attained success such as to suggest that their convergent dentition is superior to that of the Paleozoic and Mesozoic arcoids. In this regard it is worth noting that nuculoids always have had dentition similar to the con-

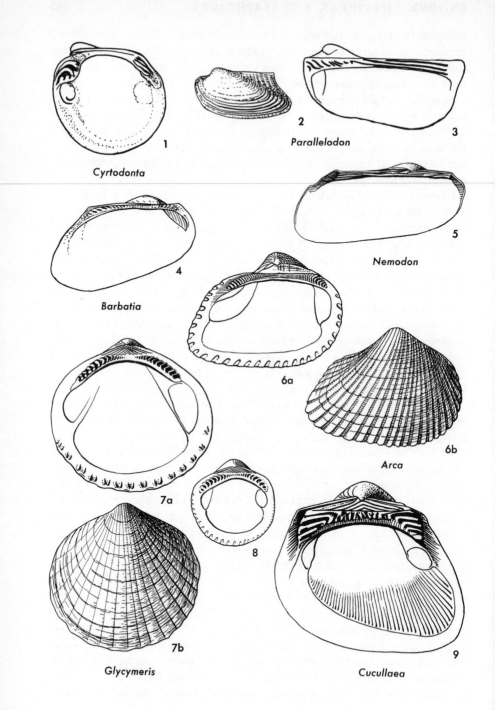

1

Cyrtodonta

2

3

Parallelodon

4

Barbatia

5

Nemodon

6a

6b

Arca

7a

8

7b

Glycymeris

9

Cucullaea

vergent type of arcoids and have been steadily represented in taxodont faunas; of course the nuculoids did not pass through as marked dental evolution as the arcoids did.

Order 2. Anisomyariida

The anterior adductor muscle of anisomyarian pelecypods either is much reduced in size or is lacking so the shell is monomyarian. Foreshortening of the shells is accompanied by major changes in the soft anatomy. It has even been discovered that torsion of the visceral mass in some shells such as *Pecten* has resulted in the two valves being dorsal and ventral instead of right and left.

Dentition is always very simple, either being unspecialized or reduced from that of more elaborate ancestors. If a very few unsymmetrically disposed teeth are present the condition is spoken of as **dysodont dentition.** If there are a few long teeth parallel to the hinge line anterior and posterior to a central ligamental pit (resilifer), the condition is spoken of as **isodont dentition.**

Loss of the anterior adductor muscle is coordinated with orderly changes in the shape of the shell among anisomyarians. Thus, pectenoids and mytiloids both progress from conditions in which the beaks and umbones lean forward (**prosocline**), through a condition in which each valve is essentially equilateral (**acline**), to a condition in which the midumbonal line leans backward (**opisthocline**).

Anomia (Fig. 9.10.7) exemplifies the ability of one animal to copy the sculpture of another shell to which it is attached. In this case the attached shell is said to have **allomorphic sculpture.** Possibly allomorphic sculpture renders the attached form less visible to creatures which might prey upon it.

Paranomia (Fig. 9.10.8) is provided with a special notch (byssal foramen) for passage of the byssal threads and thereby resembles brachiopods with a pedicle foramen.

Mytiloids. Mytiloid pelecypods have rather triangular shells which may be either equivalved or somewhat inequivalved—the latter condition being most noteworthy in forms which lie on one valve (the right valve apparently being

---

Figure 9.9 (opposite). Arcoids.
1. Interior of right valve of Cyrtodonta saffordi, 1X; Ordovician, Tennessee. 2. Exterior of left valve of Parallelodon tenuistriatus, 1X, Pennsylvanian, eastern United States. 3. Interior of right valve of Parallelodon rugosum, 1/2X, Jurassic, England. 4. Interior of left valve of Barbatia phalarca, 2X, Miocene, Maryland. 5. Interior of left valve of Nemodon grandis, 2/3X, Cretaceous, Tennessee. 6a, 6b. Interior of left valve and exterior of right valve of Arca ponderosa, 1X, Pleistocene and Recent, Atlantic Coast. 7a, 7b. Interior of left valve and exterior of right valve of Glycymeris subovata, 2/3X, Miocene, Atlantic Coastal Plain. 8. Interior of right valve of Glycymeris veatchii, 1X, Cretaceous, California. 9. Interior of right valve of Cucullaea vulgaris, 1X, Cretaceous, Tennessee.
(1 after Bassler, 1932. 2 after Morningstar, 1922. 3 after Arkell, 1930. 4 after Dall, 1895. 5, 9 after Wade, 1926. 6 after Shattuck, 1906. 7 after Gardner, 1947. 8 after Nicol, 1950.)

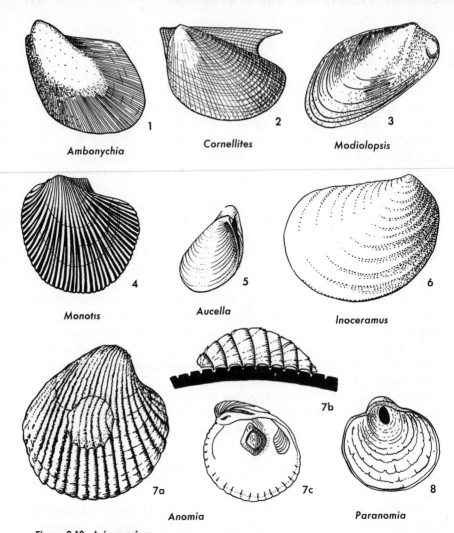

Figure 9.10. Anisomyarians.
1. Left valve of *Ambonychia bellistriata*, 1X, Ordovician, Wisconsin.   2. Left valve of *Cornellites emaceratus*, 1X, Silurian, New York.   3. Internal mold of right valve of *Modiolopsis excellens*, 2/3X, Ordovician, Minnesota.   4. Exterior of left valve of *Monotis subcircularis*, 2/3X; Triassic, western United States.   5. *Aucella piochii*, 1X, Jurassic, western United States and Russia.   6. Right valve of *Inoceramus sagensis*, 1X, Cretaceous, western interior.   7. *Anomia epihippioides*, Eocene, Gulf Coast. 7a, young specimen attached to *Venericor densata*, 1X. 7b, side view of shell showing relationship of ribs to those of host shell (black), 2X. 7c, calcified byssal plug attached to interior of an empty clam shell, 1X.   8. *Paranomia scabra* showing byssal foramen near beak of right valve, 2/3X, Cretaceous, Atlantic and Gulf Coasts.
(1, 3 after Ulrich, 1897. 2 after Grabau, 1901. 4 after Smith, 1927. 5 after Stanton, 1895. 6 after Meek, 1876. 7 after Stenzel, Krause, and Twining, 1957. 8 after Jackson, 1890.)

preferred). The anterior adductor muscle is present in a much-reduced condition in some forms, but is absent in most. Dentition is dysodont. Almost all mytiloids are marine, but a few, such as *Carbonicola,* inhabited fresh water during the Late Paleozoic (Fig. 9.19.3).

Mytiloids are represented in the Ordovician by *Modiolopsis* (Fig. 9.10.3), but the group did not become important until the Devonian, when *Modiomorpha* and the myalinoids arose; then the mytiloids began a spectacular increase in diversity and numbers. By Pennsylvanian and Permian time *Myalina* and its relatives had become major rock-makers in the midcontinent where they built shell banks analogous to those formed by oysters in Recent seas. Their morphologic changes during the Late Paleozoic are increase in size, development of a posterior extremity along the cardinal margin, slight inequilateral development of shells, and change in obliquity (Fig. 9.11). This last factor can be recognized best by visualizing the positions occupied by the imaginary, curved, **midumbonal line** which follows the greatest convexity of the valves. Several groups of mytiloids evolved along parallel lines, as shown by the rotation of the midumbonal line from a forward to a backward inclination. That is to say, the shapes of the valves progress from procline through acline to opisthocline with the passage of time. Moreover, these stages can be detected in the ontogeny of a species by tracing the various growth lines on a mature specimen. Concordance of stratigraphic series, morphologic series, and ontogenetic series among species of *Myalina* is interpreted as evidence of evolutionary history.

Paleozoic mytiloids did not survive into the Mesozoic. Instead, their place was taken by oysters and by the group of mytiloids of which *Mytilus* (Triassic? to Recent) is the standard example (Fig. 9.4.13). *Mytilus,* the edible mussel, attaches itself to the substratum by means of tough byssal threads and may accumulate in large clusters, all tied together with these threads.

A well-known possible relative of the mytiloids is *Aucella* (sometimes called *Buchia*) which migrated into Indo-Pacific regions from the north during the Jurassic and Cretaceous (Fig. 9.10.5).

Pectenoids. The pectenoids, including the scallops of commerce, constitute one of the most important of all pelecypod groups. In general the shells are subcircular, with a straight hinge margin. It is likely that the hinge margin is really anterior because of downward rotation of the ancestral dorsal hinge margin during evolutionary loss of the anterior adductor muscle scar. Nevertheless, by convention, systematists consistently illustrate pectenoid shells with the hinge margin up and refer to its position as dorsal. The shells are commonly inequivalved or opposing valves are differently sculptured. Shells range from procline to acline and opisthocline, but the umbones are consistently procline. Dentition consists of a triangular resilifer under the beaks and of one or two elongate teeth parallel to the hinge line in the isodont pattern. The large muscle scar lies just behind the center of the shell. Pectenoids range from Silurian to Recent, with about 30 Genera known from Paleozoic rocks, and 70 from the Cenozoic when pectenoids reached their greatest diversity.

Pectenoids possibly arose from *Rhombopteria* (Silurian) or a very similar form (Fig. 9.12.2). By Mississippian time they were reasonably abundant, being represented by two divergent types, *Pterinopecten* and *Aviculopecten*. The latter Genus is the most common Paleozoic pectenoid, and ranged from Mississippian into the Early Mesozoic. *Streblochondria* (Fig. 9.12.4) and *Pseudomonotis* (Fig. 9.12.3) are two other important Paleozoic Genera, the former being notable for its opisthocline shape.

Modern kinds of pectenoids, typified by *Pecten* itself, appeared in the Early Mesozoic Era and became increasingly diversified and abundant during the Cenozoic Era. In general the true pectenoids are characterized by the presence of a distinct anterior **auricle** set off from the main part of the right valve by the **byssal notch** (Fig. 9.13). Pectens are attached to the substratum, at least in their early stages, by byssal threads which are cradled in the byssal notch. Shells always lie on their right valves during the attached period; hence it is natural for the deeply indented notch to be confined to the lower or right valve. There is no corresponding notch below the anterior auricle of the left valve. Some Pectens become free-living after their early attached stage, but they still are oriented with their right valves downward. They can swim along wildly erratic courses by rapidly clapping their valves together while they eject water from first one side and then the other of the shell margins. Apparently their orientation is governed by a row of pigmented spots around the edge of the mantle; the spots are merely light-sensitive and are not capable of being focused like an eye. When Pectens remain attached to the substratum into maturity, the inner apex of the byssal notch may bear three or four spines which are jointly referred to as the **ctenolium.** A ctenolium serves as a comb to keep byssal threads separated as the shells shift about on their leashes. Absence of a ctenolium in fossil material presumably indicates that the animal led a free-living existence.

Most pectenoids bear radial ornamentation, but a few such as the so-called paper-shell Pectens are smooth or retain only concentric sculpture (Fig. 9.12.8). In general there is correlation between coarseness of ribbing and agitation of water; the coarsely ribbed forms occupy the turbulent environment near shore. Considerable importance is attached to details of surficial

---

Figure 9.11 (*opposite*). Evolution of *Myalina.*
1-5 comprise an evolutionary series in which the midumbonal line becomes more inclined, size increases, and the posterior auricle lengthens. III is another trend without the posterior auricle. Numbered growth lines on each species were selected to correspond with mature outlines of ancestral species. All illustrations are 1X.
(After Newell, 1942.)

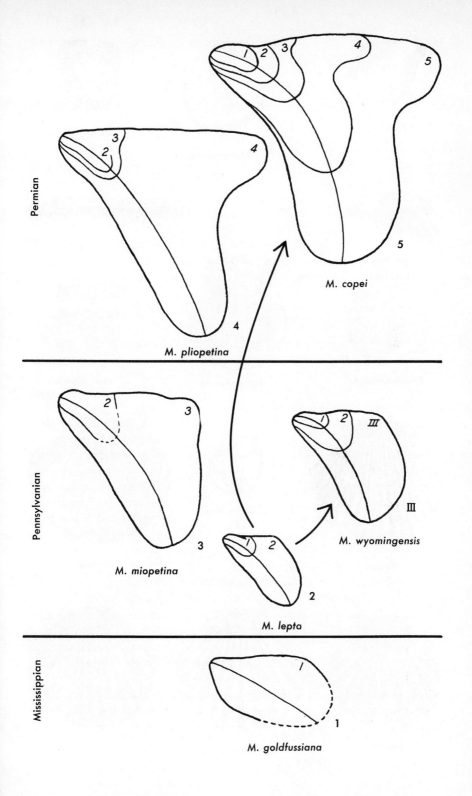

Permian

M. pliopetina

M. copei

Pennsylvanian

M. miopetina

M. lepta

M. wyomingensis

Mississippian

M. goldfussiana

Posidonia

1

2

Rhombopteria

3

Pseudomonotis

4a

6a

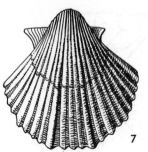

4b

Streblochondria

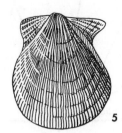

5

Aviculopecten

6b

Pterinopecten

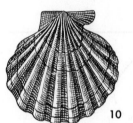

7

Pecten

8

Pseudamusium

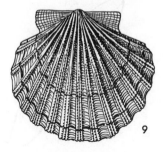

9

Lyropecten

11a

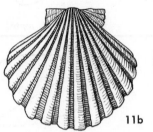

10

Lyropecten

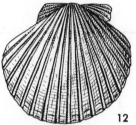

11b

Pecten

12

Lyropecten

ornamentation in identification of Pectens. Ribs may be numerous or sparse, wide or narrow, secondarily striate, separated by smooth interspaces or by ribbed interspaces, round, flat-topped, or grooved. Even the ornamentation of the anterior auricle is important in the taxonomy of pectenoids. Interior surfaces may be smooth, furrowed, or variously ribbed either in conformity with external features or in different patterns. It is customary to refer all of the Cenozoic forms to the Genus *Pecten* and to refer the smaller groups of species to Subgenera. Subgeneric names are always placed in parentheses when following generic names. Thus, *Pecten* (*Pecten*) includes all true members of the Genus *Pecten* with plano-convex shells, strong ribs, and sub-equal ears (Fig. 9.12.11). *Pecten* (*Lyropecten*) is biconvex, has striate ribs and a strong auricle (Fig. 9.12.9, 10, 12). *Pecten* (*Pseudamusium*) tends to have concentrically ornamented right valves and radially ornamented left valves (Fig. 9.12.8). In this fashion about a dozen subgeneric names are commonly used by paleontologists, particularly in the Coast Ranges of California where the pectenoids are of great practical importance in field work.

Ostreoids. Oysters were among the most important rock-makers from the Jurassic period to the Recent. Ostreoids typically are cemented to the substratum in life, although some become free after an early attached stage. Inasmuch as ostreoids conform rather closely to the configuration of the bottom, they are extremely variable in external form. It is therefore advisable, if not absolutely necessary, to have several specimens at hand when identifying a species. Size and shape of ligamental pit, concavity of the attached (almost invariably the left) valve, and position and shape of the muscle scar are all useful in identification. Surfaces may be costate or plicate, but most are smooth or lamellose.

Most Recent oysters live just below the low tide zone, but they have been reported in water as deep as 600 feet. It is assumed that fossil ostreoids predominantly lived in very shallow water. They now inhabit normal marine water but also flourish in brackish water and even can tolerate fresh water for short intervals of time. Ostreoids are known from supposedly brackish-

---

Figure 9.12 (*opposite*). Pectenoids.
1. Left valve of *Posidonia fracta*, 1 1/3X, Pennsylvanian, Ohio.   2. Left valve of *Rhombopteria mira*, 1X, Silurian, Czechoslovakia. 3. Umbonal area of left valve of *Pseudomonotis robusta*, 2X, Pennsylvanian, Kansas.   4a, 4b. Internal features of hinge of left valve (1 1/3X) and right valve (2X) of *Streblochondria sculptilis*, Pennsylvanian, Kansas.   5. Left valve of *Aviculopecten exemplarius*, 1 1/3X, Pennsylvanian, Kansas.   6a, 6b. Internal hinge features (7X) and exterior (1 1/3X) of left valve of *Pterinopecten undosus*, Devonian, New York. 7. Right valve of *Pecten quinquecostatus*, 2/3X, Cretaceous, world-wide.   8. Internal mold of left valve of *Pecten* (*Pseudamusium*) *peckhami*, 1X, Miocene, California.   9. Left valve of *Pecten* (*Lyropecten*) *madisonius*, 1/3X, Miocene, Atlantic Coastal Plain.   10. Right valve of *Pecten* (*Lyropecten*) *jeffersonius*, 1/3X, Miocene, Atlantic Coastal Plain. 11a, 11b. Lateral view and right valve of *Pecten* (*Pecten*) *hemphilli*, 2/3X, Pliocene, California. 12. Right valve of *Pecten* (*Lyropecten*) *estrellanus*, 1/2X, Miocene, California.
(1, 3-6 after Newell, 1937. 2 after Jackson, 1890. 7 after Wade, 1926. 8, 11, 12 after Arnold, 1906. 9, 10 after Clark, et al., 1904.)

water deposits in the Cretaceous System of the western interior. Assumption of a cemented habit originated among the ostreoids in the Early Mesozoic.

Ostrea ranges from Jurassic to Recent, but the more than 1000 species are generally difficult to identify. *Ostrea titan* from California and *Ostrea gravitesta* from Japan are interesting because they share honors as the biggest

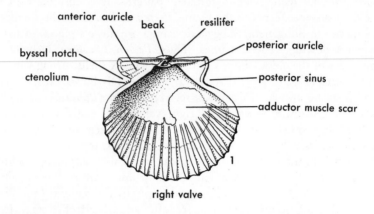

right valve

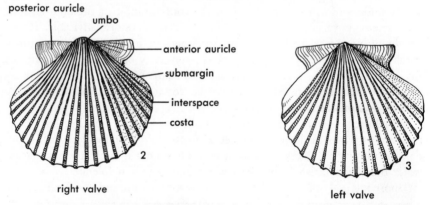

right valve

left valve

Figure 9.13. Morphology of *Pecten*.
1, 2, 3. Interior and exterior views of right valve, and exterior of left valve of *Pecten circularis* var. *aequisulcatus*, 1/2X, Pleistocene and Recent, Pacific Coast.
(After Arnold, 1906.)

oysters ever to live. These two Late Miocene species were a foot and a half long (60 cm) and contained about a quart of living animal tissue.

Some species of *Ostrea* were plicate, and individuals of one strain became so intricately plicate that they are segregated as the Subgenus *Alectryonia* (Triassic to Recent, with its greatest flare in the Cretaceous, Fig. 9.14.2, 3).

Gryphaea is a common world-wide Jurassic and Cretaceous Genus (Figs. 9.14.6; 9.15). It is ostreiform, but the beak of the large, sessile, curved, left

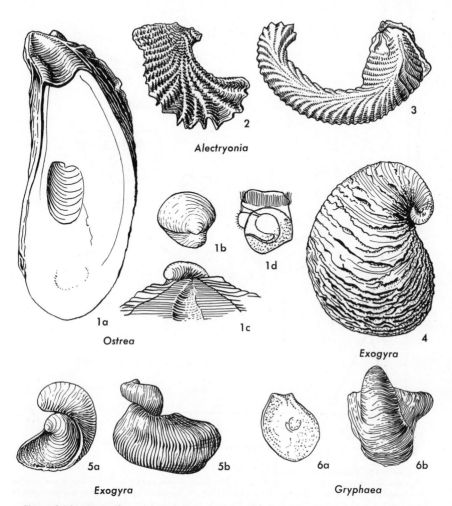

Figure 9.14. Ostreoids.
1. *Ostrea virginica*, Pliocene to Recent, Atlantic Coast. 1a, interior of left (lower) valve, 1/2X. 1b, prodissoconch, 50X. 1c, beak region of left valve with prodissoconch still attached and resilifer engraved in hinge, 50X. 1d, veliger larva, enlarged. 2. Left valve of *Alectryonia falcata*, 1X, Cretaceous, Atlantic and Gulf Coastal Plains. 3. Left valve of *Alectryonia carinata*, 2/3X, Cretaceous, Gulf Coastal Plain. 4. Left valve of *Exogyra ponderosa*, 1/2X, Cretaceous, Atlantic and Gulf Coastal Plains. 5a, 5b. Upper and side views of *Exogyra arietina*, 1X, 2/3X, Cretaceous, Gulf Coastal Plain. 6a, 6b. interior of left valve and exterior of right valve of *Gryphaea washitaensis*, 2/3X, Cretaceous, Gulf Coastal Plain.

(1a after Shattuck, 1906. 1b, 1c after Jackson, 1890. 2 after Wade, 1926. 3, 5 after White, 1884. 4 after Stephenson, 1914. 6 after Hill and Vaughan, 1898.)

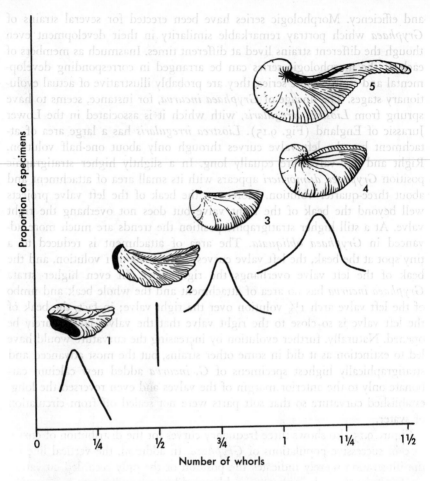

Figure 9.15 Evolution of Gryphaea.
Species are shown in side view at about 1/2X. Scars of attachment in the lower three species are shown in solid black. Variation in number of whorls is shown by distribution curves beneath three species, and a vertical line indicates the only point known for another species. All species are from the Lower Jurassic of England and are arranged in their stratigraphic order.
 1. *Liostrea irregularis.* 2. *Gryphaea dumortieri.* 3. *Gryphaea obliquata.* 4. *Gryphaea incurva.* 5. *Gryphaea* cf. *G. incurva.*
 (After Trueman, 1922.)

valve tends to arch up and to overhang the small, flat, right valve. Four main trends can be detected in the evolution of *Gryphaea:* diminution of the area of attachment and duration of attachment to the substratum; increased arching of the left valve; increase in size; and increase in the thickness of the shells. Their evolution presumably reflects the adaptation of *Gryphaea* to increased availability of calcium carbonate and the necessity for compactness and efficiency. Morphologic series have been erected for several strains of *Gryphaea* which portray remarkable similarity in their development even though the different strains lived at different times. Inasmuch as members of each of the morphologic series can be arranged in corresponding developmental and stratigraphic series, they are probably illustrative of actual evolutionary stages. The lineage of *Gryphaea incurva,* for instance, seems to have sprung from *Liostrea irregularis,* with which it is associated in the Lower Jurassic of England (Fig. 9.15). *Liostrea irregularis* has a large area of attachment but the left valve curves through only about one-half volution. Right and left valves are equally long. In a slightly higher stratigraphic position *Gryphaea dumortieri* appears with its small area of attachment and about three-quarter volution. Moreover, the beak of the left valve projects well beyond the beak of the right valve but does not overhang the right valve. At a still higher stratigraphic position the trends are much more advanced in *Gryphaea obliquata.* The area of attachment is reduced to a tiny spot at the beak, the left valve curves through about 1 volution, and the beak of the left valve overhangs the right valve. In even higher strata *Gryphaea incurva* has no area of attachment and the whole beak and umbo of the left valve arch 1⅛ volution over the right valve; in fact, the beak of the left valve is so close to the right valve that the valves could barely be opened. Naturally, further evolution by increasing the curvature would have led to extinction as it did in some other strains, but the most advanced and stratigraphically highest specimens of *G. incurva* added new calcium carbonate only to the anterior margin of the valves and even reversed the long-established curvature so that soft parts were not sealed off from circulation of water.

Figure 9.15 also shows three frequency curves for the distribution of curvature in successive populations of *Gryphaea.* In addition, the vertical line on the illustration merely indicates the position of the only recorded curvature for *G. dumortieri;* the line presumably would be expanded into a frequency curve like the others if data were available. Curves for *G. obliquata* and *G. incurva,* however, definitely overlap, indicating that some specimens in a population dominated by *G. incurva* have as few volutions as the most arcuate specimens in an underlying population dominated by *G. obliquata.* Intergradation such as this is the result of continuous variations operating through an appreciable increment of geologic time. The duration of evolution depicted in Figure 9.15, for instance, was about four or five million years. Incidentally, the *G. incurva* stock did not evolve particularly rapidly, for paleontologists are able to recognize about eight zones based upon various groups of fossils while the four or five members of this stock were evolving.

It is customary to explain overspecializations such as are exemplified by *Gryphaea* as the operation of natural selection. *Gryphaea,* however, carries the principle of overspecialization to incredible extremes because the phenomenon is repeated in several other strains at different times and in different places. Paths which are apparently orthogenetic and which are repeated ·by numerous strains of animals have been called program-evolution by some writers. For program-evolution to ◦operate as a result of natural selection (orthoselection, if you wish), it seems probable that each of the unusual series of forms should have been adapting itself to some changing physical conditions. Moreover, inasmuch as several different strains evolved in the same way, it is likely that they should all reflect some common environmental factor. Insofar as sediments are concerned, however, there does not seem to be anything much in common among the different strains, for the animals lived on sandy, chalky, or glauconitic substrata. Of course, it is possible that the animals were adapting themselves to some feature not reflected in sediment type. It is also possible that we do not understand why natural selection operates, or even that natural selection may not be the key to organic evolution of the type characterized by *Gryphaea.*

Exogyra is another Jurassic and Cretaceous Genus which resembles *Ostrea. Exogyra* differs from *Gryphaea* in having the beak of the left valve strongly twisted over to one side so that it does not overhang the right valve (Fig. 9.14.4). This twisting seems not to have been any great advantage, however, for *Exogyra* and *Gryphaea* have almost exactly the same geologic range, geographic distribution, and environmental adaptation. *Exogyra* and *Gryphaea* are the Mesozoic forerunners of *Ostrea* in ability to form shell banks. They both are present in astronomical numbers in many Cretaceous strata on the Gulf Coastal Plain and occur far north on the Atlantic Coastal Plain. One species, *Exogyra ponderosa,* characterizes a zone that has been traced with very few interruptions over a distance of 2500 miles, from New Jersey into Mexico.

Order 3.   Heterodontida

Heterodonts are dimyarian pelecypods whose dentition is not taxodont. Specifically, the heterodonts are apt to have strong cardinal teeth and weak lateral teeth. Moreover, gill structure is of the eulamellibranch type. Members are burrowing or free-living for the most part. Siphons normally are present. This group has been referred to as Eulamellibranchia or as Teleodesmacea by some specialists. Most pelecypods belong to the Heterodontida. In fact, the group is so large and so diverse that only a few of the most important forms are mentioned herein. Keys and voluminous literature are needed in order to study this great Order.

Veneroids.   The common clam, *Venus* (Fig. 9.6), and other well-known Genera such as *Pitar* and *Chione* are veneroids. According to one count, 186 Genera of veneroids were known as of 1936; possibly several thousand species are known. The group extends from Jurassic to Recent and contains many valuable guide fossils.

Trigonioids. Typical trigonioids are large triangular shells with radiating costae and radiating rows of nodes. In some cases radiating sculpture occurs in association with concentric sculpture. Cardinal teeth are unusually prominent.

Trigonia (Fig. 9.16.1) is typical of a score or more of Genera in the group. About a thousand species have been described. The group has been represented sporadically from Silurian to Recent, but was most important and distinctive during the Jurassic and Cretaceous.

Pholadoids. This group is noteworthy because of its unusual habit of boring into sediment, rock, shell, and wood. *Barnea* and *Pholadidea* are characteristic, rather normal-looking shells, but the shipworm, *Teredo,* secretes a calcareous tube as a lining for its borings in wood (Fig. 9.17). About ten Genera are known, the oldest of which are Mesozoic. Fossil borings are sometimes assigned to the Genus *Teredolites.*

Rudistoids. One of the most interesting groups of fossil pelecypods consists of the peculiar and aberrant shells called rudistoids (Fig. 9.18). Rudistoids appeared during the Jurassic and attained explosive evolutionary proportions during the Cretaceous, but they became extinct at the end of the Cretaceous Period. During their history they rather consistently occupied an oceanic belt extending along the course of the old Tethyan geosyncline from the East Indies westward to western Europe, then reappeared across the Atlantic Ocean in the western hemisphere in a region including Colombia in South America, the Gulf Coast of the United States, and the West Indies. Rudistoids were important reef-making organisms, as, for instance, in Texas, where they characterized the offshore facies of Cretaceous sediments. Other reefs were located in Baja California, near Ensenada. The northernmost Cretaceous rudistoids have been collected near Los Angeles on the Pacific Coast, from the western interior (Pierre shale), and from near the Oklahoma-Texas state line. In the Jurassic, however, rudistoids such as *Plicatostylus* (Fig. 9.18.4) lived as far north as Oregon. Cretaceous rudistoids have even been dredged from flat-topped sea mounts in the center of the Pacific Ocean 1000 miles west of Hawaii. Over 30 Genera of rudistoids have been described, most of which are only locally distributed.

Rudistoids were attached to the substratum by the apex of one much-elongated valve. So-called **normal** rudistoids are attached by the left valve and have two large teeth in the right valve and one tooth in the left valve. Normal rudistoids gave rise during the Late Jurassic to **inverted** rudistoids which are attached by the right valve and have one large tooth in the right valve and two teeth in the left valve. Subsequently both groups evolved along parallel courses involving loss or modification of teeth and sockets,

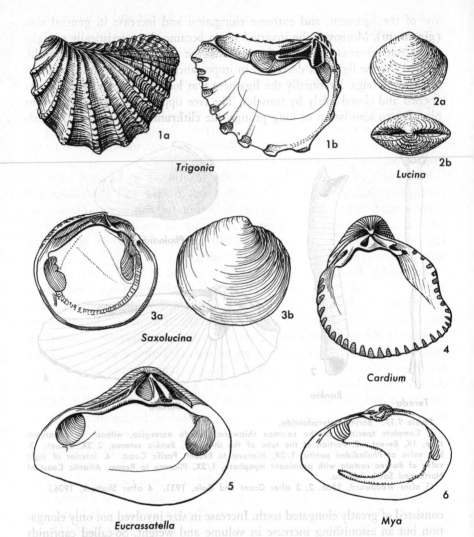

Figure 9.16 Heterodontida.

1a, 1b. Exterior and interior of the left valve of *Trigonia thoracica*, 2/3X, Cretaceous, Atlantic and Gulf Coastal Plains.　2a, 2b. Right valve and dorsal view of *Lucina occidentalis ventricosa*, 1X, Cretaceous, western interior.　3a, 3b. Interior of left valve and exterior of right valve of *Saxolucina anodonta*, 2/3X, Miocene, Maryland.　4. Interior of right valve of *Cardium medium*, 1X, Miocene, Maryland.　5. Interior of left valve of *Eucrassatella marylandica*, 2/3X, Miocene, Maryland.　6. Interior of left valve of *Mya arenaria*, 1/2X, Pleistocene to Recent, widespread.

(1 after Wade, 1926. 2 after Meek, 1876. 3, 5 after Clark, et al., 1904. 6 after Shattuck, 1906.)

loss of the ligament, and extreme elongation and increase in general size (**gigantism**). Moreover, the inverted strain became characteristically straight and erect, whereas one or both valves in the normal strain were spirally twisted. As the ligament decreased in importance the teeth became modified into long prongs. Eventually the ligament was lost and the upper valve was opened and closed solely by muscles. The free upper valve was guided into place by an association of long prongs, the **clithrum** (Fig. 9.18.5, 6), which

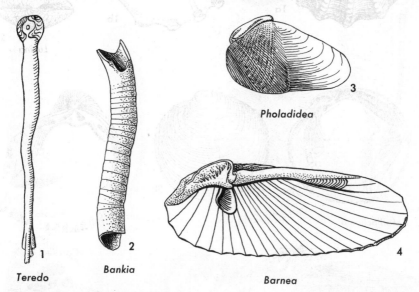

Pholadidea

Teredo *Bankia* *Barnea*

Figure 9.17. Boring Heterodontida.
1. Complete specimen of the common shipworm, *Teredo norvegica*, without its calcareous tube, 1X, Recent. 2. Portion of the tube of the shipworm, *Bankia setacea*, 2/3X, Recent. 3. Left valve of *Pholadidea penita*, 1/2X, Miocene to Recent, Pacific Coast. 4. Interior of right valve of *Barnea costata* with prominent myophore, 1/2X, Pliocene to Recent, Atlantic Coast of North and South America.
(1 after Woodward, 1866. 2, 3 after Grant and Gale, 1931. 4 after Shattuck, 1906.)

consisted of greatly elongated teeth. Increase in size involved not only elongation but an astonishing increase in volume and weight. So-called caprinids were the first rudistoids in which longitudinal chambers were developed in the middle layer of the shell, but eventually the trend toward vesicular structure of some sort was reflected in growth of all rudistoids. In some rudistoids the chambers are randomly oriented, but in others the chambers lie in horizontal layers or in radiating rows. In the last case the grooves on the exterior surface of rudistoids match the positions of the radial chambers and resemble structure of corals so closely that rudistoids have been called coralline pelecypods. Creation of internal vesicles (Fig. 9.18.1b) enabled the size of rudistoids to increase very rapidly with the most economical distribu-

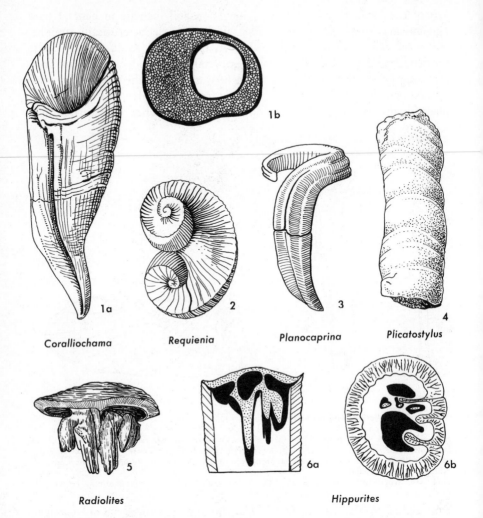

Coralliochama · Requienia · Planocaprina · Plicatostylus

Radiolites · Hippurites

Figure 9.18. Rudistoids.
1a, 1b. Cardinal side and cross section of *Coralliochama orcutti*, 1/3X, Cretaceous, California and Baja California. 2. Both spiral valves of *Requienia patagiata*, 2/3X, Cretaceous, Texas. 3. Side view of both valves of *Planocaprina trapezoides*, 1/5X, Cretaceous, Mexico. 4. Fragment of *Plicatostylus gregarius*, 1/2X, Jurassic, Oregon. 5. Side view of upper valve or operculum of *Radiolites* sp. with teeth modified into a clithrum, 1/3X, Cretaceous, Europe. 6a, 6b. Longitudinal (1/3X) and transverse (1/2X) sections of the visceral cavity of *Hippurites* sp.; visceral cavity is solid black, operculum with clithrum all stippled, inner shelly material white, and outer shelly material striate or hachured.
(1 after White, 1885   2 after Roemer, 1888.   3 after Palmer, 1928.   4 after Lupher and Packard, 1929.   5, 6 after Woodward, 1855.)

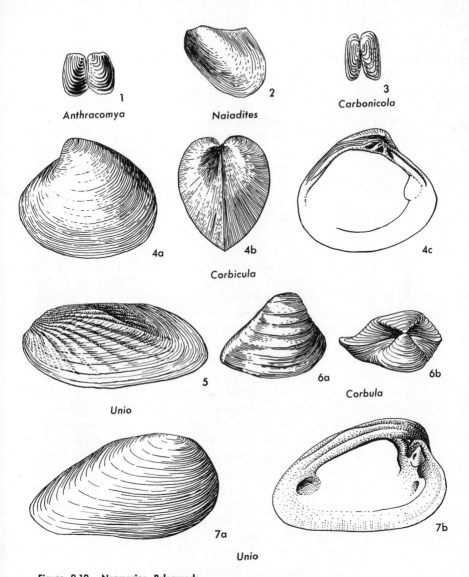

Figure 9.19. Nonmarine Pelecypods.
1. *Anthracomya elongata*, 2X, Pennsylvanian, Nova Scotia. 2. *Naiadites carbonarius*, 1X, Pennsylvanian, Nova Scotia. 3. *Carbonicola angulata*, 1X, Pennsylvanian, Nova Scotia. 4a, 4b, 4c. Left valve, anterior view, and interior of left valve of *Corbicula umbonella*, 1X, Cretaceous, Colorado. 5. Left valve of *Unio belliplicatus*, 2/3X, Cretaceous, Wyoming. 6a, 6b, Right valve and dorsal view of *Corbula undifera*, 1X, Cretaceous, Wyoming and Colorado. 7a, 7b. Right valve (1/2X) and interior of left valve (2/3X) of *Unio endlichi*, Cretaceous, western interior.

(1, 2 after Dawson, 1894. 3-7 after White, 1883.)

tion of solid skeletal substance. Accordingly, the rudistoids increased in length from a few inches to one giant, *Titanosarcolites*, from the Cretaceous of Jamaica, which stood 5 feet high. Other Genera are *Hippurites, Coralliochama, Requienia,* and *Radiolites.*

Rudistoids bear a remarkable resemblance to Paleozoic corals with dissepiments and to the unusual Permian brachiopods such as *Prorichthofenia* whose conical pedicle valves are lined with vesicles.

Cardioids. Cardioid pelecypods are characterized by peculiar dentition in which lateral teeth enroll about each other to such an extent that the two valves cannot be separated without breaking the teeth. Tooth structure of this sort commonly is referred to as **cyclodont dentition.** *Cardium* (Fig. 9.16.4) is the standard example, but it has been subdivided into more than 50 Genera and Subgenera, which all together contain about 2200 species.

Nonmarine Pelecypods. This group consists mostly of the unionoid fresh-water pelecypods. Typical representatives such as *Unio* (Fig. 9.19.7) have coarse cardinal teeth which resemble teeth of the trigonioids. The occurrence of *Corbula* and *Corbicula* (Fig. 9.19.4, 6) in some Cretaceous strata of the western interior seems to indicate that a fresh-water or brackish-water environment existed locally in the Rocky Mountain geosyncline. Unionoids also are known from nonmarine Tertiary deposits in western North America.

During the Carboniferous, fresh-water unionoids and even some mytiloid pelecypods were common in various countries; they have been studied in greatest detail in the British Isles, France, Germany, and Russia. Important representations of nonmarine pelecypods are also known in Devonian and Carboniferous deposits in the eastern United States and in southeastern Canada. *Anthracomya, Naiadites,* and *Carbonicola* are well-known Pennsylvanian Genera which are widespread (Fig. 9.19.1–3). Pre-Pennsylvanian occurrences of nonmarine pelecypods have all been questioned, but there is no question of the abundance of nonmarine pelecypods in the Pennsylvanian. Zonations based upon nonmarine pelecypods are notably consistent in distant regions, even though it does not seem that pelecypods could be transported from one body of fresh water to another very readily.

Class C.   Scaphopoda

Scaphopods comprise a relatively unimportant group of molluscs in the fossil record. All members bear a curved tubular shell which is open at both ends and generally expands gradually from the narrow posterior end to the broad anterior end (Fig. 9.20). In a few forms the anterior portion is slightly tapered so that the shells are enlarged medially. A characteristic slit is present at the posterior end of most scaphopod shells. Scaphopods are sometimes called "tusk-shells," but their resemblance is more to fangs of venomous snakes than to tusks of mammals; hence it is a bit surprising that some dramatically conceived common name is not applied to the shells of scaphopods.

In life the animal lies with most of the shell buried in sediment on the ocean floor. The posterior part of the shell projects from the sediment at an angle and is oriented with the concave side of the curved shell upward

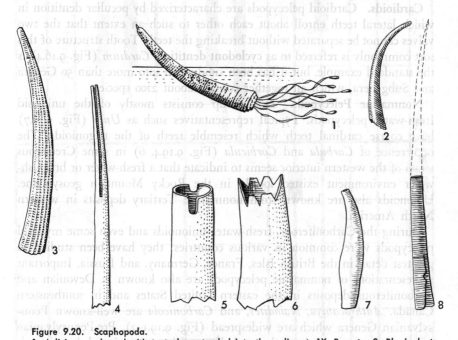

Figure 9.20. Scaphopoda.
1. A living scaphopod with tentacles extended into the sediment, 1X, Recent. 2. *Plagioglypta meekianum*, 2X, Pennsylvanian, Illinois. 3. *Dentalium attenuatum*, 2X, Miocene and Pliocene, Atlantic Coast. 4. *Dentalium stenoschizum* with unusually long apical slit, 2X, Recent. 5, 6. Two species of *Siphonodentalium* with different apical ends, enlarged, Recent. 7. *Cadulus thallus*, 5X, Miocene, Atlantic Coast. 8, *Plagioglypta canna*, 1/2X, Pennsylvanian and Permian, western United States.
(1 after Lacaze-Duthiers, 1856. 2 after Meek and Worthen, 1873. 3, 7 after Clark, et al., 1904. 4-6 after Henderson, 1920. 8 after White, 1877.)

(Fig. 9.20.1). A cylindrical or trilobed foot projects from the aperture and serves as an effective digging organ. Water circulates in and out of siphons in the posterior end and carries away refuse and reproductive bodies. No gill is present, so respiration takes place in the walls of an elongate pallial cavity. An effective radula is present. Scaphopods generally inhabit sandy or silty areas in shallow water, but they have been dredged from 15,000 feet (5000 m).

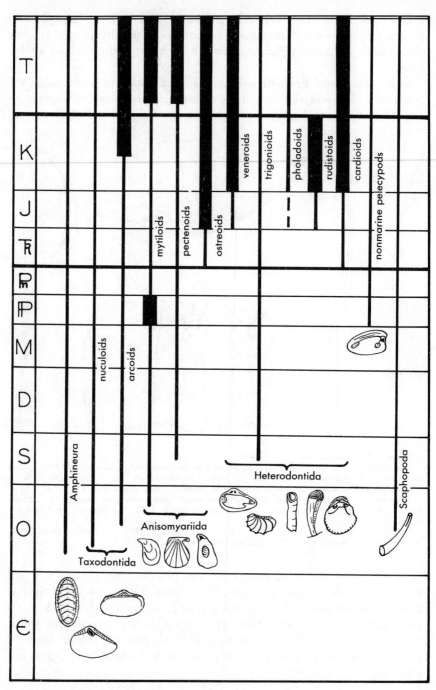

Figure 9.21. Geologic Ranges of Pelecypods, Chitons, and Scaphopods.

Scaphopoda are usually placed between the Pelecypoda and the Gastropoda in classifications because a scaphopod has the bilateral symmetry of the pelecypods and a radula such as is present among gastropods. The earliest embryonic shell is bivalved, but the adult shell is univalved.

Scaphopods range from Ordovician to Recent but are almost never common. *Dentalium,* with prominent longitudinal ribs, is the most characteristic scaphopod (Fig. 9.20.3, 4). It is something of a form Genus to which all sorts of scaphopods have been referred. *Plagioglypta* is a nearly smooth form from the Late Paleozoic, and *Cadulus* is a smooth form which extends from the Cretaceous to the Recent. About 500 Recent and fossil species are known, and these are distributed through 39 Genera.

QUESTIONS

1. How can you explain mixtures of *Ostrea* with *Unio?* How can you explain alternation of *Ostrea* and *Unio* in successive strata?
2. What climatic significance should be attached to the occurrence of rudistoids in the Jurassic of Oregon?
3. What evolutionary theory accounts for the sudden appearance of rudistoids?
4. What bearing does the geographic distribution of Cretaceous rudistoids have upon the theory of continental drift?
5. How is habit reflected in shell structure and morphology?
6. What similarities are there between ontogeny of a Permian *Myalina* and stratigraphic series of species in this Genus?
7. In view of the nature of the earliest taxodont dentition, did it reflect traces of external concentric or radial sculpture?
8. How do *Anomia* and *Petrocrania* resemble each other? How do you explain this?
9. What agents and processes brought about the widespread distribution of Carboniferous fresh-water pelecypods?
10. Why are chitons placed first in the sequences of molluscan Classes? Why are scaphopods placed after pelecypods?

BIBLIOGRAPHY

General

Adkins, W. S., 1928, Handbook of Texas Cretaceous fossils: Univ. Texas Bull. 2838.

Baker, F. C., 1898, 1902, The Mollusca of the Chicago area: Chicago Acad. Sci., Nat. Hist. Survey, Bull. 3.

Binney, W. G., 1885, A manual of American land shells: U. S. Nat. Mus., Bull. 28.

Bøggild, O. B., 1930, The shell structure of the mollusks: Kgl. Danske. Videnskab.

Selsk. Skr., Naturv. og Math. Afd., ser. 9, v. 2, pt. 2, pp. 233–326 (especially pp. 235–257).

Clark, W. B., *et al.*, 1904, The Miocene deposits of Maryland. Miocene: Maryland Geol. Survey, text and plates.

Cooke, A. H., 1927, Molluscs: Cambridge Natural History, v. 3, pp. 1–459.

Gardner, J., 1926–1947, The molluscan fauna of the Alum Bluff group of Florida: U. S. Geol. Survey Prof. Paper 142.

Girty, G. H., 1915, Fauna of the Wewoka formation of Oklahoma: U. S. Geol. Survey, Bull. 544.

Gould, A. A., 1852, Mollusca and shells: U. S. Expl. Exped., atlas.

Grant, U. S., IV, and Gale, H. R., 1931, Catalogue of the marine Pliocene and Pleistocene Mollusca of California: San Diego Soc. Nat. Hist., Mem., v. 1.

Gray, M. E., 1842, Figures of Molluscous Animals: London, Longman and Co., v. 1.

Harris, G. D., 1893, Republication of Conrad's fossil shells of the Tertiary formations of North America: Washington, D. C., R. H. Darby.

Henderson, J., 1935, Fossil non-marine Mollusca of North America: Geol. Soc. America Spec. Paper 3.

Keen, A. M., and Bentson, H., 1944, Check list of California Tertiary marine Mollusca: Geol. Soc. America Spec. Paper 56.

MacNeil, F. S., 1939, Fresh-water invertebrates and land plants of Cretaceous age from Eureka, Nevada: Jour. Paleont., v. 13, no. 3, pp. 355–360.

Shattuck, G. B., 1906, The Pliocene and Pleistocene deposits of Maryland. Pliocene and Pleistocene: Maryland Geol. Survey.

Stanton, T. W., 1895, Contributions to the Cretaceous paleontology of the Pacific Coast—the fauna of the Knoxville beds: U. S. Geol. Survey, Bull. 133.

Stephenson, L. W., 1941, The larger invertebrate fossils of the Navarro group of Texas: Univ. Texas Pub. 4101.

Turton, W., 1840, A manual of the land and fresh-water shells of the British Isles, etc.: 2nd ed., London, Longman and Co.

Wade, B., 1926, The fauna of the Ripley formation on Coon Creek, Tennessee: U. S. Geol. Survey Prof. Paper 137.

White, C. A., 1883, A review of the non-marine fossil Mollusca of North America: U. S. Geol. Survey, 3rd Ann. Rept. (1881–1882), pp. 403–550.

——, 1884, On Mesozoic fossils: U. S. Geol. Survey, Bull. 4.

——, 1885, On new Cretaceous fossils from California: U. S. Geol. Survey, Bull. 22.

Woodring, W. P., Roundy, P. V., and Farnsworth, H. R., 1932, Geology and oil resources of the Elk Hills, California: U. S. Geol. Survey, Bull. 835.

Amphineura

Berry, E. S., 1922, Fossil chitons of western North America: Proc. California Acad. Sci., ser. 4, v. 11, no. 18, pp. 399–526 (especially pp. 421–424).

Pelecypoda

Arkell, W. J., 1930, The generic position and phylogeny of some Jurassic Arcidae: Geol. Mag., v. 67, pp. 297–310, 337–352.

Arnold, R., 1906, The Tertiary and Quaternary pectens of California: U. S. Geol. Survey Prof. Paper 47.

Bernard, F., 1895, Première Note sur le Développement et la Morphologie de la Coquille chez les Lamellibranches: Bull. Soc. Géol. France, ser. 3, v. 23, pp. 104–154. (Especially pp. 104–119, but also pp. xxxvii, xxxviii, and liii–lvi.)

Cox, L. R., 1933, The evolutionary history of the rudists: Proc. Geologists' Assoc. (London), v. 44, pt. 4, pp. 379–388.

Dall, W. H., 1889, On the hinge of pelecypods and its development, with an attempt toward a better subdivision of the group: Amer. Jour. Sci., ser. 3, v. 38, pp. 445–462.

———, 1895, Tertiary molluscs of Florida, Part III: Trans. Wagner Free Inst. Sci. (Philadelphia), v. 3 (especially pp. 485–515, for morphology).

Davies, A. M., 1933, The bases of classification of the Lamellibranchia: Proc. Malacol. Soc. London, v. 20, pt. 6, pp. 322–326.

Davies, J. H., 1928, Zoning of the coal-measures by non-marine lamellibranchs: Cong. pour Adv. Études Strat. Carb., Heerlen (1927), Comptes rendus, pp. 219–222.

Dawson, J. W., 1894, Note on the Genus Naiadites, as occurring in the coal formation of Nova Scotia: Geol. Soc. London Quart. Jour., v. 50, pp. 435–442.

Dix, E., and Trueman, A. E., 1937, The valve of non-marine lamellibranchs for the correlation of the Upper Carboniferous: Deuxième Cong. Adv. Etudes Strat. Carb., Heerlen (1935), v. 1, pp. 185–201.

Douvillé, A., 1935, Les Rudistes et leur Evolution: Bull. Soc. Géol. France, ser. 5, v. 5, pp. 319–358.

Hall, J., 1879, Palaeontology: New York Geol. Survey, v. 5, pt. 2.

Hamilton, E. L., 1956, Sunken islands of the mid-Pacific mountains: Geol. Soc. America, Mem. 64.

Hill, R. T., and Vaughan, T. W., 1898, The Lower Cretaceous Gryphaeas of the Texas region: U. S. Geol. Survey, Bull. 151.

Keen, A. M., and Frizzell, D. L., 1953, Illustrated key to west North American pelecypod Genera: rev. ed., Stanford, California, Stanford Univ. Press, 32 pp.

Lang, A., 1896, Textbook of comparative anatomy, pt. II: London, Macmillan and Co., Ltd. (translated by Bernard and Bernard), 618 pp.

Lupher, R. L., and Packard, E. L., 1929, The Jurassic and Cretaceous rudistids of Oregon: Univ. Oregon Pub., Geol. Ser., v. 1, no. 3, pp. 203–212.

March, M. C., 1912, A discussion of the general classification of the Pelecypoda: Annals Mag. Nat. Hist., ser. 8, v. 10, pp. 91–116.

Meek, F. B., and Worthen, A. H., 1873, Palaeontology: Illinois Geol. Survey, v. 5, pp. 321–619.

Neumayr, M., 1884, Zur Morphologie des Bivalvenschlosses: Sitz. Kaiserlichen Akad. Wiss. Wien, Math.-Natur. Cl., v. 88, pt. 2 (1883), pp. 385–418.

Newell, N. D., 1937, Late Paleozoic pelecypods: Kansas Geol. Survey, v. 10, pt. 1.

――――, 1942, Late Paleozoic pelecypods: Mytilacea: Kansas Geol. Survey, v. 10, pt. 2.

Nicol, D., 1950, Origin of the pelecypod Family Glycymeridae: Jour. Paleont., v. 24, no. 1, pp. 89–98.

Palmer, K. V. W., 1927, The Veneridae of eastern America; Cenozoic and Recent: Palaeontographica Amer., v. 1, no. 5, pp. 209–428; plates published 1929.

Palmer, R. H., 1928, The rudistids of southern Mexico: California Acad. Sci., Occas. Papers, no. 14.

Reinhart, P. W., 1943, Mesozoic and Cenozoic Arcidae from the Pacific slope of North America: Geol. Soc. America Spec. Paper 47 (especially pp. 1–13).

Ridewood, W. G., 1903, On the structure of the gills of the Lamellibranchia: Phil. Trans. Roy. Soc. London, ser. B., v. 195, pp. 147–284.

Roemer, F., 1888, Ueber eine durch die Häufigkeit Hippuritenartiger Chamiden ausgezeichnete Fauna der oberturonen Kreide von Texas: Palaeontologische Abhand., v. 4, pt. 4.

Schenck, H. G., 1934, Literature on the shell structure of pelecypods: Mus. Roy. Hist. Nat. Belgium, v. 10, no. 34, pp. 1–20.

――――, 1936, Nuculid bivalves of the Genus Acila: Geol. Soc. America Spec. Paper 4 (especially pp. 7–30).

Sellards, E. H., Adkins, W. S., and Plummer, F. B., 1932, The geology of Texas, v. 1, Stratigraphy: Univ. Texas Bull. 3232 (especially pp. 239–518).

Stanton, T. W., 1947, Studies of some Comanche pelecypods and gastropods: U. S. Geol. Survey Prof. Paper 211.

Steinmann, G., and Döderlein, L., 1888, 1890, Elemente der Paläontologie: Leipzig, Wilhelm Engelmann, pt. I (1888), pp. 1–335; pt. II (1890), pp. 336–848 (especially pp. 230–237).

Stenzel, H. B., 1945, Paleoecology of some oysters: Nat. Res. Council, Rep. Comm. Mar. Ecol., no. 5, pp. 37–46.

――――, Krause, E. K., and Twining, J. T., 1957, Pelecypoda from the type locality of the Stone City beds (Middle Eocene) of Texas: Univ. Texas Pub. 5704.

Stephenson, L. W., 1914, Species of Exogyra from the eastern Gulf region and the Carolinas: U. S. Geol. Survey Prof. Paper 81, pp. 41–77.

――――, 1933, The zone of *Exogyra cancellata* traced twenty-five hundred miles: Bull. Amer. Assoc. Petroleum Geologists, v. 17, pp. 1351–1361.

Trueman, A. E., 1922, The use of Gryphaea in the correlation of the lower Lias: Geol. Mag., v. 59, pp. 256–268.

Ulrich, E. O., 1897, The Lower Silurian Lamellibranchiata of Minnesota: Minnesota Geol. Survey, v. 3, pt. 2, pp. 629–693.

White, C. A., 1884, A review of the fossil Ostreidae of North America, etc.: U. S. Geol. Survey, 4th Ann. Rept. (1883), pp. 273–411.

Woodward, S. P., 1855, On the structure and affinities of the Hippuritidae: Geol. Soc. London Quart. Jour., v. 11, pp. 40–61.

Yonge, C. M., 1949, On the structure and adaptations of the Tellinacea, deposit-feeding Eulamellibranchia: Phil. Trans. Roy. Soc. London, ser. B., no. 609, pp. 29–76.

Scaphopoda

Emerson, W. K., 1952, Generic and subgeneric names in the molluscan Class Scaphopoda: Jour. Washington Acad. Sci., v. 42, no. 9, pp. 296–303.

Henderson, J. B., 1920, A monograph of the east North American scaphopod mollusks: U. S. Nat. Mus., Bull. 111.

Lacaze-Duthiers, H., 1856, Histoire de l'Organisation et du Développement du Dentale: Annales Sci. Nat., Zool., ser. 4, v. 6, pp. 225–281, 319–385.

Chapter 10

SNAILS

PHYLUM XII.   MOLLUSCA (Continued)

Class D.   Gastropoda

Most gastropods are enclosed within coiled shells called **conchs**, but some gastropods occupy straight or erratically shaped shells, and others such as some of the slugs may not have shells at all. Gastropods are as diversified and abundant as pelecypods, and in addition they are more adaptable than the pelecypods are. Not only do some gastropods rest on the substratum in marine or fresh water, but they also are represented by floating groups and have even evolved into terrestrial or air-breathing strains. The number of names of living gastropods in 1949 was divided among 31,643 marine, 24,503 terrestrial, and 8765 fresh-water species. In addition, thousands of species of fossil gastropods have been described. Paleozoic species alone have been referred to about 450 Genera. In general, the numerical importance of gastropods has increased with the passage of time; hence, they are most useful in paleontologic studies of Cenozoic rocks. Possibly 30,000 species of gastropods living today may eventually be discovered as fossils in strata as old as mid-Tertiary. In addition, it is possible that an equal number of mid-Tertiary species have existed which have neither survived to the Recent nor have been discovered as fossils. Even so, gastropods and brachiopods comprise the most abundant groups of invertebrate animals which paleonologists are able to study.

Recent gastropod conchs range from microscopic tubes which compose ooze in abyssal depths, to a large conch of *Strombus* which attains a length of about a foot. Most conchs are an inch or so (2 to 5 cm) in length. Possibly the largest gastropod was *Dinocochlea,* which is found in Lower Cretaceous fresh-water or brackish-water sediments in England. This spiral shell reached a length of 7 feet 3 inches (222 cm) and a diameter of 12.5 inches (32 cm) at the body whorl. It would have been about 60 feet long if it could have been unrolled. Some difference of opinion exists, however, as to whether *Dinocochlea* is really a mollusc or is a concretion, burrow, or relic of some unknown organism.

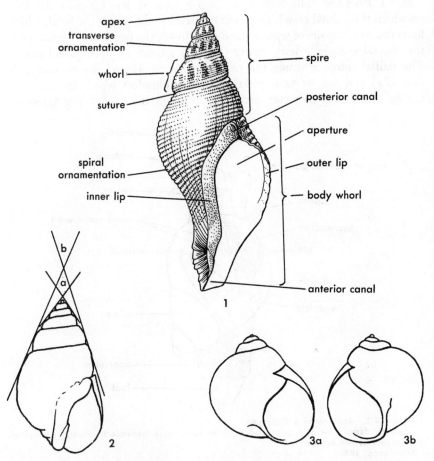

Figure 10.1. Morphology of Conchs.
1. Apertural view of *Fasciolaria acuta*, 2/3X, Miocene, Florida. 2. Apical angle (a) and pleural angle (b). 3a, 3b. Dextral and sinistral conchs of a land snail.
(1 after Dall, 1892. 2 after Shattuck, 1906. 3 after Lang, 1896.)

Conchs of typical gastropods (Fig. 10.1) consist of an expanding tube enrolled through a series of **volutions** or turns into a **spire.** That part of the tube represented by one volution is a **whorl,** and adjacent whorls are in contact along a **suture.** The last whorl, which contains most of the viscera, is the **body whorl.** The latter may be expanded into a large part of the entire conch and support the spire on its upper portion. The **apex** (pl. **apices**) which terminates the spire of a conch is posterior and the opening or **aperture** of the body whorl is anterior.

SOFT PARTS. The body rests upon a more or less flat muscular foot on which the animal crawls (Fig. 10.2). Dorsal to the foot is the head, which bears one or two pairs of tentacles and eyes. Inside the conch and surrounding the visceral mass is a fleshy lining (**mantle**) around an open **pallial cavity.** The **pallial complex** inside the pallial cavity consists of one or two gills (**ctenidia**) and one or two special organs (**osphradia**) which are used for testing the quality of water circulating through the cavity. The intestine,

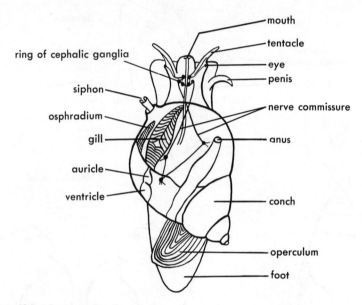

Figure 10.2. Anatomy of a Gastropod.
Schematic dorsal view of a gastropod as if the conch were translucent. Medial portions of the digestive system are omitted.
(After Lang, 1896.)

kidneys, and reproductive duct all open into the pallial cavity. In some forms one or two siphons control flow of water in and out of the pallial cavity. The mouth is commonly furnished with an effective radula, in addition to which a pair of chitinous jaws may be present. Most of the viscera normally remain within the spiral conch, but even the extended portions of the viscera can be withdrawn to the conch at will. During their withdrawal a retractor muscle first pulls in the sensitive head and then the foot, after which a chitinous or calcareous **operculum** attached to the foot slides into place and closes the aperture.

Sexes in some species are separate, but both sexes are contained within a single individual in other groups. If sexes are separate there may be some difference in size and shape of conchs belonging to individuals of opposite sexes (**sexual dimorphism**), but these differences commonly are too slight to be recognized offhand. Fertilization of eggs is internal, and the fertilized eggs are either laid or are retained within a brood pouch until they mature. Trochophore and veliger larval stages are present, and a cap-shaped dorsal shell, the **protoconch,** is secreted during early embryologic development (Fig. 10.10.1–4). Although the protoconch consists at first only of conchiolin, it is soon lined with calcium carbonate on its inner surface. Protoconchs are always smooth. In later embryologic stages a spiral conch with two to four whorls may be formed, after which the embryo either hatches from the egg or emerges from a brood pouch. The entire embryonic conch, including the protoconch and the larval whorls, is the **nucleus.** The later whorls in the nucleus are generally smooth like those of the protoconch but in some cases they bear faint ornamentation. As in the case of the protoconch, the remainder of the nucleus may consist for a time of conchiolin, but conchiolin rarely persists uncalcified into adult stages. For a while it was thought that all gastropods with similar nuclei were related, but this view is no longer held because it has been found that gastropods with dissimilar structures commonly have similar nuclei. It does appear, however, that the nucleus supplies a clue to the habits of gastropodan larvae. Thus, persistently horny nuclei are associated with pelagic existence of the larvae, and inflated nuclei with thin walls belong to larvae which seem to be restricted to deep water, no matter in what Family they occur. Geographic distribution of some gastropods no doubt is materially improved by the retention of a pelagic habit for some time before the increase of weight attendant upon calcification of the horny nucleus forces the creature to assume its normal benthonic existence.

Perhaps the most characteristic feature of gastropods is their lack of symmetry. Asymmetry is shown to a certain extent in the organization of the soft parts (Fig. 10.3). Gastropods almost certainly were derived from some bilaterally symmetrical molluscan ancestor (Fig. 10.3.1). The hypothetical ancestral form probably had a straight digestive track, a pair of gills on the posterior end, and a bilateral nervous system. If a shell were present, it may have had a central perforation. As soon as gastropods began to be confined within shells which were open at only one end (Fig. 10.3.2) it was necessary for the posterior end to swing around anteriorly to provide freedom of function for the anus and gills. The first C-shaped bending of the body, which was normally in the dorsoventral plane, is called the **flexure.** Thereafter some gastropods also underwent a lateral **torsion** in which the anal opening and the right ctenidium swung up 180 degrees in the counterclockwise direction from ventral to dorsal and occupied a position above and to the left of the head (Fig. 10.3.6). Essentially all gastropods underwent flexure, and most of them also were affected by torsion. Amazingly, a large group of gastropods such as the slugs have passed through a stage of **detorsion** in which the mouth and anus are located at opposite ends of a straight digestive track, just as was supposedly the case in the ancestral form. In

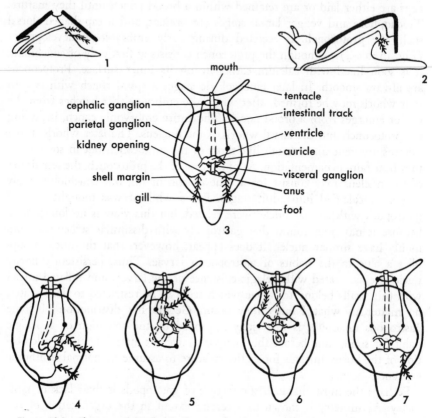

Figure 10.3. Flexure and Torsion in Gastropods.
1. Hypothetical ancestral mollusc as seen in longitudinal vertical section. 2. Ventral flexure of posterior organs as visceral mass of a gastropod is increasingly confined within a shell. 3-6. Dorsal views showing the effects of torsion. 3, primitive supposedly ancestral type. 4-6 progressive torsion leading to streptoneural anatomy. 7, complete detorsion.
All figures are schematic, and 3-7 are depicted as if the circular shell were transparent.
(Mostly modified after Lang, 1896.)

detorsion, however, the loss of morphologically left soft parts indicates that the animal has been derived from ancestors with torsional bodies (Fig. 10.3.7). Soft parts of many other gastropods represent stages of partial detorsion, in which the posterior organs habitually lie upon the right side of the visceral mass.

As torsion takes place, the morphologically left organs tend to be aborted, resulting in a notable tendency for modification of the symmetry. In its most advanced condition torsion involves loss of one gill, one kidney, and even one auricle of the heart, but the duct of the aborted, topographically right (but morphologically left) kidney is retained as the genital duct (Fig. 10.3.7). Zoologists have recognized the changes in the soft parts brought about by torsion as being of major taxonomic value. In those gastropods which are not affected by torsion or which have undergone detorsion, the two visceral nerves are disposed in a simple loop (Fig. 10.3.3, 7), whereas torsion twisted the loop of visceral nerves into a figure 8 (Fig. 10.3.6). The former gastropods are called **euthyneurans** and the latter are referred to as **streptoneurans.**

Dorsal and ventral in gastropods are ordinarily ignored in paleontologic work because of the monumental confusion with which these terms are endowed as a result of flexure, torsion, and coiling. It is generally customary for esthetic reasons to illustrate conchs with their apices (posterior ends) upward, even though most other animals are oriented with the anterior end upward.

COMPOSITION AND STRUCTURE OF CONCH. Conchs of gastropods differ structurally from valves of pelecypods because conchs rarely contain much prismatic or calcitic material. Lamellar and nacreous structure predominates, and aragonite is the most common mineralogic constituent of conchs of gastropods. Unfortunately, aragonitic structure militates against the chances that gastropods can be as well preserved as are some other molluscs.

SHAPE. If gastropods bear any trace of a shell at all, it is almost sure to exhibit some trace of **coiling.** Only a very few gastropods have straight or sinuous, conical, uncoiled shells. Coiling takes place independently of flexure or torsion of the soft parts. It is presumably an easy as well as an effective method of imparting strength and compactness to an otherwise elongate body. Spiral growth can take place according to different plans, but most methods necessitate geometric increase because the soft parts grow wider as well as longer. A characteristic gastropodan plan enables spiral growth of shells to be governed by logarithmic progression. This simply means that shells seem to increase in size at a disproportionately rapid rate. In fact, whorls of some gastropods soon reach the maximum possible diameter for convenient accommodation of the soft parts, so most of the animal's energy is devoted to increasing the thickness of the shell instead of the length. The pattern of logarithmic increase of conchs is seen best on spiral opercula (Fig. 10.9.7) and in the plan view of an abalone (*Haliotis*) shell (Fig. 10.4.10). Successive whorls may barely touch earlier whorls, or the shapes of whorls may be adjusted somewhat in order to conform to the exterior of earlier whorls. In either of the foregoing cases the whorls are all visible externally and the conchs are said to be **evolute** (Fig. 10.4.14–16). If the

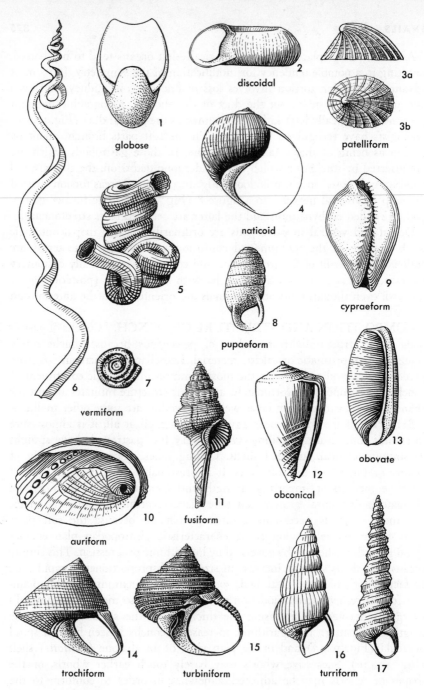

Figure 10.4. Shapes of Conchs.
(After many authors.)

most compact coiling method is employed and logarithmic growth is evident, the last whorl completely encompasses the earlier whorls and the conch
is said to be **involute** (Fig. 10.4.1, 9, 13).

Coiling takes place in two different ways, depending upon the orientation
of the axis of coiling. In its simplest form, the shell is a cup-shaped protoconch which grows anteriorly and ventrally and thereby starts to coil in one
plane around a horizontal axis. If somewhat less than one volution is present,
these shells are **patelliform** (Fig. 10.4.3). Continued coiling for several volutions in one plane produces **planispiral** conchs. Some essentially planispiral
shells are **discoidal** (Fig. 10.4.2) but others are **globose** (Fig. 10.4.1).

The second method of coiling involves twisting around a vertical axis but
not in one plane. Whorls grow forward along the projected trace of a helicoid
spiral and produce a more or less pyramidal conch which typifies these
helicoid conchs. It is customary to describe the slope of spires of helicoid
conchs in terms of the **apical angle,** which is determined by the intersection
of two lines tangent to the upper whorls of the spire; and by the **pleural
angle,** which is the angle between two lines tangent to the last two whorls
of a conch (Fig. 10.1.2). Among the descriptive terms applied to helicoid
conchs are **trochiform, turbiniform, turriform, auriform, obovate, obconical,
naticoid, vermiform, fusiform,** and **pupaeform** (Fig. 10.4.4–17).

Helicoid conchs mostly are generated along clockwise spirals; that is, they
rotate to the right when viewed down upon the apex. The same conch, if
viewed laterally with the apex up, will have the aperture on the right side.
These right-handed conchs are said to be **dextral,** whereas conchs which
spiral to the left are said to be **sinistral** (Fig. 10.1.3a, 3b). Species with normally
dextral conchs may be represented in a population by a few sinistral conchs.
A sinistral individual in the foregoing case is probably produced by an early
embryologic accident in which, for instance, the "left-handed" cell at the two-
cell stage becomes separated from its dominant "right-handed" counterpart.
Uncommon sinistral shells are not significant taxonomically because they do
not represent genetic strains or evolutionary change. On the other hand,
populations consisting mostly of sinistral shells should be considered on
statistical grounds to represent a genetic strain in which left-handedness has
become dominant.

One of the most remarkable trends in the Animal Kingdom is for some
Recent gastropods to become progressively coiled until they attain, say, a
turriform shape; but then they produce progressively more loosely constructed whorls until the whorls not only separate along the sutures, but the
anterior part of the conch grows aimlessly away from the spire. For some
reason the growth patterns of vermiform gastropods become increasingly erratic with advancing age (Fig. 10.4.5, 6). One Genus of vermiform gastropods,
Spiroglyphus (Fig. 10.4.7), is a useful marker in Tertiary strata. Incidentally,
it was originally described as a worm tube, so is truly vermiform.

In some conchs the whorls diverge and the axis of coiling lies free in the open center (**umbilicus**) of the spire. These are **phaneromphalous** conchs (Fig. 10.5.1–4). As the pleural angle decreases, the inner edges of the whorls necessarily move closer and closer to the axis of coiling until finally they touch each other, producing **anomphalous** conchs which lack an umbilicus. Or the umbilicus may be lined with secondary deposits of calcium carbonate which tend to produce the anomphalous condition. In some gastropods an inner lip covers the axis and it is not possible to decide whether the conch

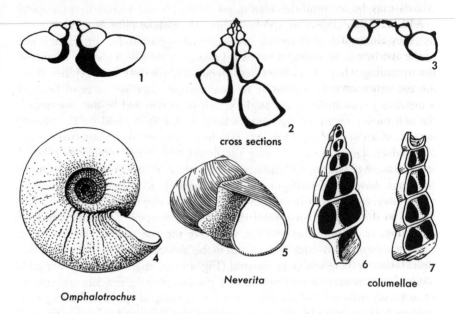

cross sections

Neverita

columellae

Omphalotrochus

Figure 10.5 Axial Structures.
1. Phaneromphalous conch with axial filling. 2, 3. narrowly and widely phaneromphalous conchs. 4. Basal view of *Omphalotrochus cochisensis* with a wide umbilicus, 1/2X, Permian, southwestern United States and Mexico. 5, *Neverita duplicata*, a cryptomphalous conch, 1X, Miocene to Recent, Atlantic Coast. 6. Cut-away diagram of an anomphalous conch with a straight columella. 7. Cut-away diagram of an anomphalous conch with a helicoid columella.
(1-3 after Ulrich and Scofield, 1897. 4 after Yochelson, 1956. 5 after Clark et al., 1904. 6, 7 after McDonald and Trueman, 1921.)

is phaneromphalous or anomphalous; hence the conchs are said to be **cryptomphalous** (Fig. 10.5.5). Anomphalous conchs apparently evolved from phaneromphalous conchs. If shell substance about the axis of coiling becomes intergrown into a compact axial rod (**columella**), the conchs are said to be **columellate.** Most columellae extend in a straight line along a straight axis (Fig. 10.5.6); but if the axis of coiling is slightly helicoid, then the columella is helicoid and appears in lateral view of broken or sectioned shells to consist of a series of oblique or *en echelon* segments (Fig. 10.5.7).

The gastropodan protoconch resembles the patelliform stage of planispiral gastropods. In many gastropods the primary conch is planispiral but the animal secretes subsequent whorls on a helicoid plan. Naturally there is a right-angle twist in a whorl at the place where the axis of coiling changes from horizontal to vertical. This bend is taken to indicate (because of application of the Law of Recapitulation) that helocoid conchs evolved from planispiral ancestors. In some cases as many as three helicoid whorls may lie along a horizontal axis at the apex of a conch, but subsequent helicoid whorls may be secreted about a vertical axis.

APERTURE. Apertures probably are basically circular in cross section, but they almost always are modified into some other shape. The free margin of the aperture is the **outer lip** and that part of the margin which abuts against the preceding whorl is the **inner lip.** Sometimes it is convenient to differentiate the inner lip into a **parietal lip** which is that portion in contact with a preceding whorl and a **columellar lip** which is that part which lies against the columella. The outer lip may be curved in profile, straight, or angular because of a **shoulder** on the whorl. The location of the inner lip commonly is clarified by the deposition of a thin layer of laminar calcium carbonate, the **inductura,** over the area. In many instances the deposition of calcium carbonate on the inner lip continues until a thick patch, the **callus,** is formed. The callus may extend axially until the umbilicus is partially or completely obscured as if a wad of wax were squeezed onto the area (Fig. 10.5.5). This condition, of course, characterizes cryptomphalous conchs.

If the margin of the aperture is delimited by smooth curves without notable indentations it is **entire** (Fig. 10.4.4). Smoothness of this kind does not preclude the presence of an outwardly directed flange (**reflected lip,** Fig. 10.6.3) or inwardly directed flange (**inflected lip,** Fig. 10.6.1). On the other hand, the margin may be indented more or less sharply where a siphon protruded from the body whorl. If the indentation is deep, it is a **notch** (Fig. 10.4.16), and if it is extended as an elongate groove it is a **canal** (Fig. 10.4.11). One large group of gastropods bears, about midway on the outer lip, a slightly depressed groove (**selenizone**) which marks the former position of the notch (Fig. 10.13). In conchs with a selenizone the rectum hung out of the notch as a slender tube. The anterior notch or canal is occupied by the incurrent siphon in siphonate gastropods. The posterior notch serves for extrusion of the rectum or for the excurrent siphon, or for both together. In general, siphonate gastropods are carnivores, whereas nonsiphonate gastropods are vegetarians, but the distinction is not consistent. Notches and canals tend to become increasingly more deeply incised into the margin of the outer lip during the growth of an individual. By application of the principle of recapitulation one may conclude that gastropods with notches and canals evolved from groups which did not have them.

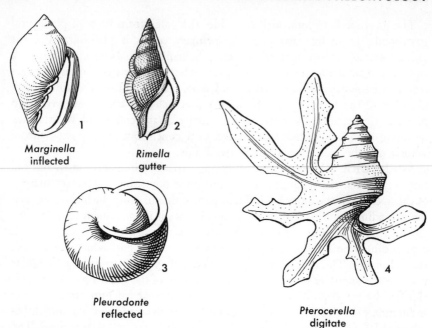

Marginella
inflected

Rimella
gutter

Pleurodonte
reflected

Pterocerella
digitate

Figure 10.6. Apertures.
1. Inflected outer lip and four columellar folds on inner lip of *Marginella elegantula*, 3X, Oligocene, Florida. 2. Long gutter where posterior siphon lay alongside the spire of *Rimella smithii*, 1 1/3X, Eocene, Florida. 3. Reflected outer lip of *Pleurodonte diespiter*, 1X, Oligocene, Florida. 4. Rear view of digitate frill on the outer lip of *Pterocerella poinsettiformis*, 1X, Cretaceous, Texas.
(1, 2, 3 after Dall, 1890.   4 after Stephenson, 1941.)

Perhaps the most extravagantly developed notches occur in *Fissurella* and *Haliotis*. In *Fissurella* there is no notch in very early larval stages, but there is a very elongate slitlike notch in the anterior margins of the conchs of late larval forms (Fig. 10.7.1a). In the most advanced larval stages the slit for the excurrent siphon has been closed off by fusion of opposite sides of the slit along the margin of the conch, forming a perforation or **trema** (Fig. 10.7.1b, 1c). With additional growth the trema is enlarged by resorption until it may encompass regions formerly occupied by the larval conch. An adult conch of *Fissurella* (Fig. 10.7.1d) bears a perforation at its apex and resembles a little volcano.

In *Haliotis* a succession of holes is developed during growth, somewhat as the trema of *Fissurella* is formed (Fig. 10.4.10). Oldest holes are sealed off progressively with shell material as growth continues, so only a few holes are functional at any one time. In *Haliotis* the posterior hole bears the anal tube, and the several anterior holes bear fingerlike projections of the mantle which are associated with the gills.

The aperture, as viewed in plan view, has a characteristic shape, ranging from circular and elliptical to quadrate, triangular, or slitlike. Moreover, the apertural outline may differ from youth to maturity; hence, in the detailed study of gastropods, it is helpful in many cases to cut a conch in half down the axis. In this way the nature of either the umbilicus or of the columella becomes apparent, in addition to the shape of the whorls. As growth progresses, there seems to be a tendency for soft parts of many gastropods to withdraw anteriorly from the apical region or to leave only a trace of the visceral sac in that region. This change may be necessitated by actual increase in the size of vital organs during growth of the individual. In any case, some gastropods partially fill in several whorls in the apical region with ridges of skeletal tissue disposed in characteristic patterns. Some ridges

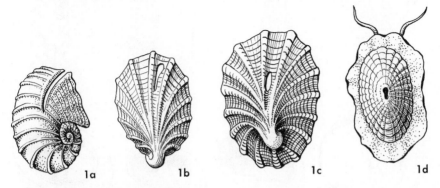

1a   1b   1c   1d

Figure 10.7.   Growth of *Fissurella*.
Growth stages of a Recent *Fissurella* from larva to adult, illustrating the development of an apical foramen (1d) from a marginal slit (1a).   1a-1c are enlarged conchs, but 1d is an adult complete with mantle and tentacles, about 1/2X.
(After Boutan, 1885).

on the inner side may extend forward into the aperture as one or two **columellar folds** (Fig. 10.6.1). In the most advanced condition, such as is found in *Nerinaea* (Fig. 10.8.5), ridges traverse outer as well as inner surfaces of the whorls. In a few gastropods (Fig. 10.8.1) the apical whorls are constricted by introduction of blisterlike vesicles with calcareous walls along the sides of the whorls in a fashion very similar to the deposition of dissepiments in rugose corals. In still other gastropods (Fig. 10.8.2) the apical portion not only may be abandoned, but it may even be deliberately broken off during the lifetime of the individual by being rapped against a rock; this process of loss of whorls is **decollation.** In *Caecum* the apical portions are sealed off by transverse partitions (**septa**) prior to decollation (Fig. 10.8.3). Decollation is particularly noticeable in some terrestrial and in some brackish-water gastropods; moreover, it has also been reported by Barrande in 24 species of cephalopods, 17 gastropods, 2 scaphopods, and 1 pteropod.

Internal whorls of some gastropods such as *Conus* may be reduced in strength by **resorption.** If this process is very extensive, as in the case of *Olivella,* the columella and internal parts of the whorls may disappear, leaving large axial cavities for the viscera. It is apparent that decollation and

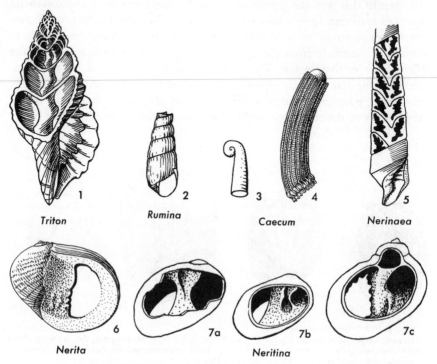

Figure 10.8.   Internal Modifications of Conchs.
1. Cut-away drawing of *Triton corrugatus* with partitions in apical whorls, 1X, Recent.   2. Decollated conch of *Rumina decollata,* 3X, Recent.   3. Juvenile conch of *Caecum* sp. with coiled apex, 13X, Recent.   4. Decollated conch of *Caecum coronellum* with convex septum at truncated end, 6X, Miocene, Florida.   5. Cut-away section of *Nerinaea trochea* with internal ridges on whorls, slightly enlarged, Recent.   6. *Nerita tampaensis* with callus extending across part of the aperture, 3X, Miocene, Florida.   7a, 7b, 7c. Cut-away posterior views of three species of *Neritina* arranged in a morphologic series to show progressive loss of columella and growth of apertural flange as in 6.
(1, 5 after Woodward, 1880. 2 after Turton, 1840. 3 after Woodward, 1866. 4, 6 after Dall, 1892. 7 after Woodward, 1892.)

resorption, as well as the external effects of erosion peculiar to some molluscs, all conspire to make some gastropods seem to be less well preserved than they actually are.

Even more peculiar is the behavior of various species of *Neritina* and its relatives, in which the inner wall of the whorls is resorbed and a flange is built out to one side of the inner wall and just behind the aperture; then the retractor muscle is attached to the flange (Fig. 10.8.6, 7). Ultimately the flange and inner portions of the enlarging callus extend like a false columella from top to bottom of the interior cavity of the conch. The flange and callus, however, lie athwart the space through which the viscera must pass as the animal grows forward; therefore, the neritids have evolved into a paradoxical situation in which some calcium carbonate is deposited on the front of the callus while other calcium carbonate is being resorbed from back of it. The process has been likened to that in which a man digs out the floor of a shack in order to raise the roof.

OPERCULUM.   Several unrelated groups of gastropods possess means of closing off all or part of the aperture after the soft parts have been withdrawn into the conch. They may seal themselves off for protection against enemies, or they may protect themselves against dehydration during a dormant period. Thus, when terrestrial snails become dormant during dry summer weather they are said to be in **estivation** (**hibernation** is dormancy in the winter.) The

Figure 10.9. Opercula.
1. External surface of operculum of *Turbo rhectogrammicus*, 1X, Miocene, Florida. 2. Exterior surface of operculum of *Natica precursor*, 3X, Miocene, Florida. 3. Exterior surface of a corneous operculum of *Viviparus intertextus*, 1 1/2X, Recent.   4. Silicified operculum of *Ceratopea keithi*, 1X, Ordovician, Appalachians, Ouachitas, and Texas. 5. *Ampullaria* sp. in living position with operculum at rear and branchial siphon extended to left, 1X, Recent. 6. *Turritella* sp. in living position and bearing a multispiral corneous operculum, 1X, Recent. 7. Exterior of operculum of *Littorina littorea*, 2X, Recent.
(1 after Dall, 1892. 2 after Gardner, 1947. 3 after Woodring, Roundy, and Farnsworth, 1932.   4 after Butts, 1926. 5 after Woodward, 1880. 6 after Gray, 1842. 7 after Woodward, 1866.)

land snails secrete over the aperture a mass of calcified mucus which dries to form an **epiphragm.** Return of moisture softens the epiphragm and the snail resumes its activities.

The common kinds of durable apertural covers consist of conchiolin, or of calcium carbonate, or of the two substances together; any one of these structures is an **operculum.** Opercula are almost restricted to those gastropods in which there is an outer calcitic layer of the conch. In cases wherein the operculum is preservable, it may be shaped or sculptured in such a manner that it is useful in identification of species. Some opercula, however, are merely smooth elliptical plates. Others commonly consist of a spirally enrolled plate with an inner flat side and an outer convex side. Convex sides of opercula may bear intricately contrived ornamentation which facilitates identification (Fig. 10.9). The opercular spire, incidentally, always is generated in the direction opposite to that of the conch.

Opercula may be useful stratigraphic markers, as, for instance, in the Lower Ordovician from Oklahoma to Tennessee where several zones of silicified opercula of *Ceratopea* are recognized. Incidentally, the conchs into which *Ceratopea* might fit have not been found with the opercula. In several oil fields in California one Pliocene faunal zone is characterized by the presence of numerous opercula belonging to *Scalez.* Inasmuch as conchs do not occur with *Scalez,* the opercula were thought for a long time to be scales of fish—hence the generic name. Opercula might be separated from conchs by current action, in addition to which the difference in chemical and mineralogic constitution of the opercula and conchs might affect their chances of preservation.

ORNAMENTATION. Variations in ornamentation are of major importance in identifying gastropods and in understanding the evolution of some strains. In a sense even smooth conchs are ornamented because they bear **growth lines** which record faithfully the former margin of the outer lip. Growth lines are very useful to a taxonomist because the fragile body whorl need not be preserved in order for a paleontologist to reconstruct the outline of the aperture. Growth lines may extend across the exposed surface of the whorl in a single arc or in S-shaped curves called **sinuses** (Fig. 10.17.1–7). If the curvature of a growth line is convex in the direction of growth the arc represents a **spiral sinus,** whereas it is an **antispiral sinus** if it is concave forward. Moreover, a **growth-line angle** can be measured between the axis of the conch and a line connecting the two exposed ends of a growth line on a whorl.

Ornamented conchs bear one or both of two main kinds of ornamentation (Fig. 10.1). **Spiral ornamentation** consists of fine to coarse **ribs** which continue forward in the direction of growth; that is, the ribs lie parallel to the sutures. On the other hand, **transverse ornamentation** consists of ribs which extend across the whorls more or less parallel to the growth lines, that is, approximately at right angles to the sutures. In numerous instances both spiral and transverse ribs are present on the same conch. Naturally, it is necessary to modify the word "rib" with "spiral" or with "transverse" in order to make clear which kind of ornamentation is being considered.

Spiral ribs arise from irregularities in the margin of the mantle and presumably strengthen the shell. Although an adult whorl may bear numerous spiral ribs, the early whorls bear fewer and fewer ribs; thus, it is very important to see the apical whorls of a conch in order to determine how many and in what order the first spiral ribs appear. It commonly develops that only one to three primary spiral ribs are present.

Transverse ribs apparently arise from variations in the rate of forward growth of the outer lip. As in the case of spiral ribs, the nuclear whorls may be smooth, after which spiral ribs appear. Some transverse ribs project away from the shell as prominent flanges (Fig. 10.17.8). Presumably the transverse ribs also strengthen the conchs.

Increased complexity of ornamentation commonly represents interplay between spiral and transverse ornamentation as is shown by two species on Figure 10.10. In Figure 10.10.9 the protoconch and whorl I are smooth. Between whorls V and VII distinct spiral ribs and weak transverse ribs are developed. In whorl X the transverse ribs are as strong as the spiral ribs; hence the pattern is reticulate. Moreover, the intersections of the two kinds of ribs are surmounted by a node; therefore this pattern can be termed **nodose-reticulate.** In another species (Fig. 10.10.10) the protoconch and whorl I are smooth as in the foregoing case. In whorl V, however, a strong set of transverse ribs has arisen. These are joined by spiral ribs at whorl VII and the two combine to produce a nodose-reticulate pattern in whorl VIII. Although sculpture of the mature whorls of both illustrated species is remarkably similar, the two sculptures were derived in very different fashions; they thus epitomize the concept of convergence in evolution. Even gastropods of very different geologic ages and of no genetic relationship may resemble each other rather closely because of convergence.

Nodose-reticulate sculpture is the acme of complexity, but evolution proceeds even further in many gastropods by modification of that pattern. Thus, one or both sets of ribs may diminish in strength, leaving a dominantly nodose sculpture. In some cases the process of simplification goes so far that all trace of sculpture is lost and the mature whorls resemble the protoconch (Fig. 10.10.11, 12). Causes of retrogressive evolution such as loss of sculpture can only be explained by discovering why natural selection began to favor different qualities. For instance, reduction in strength of ornamentation would produce relative lightness in adult stages and also less frictional resistance to water, substratum, or vegetation.

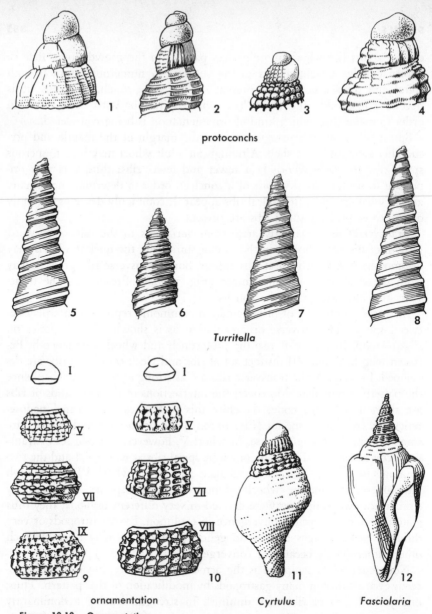

protoconchs

Turritella

ornamentation   Cyrtulus   Fasciolaria

Figure 10.10. Ornamentation.
1-4. Nuclei of four Genera showing smooth protoconchs, 6X to 10X. 5-8. Apical whorls of *Turritella* sp. showing early patterns of spiral ribs Cenozoic, California. 5. *Turritella uvasana* stock with bicostate whorls, 6X. *Turritella buwaldana* stock, tricostate, 7X. 7. *Turritella broderipiana* stock, mesocostate, 3X. 8. *Turritella cooperi* stock, cingulate, 7X. 9, 10. Two species of Jurassic gastropods with sculpture of four whorls shown in growth sequence (Roman numerals). 11. Loss of sculpture and development of loose whorls in *Cyrtulus serotinus*, 2/3X, Recent. 12. Reversion from nodose to spiral ornamentation in *Fasciolaria apicina*, 3X, Pliocene, North Carolina.

(1 after Grabau, 1904. 2, 11 after Smith, 1945. 3, 4 after Smith, 1946. 5-8 after Merriam, 1941. 9, 10 after McDonald and Trueman, 1921. 12 after Grabau, 1906.)

Smoothness may also be brought about by encasing mature whorls in secondary skeletal layers when mature conchs are partially invested by the mantle. In this case the change to smoothness is presumably associated with altered habits in which increased weight of the conch is advantageous.

The rate at which new sculptured features are added to over-all patterns varies in different species. Nodose-reticulate pattern is attained by whorl X in Figure 10.10.9, but it is attained by whorl VIII in Figure 10.10.10. A speeding up of the rate of change in this fashion is **acceleration.** Acceleration reflects the tendency of sculptural patterns to occupy earlier and earlier whorls in the ontogeny of specimens in a genetic strain. For example, purely transverse sculpture occupies only one whorl or less in the nucleus of Figures 10.10.2 and 10.10.4. Ultimately there can be so much crowding of patterns back into early ontogentic stages that some of the patterns are eliminated. Thus, when a nodose pattern is the first sculpture to appear on the nucleus (Fig. 10.10.3) it suggests that earlier ribbed stages have been crowded out.

On the other hand, one pattern may persist on several whorls an unusually long time in some species. This is **retardation.** As in the case of acceleration, retardation presumably reflects adaptation of conchs to changing environmental requirements, but retardation does not necessarily have any bearing on the evolutionary history of the species. In fact, the effects of both acceleration and retardation are major obstacles in the quick interpretation of the evolutionary history of gastropods. For a while biologists hoped that gastropods would provide indisputable proof of the Theory of Recapitulation. After all, developmental stages of conchs are exposed for inspection, and the stratigraphic record provides evidence about the general evolutionary succession of forms. General evolutionary patterns of gastropods seem to be manifested by increasing complexity of sculpture, followed in some cases by loss of ornamentation. If the Theory of Recapitulation operated with mechanical consistency, the early whorls should bear the same ornamentation that adult whorls bore on ancestral forms. Acceleration and retardation are so widespread among gastropods, however, that ontogenies are not always clearly apparent on spires, nor can an isolated species always be placed accurately in the evolutionary fabric of similar gastropods by study of ornamentation. Nevertheless, experience has shown that ontogenetic studies can be of great value in grouping some gastropods into genetic series. In *Turritella,* for instance, all ornamentation consists of spiral ribs, but the ribs arise according to different plans in the nuclear whorls. Four genetic groups are illustrated by typical species of *Turritella* in Figure 10.10.5–8; nuclear whorls are, respectively, bicostate, tricostate, mesocostate, and cingulate (bicostate but with a broad depressed region between ribs). Mature sculpture of species from different groups may be similar, but juvenile sculpture is consistently different.

CLASSIFICATION. Zoologic classifications of gastropods can be quite satisfactory for study of Recent conchs, but they are rather unsatisfactory if applied to fossil conchs, except in cases in which there is such close correlation between shapes of fossil and Recent conchs that it is safe to assume that soft anatomy of fossil and Recent gastropods also was the same. On the other hand, paleontologically inspired classifications are too inexact for use by zoologists. In the face of the foregoing incompatibilities it is likely that fossil gastropods are the most difficult organisms to classify in paleontology.

Subdivision of the gastropods into readily recognized categories which bear consistent genetic relationship with one another seems to be impossible. There is so much convergence in shape and ornamentation that one Subclass cannot even be distinguished in all cases from other Subclasses. Fortunately, a wealth of published material is available to which the interested person may refer. Moreover, some useful keys of great regional importance are available, as, for instance, the key published by Keen and Pearson (1952) for the Pacific Coast.

The dependence of paleontology upon zoology is possibly never shown more clearly than in the following key to Subclasses of gastropods. Comprehension of relationships among great groups of gastropods is based upon understanding certain fundamental structures of soft parts.

KEY TO SUBCLASSES OF GASTROPODS

   I. Symmetrical soft parts (mostly assumed) .... Protogastropoda
  II. Asymmetrical soft parts
     A. Streptoneuran .... Prosobranchia
     B. Euthyneuran
       1. Gill present (largely marine) .... Opisthobranchia
       2. Gill absent (largely terrestrial) .... Pulmonata

SUBCLASS 1. PROTOGASTROPODA

Protogastropods bear simple, patelliform, and mostly planispiral conchs with almost entirely symmetrical conchs and soft parts. The apices of some conchs referred to this Subclass are inclined anteriorly instead of in the posterior direction customary to other gastropods. Extinct representatives of the group ranged from Early Cambrian to Permian, and there is one Recent species. *Tryblidium* (Ordovician and Silurian) is a rather well-known Genus.

It has long been supposed that gastropods arose from a bilaterally symmetrical ancestor because they exhibit traces of bilaterality, as in the structure of the head, nervous system, and in some cases in other organs (Fig. 10.3). Recently, 13 specimens of a living species of mollusc were dredged from a depth of almost 11,000 feet (3590 m) off the Pacific coast of Mexico. Soft anatomy of these creatures supports the hypothetical contention that there is a group of bilaterally symmetrical molluscs with patelliform shells. Thus,

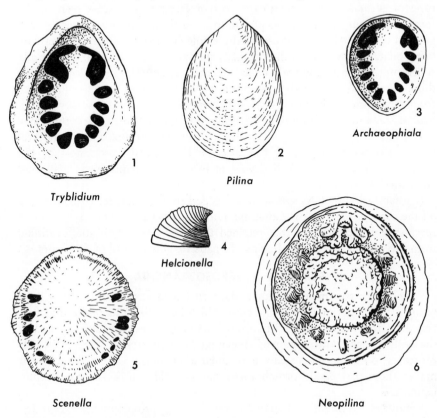

Figure 10.11. Protogastropoda.
 1. Interior of *Tryblidium reticulatum* showing five pairs of small muscle scars and an anterior pair of large markings, 1 1/3X, Silurian, Sweden. 2. Dorsal view of *Pilina unguis*, 2/3X, Silurian, Sweden. 3. Interior of *Archaeophiala antiquissima* with same muscle scars as in 1, 1X, Ordovician, Sweden. 4. Side view of *Helcionella subrugosa*, 1X, Lower Cambrian, New York. 5. Interior of *Scenella* sp. showing six pairs of muscle scars, 3X, Middle Cambrian, British Columbia. 6. Schematic ventral view of *Neopilina galatheae* showing central muscular foot surrounded by five pairs of gills, 1 1/2X, Recent.
 (1, 2 after Knight, 1941. 3, 4 after Knight, 1952. 5 after Rasetti, 1954. 6 after Lemche, 1957.)

the Subclass Protogastropoda must be extended into the Recent. These abyssal Recent protogastropods have been named *Neopilina* in allusion to their similarity to *Pilina* from the Silurian (Fig. 10.11.6, 2).

Muscle scars are not impressed into the thin shell of *Neopilina*, but five pairs of strong muscles connect the foot to points on the shell at the sites of the five pairs of gills. These muscles and gills correspond remarkably well to the five small pairs of muscle scars in *Tryblidium* and in *Archaeophiala* (Fig. 10.11.1, 3). Other patches of muscles around the A-shaped oral structures of *Neopilina* conform to the pair of large muscle scars seen in the foregoing fossils. There is a nephridium at each gill. An auricle serves each gill and two ventricles are present—the whole circulatory apparatus therefore being bilaterally symmetrical. Externally the apex of the shell bears a dextrally coiled protoconch of one and one-half whorls. Although some paleontologists think that coiled gastropods arose from patelliform ancestors, it would appear from the nature of the protoconch that *Neopilina* represents a somewhat advanced stage in the evolutionary development of shell form. *Neopilina* may have lived with the shell down and the gills uppermost, inasmuch as respiration seems better assured if this attitude is assumed; also, most of the apical portion of the conch is devoid of incrusting organisms, as if it were embedded in sediment.

A second species of *Neopilina* was dredged from 19,140 feet (6380 meters) off the coast of Peru by the Columbia University vessel, *Vema,* in 1958. Four specimens were recovered that retained their soft parts. This species differs from the original species in having six pairs of gills instead of five pairs.

SUBCLASS 2.   PROSOBRANCHIA

Prosobranch gastropods comprise those in which flexure and torsion have brought the posterior part of the body which bears the gills forward at first and then over the anterior portion until the gills lie near the anterior end of the body (hence, "prosobranch," meaning "gill in front"; Fig. 10.3.5, 6). Moreover, only one gill usually is retained after torsion. The torsion which makes these gastropods prosobranchs naturally also makes them streptoneurans.

Almost all commonly observed gastropods are prosobranchs, except for most land snails. The Prosobranchia are largely marine, although many fresh-water representatives are known and a few air-breathing prosobranchs have been described. Some gill-bearing marine prosobranchs such as *Littorina* can invade the subaerial environment for short periods of time. Most of the strictly air-breathing prosobranchs have lost their gills just as the Pulmonata have, but intermediate forms may retain remnants of a gill or may carry on respiration with a gill and a lung simultaneously. Thus, in *Ampullaria,* water can be circulated through a gill chamber, and air can be taken into a pulmonary chamber through a snorkellike tube which can be extended out of the water (Fig. 10.9.5).

The bewildering array of prosobranch gastropods is herein divided arbitrarily into general groups in order to illustrate the main kinds of variation. No evolutionary or genetic significance should be attached to these groups.

All together, at least 100 Families of prosobranchs are known, and these may comprise several thousand Genera and tens of thousands of species.

Some systematists find it convenient to divide the prosobranchs into three general groups on the basis of shell features more or less in line with a classification adopted by Thiele (1931). Thus, archaeogastropods bear a selenizone, mesogastropods have entire apertural margins, and neogastropods have notches or canals in the margin of the aperture. Unfortunately, the three foregoing groups are not consistently exclusive on other grounds; hence, the separation is not used herein.

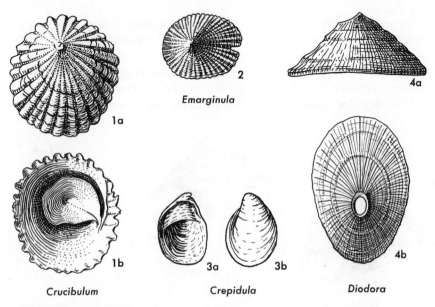

Figure 10.12. Patelloids.

1a, 1b. Dorsal and ventral views of *Crucibulum costatum* var. *pileolum*, 1X, Oligocene and Miocene, Atlantic Coast. 2. Dorsal view of *Emarginula marylandica*, 1X, Miocene, Maryland. 3a, 3b. Ventral and dorsal views of *Crepidula fornicata*, 1 1/2X, Oligocene to Recent, Atlantic Coast. 4a, 4b. Side and dorsal views of *Diodora marylandica*, 1X, Miocene, Maryland.

(1, 2, 4 after Clark, et al., 1904. 3 after Shattuck, 1906.)

Patelloids. Patelloid gastropods include many cap-shaped conchs and some other kinds which are not distinctly planispiral or helicoid (Fig. 10.12). *Fissurella* and *Patella* (Fig. 10.4.3) are common Recent Genera which are known from Tertiary rocks. In *Crepidula* a horizontal shelf extends across the posterior half of the shell. *Crucibulum* bears an extra little conical skeleton inside the large patelliform outer shell. One Genus of Miocene patelloid gastropods, *Emarginula* (Fig. 10.12.2), is characterized by the presence of a slot in the margin of adult conchs and therefore resembles early growth stages of the living *Fissurella* described before (Fig. 10.7). Patelloids charac-

teristically fasten themselves to rocks on barren headlands and manage to
survive temporary exposure in the intertidal zone during low tide.

The patelliform shape characterizes adult conchs in various groups of
gastropods, and it is widely present as the initial shell at the tips of many
protoconchs. Perhaps because of this latter phenomenon, many biologists
believe that patelliform gastropods may be ancestral to numerous other
gastropods. There does not seem to be any significant relationship between
soft parts of Protogastropoda and patelliform prosobranchs, however, and
therefore the patelliform shape may be merely an adaptation of no genetic
significance.

Pleurotomarioids. All members of this group have a deep notch on the
outer lip and a selenizone on the surface of the conch to mark the former
position of the notch as it became filled in with shell material (Fig. 10.13).
Conchs are mostly helicoid spirals, but *Haliotis* (Fig. 10.4.10) is broadly
convex. *Hormotoma* (Ordovician and Silurian), *Bembexia* (Devonian),
Glabrocingulum (Mississippian to Permian), and *Pleurotomaria* (Recent)

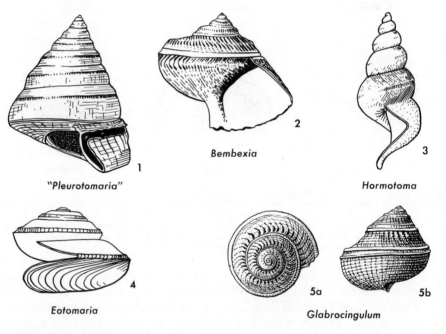

"Pleurotomaria"　　　　*Bembexia*　　　　*Hormotoma*

Eotomaria　　　　*Glabrocingulum*

Figure 10.13. Pleurotomarioids.
　　1. *"Pleurotomaria"* [*Entemnotrochus*] *adansoniana*, 1/4X, Recent. 2. *Bembexia sulcomarginata*,
2X, Devonian, New York. 3. *Hormotoma trentonensis*, 1X, Ordovician, Minnesota. 4. *Eotomaria
supracingulata*, 1X, Ordovician, Wisconsin. 5a, 5b. Spire and posterior of *Glabrocingulum grayvillense*, 3X, Pennsylvanian, Oklahoma.
　　(1 after Knight, 1952. 2 after Hall, 1879. 3, 4 after Ulrich and Scofield, 1897. 5 after
Girty, 1915.)

are typical Genera. The pleurotomarioids reached their culmination in diversity during the Paleozoic and were once thought to have become extinct during the Tertiary Period; however, living specimens were discovered in the middle of the last century. Possibly 1500 species of fossil pleurotomarioids are known and about half a dozen living species have been described. Pleurotomarioid gastropods are thought to be rather primitive.

Bellerophontoids. Planispiral conchs with marginal slits range from Ordovician to Triassic and include some of the most primitive gastropods. *Bellerophon* (Ordovician to Triassic) and *Euphemites* (Mississippian to Permian) have globose conchs with flaring apertural rims (Fig. 10.14.1, 2).

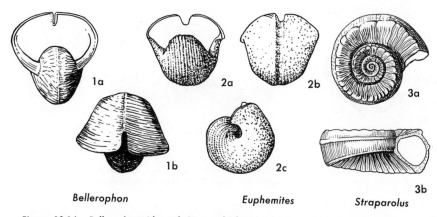

Figure 10.14. Bellerophontoids and Straparoloids.
1a, 1b. Apertural and rear views of *Bellerophon* sp., 1X, Mississippian, Indiana.   2a, 2b, 2c. Apertural, rear, and side views of *Euphemites vittatus,* 1X, Pennsylvanian, midcontinent.   3a, 3b. Spire and apertural view of *Straparolus subquadratus,* 1X, Pennsylvanian, Illinois.
(1 after Knight, 1952.   2 after White, 1884.   3 after Meek and Worthen, 1873.)

Bellerophontoid conchs are precisely planispiral; hence they typify the exact bilateral growth termed **isostrophic.** According to some views bellerophontoids are very primitive gastropods which share features with the patelloids and the pleurotomarioids. Bellerophontoids, for instance, have a notch like that of the pleurotomarioids, although the orientation of soft parts in the conchs may be different (no soft parts of bellerophontoids are known). Similar but later planispiral conchs, such as occur in Cretaceous to Recent fresh-water deposits, belong to the Pulmonata.

Straparoloids. *Straparolus* (Silurian to Permian) is typical of nearly planispiral but really discoidal gastropods (Fig. 10.14.3). There is no notch in the rim such as is present among the bellerophontoids. Spires are very low and conchs are widely phaneromphalous. Whorls vary in cross section from circular to those having an angular shoulder. Straparoloids occur in strata as old as Cambrian. They are usually placed among the primitive prosobranchs, even though no soft parts are known.

Macluritoids. Those conchs which seem to have grown posteriorly up around the axis instead of anteriorly down around it are said to be **hyperstrophic** (Fig. 10.15). Considered another way, what appears to be the spire of a hyperstrophic conch is homologous with the base of a common gastropod with an **orthostrophic** conch. If macluritoids are oriented according to the view that they are orthostrophic, the conch will appear to be sinistral, but the conchs are dextral if a hyperstrophic orientation is chosen. In all gastropods with spiral opercula, the opercula twist in the opposite direction

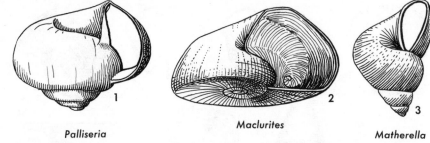

Palliseria   *Maclurites*   *Matherella*

Figure 10.15. Macluritoids.
1. *Palliseria robusta*, 2/3X, Ordovician, Nevada, California. 2. *Maclurites logani* with operculum in place, 2/3X, Ordovician, Ontario. 3. *Matherella saratogensis*, 4X, Cambrian, New York.
(After Knight, 1952.)

from the coiling of the conch; thus, a clockwise or dextral conch produces an operculum with a counterclockwise spiral. In *Maclurites* the operculum is counterclockwise; hence, the conch is dextral and hyperstrophic. About 16 other Genera are united with *Maclurites* in the group. They range from Cambrian to Devonian. Later hyperstrophic conchs arose from other groups.

Trochoids and Turritelloids. The great majority of prosobranchs have some sort of distinctly spiral conch, the shape of which is best indicated by reference to the pleural angle (Figs. 10.16; 10.17). Numerous trends in modification of shape are apparent, such as elongation of the spire and elongation of the body whorl by extension of the anterior canal so that a

Figure 10.16 (opposite).   Miscellaneous Prosobranchs.
1. *Strombus aldrichi*, 1X, Miocene, Florida.   2. Rear view of *Anchura lobata*, 1X, Cretaceous, Tennessee.   3. *Conus floridanus*, 1X, Miocene, Florida.   4. *Olivella alabamensis*, 2X, Eocene, Alabama.   5. *Ecphora quadricostata*, 1X, Miocene, widespread.   6. *Clathrodrillia incilifera*, 2 1/2X, Miocene, Atlantic Coast.   7. "*Drillia*" boring through pelecypod valve, 7X, Miocene, Florida.   8. *Cypraea heilprini*, 1 1/3X, Miocene, Florida.   9. *Ficus eopapyratia*, 1 1/3X, Miocene, Florida.   10. *Busycon canaliculatum*, 2/3X, Pliocene to Recent, Atlantic Coast.
(1 after Dall, 1890.   2 after Wade, 1926.   3 after Gardner, 1937.   4 after Harris, 1893. 5, 6, 10 after Clark, et al., 1904.   7-9 after Gardner, 1947.)

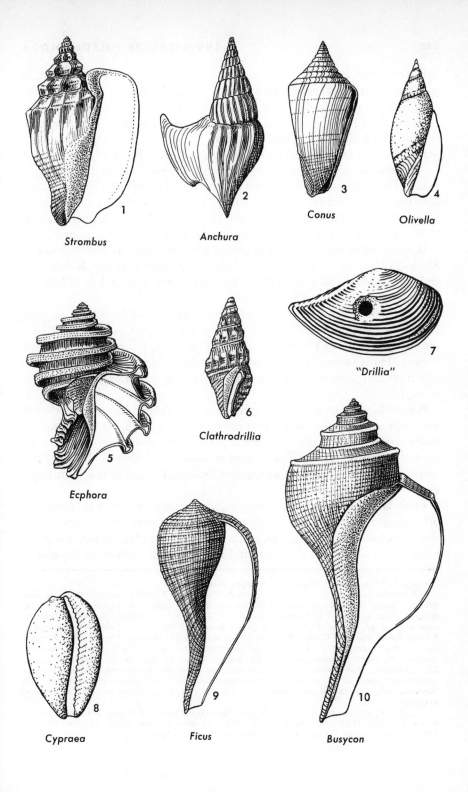

1   *Strombus*

2   *Anchura*

3   *Conus*

4   *Olivella*

5   *Ecphora*

6   *Clathrodrillia*

7   "*Drillia*"

8   *Cypraea*

9   *Ficus*

10   *Busycon*

fusiform conch is produced. In association with the latter feature there is transition from gastropods with an entire margin of the outer lip to gastropods with a notched outer lip.

Turritella is probably used more than any other Genus of gastropods for correlation of Cenozoic strata. Hundreds of species have been described, many of which are well-known index fossils (Figs. 10.17; 10.10). Species can be differentiated on the basis of whorl profile, growth lines, mature sculpturing, and nuclear sculpturing. Genetic strains, for instance, are based in large part upon the number and distribution of revolving ribs on early whorls (Fig. 10.10.5–8). *Turritella* is abundant in warm shallow water today. Fossil turritellas locally are abundant enough to comprise veritable coquinas.

In Paleozoic strata the turriform conchs are represented by *Meekospira* and *Subulites* (Fig. 10.17.14, 15), both of which are unornamented. *Mesalia* is a common Genus which resembles *Turritella* except that it has a reflected inner lip (Fig. 10.17.11, 12).

Among the most interesting of gastropods are the "drills" which use their radulae to bore into other gastropods or into various pelecypods. *Clathrodrillia* (Fig. 10.16.6) and *Urosalpinx* (Fig. 10.17.9) are two well-known Genera. Holes bored by gastropods cannot be assigned with confidence to any particular Genus but are usually referred to as *Drillia* borings (Fig. 10.16.7).

Naticoids. Naticoid conchs are more or less globose because the spire is very depressed and the body whorl expands so rapidly that it dominates the entire conch (Fig. 10.18). A callus is present very commonly. Surfaces are generally smooth; hence identification of naticoids is difficult. *Natica, Polynices,* and *Amaurellina* are characteristic Genera. The group ranges throughout the Mesozoic and Cenozoic.

Fresh-Water Forms. These prosobranchs mostly have smooth shells and are difficult to identify, but they do occur as fossils commonly enough to warrant recognition as a significant group of gastropods (Fig. 10.19). *Viviparus* occurs from Cretaceous to Recent and is common in fresh-water deposits in

Figure 10.17 (opposite).   Miscellaneous Prosobranchs.
1. *Turritella humerosa*, 2/3X, Eocene, Atlantic Coast.   2. *Turritella mortoni*, 2/3X, Eocene, Atlantic Coast.   3. *Turritella trilira*, 2X, Cretaceous, Gulf Coast.   4. *Turritella plebeia*, 1X, Miocene, Atlantic Coast.   5. *Turritella postmortoni*, 2/3X, Eocene, Atlantic Coast.   6. *Turritella arenicola* 1 1/3X, Eocene, Gulf Coast in United States and Mexico.   7. *Turritella alabamiensis*, 1 1/3X, Paleocene, Gulf Coast.   8. *Murex chipolanus*, 1 1/3X, Miocene, Florida.   9. *Urosalpinx cinereus*, the "oyster drill", 1 1/2X, Miocene, Atlantic Coast.   10. *Terebra langdoni*, 3X, Miocene, Florida.   11. *Mesalia alabamiensis*, 1 1/3X, Eocene, Alabama.   12. *Mesalia seriatim-granulata*, 2X, Cretaceous, Gulf Coast.   13. Oblique apertural view of *Mesalia martinezensis* showing rudimentary canal at inner lip, 1X, Paleocene, California.   14. *Meekospira peracuta*, 1X, Pennsylvanian, midcontinent and eastern United States.   15. *Subulites regularis*, 1X, Ordovician, Kentucky.
(1, 2, 5-7, 11 after Bowles, 1939.   3 after Stephenson, 1941.   4, 9 after Clark et al., 1904. 8 after Gardner, 1947.   10 after Gardner, 1937.   12 after Roemer, 1852.   13 after Merriam, 1941.   14 after White, 1884.   15 after Ulrich and Scofield, 1897.)

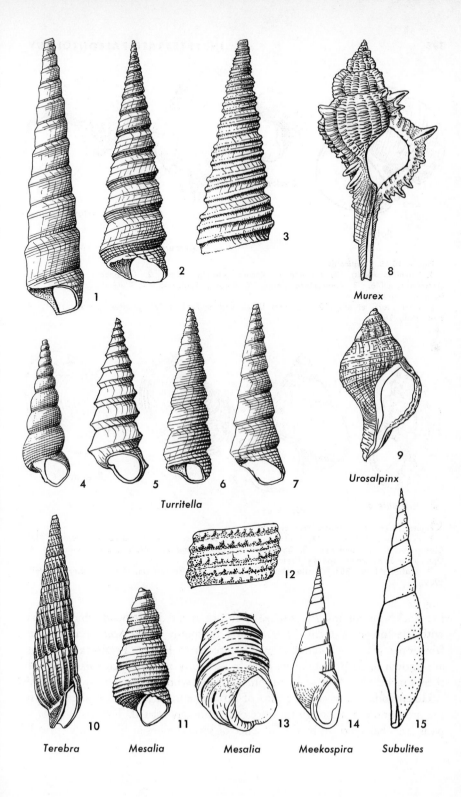

1

2

3

8

Murex

4

5

6

7

Turritella

9

Urosalpinx

10

11

12

13

14

15

Terebra   Mesalia   Mesalia   Meekospira   Subulites

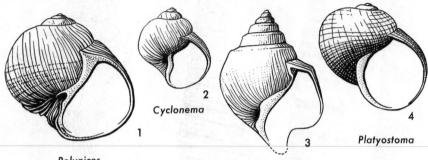

Figure 10.18. Naticoids.
1. *Polynices heros*, 1X, Miocene to Recent, Atlantic Coast. 2. *Cyclonema limatum*, 1X, Ordovician, Ohio. 3. *Amaurellina clarki*, 1X, Eocene, California. 4. *Platyostoma lineata*, 1X, Devonian, New York.
(1 after Clark, et al., 1904. 2 after Ulrich and Scofield, 1897. 3 after Stewart, 1927. 4 after Hall, 1879.)

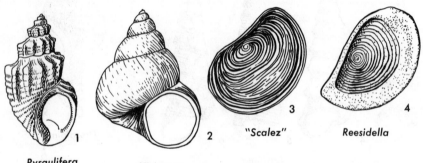

Figure 10.19. Fresh-Water Prosobranchs.
1. *Pyrgulifera humerosa*, 1X, Cretaceous, Rocky Mountains. 2. *Viviparus raynoldsanus*, 1X, Cretaceous, Rocky Mountains. 3. Operculum of *"Scalez" petrolia*, 4X, Pliocene, California. 4. Operculum of *Reesidella* sp., 4X, Cretaceous, Montana.
(1, 2 after White, 1883. 3 after Woodring, Roundy, and Farnsworth, 1932. 4 after MacNeil, 1939.)

the Rocky Mountains. *Pyrgulifera* is an ornamented gastropod which occurs with the foregoing Genus. *Reesidella* (commonly called *Scalez*) is known from opercula which range from Cretaceous to Recent. Fresh-water forms are known to be prosobranchs only by carefully matching characteristics of their conchs with those of living prosobranchs whose soft anatomy is known.

Heteropods. One small group of streptoneurans is usually placed with the prosobranchs, although they are only remotely related. These, the heteropods, are characterized by the presence of several lobes or fins on the spreading foot, and by a coiled conch such as in *Atlanta* (Fig. 10.21.1). Heteropod conchs range in size from microscopic to about 3 centimeters in diameter. Living heteropods float in the upper zones of the ocean in incalculable numbers. After death their conchs accumulate on the sea floor in conjunction with the globigerine oozes. About 60 Recent species have been described, and the group occurred as long ago as the Cretaceous.

SUBCLASS 3.   OPISTHOBRANCHIA

Opisthobranchs receive their name because the gills lie near the posterior end of the body. This feature also indicates that the nerve system tends to be euthyneurous (Fig. 10.3.7). Opisthobranchs seem to have been derived from prosobranchs (streptoneurans) because opisthobranchs have only one gill, one kidney, and one auricle in the heart. It would seem, therefore, that opisthobranchs are gastropods which have undergone detorsion.

There is a notable tendency among opisthobranchs for a decrease in size and strength of the conch until it is absent in some of the sea hares. Moreover, opercula are very rare among opisthobranchs. Whereas conchs diminish in size, the foot of opisthobranchs tends to increase in size until it encloses all or part of the conch. Those conchs which have thus become secondarily internal tend to be covered with a thin layer of inductura over their surface. At the same time the foot may spread out by development of lateral vanes which are used for swimming. All opisthobranchs are marine. The Subclass ranges from Carboniferous to Recent and is represented by about 70 Families. Assignment of conchs to the Opisthobranchia depends upon recognition of asymmetrical soft anatomy or matching conchs with living opisthobranchs whose anatomy is known.

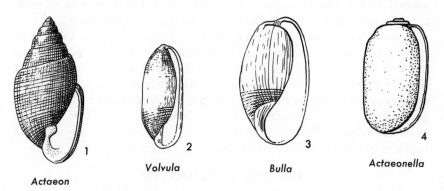

Volvula   *Bulla*   *Actaeonella*

Actaeon

Figure 10.20.   Opisthobranchs.
1. *Actaeon ovoides*, 3X, Miocene, Maryland.   2. *Volvula iota* var. *patuxentia*, 5X, Miocene, Maryland.   3. *Bulla striata waltonensis*, 2X, Miocene, Florida.   4. *Actaeonella oviformis*, 1X, Cretaceous, California.
(1, 2 after Clark, et al., 1904.   3 after Gardner, 1937.)

Actaeonella (Cretaceous) and *Actaeon* (Cretaceous to Recent) represent the normal, more or less helicoid gastropodan shape of the conch. *Bulla* (Jurassic to Recent) represents those opisthobranchs with a thin, largely internal shell (Fig. 10.20). *Actaeon* is especially interesting because it retains streptoneuran nerves but has its gills located posteriorly. It seems to stand close to the prosobranchs. *Tethys* is a Recent sea hare with a large sluglike body and a rudimentary internal conch.

Pteropods. These opisthobranchs bear a laterally expanded foot which projects anteriorly as two broad fins, and they either bear a minute conch or lack a shell. They are the pteropods or "wing-feet" (Fig. 10.21). All pteropods are small and most of the Recent ones are microscopic. They swarm in vast numbers in the ocean, particularly in northern latitudes, and constitute the principal food of plankton-feeding whales. Some pteropod shells are elongate cones, but others are coiled. Pteropods are symmetrical externally but their soft parts are notably asymmetrical. A radula is present and opercula are known. Gills may be absent. According to different ideas, pteropods have been grouped with gastropods or cephalopods or have been placed in a separate Class by themselves. More than 160 species of Recent pteropods are known. *Limacina* and *Clio* are common Recent Genera (Fig. 10.21.2, 3).

True pteropods are thought to range from Cretaceous to Recent, but they are not important rock-makers in ancient sediments. On the other hand, pteropods occur in tremendous abundance in some deep-sea sediments today. In fact, some varieties of globigerine ooze contain so many pteropod conchs that they have been called **pteropod ooze.** Pteropod ooze is characteristically developed in water of moderate depth on seamounts and on the flanks of islands in warm waters. Pteropods and heteropods usually occur together and are both included in the oozes; moreover, pteropods and heteropods are probably grouped together as "pteropods" in some oceanographic studies.

Pteropodlike animals also are known from Lower Cambrian to Permian rocks. Shells of these creatures are shaped like pteropods, but generally are much larger and contain much more calcitic shell substance than do the shells of Recent pteropods. According to various ideas, the ancient pteropods are grouped with modern pteropods or are put in a separate Class, or are grouped in part with conularioids in the Coelenterata. *Hyolithes* is known from Cambrian to Permian, and *Tentaculites* is a Genus of very common fossils in Silurian and Devonian rocks (Fig. 10.21.5, 7–9).

SUBCLASS 4.   PULMONATA

Pulmonate gastropods typically are air-breathers in which the gills are lost. Respiration takes place through the surface of the mantle cavity or, in part, through the exterior surface of the body. Respiration is improved by an increase in the number of blood vessels in the wall of the mantle cavity, and

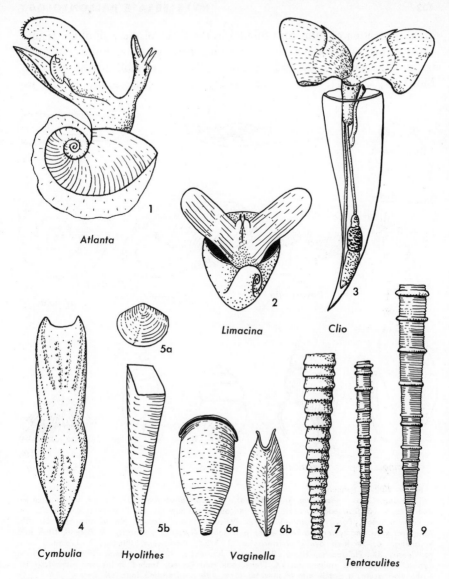

Atlanta

Limacina

Clio

5a

Cymbulia   Hyolithes

Vaginella

Tentaculites

4   5b   6a   6b   7   8   9

Figure 10.21.   Heteropods, Pteropods, and Allied Forms.
1. A complete heteropod, *Atlanta cunicula*, 10X, Recent.   2. A complete pteropod, *Limacina scaphoides*, 5X, Recent.   3. A complete pteropod, *Clio virgula*, 10X, Recent.   4. *Cymbulia parvidentata*, 1 1/3X, Recent.   5a, 5b. Operculum and side view of *Hyolithes princeps*, 1X, Cambrian, Newfoundland and Massachusetts.   6a, 6b. Ventral and side views of *Vaginella chipolana*, 6X, Miocene, Florida.   7. *Tentaculites scalariformis*, 3X, Devonian, New York.   8. *Tentaculites niagarensis*, 6X, Silurian, eastern United States.   9. *Tentaculites gyracanthus*, 6X, Devonian, New York.
(1-3 after Gould, 1852.   4 after Pelseneer, 1888.   5 after Walcott, 1890.   6 after Gardner, 1937.   7 after Hall, 1879.   8, 9 after Hall and Clarke, 1888.)

even by creation of numerous tubules in the tissue of the wall of the mantle cavity. Unfortunately, not all air-breathing gastropods are Pulmonata; only those euthyneuran gastropods without gills are referable to this Subclass. Moreover, not all Pulmonata are air-breathers, because some, having per-

Figure 10.22. Pulmonata.
1. A slug, *Limax antiquorum*, 1/2X, Recent. 2. *Pupa muscorum*, 10X, Recent, North America and Europe. 3. *Dawsonella meeki*, one of the oldest pulmonates, 6X, Pennsylvanian, Illinois. 4. A common snail, *Polygyra albolabris*, 1X, Pleistocene and Recent, North America. 5a, 5b. Apertural view and spire of a fresh-water pulmonate, *Gyraulus utahensis*, 1X, Eocene, Utah and Wyoming. 6. *Succinea ovalis pleistocenica*, 1 1/2X, Pleistocene, Illinois. 7. *Lymnaea bonnevillensis*, 3X, Pleistocene, Utah. 8. *Vertigo loessensis*, 10X, Pleistocene, Illinois. 9. *Physa gyrina*, a fresh-water pulmonate, 1X, Pleistocene and Recent, United States and Canada. 10. *Siphonaria acuta*, a patelliform fresh-water form with a spreading foot, 1X, Recent.
(1 after Turton, 1840. 2-4 after Binney, 1885. 5 after White, 1883. 6, 8 after Baker, 1931. 7 after Baker, 1911. 9 after Baker, 1902. 10 after Gray, 1842.)

fected the air-breathing ability, have returned secondarily to a subaqueous existence, just as whales and porpoises among mammals have returned to the oceans. In the case of gastropods, however, some subaqueous Pulmonata circulate water through the mantle cavity, whereas no air-breathing vertebrate ever became adapted to circulating water through its lungs. Subaqueous

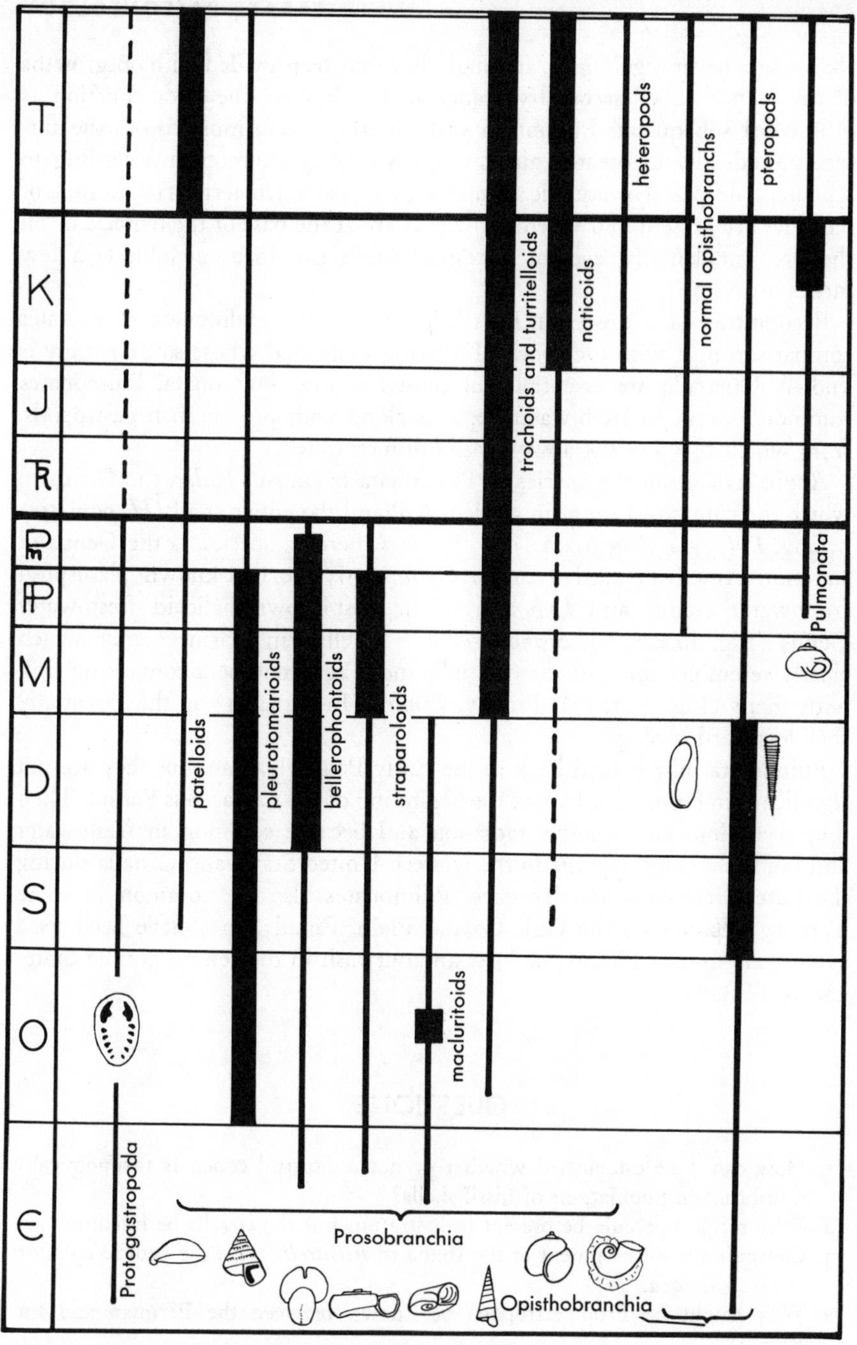

Figure 10.23. Geologic Range of Gastropods.

Pulmonata never regain gills, although they may be provided with outgrowths of the mantle called **secondary branchiae** which serve the same function as gills. Most subaqueous Pulmonata such as *Ampullaria* must rise to the surface periodically to breathe air. Zoologists classify Pulmonata according to whether one pair (in aquatic forms) or two pairs (in terrestrial forms) of tentacles are present and whether the eyes are at the base of the tentacle or on the tips. Incidentally, eyes of terrestrial snails can focus on objects a few inches away.

Recognition of a fossil conch as belonging to the Pulmonata necessitates comparison of it with the conch of a living gastropod whose soft anatomy is known. Opercula are essentially unknown among Pulmonata. Pulmonates commonly occur in fresh-water deposits along with prosobranch gastropods, from which they are not always easily differentiated.

About half of all the species of Pulmonata belong to *Helix,* the Genus to which the common European garden snail and the edible snail (*H. pomatia*) belong. *Polygyra* (Fig. 10.22.4), with 125 American species, is the Genus of common American garden snails. *Gyraulus* is the best-known planispiral fresh-water Genus and *Lymnaea* is the best-known helicoid fresh-water Genus (Fig. 10.22.5, 7). *Siphonaria* is a patelliform marine Genus which closely resembles some of the opisthobranchs and may be a connecting link with them (Fig. 10.22.10). Finally, *Limax* (Fig. 10.22.1) is the essentially shell-less garden slug.

Pulmonata may extend back to the Early Pennsylvanian, but they are not significant in faunas until about the beginning of the Cretaceous Period. Then they went into an explosive radiation and became common in fresh-water and brackish-water deposits in the western United States and Canada during the Late Cretaceous and Tertiary. Pulmonates also are common in some Tertiary deposits on the Gulf Coastal Plain. Finally, they have been used extensively to date Pleistocene loess and outwash in the central United States and in Canada.

QUESTIONS

1. How can it be established whether or not a sinistral conch is taxonomically significant in populations of fossil shells?
2. Why might opercula be present in a stratum but the conchs be missing?
3. Compare the development of the trema in *Fissurella* with the pedicle opening in *Orbiculoidea*.
4. Why might no Protogastropoda be known between the Permian and the Recent?
5. Why is nuclear sculpture important?

6. Why do some gastropods abandon early parts of their conchs, and how do they accomplish this?
7. Why were biologists so sure that the Protogastropoda existed in modern seas, and what bearing does *Neopilina* have on the subject?
8. How do Amphineura resemble gastropods? Why are the two Classes separated from each other?
9. In a mixture of pelecypods, gastropods, and brachiopods, which would be best preserved? Least well preserved? Why?
10. What bearing does the Law of Irreversibility of Evolution have upon the adaptations of pulmonates to a strictly aquatic existence?

BIBLIOGRAPHY

Baker, F. C., 1911, Lymnaeidae of North and Middle America, Recent and fossil: Chicago Acad. Sci., Spec. Pub. 3 (especially pp. 1–86).

——, 1931, Pulmonate Mollusca peculiar to the Pleistocene Period, particularly the loess deposits: Jour. Paleont., v. 5, no. 3, pp. 270–292.

Boutan, L., 1885, Recherches sur L'Anatomie et le Développement de la Fissurelle: Arch. Zool. Exp. Gén., ser. 2, v. 3, supp., pp. 1–173.

Bowles, E., 1939, Eocene and Paleocene Turritellidae of the Atlantic and Gulf Coastal Plain of North America: Jour. Paleont., v. 13, no. 3, pp. 267–336.

Clarke, A. H., Jr., and Menzies, R. J., 1959, *Neopilina (Vema) ewingi,* a second living species of the Paleozoic Class Monoplacophora: Science, v. 129, no. 3355, pp. 1026, 1027.

Dall, W. H., 1924, On the value of nuclear characters in the classification of marine gastropods: Jour. Washington Acad. Sci., v. 14, no. 8, pp. 177–180.

Eales, N. B., 1950, Torsion in Gastropoda: Proc. Malacol. Soc. London, v. 28, pts. 2 and 3, pp. 53–61.

Grabau, A. W., 1904, Phylogeny of Fusus and its allies: Smithsonian Misc. Coll., v. 44, no. 1417.

Keen, A. M., and Pearson, J. C., 1952, Illustrated key to west North American gastropod Genera: Stanford, California, Stanford Univ. Press, 39 pp.

Knight, J. B., 1941, Paleozoic gastropod genotypes: Geol. Soc. America Spec. Paper 32 (especially pages 9–28).

——, and Yochelson, E. L., 1958, A reconsideration of the relationships of the Monoplacophora and the primitive Gastropoda: Proc. Malacol. Soc. London, v. 33, pt. 1, pp. 37–48.

Lemche, H., 1957, A new living deep-sea mollusc of the Cambro-Devonian Class Monoplacophora: Nature (London), v. 179, no. 4556, pp. 413–416.

McDonald, A. I., and Trueman, A. E., 1921, The evolution of certain Liassic gastropods, with special reference to their use in stratigraphy: Geol. Soc. London Quart. Jour., v. 77, pt. 4, pp. 297–344.

Merriam, C. W., 1941, Fossil Turritellas from the Pacific Coast region of North America: Univ. California Pubs., Bull. Dept. Geol. Sci., v. 26, no. 1, pp. 1–214.

Moseley, H., 1838, On the geometrical forms of turbinated and discoid shells: Phil. Trans. Roy. Soc. London, 1838, pt. II, pp. 351–370.

Pelseneer, P., 1888, Report on the Pteropoda collected by H. M. S. "Challenger" during the years 1873–76, pt. 3, Anatomy: Report on the scientific results of the exploring voyage of H. M. S. "Challenger": Zoology, v. 23, pt. LXVI.

Pennak, R. W., 1953, Fresh-water invertebrates of the United States: New York, Ronald Press, 769 pp., 470 ills.

Rasetti, F., 1954, Internal shell structures in the Middle Cambrian gastropod *Scenella* and the problematic Genus *Stenothecoides:* Jour. Paleont., v. 28, no. 1, pp. 59–66.

Roemer, Ferdinand, 1852, Die Kreidebildungen von Texas und ihre organischen Einschlüsse: Bonn, Adolph Marcus, 100 pp., 11 pls.

Stewart, R. B., 1927, Gabb's California fossil type gastropods: Proc. Acad. Nat. Sci. (Philadelphia), v. 78, pp. 287–447.

Thiele, Johannes, 1931, Handbuch der systematischen Weichtierkunde, Jena, Gustav Fischer, 2 vols.

Ulrich, E. O., and Scofield, W. H., 1897, The Lower Silurian Gastropoda of Minnesota: Minnesota Geol. Survey, v. 3, pt. 2, pp. 813–1081.

von Linden, M., 1896, Die Entwicklung der Skulptur und der Zeichnung bei den Gehäuseschnecken des Meeres: Leipzig, Zeitschr. Wiss. Zool., v. 61, pp. 261–317.

Walcott, C. D., 1890, The fauna of the Lower Cambrian or Olenellus zone: U. S. Geol. Survey, 10th Ann. Rept., pt. 1, pp. 509–774.

White, C. A., 1884, The fossils of the Indiana rocks, no. 3: Indiana Dept. Geol. Nat. Hist., 13th Ann. Rept., pt. 2, pp. 107–180.

Wood, E., 1910, The phylogeny of certain Cerithiidae: Annals New York Acad. Sci., v. 20, pt. 1, pp. 1–92.

Woodring, W. P., Roundy, P. V., and Farnsworth, H. R., 1932, Geology and oil resources of the Elk Hills, California: U. S. Geol. Survey, Bull. 835 (especially pp. 33–39).

Woodward, B. B., 1892, On the mode of growth and the structure of the shell in *Velates conoideus,* Lamk., and other Neritidae: Proc. Zool. Soc. London (1892), pt. 3, pp. 528–540.

——, 1922, On *Dinocochlea ingens,* n. gen. and sp., a gigantic gastropod from the Wealden beds near Hastings: Geol. Mag., v. 59, pp. 242–247, 248.

Yochelson, E. L., 1956, Permian Gastropoda of the southwestern United States: Bull. Amer. Mus. Nat. Hist., v. 110, art. 3, pp. 173–276.

——, and Bridge, J., 1958, The Lower Ordovician gastropod *Ceratopea:* U. S. Geol. Survey Prof. Paper 294-H, pp. 281–304.

Chapter 11

CEPHALOPODS

PHYLUM XII. MOLLUSCA (Continued)

Class E. Cephalopoda

Ever since William Smith discovered, just before 1800, that the Jurassic rocks of England could be subdivided on the basis of invertebrates, the study of cephalopods has progressed until this class of molluscs probably has received more attention than has any other group of fossil invertebrates. Cephalopods have proved to be wonderfully suited to the study of principles of evolution and to the application of these principles in the correlation of sedimentary rocks. Not only are conchs of cephalopods widespread and common, but they occur in strata of various composition and texture, and many cephalopods are readily identified. Moreover, the rate of evolution of cephalopods was so rapid that they characterize rather narrow vertical successions of strata. The principal difficulties in identification of cephalopods are the increasing refinement with which morphologic features must be differentiated, the appalling number of Genera and species which are available, and the tendency of unrelated forms to resemble each other through convergence. About 3000 Genera of fossil cephalopods have been described. As is the case with other intensively studied groups, increased knowledge requires specialization; hence the detailed interpretation of cephalopods has come to rest in the hands of relatively few individuals. Even so, the importance of cephalopods remains very great; hence, it is necessary for geologists who are concerned with stratified rocks of most ages to know something of cephalopods in order to make intelligent use of this valuable Class of invertebrates.

The most common living cephalopods are squids and octopods, which together more or less typify the Class, except that the chambered conch which is so diagnostic of fossil cephalopods is reduced or lost in the common Recent cephalopods. In general, conchs of cephalopods resemble conchs of gastropods externally, but most cephalopod conchs are planispiral, whereas most gastropod conchs are helicoid. Conchs of the same shape in the two

Classes sometimes may only be differentiated by noting whether they are chambered or not. Aside from the chambered conchs, cephalopods are characterized by the presence of tentacles bearing suckers and by a peculiar method of locomotion. Cephalopods swim by a system of jet propulsion in which water is ejected from the mantle cavity through a tubular fleshy **funnel** or **hyponome.** The funnel is directed forward from the aperture; hence, the stream of water ejected from it forces the conch backward through the water. Presence and location of the funnel, therefore, are of fundamental significance in studies of most cephalopods. If the funnel is located at the ventral part of the animal, a reëntrant **(hyponomic sinus)** in the margin of the aperture accommodates it.

Although about 300 species of Recent cephalopods are known, very few of these are provided with much, if any, shelly material. If conchs are present, they are almost invariably internal. Of all the living cephalopods, *Nautilus* is the most important Genus to paleontologists because it provides a link with the 10,000 or more fossil cephalopods with chambers which have been described. Primary considerations of orientation and behavior of fossil cephalopods, therefore, depend in large measure upon interpretation of the anatomy and habits of *Nautilus*.

CONCH.   In its simplest form the cephalopod conch is a straight cone in which the aperture is anterior and the apex is posterior. If a hyponomic sinus is present, it is always ventral. During the course of the progressive coiling which affected most cephalopods, the conch became enrolled so that orientation of conchs of cephalopods is almost as confusing as is orientation of gastropods. If the ventral margin of a planispirally coiled conch is traced posteriorly it lies at one instance on the uppermost part of the conch above its starting position. Obviously, ventral and dorsal have one meaning when applied to soft anatomy and would have other meanings if applied to different points on the periphery of the conchs. The same confusion affects use of the terms anterior and posterior when applied to coiled cephalopod conchs. Accordingly, a special set of terms has been created to describe orientation of the conchs of coiled cephalopods. That portion of the conch which is nearest the aperture is **adapertural,** whereas the portion of the conch nearest the apex is **adapical.** Adapertural and adapical also can be applied to forward and backward directions, respectively. That part of the conch which lies along the periphery or midventral line of each whorl is the **venter.** The venter is simply the imaginary trace of former ventral positions of the soft parts and of the hyponomic sinus.

The large open receptacle for the soft parts is the **living chamber.** It may occupy between one-quarter of a volution and almost one volution. Behind the living chamber (that is, adapically) lies the chambered portion of the conch called the **phragmocone.** Finally, that portion of the conch which is uppermost is the **dorsum.** The dorsum may include part of the phragmocone or part of the living chamber as well, depending upon the sizes of the phragmocone and living chamber.

In its normal swimming position *Nautilus* carries itself with the plane of the conch vertical and the aperture facing slightly upward (Fig. 11.1). In spite of the natural orientation of *Nautilus* paleontologists have adopted a conventional orientation for conchs of coiled cephalopods in which the living chamber is placed uppermost and the lateral margin of the aperture is vertical. This conventional position is almost exactly inverted from the normal living

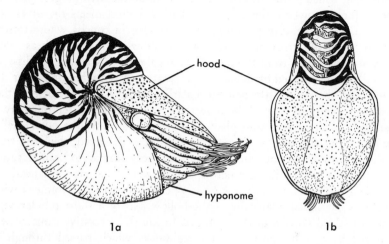

Figure 11.1. The Pearly Nautilus.
1a. Side view of *Nautilus pompilius* in the normal position of rest, about 1/3X, Recent. 1b. Apertural view with the tentacles and siphon almost completely retracted and covered by the hood.
(After Dean, 1901.)

position. Conchs of straight cephalopods conventionally are oriented with the long axis vertical and the aperture up, although they presumably lived with the conch disposed horizontally.

Interiors of conchs are divided into chambers (**camerae**) by transverse partitions, the **septa.** Septa may be evenly concave like a saucer or they may be intricately scalloped. During life all chambers of *Nautilus* are filled with a nitrogen-rich gas which provides just the right amount of buoyancy in order to keep the complete organism in a state of equilibrium with the pressure at a particular depth. Chambers of phragmocones decrease in size adapically until the first chamber, or **protoconch,** is encountered. New septa are added behind the visceral mass after it moves forward in the living chamber. It is apparent, therefore, that the secretion of new septa reflects adjustment of the volume and length of the living chamber to corresponding changes in the shape and to the proportions of the soft parts. Thus, the growth of a cephalopod is recorded by changes in shape and in secretion of successive septa. Cephalopods are especially well suited for ontogenetric studies because the phragmocones containing the early chambers are carefully preserved for examination, even though some chambers may be enclosed within later whorls.

Each septum consists of three parts. The **mural portion** is a wide rim which is plastered against the inner surface of that portion of the shell which forms the living chamber, whereas the **free portion** of the septum is the concave diaphragm which forms the actual partition across the shell (Fig. 11.3.2). The line of juncture where the free portion of a septum meets the outer shell of the conch is the **suture.** Sutures are best seen in conchs whose camerae have been filled with sediment or some crystallized mineral such as calcite. They are not visible from the outside unless the shell is eroded or dissolved naturally or is removed by deliberate preparation. Even when the outer shell is removed the sutures do not particularly resemble sutures such as those separating bones in a skull, because the free portion of a septum may remain in the suture as a thin plate. If, however, not only the outer shell of the conch but the free portion of the septum is dissolved, then the traces of the sutures across the internal mold are very similar to cranial sutures in vertebrates in that they are both spaces between adjacent substances.

In the free portion of each septum is a perforation (**septal foramen**) which usually is continued adapically as the hollow axis of a short tubular **septal neck** (the third portion of the septum). In life the successive camerae were traversed by a continuous tube, the **siphuncle,** which passed through the septal foramina and the septal necks. The siphuncle ended at a chitinous-walled chamber, the **caecum,** which was located just adaperturally from the protoconch. Sides of the siphuncle consist of porous, spicular, chitino-calcare-ous **connecting rings,** which naturally extended from the septal necks of one septum to the septal foramen of the next septum. Far from being ringlike, connecting rings are really tubes. After the death of the animal, the siphuncular walls often collapsed, and sediment or mineral matter infiltrated the camerae. Incidentally, it seems incredible that the infiltration by sediment can have been so complete as it usually is in phragmocones. In the case of mineralization, unusual minerals in some cases occur in vugs in cephalopods. Moreover, in cephalopods of many ages these cavities seem to be singularly suited to the accumulation of crude oil, so that collectors have been known to be splattered with petroleum when trying to break fossil conchs out of their matrix.

CLASSIFICATION. It is convenient to divide the Class Cephalopoda into three Subclasses, of which the Nautiloidea are characterized by straight to increasingly coiled external conchs with subcentral siphuncles and unpleated sutures. Ammonoidea have mostly ventral siphuncles (one group has dorsal siphuncles), coiled or secondarily uncoiled conchs, and generally complexly pleated sutures. The Coleoidea are characterized by progressive reduction or loss of an internal shell.

SUBCLASS 1.   NAUTILOIDEA

The nautiloid cephalopods are the oldest, most primitive, and probably the best adapted of all the cephalopods. At least they lived longer than the other groups and seem to have given rise to the other two Orders. Nautiloids range from Late Cambrian to Recent and reached their greatest importance during the Paleozoic. In fact, the longest shells of invertebrates ever discovered are the 15-foot-long (5 m) cephalopod shells in the Ordovician. The Order is typified by *Nautilus,* which is the only Genus with living representatives remaining from the large number of fossil Genera. Most people have at least heard that *Nautilus* is chambered, that it has a pearly conch, or that it has been said to drift about on the surface of the oceans using its foot as a sail. A few lines of poetry by Holmes and by Pope have immortalized some of these concepts, even though the idea that nautiloids sail about on the surface is not supported by observations. On more mundane grounds, however, scientists are intensely interested in *Nautilus* because it is a veritable living fossil and provides the only link between the ammonoids and nautiloids on the one hand and the squids and octopods on the other hand. *Nautilus* is represented by three living species, all of which inhabit the western Pacific Ocean in a great area extending from Australia and New Zealand north to the Philippine Islands and east to Fiji. Beyond this region empty conchs have drifted as far north as Japan. *Nautilus* rarely rises into water as shallow as 12 feet (4 m) and then only at night, normally. In the daytime the animals live as deep as 2300 feet (about 770 m) and are caught in traps very commonly at less than 1000 feet (about 330 m). There seems to be no substantiated report as to how *Nautilus* moves at its normal depth, but all captured individuals swam rather than crawled. One individual at rest in an aquarium held fast to the wall with its tentacles and did not crawl about.

SOFT PARTS. It is convenient to consider the soft parts of a *Nautilus* as resembling a squidlike animal contained within the living chamber. Thus, the aperture is filled with 88 subequal slender tentacles grouped on 8 stout bases. When the animal is alarmed it pulls itself within the living chamber by contraction of a pair of retractor muscles which are attached to opposite sides of the living chamber. It then covers the aperture by lowering a very stiff hood which otherwise overlies the dorsal portion of the extendable parts (Fig. 11.1.2). The retractor muscles also seem to be involved in locomotion, because water is forced out of the mantle cavity and through the funnel when the retractor muscles pull the viscera back forcefully into the living chamber. During swimming the animal can alter its depth in the water by pointing the muscular funnel up or down, or can spin around topwise by ejecting water from the funnel when the funnel is directed sidewise.

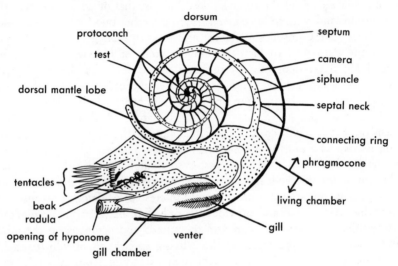

Figure 11.2. Anatomy of *Nautilus*.
Diagrammatic section in the plane of coiling. Only two of the four gills are visible. (After Flower, 1945.)

The mouth is located centrally within the circle of tentacles and is equipped with very stout chitinous jaws, as well as with an effective radula (Fig. 11.2). The jaws are formidable instruments with powerful muscles to activate them. The upper jaw lies within the larger lower jaw and the two resemble an inverted parrot's beak. Not only are the cutting edges of some nautiloid jaws slightly calcified, but a few fossil jaws have been described from Mesozoic strata. The Genus *Rhyncholithes* is based upon jaws from the Triassic of Germany. Only one example of Paleozoic (Carboniferous) nautiloid jaws is known, in spite of the abundance of conchs in various places.

Respiration in *Nautilus* takes place through four gills which are suspended in the mantle cavity. Inasmuch as all other living cephalopods have only two gills, the number of gills is accorded great importance in differentiating coleoids from nautiloid cephalopods. The digestive track is slightly contorted and opens into the mantle cavity. No ink sac is present in nautiloids. The nervous system is highly organized, with balancing organs and other specialized sensory devices, of which the eyes are the most noteworthy. The two eyes of *Nautilus* consist of rather triangular bodies with an elongate slitlike aperture through which light passes without benefit of a lens. In

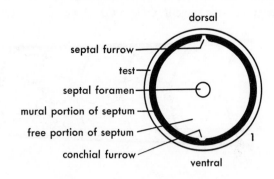

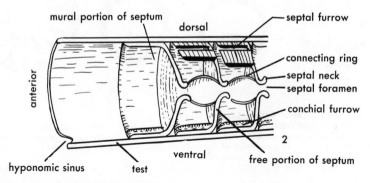

Figure 11.3. Septal Anatomy of Nautiloids.
1. Transverse section through the center of a camera.   2. Diagrammatic longitudinal section of a straight cephalopod.
(After Flower, 1945.)

fact, sea water communicates freely through the slit into the interior of the eyes, rendering each of them a kind of subaqueous, pinhole camera.

In *Nautilus* a branch of the circulatory system extends posteriorly within the siphuncle. It is likely that the siphuncle can maintain some control over the gas pressure within the chambers as the animal changes its depth; otherwise it seems as though the conch would be crushed. On the other hand, extension of living tissue back to the caecum appears to be a liability because damage to the phragmocone ordinarily is not repaired, although damage to the living chamber commonly is repaired. Apparently very little regenerative ability is retained in most phragmocones.

Conchs of many nautiloids bear a shallow groove, the **conchial furrow,** at the midventral position on the inner surface of the shell (Fig. 11.3.1). This furrow, in association with the hyponomic sinus, is useful in the orientation of conchs. The function of the conchial furrow is not known. Unlike the conchial furrow, which is not invariably present, the **septal furrow** is always present at some stage in the growth of a conch. It consists of a shallow groove

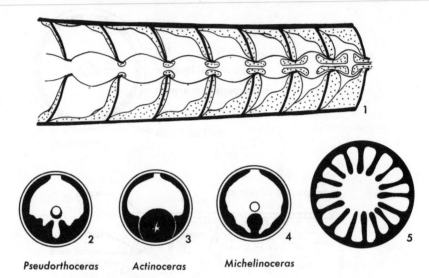

Pseudorthoceras   *Actinoceras*   *Michelinoceras*

Figure 11.4. Cameral and Siphuncular Deposits.
1. Schematic longitudinal section of a straight nautiloid showing progressive change in cameral and siphuncular deposits and in shape of connecting rings. 2-4. Transverse sections of three conchs showing concentration of cameral deposits ventrally. 5. Transverse section of the siphuncle of an actinosiphonate nautiloid.
(1 after Flower, 1945 and 1957. 2, 3 after Flower, 1957. 4, 5 after Flower, 1945.)

which extends completely through the mural portions of the septa and exposes the outer shell substance along the dorsal midline of each camera. Septal furrows are discontinuous on inner surfaces of shells because mural portions of septa do not extend all the way adaperturally to the next septum. Septal furrows can be preserved in original shells, or in molds, or in casts, hence, they can be very useful for orienting shells.

Connection between the camerae and the living chamber was not lost after secretion of one or more septa. Instead, the mantle which lined the inner surfaces of the camerae continued to secrete calcium carbonate in the form of **cameral deposits** which lined the interiors of camerae (Fig. 11.4.1-4).

Moreover, the amount of cameral deposits was greatest in progressively older camerae and tended to be thickest on the ventral region. It has been suggested that the tendency to fill up camerae with skeletal material is a feature connected with racial old age, but it is more apt to be a method of adding ballast in order to offset increased buoyancy as new camerae are added.

SHAPE OF CONCHS. For a long time it has been observed that nautiloids showed a general tendency for progressively tighter coiling of their conchs. Thus, most of the Cambrian and Ordovician nautiloids are straight or are only slightly curved, whereas the tightly coiled forms are characteristic of younger strata. Between these two extremes are all intermediate stages of coiling. It is rather natural to conclude from the foregoing that a nautiloid can be classified or located in an evolutionary series by its stage of coiling. Unfortunately, there are so many variations in (or outright reversals of) the general trend that systematists are rather wary about indiscriminately assigning taxonomic or phylogenetic value to shapes of conchs. For instance, coiling took place along the same lines in various strains of nautiloids at different rates and at different times. The result is that degree of coiling has to be evaluated in relation to other morphologic changes in order to be significant.

Evolving from more or less straight conchs, cephalopods could coil up in either of two directions. Most cephalopods are enrolled so that the hyponomic sinus (or other ventral features such as the conchial furrow) is on the convex side—that is, it is on the side of the aperture away from the axis of coiling. Conchs of this sort are **exogastric** (Fig. 11.5.5–7, 9–12). Their potential ability to become more enrolled is almost unlimited. On the other hand, **endogastric** conchs are enrolled with the hyponomic sinus on the concave or inner side of curvature (Fig. 11.5.1, 4). Curvature among endogastric conchs rarely progresses beyond an arcuate or banana-shaped stage because operation of the hyponomic funnel would be inhibited by interference with the preceding whorl. Accordingly, it is not surprising to discover that endogastric conchs are rather diagnostic of Early Paleozoic strata. *Phragmoceras,* from the Silurian, is the most enrolled endogastric nautiloid. It passes through about $1\frac{1}{2}$ whorls, hence it corresponds to *Gyroceras* among exogastric conchs.

Returning now to the exogastric conchs, the straight conchs are typified by the Genus *Michelinoceras,* which formerly was known as *Orthoceras* (Fig. 11.5.3). Conchs of this kind are said to be **orthoceracones.** The next stage of curvature in a morphologic series is the arcuate form with less than one volution; it is typified by *Cyrtoceratites;* hence, these conchs are **cyrtoceracones** (Fig. 11.5.5). Conchs with as many as about two free volutions are typified by *Gyroceras;* hence they are **gyroceracones** (Fig. 11.5.7). *Tarphyceras* typifies **tarphyceracones,** in which the whorls are in contact (Fig. 11.5.9). Compactness is increased after the tarphyceraconic stage by the partial envelop-

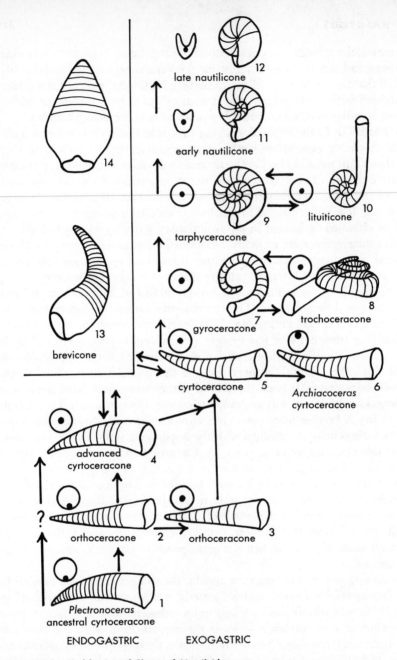

Figure 11.5. Modification of Shape of Nautiloids.
Conchs are mostly oriented ventral side down and seen in side view. Cross sections along-side most of the conchs show the position of the siphuncle by a black dot. Arrows indicate directions of change which have been recognized in various morphologic series. In general, the evolutionary progress is thought to have proceeded from bottom to top of the figure.
1 is *Plectronoceras*. 6 is *Archiacoceras*.
(After Flower, 1946 and 1954.)

ment of one whorl within the succeeding whorl to produce a condition known generally as **convolute.** More precisely, the overlap of one whorl on an earlier whorl may be very slight (**evolute**) or very considerable (**involute**). In *Nautilus,* for instance, convolution is so extreme that the last whorl completely covers the earlier portion of the conch. Any involute conch is a **nautilicone,** however (Fig. 11.5.11, 12). The degree of convolution can be expressed in different ways. A simple method is to refer to the height of the **impressed zone,** which is the distance one whorl is involved in another whorl when the conch is viewed from the aperture. Or the ratio of height of the impressed zone to the height of the aperture may be cited. As viewed from the side, however, the degree of convolution is reflected in the width of the exposed central or axial whorls within the inner edge of the last whorl. This concave region near the axis of coiling is the **umbilicus.** It can be defined in terms of its degree of concavity, presence or absence of a perforation at the axis of coiling, and slope of its sides. As a result of changes in the shapes of whorls during growth, diagrammatic **whorl sections** customarily are illustrated for many cephalopods; moreover, it may be necessary to cut through a conch along the axis of coiling in order to show whorl sections at various stages.

In addition to the foregoing forms, a few special shapes are worth noting. The first of these is the helicoid spiral which resembles loosely coiled conchs of gastropods; these conchs are called **trochoceracones,** after *Trochoceras* (Fig. 11.5.8). Compact conchs with shortened phragmocones and rather swollen adapertual regions are **brevicones** (Fig. 11.5.13, 14). *Brevicoceras* was named for this form of conch, instead of vice versa. Strangely, apertures of brevicones customarily are restricted to slots or some other form of narrow opening (Fig. 11.7). The last shape to be considered is the **lituiticone,** named after *Lituites,* which coils up in its early stages as a typical nautilicone and then, in its later development, grows straight like an orthoceracone (Fig. 11.5.10). Lituiticonic uncoiling of nautiloid conchs foreshadows much more extensive development of a similar trend among some Cretaceous ammonoids.

It was formerly thought that most of the foregoing stages constituted an evolutionary series, that is, that increasingly compact conchs were always produced. It is now known that the shape of a conch may revert to an early stage after some later stage was attained. Thus, there is a sort of oscillation between cyrtoceraconic and orthoceraconic conchs in some strains, and some paleontologists think that all known cephalopods, straight or curved, have been derived from a coiled ancestor. Flower and Kummel (1950) mention a case among *Oncoceras* and its allies in which the ancestral form is breviconic and exogastric, but it gave rise to endogastric as well as exogastric descendants; of the two strains, the exogastric line evolved up to the stage of being trochoceraconic and then different members reverted back through the gyroceraconic form into the original breviconic shape from which the oncoceroids started.

ADAPTATIONS OF CONCHS. So far as is known now, the oldest cephalopods are slightly cyrtoceraconic, the siphuncle is located at the ventral margin, there are no connecting rings, and the shape is endogastric. This stage is characterized by *Plectronoceras,* from the Upper Cambrian of China (Fig. 11.5.1). From it arose *Ellesmeroceras* and its allies, in which there is some tendency for orthoceracones to develop (Fig. 11.5.2); moreover, connecting rings are developed. Very rapidly thereafter, in Ordovician time, orthoceraconic shells became dominant, and the siphuncle migrated into a subcentral position; in fact, this last arrangement of shape and siphuncular position is considered to be the generalized early form of nautiloid cephalopods (Fig. 11.5.3).

From a study of color markings and shapes of conchs it seems probable that early nautiloids were bottom-dwellers or returned to the bottom after short excursions into the pelagic realm, or lived horizontally as free-swimming organisms. For example, symmetrical color markings of some straight conchs are absent on the ventral surface, whereas color markings should have encircled the conch if the animal hung suspended from a floating conch. Other conchs are ventrally flattened, suggesting that the animal was a burrower or a groveler in the surficial sediments of the ocean floor.

It is even probable that some early nautiloids gave up the ability to swim and adopted a creeping habit. Evidence for change of habit is found in **decollation** (truncation) of apical portions of phragmocones in the same way that some gastropods cast away apical parts of their conchs. Barrande, for instance, described how *"Orthoceras" truncatum* from Europe cast away about four camerae at a time and then sealed off the exposed septal foramen with a striated conical to spherical deposit of calcite which also tended to streamline the new apex somewhat (Fig. 11.6.10). Unlike *Nautilus* with its numerous, small, unequal arms, ancient nautiloids such as *"O." truncatum* presumably had some small arms and two large tentacular arms such as are present among squids today and which were long enough to reach around and lie upon the septal face exposed by decollation. Tentacular arms must have had the power to secrete calcium carbonate in the same way that some female octopods secrete a brood pouch from the surface of two specialized arms. By decollation the nautiloids destroyed most of the adapical buoyancy of their bodies. Thereafter, decollated nautiloids must have lived horizontally, whether they were active swimmers or were strictly bottom-dwellers. All together, 3 Genera and 24 species of Paleozoic nautiloids are believed to have decollated their conchs.

Most nautiloids adopted a pelagic existence in which buoyancy was a paramount consideration. The straight conchs, being external, tended to buoy up the posterior part of the animal progressively with addition of new chambers; therefore, some method of controlling buoyancy would be beneficial. Secondary deposits of calcium carbonate accumulated like ballast within the adapical portions of many conchs and tipped the apices of the phragmocones down so that the conchs lay upon an even keel.

Buoyancy also was controlled in conchs which were coiled up into a compact spiral because the center of buoyancy would be located in the phragmocones above the center of gravity in the living chambers. Thus, the living chambers would always be pendent beneath the camerate portions of the conchs. Additional adjustments in buoyancy during growth took place by involution of the whorls or by compression of the conch along the axis of coiling. Similar changes in buoyancy characterized conchs of ammonoids.

The major obstacle to progressive compactness of coiling would seem to be encountered at the cyrtoceraconic stage. The difficulty is readily understood because a cyrtoceracone is the most poorly designed conch to control during its movement through the water. If it were propelled rapidly it would tend to describe a series of loops; in fact, it would be no more controllable than a banana-shaped rocket. One solution to the locomotor difficulty lay in development of short phragmocones which would have a less adverse rudderlike effect on the trajectory of the conchs. The resulting shortened conchs or brevicones are particularly common among cyrtoceraconic nautiloids. Moreover, many brevicones also are swollen midway along the conch in a fashion which provides necessary increase in displacement in one region at the same time that shortening reduced displacement in another region; in this way a nice adjustment of buoyancy could be maintained.

Changes in shape bear upon a fundamental concept in evolution which is called Dollo's Law or the Law of Irreversibility of Evolution (page 42).

SIPHUNCLE. Siphuncles consist of a fleshy axis and a calcareous sheath or wall. In *Nautilus* the axis is traversed by a branch of the circulatory system, but in fossil cephalopods the sheath is quite naturally hollow. In its simplest form the sheath consists of the septal necks without connecting rings. Part of the original fleshy material either was contained within a chitinous sheath or was exposed in the camerae. Septal necks of nautiloids always are directed adapically in a plan called **retrochoanitic** (Fig. 11.3.2).

The remarkable diversity of the siphuncular sheath has led to exhaustive study of it among nautiloids. Examinations are made possible by preparing polished surfaces of specimens sliced along the plane of coiling or by making thin sections of siphuncles in the same plane. It seems that the siphuncle is located near the ventral margin in primitive cephalopods and may indicate a low center of gravity associated with bottom-dwelling existence of the animals. The siphuncle of nautiloids tended to migrate to a central or subcentral position and even may be located dorsally in some advanced conchs in which the center of buoyancy is located high above the center of gravity. Moreover, the position of the siphuncles moves from ventral to subcentral in some individual conchs as they grow larger. And the position of the siphuncle also may shift slightly after it has attained its normal subcentral location.

Most siphuncular modifications, however, pertain to the manner in which the sheath expands, thickens, or is reinforced with secondary deposits. In cases in which the septal necks and siphuncular walls are cylindrical, the siphuncle is said to be **orthochoanitic.** In other cases the septal necks and connecting rings comprise a bulbous structure within each camera and a restriction at each septum, whereupon the siphuncle resembles a string of beads or balls (Fig. 11.3.2); these are **cyrtochoanitic** siphuncles. Both kinds of siphuncles can occur in one conch and transitional forms also are known.

Siphuncular walls may consist of thin skeletal tissue (**eurysiphonate**) or of thickly constructed tissue (**stenosiphonate**). Close attention is paid to the disposition of connecting rings, septal necks, and of any unusual processes or structures inside or outside of the siphuncular wall. Thus, a series of invaginated cones (**endocones**) may occupy the apical portions of some siphuncles or thin diaphragms may cross the siphonal tube. Some sort of secondary deposit of calcium carbonate largely fills siphuncles of some cephalopods, particularly the siphuncles of straight conchs. **Siphuncular deposits** are comparable to cameral deposits, but the latter seem to have been deposited by extensions of the mantle, whereas siphuncular deposits arise from siphuncular tissues. Siphuncular deposits most commonly comprise doughnutlike rings of sclerenchyme which are thickest and best developed farthest toward the apex of the conch. Siphuncles in which deposits consist of plates radiating from the axis are said to be actinosiphonate. In transverse section actinosiphonate siphuncles resemble transverse sections of some corals (Fig. 11.4.5). Actinosiphonate structure occurs in several unrelated groups of nautiloid cephalopods ranging from the Upper Ordovician to the Upper Devonian and is particularly common in brevicones of the Middle Silurian and Middle Devonian.

There is some significance in the change in size of the siphuncles of nautiloids. Siphuncles of primitive nautiloids such as *Endoceras* had relatively large diameters, but by Late Ordovician time the siphuncles of nautiloids were dominantly rather slender—a condition retained in *Nautilus.* It is likely, therefore, that the branch of the circulatory system which traverses the siphuncle of *Nautilus* is merely a relic of a formerly important region of the body.

ORNAMENTATION. Nautiloid conchs tend to be smooth and covered with growth lines, no matter whether the conchs are straight or curved. If ornamentation is present, it may be **annular** and consist of fine to coarse encircling ornamentation or be radial and consist of fine to coarse ribs running longitudinally with the growth of the shell.

CLASSIFICATION. Although considerable progress now is being made in the study of nautiloids, the residue of unsolved problems is still too great to enable a clear-cut classification to be constructed. Several evolutionary series are known very well; however, the differentiation of stages in these series requires a rather high degree of specialization. A lucid breakdown of nautiloids into 14 Orders and 75 Families has been presented by Flower and Kummel (1950). They also present range data and a tentative phylogeny of the Subclass. Among the various nautiloids, the groups mentioned below are particularly noteworthy.

Ellesmeroceratids. These are seemingly the parent stock of all cephalopods and lived during the Cambrian and Ordovician. They are mostly orthoceracones and endogastric cyrtocones with a large ventral siphuncle. *Plectronoceras,* the oldest cephalopod, from the Upper Cambrian of China, belongs here (Fig. 11.5.1). It is endogastric, cyrtoceraconic, and rather small.

Endoceratids. *Endoceras* and its allies are very common in Ordovician strata. They are mostly orthoceracones with large subcentral siphuncles which bear endocones (Fig. 11.6.9).

Michelinoceratids. This group contains the majority of orthoceracones and ranges from Ordovician to Triassic. The siphuncle is slender and subcentral. Characteristic Genera are *Michelinoceras* (Ordovician) and *Mooreoceras* and *Pseudorthoceras* (Late Paleozoic) (Fig. 11.6.8, 1, 2).

Oncoceratids. Almost all cyrtoceracones and brevicones belong here, whether they are exogastric or endogastric. Moreover, the apertures of oncoceratid conchs are very commonly constricted in some characteristic pattern (Fig. 11.7). The group ranged from Ordovician to Pennsylvanian but reached its peak in the Silurian. Typical Genera are *Oncoceras* (Ordovician); *Austinoceras, Hexameroceras,* and *Gomphoceras* (Silurian); *Cranoceras* (correct name for *"Cyrtoceras"*) (Devonian). The group also contains the unique Genus *Archiacoceras* (Devonian), which is exogastric, but has a dorsal siphuncle instead of a ventral or subcentral siphuncle (Fig. 11.5.6).

Ascocerids. A group of brevicones related to *Ascoceras* merits special attention because of the interesting ways in which the buoyancy of members of the group is controlled. *Ascoceras* (Fig. 11.8.9b) was slender and slightly cyrtoceraconic until maturity, when it developed an expanded living chamber. On at least one occasion during the life of each individual and probably at other times, *Ascoceras* cast off a series of the cyrtoceraconic camerae by decollation, until only the living chamber remained (Fig. 11.8.9c). The living chamber was further modified by development of a row of dorsal chambers or floats through modification of septa (Fig. 11.8.9a). Stages in the evolutionary descent of ascocerid cephalopods seem to have

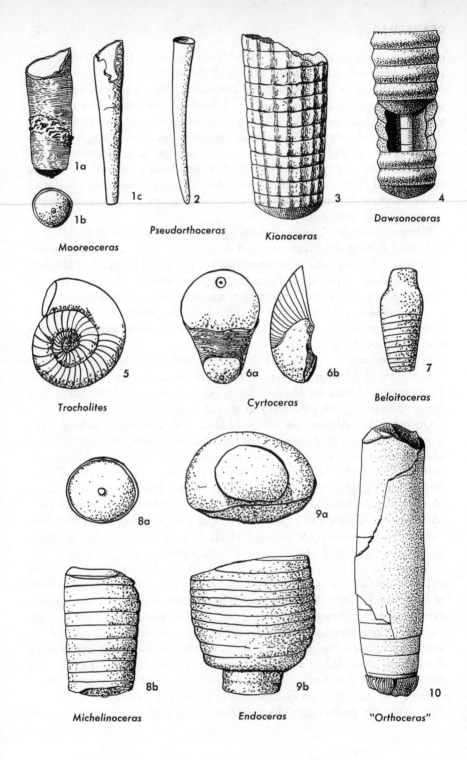

1a

1b

1c
Mooreoceras

2
Pseudorthoceras

3
Kionoceras

4
Dawsonoceras

5
Trocholites

6a

6b
Cyrtoceras

7
Beloitoceras

8a

8b
Michelinoceras

9a

9b
Endoceras

10
"Orthoceras"

arisen from simple forms such as *Montyoceras* (Fig. 11.8.1) in which the septa are mostly widely spaced and merely incline forward somewhat at their dorsal edges. From this stage onward, the principal evolutionary tendencies consist of crowding of septa in old age; change in outline of siphuncle from almost parallel-sided (actually plano-convex dorsoventrally) to biconvex; expansion of the living chamber; and development of S-shaped convex camerae without siphuncles along the inside of the dorsal part of the living chamber. The ascocerids are Ordovician and Silurian.

Biconvex siphuncles first arose in the anterior septa of *Hebetoceras* (Fig. 11.8.2), but eventually all siphuncular segments became biconvex and the number of segments with a plano-convex profile disappeared. At the same time some septa were aborted and the single compound camera which remained then consisted of more than one siphuncular segment. Siphuncular transition is shown in the change from *Schuchertoceras* either to *Billingsites* or to *Lindstroemoceras*. Thus, *S. iowaense* is notable because the large posterior camera retains relics of three siphuncular segments, two of which are biconvex and one of which is plano-convex (Fig. 11.8.4). Only two segments (both biconvex) are present in *S. anticostiense* (Fig. 11.8.5), and only one is present in both *Billingsites* and *Lindstroemoceras* (Fig. 11.8.6, 7).

The most diagnostic feature of ascocerid nautiloids is the progressive appearance of S-shaped camerae which are fused together in overlapping series on the dorsal side of the living chamber. Two dorsal camerae first appear in *Schuchertoceras* (Fig. 11.8.4, 5) and finally the number increases to about 7 in advanced forms (Fig. 11.8.9), with a maximum of 12. Septa on the ventral sides of living chambers usually are short and straight. *Choanoceras* is a parallel offshoot of ascocerids which reveals an incipient ascocerid septum but has septa fused together on the ventral side (Fig. 11.8.3).

One of the most amazing of all nautiloids is *Pseudascoceras*, which began to seal off the posterior part of the living chamber with concave or normal

---

Figure 11.6 (*opposite*). Nautiloids.

1. *Mooreoceras* sp., Mississippian, Nevada. 1a, side view of a fragmentary conch with surface ornamentation, 1 1/3X. 1b, lower end of 1a showing septum and siphuncle, 1 1/3X. 1c, nearly complete conch, 1/2X. 2. *Pseudorthoceras knoxense*, 1/2X, Pennsylvanian, midcontinent. Somewhat diagrammatic side view showing curved apical region. 3. *Kionoceras austini*, 2/3X, Silurian, Ohio. 4. Partially cut-away conch of *Dawsonoceras hyatti*, 1/2X, Silurian, Ohio. 5. *Trocholites ammonius*, 2/3X, Ordovician, New York. 6a, 6b. Dorsal and side views of *Cyrtoceras depressum*, 1/2X, Devonian, Germany. 7. Ventral view of *Beloitoceras lycum*, 2/3X, Ordovician, Wisconsin. 8a, 8b. Broken phragmocone with septal surface, and side view of part of phragmocone of *Michelinoceras sociale*, 2/3X, Ordovician, eastern United States. 9a, 9b. Broken cross section and side view of fragment of *Endoceras proteiforme*, 1/4X, Ordovician, eastern United States. 10. Side view of truncated conch of "*Orthoceras*" *truncatum* with callus over broken end, about 1X, Lower Paleozoic, Czechoslovakia.

(1 after Youngquist, 1949. 2 after Miller, Dunbar, and Condra, 1933. 3, 4 after Foerste, 1928. 5 after Hall, 1847. 6 after Foerste, 1926. 7 after Foerste, 1924. 10 after Barrande, 1860.)

nautiloid septa after it had restricted the living chamber with ascocerid septa (Fig. 11.8.8). Some paleontologists think that *Pseudascoceras* indicates a reversion to early youthful or to ancestral septal conditions which characterized the long, narrow, molted portion of the conch.

Nautilids. This narrowly defined group within the larger category of nautiloids is characterized by conchs whose coiling is evolute to involute. *Nautilus* is the classic example, but almost identical conchs are present in Devonian strata. Nautilids became numerically important in the Mesozoic and Cenozoic.

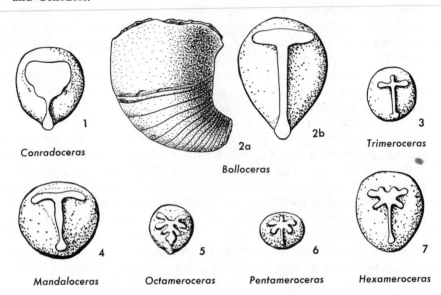

Figure 11.7. Apertures of Breviconic Nautiloids.
Bolloceras is Devonian, but the rest are Silurian. Mostly slightly reduced.
(After Foerste, 1926.)

The siphuncle in nautilids either is subcentral or occupies a distinctly dorsal position reminiscent of that in the cyrtoceraconic *Archiacoceras* (Fig. 11.5.11, 12). During the Paleozoic a few nautilids showed a short-lived tendency to develop slightly sinuous sutures, and this tendency became important in the Mesozoic. By Cretaceous time only the tightly coiled nautilids survived. The latter are represented by two strains, both of which

Figure 11.8 (*opposite*). Evolution of Ascocerid Nautiloids.
The external appearance of a fossil specimen is shown in 9c at 2/3X. All other illustrations are vertical longitudinal sections of conchs. Only 9b is essentially complete, whereas all of the others are truncated at their right (posterior) ends. Arrows indicate probable evolutionary paths.
(1-9a after Flower, 1941. 9b, 9c after Lindström, 1890.)

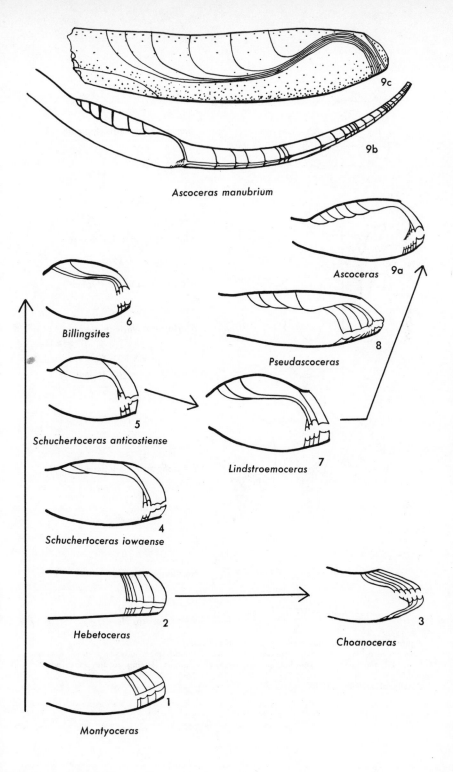

9c

9b

Ascoceras manubrium

Ascoceras 9a

6

Billingsites

8

Pseudascoceras

5

Schuchertoceras anticostiense

7

Lindstroemoceras

4

Schuchertoceras iowaense

2

Hebetoceras

3

Choanoceras

1

Montyoceras

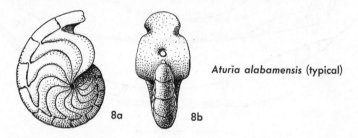

Aturia alabamensis (typical)

8a   8b

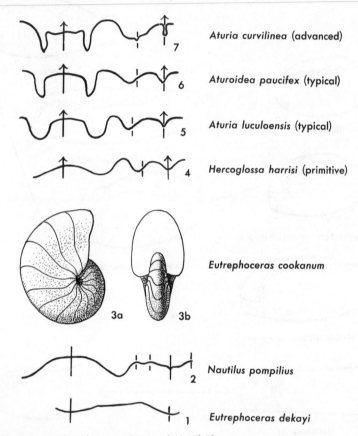

Aturia curvilinea (advanced)   7

Aturoidea paucifex (typical)   6

Aturia luculoensis (typical)   5

Hercoglossa harrisi (primitive)   4

Eutrephoceras cookanum

3a   3b

Nautilus pompilius   2

Eutrephoceras dekayi   1

Figure 11.9. Final Evolutionary Stages of Nautiloids.
Eutrephoceras and *Nautilus* represent the simplest and most advanced true nautiloids. Sutures 4-7 represent the morphologic sequence of changes leading to the most advanced aturoids.
(Mostly after Miller, 1947.)

probably arose from a form such as *Eutrephoceras* with almost straight sutures (Fig. 11.9). One strain culminated in the living pearly nautilus, of which *Nautilus pompilius* is an example.

The other nautilids branched out into several Genera in which the sutural patterns of the long-extinct goniatites were duplicataed. Their ascendancy seems to be geared to the extinction of the ammonoids at the close of the Cretaceous. Even by Paleocene and Eocene time the coiled nautilids increased somewhat in abundance and diversity. It was then that *Aturia* and its relatives began to exhibit a sharply angular lobe in their sutures (Fig. 11.9). Increasing complexity of sutural trace in the aturoid strain is exemplified in Figure 11.9 by *Hercoglossa, Aturia,* and *Aturoidea* which are arranged in a morphologic series. They are not known to comprise an evolutionary series as depicted, however. The aturoids became extinct during the Pliocene when they had attained sutures only as complex as those which the simplest ammonoids (goniatites) developed. All together, 8 Genera and about 75 species of Tertiary nautilids are known.

Only *Nautilus* survived into the Pleistocene and Recent, and it now represents the last survivor of the whole Subclass Nautiloidea.

BUOYANCY AND FORM OF NAUTILOID CONCHS. It is generally believed that cephalopods arose from some gastropodlike molluscan ancestor, within or near the gastropods, although no intermediatae stages are known, either living or extinct. All of the early cephalopods are straight or are slightly curved (in the endogastric fashion). Compartmentation of the conchs at first involved construction of closely arranged septa—there being as many as eight times as many septa in a given distance in early forms as in later forms. It also was possible that the early chambers were occupied to some extent by soft tissue. Moreover, some early forms such as *Endoceras* had unusually large siphuncles which must have been filled with tissue at least near the living chamber. All in all the primitive cephalopods seem to have been heavily constructed and to have been suited mostly for existence as bottom-dwellers which carried their conchs horizontally.

When gas began to lighten the weight of conchs, a marvelous succession of evolutionary changes and ecologic adaptations was instigated. In the first place, the tips of the new buoyant conchs tended to rise so that straight conchs were carried higher or conchs became curved exogastrically. Thus, the living chamber could remain horizontal although the center of buoyancy tended to rise above it. Continued curvature eventually produced tightly coiled conchs. Presumably there was always a strong trend to acquire or to maintain a nice adjustment between the buoyancy of the animal and its weight, as is known to be true of *Nautilus* today. Moreover, the habits of the animal surely reflected the buoyancy of the conch—the more buoyant the conch, the more probable that the animal was a good swimmer.

Another group, which probably consisted of active swimmers, retained long tapering conchs with more distantly spaced septa and thereby became involved in serious engineering problems because their center of buoyancy was located far adapically of their center of gravity. Although the normal attitude of an orthocone is presumed to have been horizontal, the center of buoyancy would be about in the center of the phragmocone and the center of gravity would be in or near the living chamber; therefore at rest the animal would be suspended vertically with the aperture down. This is patently a poor position for jet propulsion or feeding. Many orthoceraconic nautiloids reduced their buoyancy and moved the apex of the conch back to horizontal by adding a lining of secondary calcareous material within the camerae and within the siphuncle. Secondary deposits served to shift the center of buoyancy adaperturally and the center of gravity adapically until they lay very close together. Addition of a little extra material as ballast on the ventral side in many instances helped to stabilize the conch with its ventral side down. Stabilization would be maintained during later growth stages by addition of secondary deposits progressively farther forward and thickening of deposits near the apex until camerae were nearly filled.

Not all nautiloid conchs became lighter, nor did the animals become potentially more effective swimmers when the buoyancy of the conchs was increased. Some short, but rapidly expanding, pear-shaped conchs had only a few camerae but large living chambers. It is a peculiar feature of many breviconic nautiloids that their apertures were constricted into various slit-like or cruciform patterns. Probably the brevicones with narrow apertures were not carnivorous, or if they were, they fed on small prey. They probably were good swimmers. Other nautiloids which normally occupied long tapered conchs took a precipitously direct approach to becoming breviconic and cast off some of the apical portion of the conch by decollation very much in the same fashion that a few gastropods are known to do. Of all the breviconic nautiloids, however, *Ascoceras* and its allies are the most bizarre. Members of the ascocerid group arose from orthoceraconic or cyrtoceraconic ancestors and consisted of slender, tapering, apical portions which led to straight or swollen living chambers. Apparently at maturity they truncated the slender apical portion of the conch just behind the living chamber. Inasmuch as the apical portion contains no cameral deposits, it probably was buoyant enough to keep the creature suspended vertically in the water. After molting, however, the ascocerid cephalopods seem to have maintained a horizontal position, owing to the presence of special buoyant camerae along the dorsal interior of the living chamber.

SUBCLASS 2. AMMONOIDEA

No soft tissues have been discovered for any ammonoid, but the animals are assumed to have had essentially the same anatomy as the nautiloids because the shapes of conchs in the two groups are similar. Whereas the development of nautiloids is traced largely in changes in the shape of the conch and position of the siphuncle, the evolution of ammonoids is traced largely through study of the sutures. Most ammonoid conchs are more or less involute from their earliest appearance and therefore do not change much in shape. On the other hand, sutural development is so marvelously diverse that ammonoids provide ideal material for study of the change in morphology with the passage of time. No doubt there has been more attention devoted to ammonoids and more significance attached to them for evolutionary studies than to any other group of animals. Because of the wealth of information, ammonoids are looked upon as ideal material for correlation of strata. As a result of concentrated study, about 10,000 species of ammonoids have been described. They range in age from Early Devonian to Late Cretaceous.

SHAPE OF CONCHS. Ammonoids are almost entirely planispiral and involute (Fig. 11.10)—a form which is termed nautiliconic among nautiloids and which has been termed ammoniticonic among ammonoids. Various other special descriptive terms are available for normal, depressed, and compressed conchs of planispiral ammonoids, depending also upon the degree of their involution (that is, upon the width of the umbilicus). In general the shape of planispiral conchs tends to change from evolute to involute and from globose to discoidal (that is, from depressed to compressed). There are, however, many reversals of these trends.

The most readily recognized conchs are those which depart from the orthoceraconic and the planispiral forms. A few Paleozoic and a few more Mesozoic conchs became enrolled in helicoid spirals like gastropods, but the most interesting of all are the bizarre conchs which uncoiled somewhat. This tendency for uncoiling appeared only rarely among nautiloids during the Paleozoic, but it appeared several times among ammonites during the Mesozoic and finally characterized one whole Suborder of ammonites during the Cretaceous. In fact, uncoiling is the predominant trait of ammonites just before their extinction.

APERTURE. Apertures of most ammonoids differ notably from apertures of nautiloids. In nautiloids the margin of the aperture is a smooth curve except where it may be indented by the hyponomic sinus. Among ammonoids, on the other hand, the venter is apt to be produced into a pointed

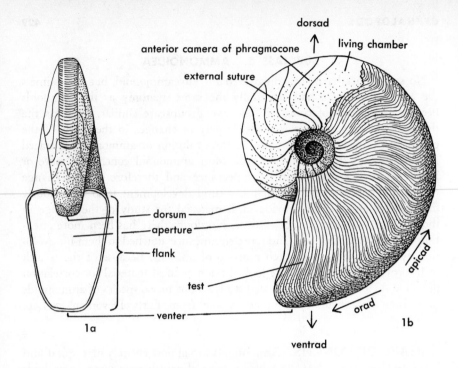

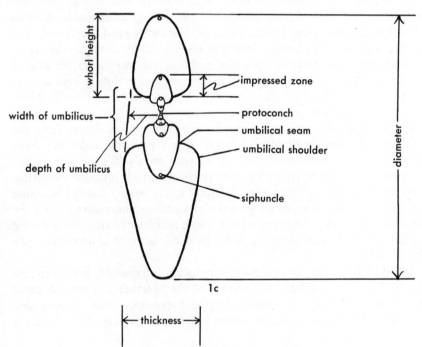

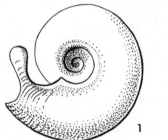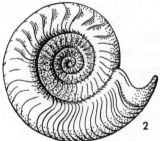

Figure 11.11. Morphology of Ammonoids.
1. *Harpoceras aalense,* showing very prominent lappet on the flanks of the aperture, 1/2X, Jurassic, England. 2. *Harpoceras levinsoni,* with a prominent rostrum on the venter, 1/5X, Jurassic, England.
(After Wright, 1878.)

rostrum instead of being indented as a sinus (Fig. 11.11.2). Moreover, each of the two sides of the aperture also may be produced into a fingerlike extension called a **lappet** (Fig. 11.11.1). Rostra and lappets normally are developed in mature stages only.

Many ammonoids secreted opercula called **aptychi** (sing. **aptychus**), whereas opercula are unknown among nautiloids. Ammonoid opercula consist either of one calcerous or chitinous plate or of a pair of calcareous plates (Fig. 11.12). Single-plated **anaptychi** range from Devonian to Cretaceous, but bivalved **aptychi** are all Mesozoic. Aptychi are particularly common in Jurassic and Lower Cretaceous strata. Aptychi and anaptychi have been controversial objects because they formerly were assigned variously to the arthropods, pelecypods, echinoderms, worms, birds (beaks), fish, and gastropods. As in the case of opercula of gastropods, aptychi may be abundant in strata in which conchs are not present. Aptychi and conchs may have been selectively sorted by oceanic currents; or aptychi could have been dropped on the sea floor from drifting conchs of dead animals; or possibly aptychi, being calcitic or chitinous, may not be dissolved by ground water, whereas fossil conchs, being aragonitic and generally lacking a periostracum, are more readily dissolved than are the aptychi.

Aptychi have been reported commonly from Europe and less commonly from the New World. Specialists recognize 15 "form" Genera of aptychi and anaptychi.

SIPHUNCLE. Siphuncles of ammonoids are simpler than those of

Figure 11.10 (*opposite*). Terminology for Ammonoid Conchs.
Conchs are oriented ventral side down in this figure, although they are customarily oriented ventral side up.
1a, 1b, apertural and side views. 1c, vertical section.
(After Miller, 1938 and Plummer and Scott, 1937.)

nautiloids. Septal necks of early ammonoids are retrochoanitic (adapically directed) as in the case of nautiloids, but septal necks of later ammonoids are **prochoanitic;** that is, they are directed adeperturally. The wall of the siphuncle consists of a chitinous sheath which became progressively indurated with calcium phosphate during growth to form the connecting rings.

Position of the siphuncle in ammonoids is ventral in all but one small group of Devonian ammonoids including *Clymenia* and its allies. In the clymeniids the siphuncle is dorsal. The dominantly ventral position of the siphuncle could represent a relic of the primitive condition in ancestral

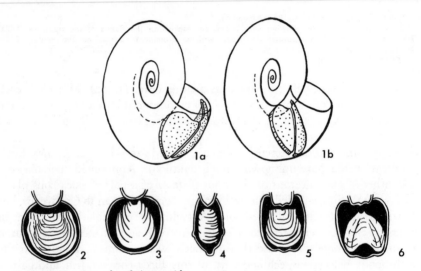

Figure 11.12. Opercula of Ammonoids.
1a. Oblique view of *Aspidoceras* with the aptychus in the open position. 1b, the same conch with the aptychus in the closed position. Conchs are in living posture. 2-6. Apertures bearing anaptychi. Notice how an anaptychus fails to close the aperture completely.
(1 after Trauth, 1927. 2-6 after Schmidt, 1929.)

nautiloids. Siphuncles of ammonoids are of the same relative size as those of most of the advanced nautiloids; that is, they are slender.

ORNAMENTATION. Smooth ammonoids are common but they are not characteristic of the Subclass. Most conchs bear some sort of transverse ornamentation and some bear longitudinal ornamentation. Growth lines are always present although they may be faint. On the other hand, growth lines may be prominent and even raised into ridges and lamellae. Ribs occur singly or in groups and increase by division or by intercalation. In some cases the ribs bear nodes, in which cases the nodes are largest near the venter. In a few cases the nodes may be produced into spines. Over the whole course of ammonoid evolution, there has been a general tendency for change in ornamentation from growth lines to fine ribs, coarse ribs, and finally to nodes and spines. Unfortunately, several reversals of this trend are known, and reversals presumably could have started at any place along the course. Haas (1942), for instance, mentions some reversals in which the trend in character of ornamentation is from coarse to fine. It follows, therefore, that changes in transverse ornamentation must be studied in relationship to other features before their evolutionary significance can be evaluated.

Longitudinal (spiral) ornamentation is less common than transverse ornamentation in ammonoids. Flattening of the venter is a phenomenon encountered in various ammonoids and is almost equally related to change in whorl profile as to ornamentation. But whether flattened or not, various ammonoids tend to develop one or more **keels** on the venter or perhaps to develop one or more ventral grooves. Other spiral ornamentation usually takes the form of striae on the flanks of the whorls. Coarse spiral ornamentation rarely is developed.

Although not strictly part of the ornamentation, transverse shallow **constrictions** indent the internal molds of various ammonoids. From one to three constrictions are present in each volution. Constrictions represent the location of transverse ribs on the internal surfaces of the shell.

According to some views, development of ornamentation is a manifestation of adaptation to environment. Heavy ornamentation near the aperture, for instance, could serve to keep the center of gravity below the center of buoyancy in expanding conchs. According to other views, progressive development of ornamentation reflects a method of disposing of excess calcium carbonate when optimum growth of the conch was being attained. Extreme supporters of the latter theory have even maintained that heavy ornamentation indicates approaching racial senility and extinction.

SUTURES. Sutural pattern is not only the basis of differentiating ammonoids from nautiloids, but it is the principal means of differentiating the various subgroups of ammonoids. Whereas (except in aturoids) nautiloid sutures are either straight (traces of right conical sections, geometrically speaking) or are very broadly scalloped, ammonoid sutures are pleated into a series of folds which are alternately convex and concave adaperturally (Fig. 11.13). Those parts of a suture whose convex curvature is toward the aperture are **saddles,** whereas the concave members are **lobes.** Lobes and saddles occur alternately along the flanks of the whorls until they disappear under the **umbilical seam** where two whorls come in contact. The exposed portion of a suture is the **external suture** and the hidden portion is the **internal suture.**

It is customary to represent a suture by an expanded tracing in a plane rather than by showing it in different perspective views around a whorl. These schematic tracings or **sutural diagrams** are oriented with the saddles upward. The position of the imaginary midventral line is indicated by an

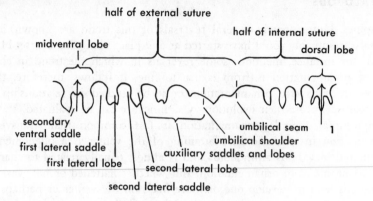

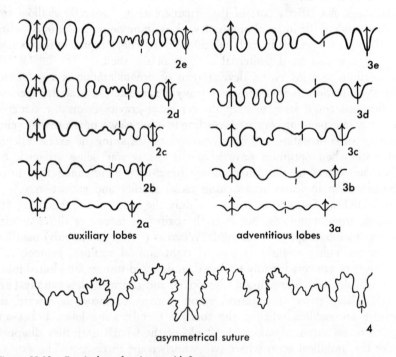

Figure 11.13. Terminology for Ammonoid Sutures.
1. One half of the complete suture of *Shumardites uddeni*, Pennsylvanian, Texas. When an umbilical shoulder is not present in an ammonoid, only one dashed line is used to partition a suture. 2a-2e. Ontogenetic changes in sutures of *Adrianites dunbari* from the Permian of Mexico, showing how auxiliary lobes arise near the umbilical seam. 3a-3e. Ontogenetic changes in sutures of *Agathiceras uralicum* from the Pennsylvanian of Russia, showing how adventitious lobes arise by subdivision of the first lateral lobe near the venter. 4. Asymmetrical mature suture of a Jurassic ammonite from England.

(1-3 after Miller and Furnish, 1940a and 1957. 4 after Swinnerton and Trueman, 1917.)

arrow pointing adaperturally (also being upward on the page). The position of the umbilical seam is shown by a short vertical line or by a row of vertical dashes. If the internal suture can be traced to the middorsal position, that imaginary line also is indicated by an anteriorly directed arrow. Internal sutures are available only from much weathered or from specially prepared specimens. The great majority of ammonoid sutures are symmetrical on both sides of the midventral line; hence, it is customary to depict only one half of the external suture plus the remaining flank of the **midventral lobe.** Thus, the midventral arrow used in orientation bisects the midventral lobe. If asymmetrical sutures are present, then it may be desirable to depict the whole external suture (Fig. 11.13.4).

In view of the great importance attached to even slight variations in ammonoid sutures, various systems of nomenclature have been proposed which enable a paleontologist to designate a certain lobe or saddle accurately (Fig. 11.13.1). Thus, the midventral lobe lies along the venter and may be modified by the development within it of a **ventral saddle.** Moreover, ventral saddles may be simple, bifid, or otherwise modified, and their height, width, and shapes are significant. The **first lateral saddle** lies adjacent to the midventral lobe and the two share a common flank just as limbs of anticlines and synclines are shared in a series of folds. The **first lateral lobe** lies on the umbilical side of the first lateral saddle and is progressively flanked by the **second lateral saddle** and the **second lateral lobe** (or **umbilical lobe,** as it is called by some workers because it straddles the umbilical seam). If the internal suture can be examined, then a **dorsal lobe** will be found in the median position there. Although the basic ammonoid sutural pattern consists of six lobes with intervening saddles, a few very primitive ammonoids have only three or four lobes.

Ammonoid sutures are affected by a very strong tendency for increase in the number of lobes and saddles. Thus, the normal trend is for new lobes and saddles to arise at the sides of the umbilical lobe and to migrate laterally. These are the **auxiliaries** (Fig. 11.13.2). Eventually they may increase to a size equal to that of the primary lobes and saddles. On the other hand, new **(adventitious)** saddles and lobes also can arise by subdivision of primary saddles and lobes near the venter and grow to be equal to the original saddles and lobes in size and shape (Fig. 11.13.3). It follows, therefore, that a paleontologist must know manner of origin of the lobes and saddles in order to differentiate among primary, auxiliary, and adventitious kinds.

Increase in the number of lobes and saddles progresses more or less in coordination with minor complication of the trace of each saddle or lobe. Early forms of ammonoid sutures are smooth curves, whether on lobes or on saddles, but the first modification affects the lobes so that they become V-shaped whereas the saddles remain rounded. Ammonoids of this sort have a

goniatitic suture (Fig. 11.14.1). Further modification of the goniatitic suture produces a series of tiny serrations along the arcs of the lobes to form a **ceratitic** suture (Fig. 11.14.2). Finally, the saddles also become serrate and an **ammonitic** suture is evolved (Fig. 11.14.3). It is noteworthy that serrations

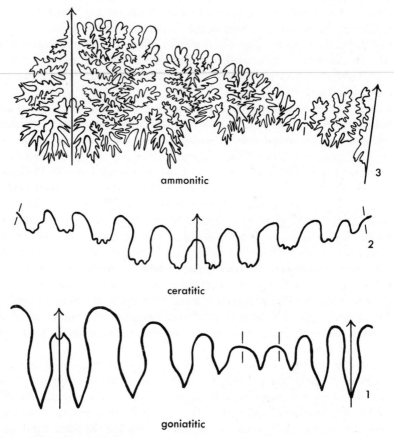

ammonitic

ceratitic

goniatitic

Figure 11.14. Ammonoid Sutures.
1. Goniatitic suture of *Metalegoceras* sp., Permian. One half of the complete external and internal suture is shown. 2. Ceratitic suture of *Owenites* sp., Triassic. Both halves of the external suture are shown. 3. Ammonitic suture of *Parapachydiscus* sp., Cretaceous. The right half of the complete external and internal suture is shown.
(1 after Miller and Furnish, 1940a. 2 after Smith, 1932. 3 after Stephenson, 1941.)

first appear near the venter on old lobes and saddles and progressively affect inflections farther laterally, whereas new lobes arise laterally at the umbilical seam as though in anticipation of the advancing serrations.

Concentration of attention on sutural diagrams has led to the development of ingenious methods for drawing them. Freehand sketching is inexact, and drafting on a grid with use of calipers is tedious and rather inexact; hence, mechanical systems for tracing are much in vogue. Some systems involve various sorts of pantographs in which a stylus held in the hand is used to trace the suture on an oriented conch while a pen automatically records the suture on a flat surface. Or, a camera lucida enables direct tracing of sutures projected on a paper. The simplest system, however, is to wrap a piece of transparent plastic around a conch and to trace the suture directly on the plastic, after which the tracing can be projected to any desired size with an enlarger or an optical projector.

It is not known why ammonoid septa become so intricately folded, although several advantages accrue from this development. In the first place, ammonoid conchs are much more strongly constructed than are the conchs of any other molluscs. Whether enrolled or not, the invaginated construction of septa on the mortise and tenon principle gives great structural strength to the conchs. Second, the pleated septa require more calcium carbonate than do simple transverse septa of nautiloids. It is likely that cephalopods share a problem in common with many groups of animals, namely, how to dispose of excess calcium carbonate constructively. Nautiloids add excess calcium carbonate to the conchs as cameral deposits and as siphuncular deposits, but neither of these deposits is known among ammonoids. Possibly the increasingly pleated septa laid down during growth serve the same physiologic purpose as the secondary deposits did among nautiloids. Third, the unusually large amount of substance used in making pleated septa may help to maintain the center of gravity below the center of buoyancy. Fourth and finally, pleating of septa may help to increase the over-all density of the conch in proportion to the increase in displacement when a new and larger gas-filled camera is sealed off.

CLASSIFICATION. The three fundamental sutural patterns among ammonoids have served for a long time to characterize three major taxonomic categories—the goniatites, ceratites, and ammonites. At first these groups were recognized as Genera (*Goniatites, Ceratites,* and *Ammonites*), but only the first two names still are retained in a generic sense. In addition, however, the Genera have been used as the roots for names which characterize ever higher and higher taxonomic categories. Systematists now tend to recognize the three taxa as about the magnitude of Orders or Subclasses. Detailed studies also have shown the existence of transitional forms among the taxa so that they are not as distinct as once they were thought to be. The result is that clear-cut distinctions are not possible in classifications of Ammonoidea. Relatively simple classifications such as the one used herein do not account for various intermediate (but fortunately, rather rare) forms. On the other hand, carefully differentiated taxa in use by specialists require a degree of proficiency in ammonoid lore which is rarely attained by geologists. Accordingly, the following classification is designed to lead the student into the relationships of ammonoids and to prepare him, if necessary, for the more exacting subdivisions thought to be based upon phylogenetic grounds (Arkell, Furnish, Kummel, Miller, Schindewolf, and Wright, in *Treatise on Invertebrate Paleontology,* pt. L, 1957, Lawrence, Univ. Kansas Press, pp. L7-L10).

Subclass 2. Ammonoidea
  Order a. Goniatitida
    Suborder (1). Anarcestina
    Suborder (2). Goniatitina
  Order b. Clymeniida
  Order c. Ceratitida
    Suborder (1). Prolecanitina
    Suborder (2). Ceratitina
  Order d. Ammonitida
    Suborder (1). Phylloceratina
    Suborder (2). Lytoceratina
    Suborder (3). Ammonitina

KEY TO ORDERS AND SUBORDERS OF AMMONOIDEA

I. Siphuncle dorsal .... Order Clymeniida
II. Siphuncle ventral
  A. Sutures not crenulate .... Order Goniatitida
    1. Sutures sinuous .... Suborder Anarcestina
    2. Sutures angular .... Suborder Goniatitina
  B. Sutures crenulate
    1. Saddles smooth .... Order Ceratitida
      a. Some lobes smooth .... Suborder Prolecanitina
      b. No lobes smooth .... Suborder Ceratitina
    2. Saddles crenulate or foliate .... Order Ammonitida
      a. Sutures foliate .... Suborder Phylloceratina
      b. Sutures not foliate
        (1) Conch evolute or uncoiled ..... Suborder Lytoceratina
        (2) Conchs involute .... Suborder Ammonitina

Order a.   Goniatitida

The Goniatitida encompass all ammonoids with simple nonserrate sutures, in addition to which some of the most specialized Genera are characterized by the presence of serrations on some lobes near the venter. Two intergrading groups are recognized within the Order, depending upon whether the sutures are entirely sinuous or have angular lobes. The Order ranges from Lower Devonian to Permian and includes the dominant Paleozoic ammonoids. As loosely construed, the term "goniatite" can be applied to these ammonoids.

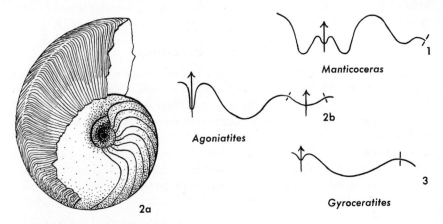

Figure 11.15. Goniatitida (Anarcestina).
1. Suture of Manticoceras simulator, New York. 2a, 2b. Side view (1/5X) and suture of *Agoniatites vanuxemi*, New York. 3. Suture of *Gyroceratites gracilis*, Germany.
All species are Devonian.
(After Miller, 1938.)

SUBORDER (1).   ANARCESTINA

Anarcestine goniatites are characterized by broadly sinuous sutures in which neither the saddles nor the lobes are serrate (Fig. 11.15). Conchs of some of the simplest forms such as *Gyroceratites* (Devonian) have perforate umbilici and lack any impressed zone. More advanced Devonian forms such as *Agoniatites* and *Manticoceras* become involute and the sutural pattern

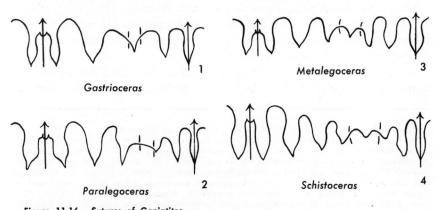

Figure 11.16. Sutures of Goniatites.
1. Gastrioceran suture of *Gastrioceras branneri*, 1 1/3X, Lower Pennsylvanian, midcontinent. 2. Paralegoceran suture of *Paralegoceras texanum*, 1 1/3X, Lower Pennsylvanian, Texas. 3. Early schistoceran suture of *Metalegoceras evolutum*, 1X, Permian, Timor. 4. Typical schistoceran suture of *Schistoceras missouriense*, 4 1/2X, Upper Pennsylvanian, southwestern states and midcontinent.
(1, 2 after Miller and Furnish, 1940c. 3, 4 after Plummer and Scott, 1937.)

even merges with that of the true goniatitic type. Anarcestine goniatites appeared in the Early Devonian and became extinct by the end of the Devonian.

SUBORDER (2). GONIATITINA

These, the typical goniatites, are characterized by their angular lobes, but the most advanced forms develop serrations of lobes near the venter analogous to serrations of all lobes among the ceratites. There is a rather persistent trend among some goniatites toward an increase in the number of lobes. Thus, the earliest true goniatites (*Tornoceras,* Devonian) have 6 lobes; most goniatites (*Gastrioceras,* Pennsylvanian) have 8 lobes, and some add auxiliaries until 12 lobes (*Metalegoceras,* Permian), or 14 lobes (*Schistoceras,* Pennsylvanian), or 16 lobes are present. In this way gastrioceran (8 lobes), paralegoceran (10 lobes), or schistoceran sutures (12 to 16 lobes) are recognized (Fig. 11.16).

Subtle changes in the shape of sutures of the Goniatitina also are important. For instance, V-shaped lobes of early goniatites are supplanted by bottle-shaped lobes in later goniatites. Finally, surficial ornamentation becomes important in identification of some Goniatitina. Students of Carboniferous goniatites in Europe have discovered systematic changes in relationships between transverse and spiral fine ribbing. Similar changes in ornamentation have been recognized in America and elsewhere. Thus, even external fragments of conchs devoid of suture lines can be identified when placed in the hands of experts.

Other characteristic typical Goniatitina are *Imitoceras* and *Eumorphoceras* (Mississippian), *Goniatites* and *Cravenoceras* (Mississippian and Pennsylvanian), and *Agathiceras* (Pennsylvanian and Permian) (Fig. 11.17). Goniatitina appeared in the Late Devonian and became extinct before the end of the Permian. During that interval they became the dominant and most characteristic Late Paleozoic cephalopods.

Toward the end of their reign in the Permian the sutural development of some goniatites progressed far beyond the normal goniatitic stage and be-

---

Figure 11.17 (*opposite*).   Goniatitida (Goniatitina or Typical Goniatites).

1a, 1b, 1c. Side and aboral views (2/3X) and suture of *Cravenoceras hesperium,* Mississippian, western United States.   2a, 2b, 2c. Apertural and side views (2/3X) and suture of *Goniatites choctawensis,* Mississippian, widespread in United States.   3a, 3b, 3c. Side and apertural views (2/3X) and suture of *Tornoceras uniangulare,* Devonian, New York.   4a, 4b, 4c. Aboral and side views (2/3X) and suture of *Eumorphoceras bisulcatum,* Mississippian, widespread in United States.   5. Suture of *Munsteroceras parallelum,* Mississippian, Indiana.   6a, 6b. Side view (2/3X) and suture of *Agathiceras frechi,* Pennsylvanian, Texas.   7a, 7b, 7c. Side and apertural views (2/3X) and suture of *Imitoceras rotatorium,* Mississippian, Indiana.   8a, 8b. Side view (2/3X) and suture of *Pseudoparalegoceras williamsi,* Pennsylvanian, Arkansas.

(1 after Youngquist, 1949. 2a, 2b, 4 after Miller and Youngquist, 1948. 2c after Miller, Downs, and Youngquist, 1949. 3 after Miller, 1938. 5 after Miller and Collinson, 1951. 6a after Miller and Furnish, 1940a. 6b after Plummer and Scott, 1937. 7a, 7b after Smith, 1903. 7c after Foord and Crick, 1897. 8 after Miller and Downs, 1948.)

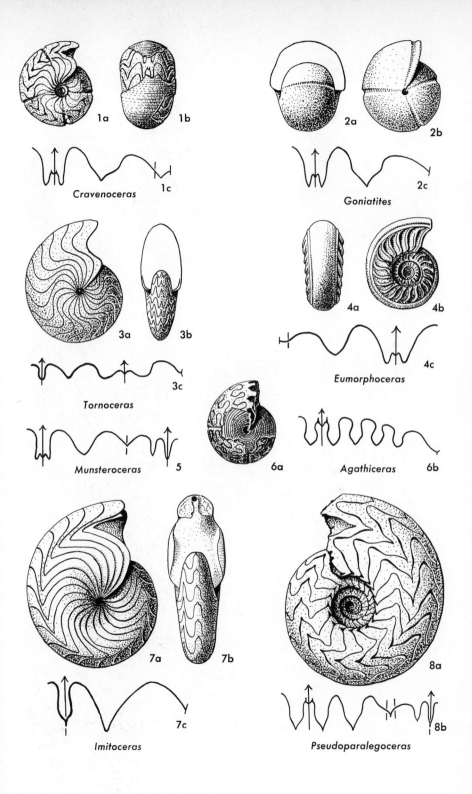

1a   1b

Cravenoceras   1c

2a   2b

Goniatites   2c

3a   3b

Tornoceras   3c

4a   4b

Eumorphoceras   4c

Munsteroceras   5   6a   *Agathiceras*   6b

7a   7b

Imitoceras   7c

8a

Pseudoparalegoceras   8b

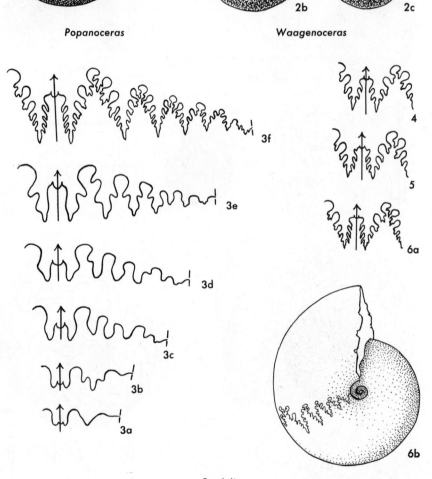

1a

2a

Popanoceras

Waagenoceras

2b

2c

3f

4

3e

5

3d

6a

3c

3b

3a

Perrinites

6b

came ceratitic or even ammonitic. Thus, *Popanoceras* resembles true ceratites, whereas *Waagenoceras* and *Perrinites* can be differentiated from some true ammonites only by recognizing goniatitic early sutural development in their conchs. In Figure 11.18, for instance, young stages 3a-3c of *Perrinites hilli* are clearly goniatitic; the first indications of crenulations appear at stage 3d, and crenulations are perfected in mature stages 3e and 3f. Perhaps because of the need for paying close attention to sutural detail, specialists have become able to recognize not only species but also subspecies of *Perrinites* on the basis of minor changes in crenulations in the midventral lobe and the first lateral saddle (Fig. 11.18.4–6a).

None of the foregoing goniatites gave rise to any true ceratites or ammonites—the resemblance of goniatites to later forms is due merely to remarkable instances of convergence. There is no particular word to denote the

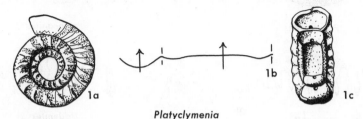

Platyclymenia

Figure 11.19.   Goniatitida (Clymeniina).
1a, 1b, 1c. Side view, suture, and broken conch of *Platyclymenia americana*, 1X, Devonian, Montana.
(After Miller, 1938.)

close relatives of true goniatites which developed ammonitic sutures, but perhaps "pseudoammonites" would be a helpful addition to our vocabulary. This addition would be particularly suitable in view of the recurrence of other pseudoammonites among ceratites and the well-known rise of pseudoceratites among true ammonites (which latter phenomenon is described in the section on Ammonitina hereafter).

Order b.   Clymeniida

Clymeniid ammonoids differ from all other ammonoids because the siphuncle is located on the dorsal side in adult camerae (Fig. 11.19). In

---

Figure 11.18 (*opposite*).   Goniatitida (Specialized Goniatitina).
1a, 1b. Suture and side view (1X) of *Popanoceras bowmani* showing some coarsely ceratitic lobes, Permian, Texas.   2a, 2b, 2c. Suture and side and apertural views (1X) of *Waagenoceras guadalupensis* showing almost completely ammonitic suture, Permian, Texas.   3a-3f. Ontogenetic stages in the growth of *Perrinites hilli multistriatus*, Permian, Texas. 3a corresponds to the mature suture of *Goniatites*; 3b, to *Neoshumardites*; 3c, to *Shumardites*; 3d, to *Peritrochia*; and 3e, to *Properrinites*—all of which occur in ascending stratigraphic order.   4-6a illustrate how ventral lobes of sutures characterize subspecies.   4 is *Perrinites hilli tardus*.   5 is *Perrinites hilli gouldi*.   6a is *Perrinites hilli hilli*.   6b, side view of *Perrinites hilli hilli*, 1/2X, Permian, Texas.
(After Miller and Furnish, 1940a.)

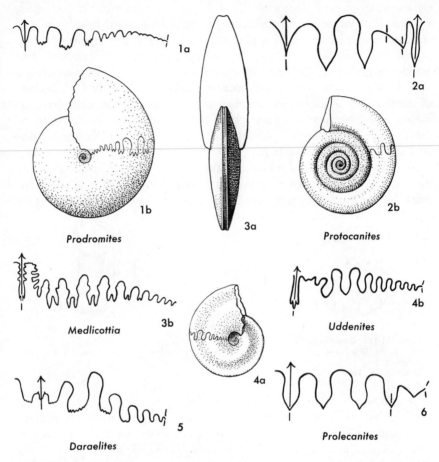

Figure 11.20. Prolecanitina.
1a, 1b. Suture and side view (2/3X) of *Prodromites gorbyi,* Mississippian, Indiana. 2a, 2b. Suture and side view (1/2X) of *Protocanites lyoni,* Mississippian, east-central United States. 3a, 3b. Apertural view (1X) and suture of *Medlicottia burckhardti,* Permian, Texas. 4a, 4b. Side view (2/3X) and suture of *Uddenites schucherti,* Pennsylvanian, Texas. 5. Suture of *Daraelites meeki,* Permian, Sicily. 6. External suture of *Prolecanites discoides,* 1 1/3X, Carboniferous, England.
(1, 2a after Miller and Collinson, 1951. 2b after Smith, 1903. 3 after Miller and Furnish, 1940a. 4 after Smith, 1932. 5 after Miller and Furnish, 1940b. 6 after Foord and Crick, 1897.)

juvenile camerae, however, the siphuncle is ventral, so clymeniids seem to have been derived from typical ammonoids rather than from a separate branch of nautiloids. Sutures of clymeniids resemble those of the Anarcestina. *Clymenia* is the typical example of the Clymeniida. The entire group is confined to the Upper Devonian. Although a few forms have been found in New York and Montana, the Order is most common in Europe.

Order c. Ceratitida

Those ammonoids whose sutures all characteristically bear serrate lobes comprise the ceratites. The Order intergrades with some of the advanced Goniatitina from which it arose and with the Ammonitida to which it gave rise. Thus, some primitive prolecanitine ceratites lack serrate lobes but are assigned to the Ceratitida because they gave rise to cephalopods with entirely serrate lobes. The Order appeared in the Late Devonian and became extinct before the end of the Triassic. Two Suborders are recognized on the basis of sutural expression, shape of conchs, and degree of external ribbing.

SUBORDER (1). PROLECANITINA

Prolecanitine ceratites are mostly rather notably compressed into discoidal conchs. Unlike other rather advanced ammonoids, the septal necks in this Suborder are retrochoanitic. Characteristically there are numerous auxiliary lobes and saddles, as many as 24 or possibly more being visible on the external suture in some Genera. Perhaps the principal interest in the Suborder, however, arises from the tendency of Genera like *Daraelites* to develop serrations in lobes near the venter, thus passing from goniatitic to ceratitic sutures (Fig. 11.21). Indeed, specialists conclude that the Ceratitina evolved from an offshoot of the daraelitids in mid-Permian time. Typical prolecanitine ceratites are *Prolecanites* and *Prodromites* (Mississippian), *Uddenites* (Pennsylvanian), and *Daraelites* (Permian, Fig. 11.20). The Suborder arose in the Late Devonian and became extinct in the Permian, except for one Family which was represented in the Triassic.

The relationship between the supposed evolutionary history of a group of cephalopods and the known growth stages of an advanced individual in the group is ideally illustrated by *Daraelites* and some of its relatives.

Figure 11.21.1–7a is arranged in a morphologic series in the order of increasing complexity of sutural pattern. Moreover, the species also appear in successive stratigraphic order, except that species 2 and 3 lived almost at the same time. The several species lived at different places remote from each other and evolved over a period of about 25 million years. *Prolecanites* (Upper Mississippian, Fig. 11.21.1) has a typical goniatitic suture whose angular lobes became rounded in passing into *Epicanites* (Upper Mississippian, Fig. 11.21.2). Crenulations in the first lateral lobe appear in *Praedaraelites* (Upper Mississippian, Fig. 11.21.3). The foregoing three Genera all have three saddles, but *Boseites scotti* has three auxiliary lobes (Fig. 11.21.4). *Boseites texanus* (Upper Pennsylvanian) has another auxiliary lobe and faint new crenulations appear in the second lateral lobe and the midventral lobe (Fig. 11.21.5). *D. leonardensis* (Lower Permian, Fig. 11.21.6) and *D. meeki*

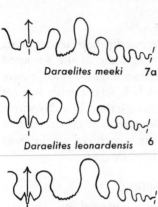

Daraelites meeki   7a

Daraelites leonardensis   6

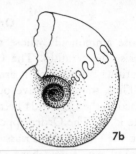

7b

Boseites texanus   5

Boseites scotti   4

"Predaraelites" culmiensis   3

Epicanites sandbergi   2

Prolecanites discoides   1

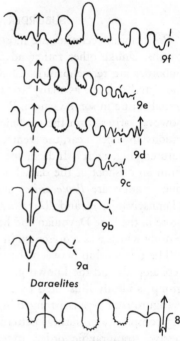

9f

9e

9d

9c

9b

9a

Daraelites

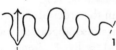

8

Xenaspis carbonaria

Figure 11.21. Prolecanitina. Evolution of *Daraelites*.

1-7a. Mature sutures of seven prolecanitid species arranged in a morphologic series. They occupy progressively younger stratigraphic positions, except that 2 and 3 are of about the same age. 7b. Side view of *Daraelites meeki*, the genotype of *Daraelites*, 1 1/3X, Permian, Sicily. 8. Suture of *Xenaspis carbonaria*, a very early true ceratite, Permian, India. It is introduced on this plate for comparison with the daraelitids; it has fewer lobes than *Boseites* and *Daraelites*, but all of the external lobes are crenulate. 9a-9f. Ontogenetic change in sutures during growth of *Daraelites elegans*, Permian, Russia. Stages 9a to 9f can be matched with species in 1 to 7a.

(1-3 after Miller and Furnish, 1940b. 4-8 after Miller and Furnish, 1940a. 9 after Tchernow, 1907.)

(Middle Permian, Fig. 11.21.7a) have crenulations out into the third lateral lobe; the strength of previous crenulations is increased but no new auxiliary lobes appear.

Successive growth stages of an advanced species of *Daraelites* are illustrated by sutures in Figure 11.21.9a–9f. Stages 9a to 9c correspond with species 1 and 2 in the foregoing morphologic series. Ontogenetic stages 9d and 9e correspond with species 5 and ontogenetic stage 9f corresponds with species 7a, only not so many auxiliary lobes are present in 9d–9f as in species 5–7a. Nevertheless, it is apparent that the ontogeny of *Daraelites elegans* (9a–9f) depicts with reasonable faithfulness the morphologic and stratigraphic series leading from *Prolecanites* to *Daraelites* (1–7a). In view of the concordance of all three series, paleontologists interpret species 1–7a as representing the essential course of actual evolution of the daraelitids. In like manner, ontogenies of other ammonoid sutures have been shown to recapitulate stages through which a particular group evolved.

SUBORDER (2). CERATITINA

This Suborder is characterized by the presence of ceratitic sutures in all lobes. Unlike the sparse Goniatitina in the Paleozoic which tended toward having ceratitic sutures but retained smooth conchs, the true ceratites bear various kinds of external ornamentation. Most commonly some form of coarse, transverse ribbing is present.

Xenodiscus (Permian and Triassic) is the oldest true ceratite and seems to have arisen from some relative of the prolecanitid, *Daraelites* (Fig. 11.22.3). In the Triassic the true ceratites were involved in a spectacular expansion in their diversity and numerical abundance, there being about 492 Genera of Ceratitina recognized. Other well-known Triassic Genera from America are *Inyoites, Owenites, Meekoceras, Nevadites, Clionites,* and *Tropigastrites* (Fig. 11.22). No ceratite survived into the Jurassic, but the Ceratitina produced an offshoot in Early Triassic time from which the Ammonitida arose.

One of the most extraordinary developments known in paleontology is the continued progression of serrations onto saddles of Ceratitina. Saddles of *Juvavites* and *Gymnotoceras* (Fig. 11.23.1, 2) bear weak serrations, but a few Genera such as *Ussaria, Trachyceras, Gymnites,* and *Arcestes* (Fig. 11.23.4–7) developed typical ammonitic sutures. These latter Genera are appropriately called pseudoammonites, just as Genera were designated among the Goniatitina because they bore similar sutural patterns. Expert training is required in order to differentiate evolutionary dead ends among the Ceratitina from convergent stages within the Ammonitida.

Not long before false ammonitic sutures evolved among some of the ceratites, other groups typified by *Cordillerites* (Fig. 11.23.3) and *Choristo-*

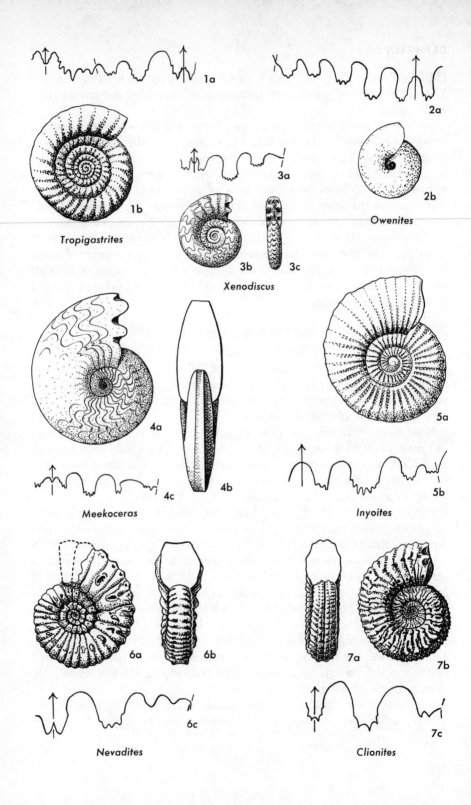

1a

2a

3a

2b

Owenites

1b

Tropigastrites

3b 3c

Xenodiscus

4a

4b

5a

4c

Meekoceras

5b

Inyoites

6a 6b

Nevadites

6c

7a 7b

7c

Clionites

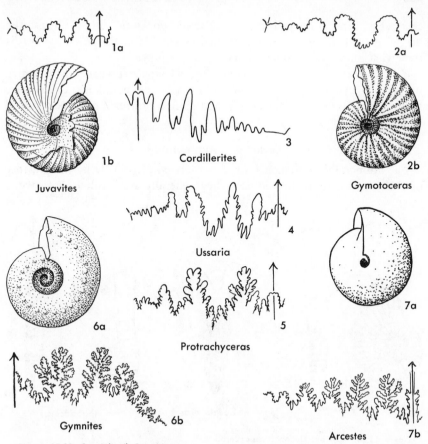

Figure 11.23. Specialized Ceratitina.
1a, 1b. Suture and side view (2/3X) of *Juvavites strongi*, Upper Triassic, California.
2a, 2b. Suture and side view (2/3X) of *Gymnotoceras [Ceratites] beckeri*, Middle Triassic,
Nevada. 3. Suture of *Cordillerites angulatus*, 1X, Lower Triassic, Idaho. 4. Suture of *Ussaria
occidentalis*, 1X, Lower Triassic, Idaho. 5. Suture of *Protrachyceras lecontei*, 1X, Upper Triassic,
California. 6a, 6b. Side view (1/3X) and suture of *Gymnites alexandrae*, Middle Triassic,
Nevada. 7a, 7b. Side view (2/3X) and suture of *Arcestes gabbi*, Middle Triassic, Nevada.
Although the suture of *Cordillerites* resembles that of Paleozoic goniatites, and the others
resemble sutures of Jurassic and Cretaceous ammonites, all of these forms are believed to be
closely related to the typical ceratites and to be unrelated to goniatites or true ammonites.
(1, 5 after Smith, 1927. 2, 6, 7 after Smith, 1914. 3, 4 after Smith, 1932.)

Figure 11.22 (*opposite*). Typical Ceratitina.
1a, 1b. Suture and side view (2/3X) of *Tropigastrites trojanus*, Middle Triassic, Nevada.
2a, 2b. Suture and side view (2/3X) of *Owenites koeneni*, Lower Triassic, California. 3a, 3b, 3c.
Suture and side and apertural views (2/3X) of *Xenodiscus waageni*, Lower Triassic, Idaho and
California. 4a, 4b, 4c. Side and apertural views (2/3X) of *Meekoceras gracilitatis*, Lower
Triassic, Idaho and California. 5a, 5b. Side view (2/3X) and suture of *Inyoites oweni*, Lower
Triassic, California. 6a, 6b, 6c. Side and apertural views (2/3X) and suture of *Nevadites
whitneyi*, Middle Triassic, Nevada. 7a, 7b, 7c. Apertural and side views (2/3X) and suture of
Clionites americanus, Upper Triassic, California.
(1, 6 after Smith, 1914. 2-5 after Smith, 1932. 7 after Smith, 1927.)

ceras (Fig. 11.24.1) seemed to produce rather goniatitic sutures because the height of the lobes and saddles increased notably. Moreover, *Choristoceras* is somewhat more evolute than are most other ceratites.

Rhabdoceras (Fig. 11.24.3–5) is an unusual Upper Triassic Genus which uncoiled in maturity just as *Lituites* did among the nautiloids. *Cochloceras* (Fig. 11.24.2) is peculiar because it coiled up like a turreted gastropod instead of being planispiral.

Order d.   Ammonitida

The ammonitid ammonoids are characterized principally by the presence of ammonitic sutures. In addition, they generally are involute, but several

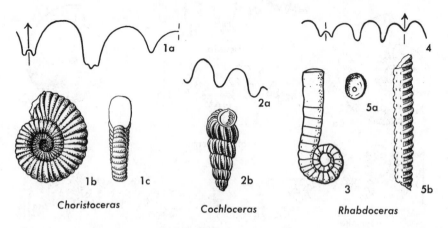

Figure 11.24. Aberrant Upper Triassic Ceratites.
1a, 1b, 1c. Suture and side and apertural views (2/3X) of *Choristoceras kellyi*, Nevada. There is no impressed zone. 2a, 2b. Suture and side view (2/3X) of *Cochloceras fischeri*, Europe.   3. Coiled apical portion of *Rhabdoceras* sp., 10X.   4. Suture of *Rhabdoceras suessi*, Europe. 5a, 5b. Cross section and side view of the straight portion of *Rhabdoceras russelli*, 1X, California.
(1, 5 after Smith, 1927. 2, 4 after von Hauer, 1860. 3 after Spath, 1933.)

strains became secondarily uncoiled. Detailed studies starting in about 1865 have revealed and supported the differentiation of at least two great genetic series of ammonites, the phylloceratines and the lytoceratines. More recently (since work by Salfeld, 1913) opinion among authorities on ammonites has been growing that ammonites should be divided into three groups. According to these ideas the phylloceratines gave off the lytoceratines in the Early Jurassic. Both of these groups persisted as conservative ammonites but produced offshoots of vigorously evolving ammonites at several times. The foregoing developmental scheme is the classic example of **iterative evolution** (iterate means to repeat). All three of the foregoing strains of ammonites currently are grouped into the taxonomic category of Ammonitida as most rigidly defined.

The Ammonitida range from Early Triassic to the end of the Cretaceous. During that time they were the most diverse elements in the known marine faunas, there being perhaps 8000 species of Mesozoic ammonites which are referred to about 900 Genera.

SUBORDER (1).   PHYLLOCERATINA

Phylloceratine ammonites are characterized principally by phylloid (leaf-like) sutures in which minor indentations of sutures may lead to single, bifid,

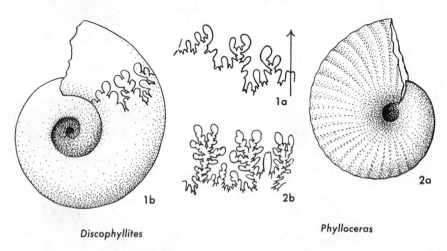

Discophyllites

Phylloceras

Figure 11.25. Ammonoida (Phylloceratina).
1a, 1b. Side view (2/3X) and suture of *Discophyllites patens*, Triassic, California. 2a, 2b. Side view (2/3X) and partial suture of *Phylloceras grossicostatum*, Jurassic, Alaska.
(1 after Smith, 1927. 2 after Imlay, 1953.)

trifid, or more complex subdivisions. Among the most readily recognized sutural patterns of the ammonites are those in which outer terminations are convexly rounded. A complete saddle, for instance, vaguely resembles a compound leaf of a fern in which the leaflets are analogous to the rounded minor terminations of the saddle (Fig. 11.25.1a, 2b). Conchs are apt to be small and smooth, or only feebly ornamented.

Of the 34 recognized Genera of Phylloceratina, *Phylloceras* is a well-known and nearly world-wide Jurassic and Cretaceous representative. The Phylloceratina range from Early Triassic to Late Cretaceous, during which time they were particularly abundant in the equatorial regions. Compared to other Ammonitida, however, the phylloceratines are not particularly abundant, except locally.

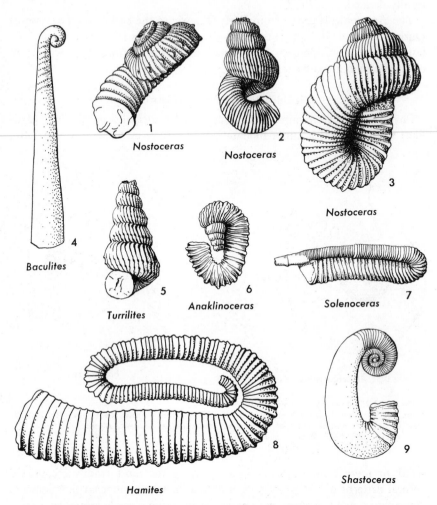

Figure 11.26. Ammonoida (Typical Cretaceous Lytoceratina).
1. *Nostoceras crassum*, 2/3X, Texas. 2. *Nostoceras colubriformis*, 1X, Texas. 3. *Nostoceras stantoni*, 2/3X, Texas. 4. *Baculites ovatus* showing the small apical end with the tiny coiled portion, 7X, Wyoming. 5. *Turrilites splendidus*, 1X, Texas. 6. *Anaklinoceras reflexum*, 2/3X, Texas. 7. *Solenoceras reesidei*, 1 1/3X, Texas. 8. *Hamites phaleratus*, 2/3X, Germany. 9. *Shastoceras behemoth*, 1/30X, California.

All specimens are Cretaceous. Conchs are oriented in their theoretical living position.

(1-3, 5-7 after Stephenson, 1941. 4 after Reeside, 1927. 8 after Griepenkerl, 1889. 9 after Anderson, 1938.)

SUBORDER (2). LYTOCERATINA

Lytoceratine ammonites are characterized by a combination of two or three features. In the first place, the conchs tend to be evolute or even to have their

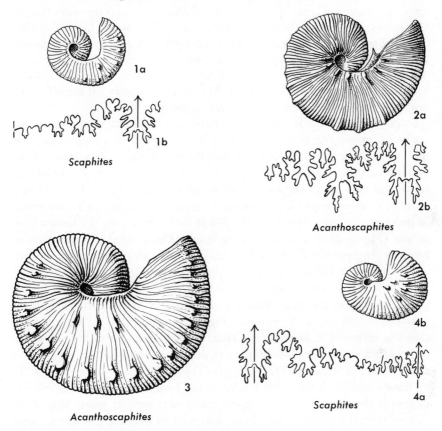

Figure 11.27. Lytoceratina (Cretaceous Scaphitids).
1a, 1b. Side view (2/3X) and suture of *Scaphites leei* var. *parvus*, New Mexico. 2a, 2b. Side view (2/3X) and suture of *Acanthoscaphites roemeri*, western interior. 3. Side view of *Acanthoscaphites nodosus* var. *brevis*, 2/3X, western interior. 4a, 4b. Side view (2/3X) and suture of *Scaphites hippocrepis*, western interior.
(1, 4 after Reeside, 1927b. 2, 3 after Meek, 1876.)

whorls slightly separated (Fig. 11.26). Minor sutural elements are rather sharply terminated, instead of being rounded as among the Phylloceratina. Finally, the Lytoceratina are most renowned for the remarkable uncoiling to which most (but not all) strains were subject. Unfortunately, the few primitive representatives of the Lytoceratina resemble some of the Ammonitina so closely that special attention must be devoted to sutural development in order to differentiate the two groups. The Suborder ranged from Early Jurassic to Late Cretaceous.

Uncoiling alone is enough to warrant recognition of spectacularly aberrant Genera such as *Bochianites* (Upper Jurassic and Lower Cretaceous), *Shastoceras* and *Hamites* (Lower Cretaceous), and *Baculites* and *Nipponites* (Upper Cretaceous, Fig. 11.26). Another aberrancy is typified by the helicoid coiling of *Turrilites* (Lower Cretaceous) and its partly uncoiled analogue, *Nostoceras* (Upper Cretaceous). Various strange lytoceratine ammonites occur commonly in Cretaceous strata on the Gulf Coast and in sediments of the Rocky Mountain geosyncline from the United States into Canada. Of these Genera, *Scaphites* and *Baculites* are the most well known.

Scaphitid cephalopods are only partially uncoiled and their sutures are normally ammonitic (Fig. 11.27). Conchs bear weak to strong costae and one or more rows of nodes on the flanks. Because of their abundance and the rapidity of their evolution, the scaphitids have become very useful in correlation of Cretaceous deposits in the western interior. Five species out of a series of 13 are arranged in Figure 11.28 in ascending stratigraphic succession in order to illustrate how variation differs with time. Size, for instance, increases (Fig. 11.28.1a–4a) and then decreases (Fig. 11.28.5a). Ornamentation becomes progressively finer. Shapes change from more evolute to less evolute, which is the reverse of what one might expect; earlier evolution, however, presumably progressed from an involute ancestor through a series of more evolute conchs to the stage shown in Figure 11.28.1a. In their over-all appearance, the suture of *S. warreni* (Fig. 11.28.2b) is in some ways simpler than the suture of *S. larvaeformis* (Fig. 11.28.1b), but thereafter sutures become increasingly complex (Fig. 11.28.3b, 4b) before reverting again to a distinctly simple pattern (Fig. 11.28.5b). The evolutionary progression of the 13 known species in the series is represented herein by only the 5 species illustrated; the series possibly occupied about nine million years. Minute details of sutural expression also have been used to evaluate changes in some of the group of scaphitid cephalopods discussed heretofore. In Figure 11.28 the first lateral lobes of six species of scaphitids are shown. The basic bifid pattern (Fig. 11.28.6a or 2c) is modified into a trifid pattern (Fig. 11.28.6f or 5c) because a large prong on the right side of the lobe increases in size disproportionately and migrates down to occupy the central position.

In some ways *Baculites* epitomizes the evolution of aberrant Cretaceous cephalopods, for it has uncoiled secondarily until only a minute involute conch remains at the apex of a long straight shaft (Fig. 11.26.4). Evolution of species of *Baculites* is traced primarily through changes in the size of conchs and through complexity of sutures. In species of *Baculites* from the western interior (Fig. 11.29) the size increases regularly and culminates in *B. grandis,*

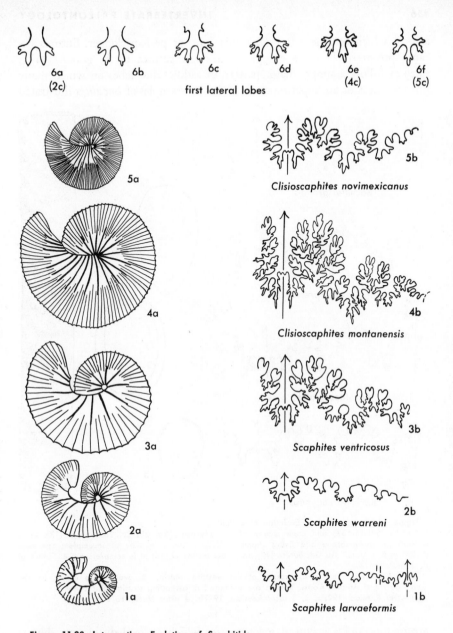

6a
(2c)

6b

6c

6d

6e
(4c)

6f
(5c)

first lateral lobes

5a

5b

Clisioscaphites novimexicanus

4a

4b

Clisioscaphites montanensis

3a

3b

Scaphites ventricosus

2a

2b

Scaphites warreni

1a

1b

Scaphites larvaeformis

Figure 11.28. Lytoceratina. Evolution of Scaphitids.
1-5. Side views (2/3X) and mature sutures of several Cretaceous scaphitids are shown in ascending stratigraphic order. 6a-6f. Details of crenulations in the first lateral lobe of six species. Some species in series 1-5 are duplicated.
(After Cobban, 1951.)

a form which became 4 feet (120 cm) long or perhaps longer. Sutures became progressively more complex, although sutures of *B. grandis* (Fig. 11.29.4) follow a simple major pattern of saddles and lobes on which many fine crenulations are superimposed. The four examples of *Baculites* illustrated

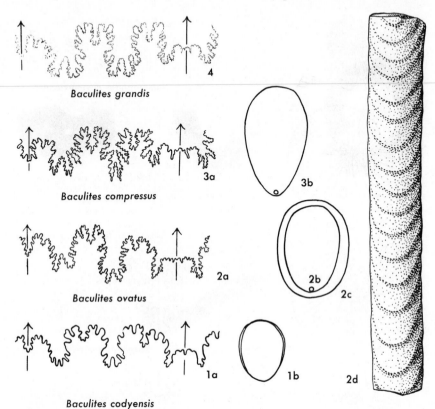

Baculites grandis

Baculites compressus

Baculites ovatus

Baculites codyensis

Figure 11.29. Lytoceratina. Evolution of *Baculites*.
1a, 1b. Suture (3X) and cross section of *B. codyensis*. 2a, 2b, 2c, 2d. Suture (1X), cross sections of phragmocone and living chamber (2/3X), and side view of incomplete specimen (2/3X) of *B. ovatus*. 3a, 3b. Suture (1X) and cross section (2/3X) of *B. compressus*. 4. Suture of *B. grandis* (1/2X).
All species occur in the Cretaceous of the western interior. *B. ovatus* also occurs on the Gulf Coast and Atlantic Coast. Species are arranged in ascending stratigraphic order.
(1 after Reeside, 1927a. 2, 3 after Reeside, 1927b. 4 after Meek, 1876.)

are members of a group of seven species which evolved during possibly 20 million years.

UNCOILING OF CEPHALOPODS. For many years the uncoiling of cephalopods was interpreted as some sort of a degenerate phenomenon associated with racial old age just before the extinction of the affected lineages. This concept was enhanced by the fact that lytoceratine ammonites, which typify uncoiling, reached the peak of their development during the Cretaceous Period. The fact is, however, that lytoceratines are not the only ammonites which uncoiled, because some ceratites also uncoiled. Moreover, uncoiling took place at several times—not just before the extinction of the ammonites. In

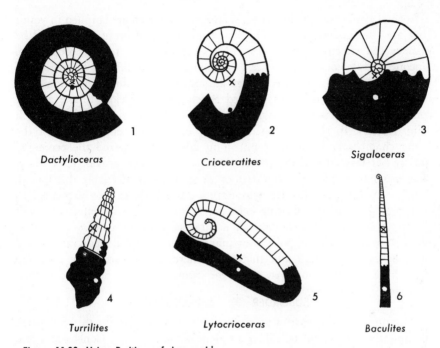

1. *Dactylioceras* 2. *Crioceratites* 3. *Sigaloceras*

4. *Turrilites* 5. *Lytocrioceras* 6. *Baculites*

Figure 11.30. Living Positions of Ammonoids.
1, 3. Involute Jurassic ammonoids (Ammonitina). As the living chambers became shorter, the center of gravity was located farther from the axis of coiling. 2, 4-6. Evolute Cretaceous ammonoids (Lytoceratina). Further lowering of the center of gravity accompanied the process of uncoiling.
X-center of buoyancy. ●-center of gravity. Living chambers are solid black. No scale is implied, but all figures are reduced and are schematic.
(After Trueman, 1941.)

addition, some nautiloids uncoiled far back in the Paleozoic. Finally, cephalopods were evolving vigorously and were exceedingly abundant just before their extinction. In view of all of these things, paleontologists began to look for explanations of uncoiling other than racial senility and evolutionary debility.

Uncoiled cephalopod conchs rather consistently have large living chambers, whereas most coiled conchs have relatively small living chambers. The diameter of the living chamber remains about the same at maturity, and only the length increases significantly. Inasmuch as great bodily changes probably did not suddenly in adulthood affect the structure of the animal which inhabited the living chamber, it seems probable that the extra volume in the living chamber merely represents increased volume of the mantle cavity which could provide more effective jet propulsion and might be correlated with a change in habits.

Normal evolute or involute conchs, and conchs which are enrolled in youth (but are subsequently uncoiled), are streamlined and presumably could be maneuvered effectively with a small reserve of water for jet propulsion. Uncoiled adult conchs, however, are unwieldy and difficult to negotiate; therefore they might require a large amount of water for locomotion. The center of buoyancy in normal coiled conchs is rather close to the axis of coiling, and the center of gravity lies well within the outline of the conch (Fig. 11.30.1). In aberrant conchs, on the other hand, enlargement of the living chamber and attendant uncoiling effectively lowered the center of gravity but insured that the coiled phragmocone which provided the buoyancy usually tended to be compact or at least not ineffectively distributed. Thus, even the most bizarre lytoceratine ammonites can be explained as merely adaptations to a floating existence in which increased effectiveness of jet propulsion was of advantage in natural selection (Fig. 11.30.2–6). It is likely, however, that the posture of many uncoiled cephalopods was altered radically between youth and maturity. There is not necessarily anything degenerate or senile, however, about the assumption of a floating existence.

SUBORDER (3). AMMONITINA

Ammonites in the narrowest sense of the word comprise this Suborder. Technically, they could be called ammonitine ammonites. Conchs are generally rather involute and also tend to be ornamented with transverse ribs and longitudinal keels and to bear nodes and spines. Sutures mostly are very complex, but may resemble those of the Lytoceratina so closely as to require expert knowledge for their discrimination. To this Suborder can be referred the vast majority of conchs to which the name "ammonite" customarily is applied. Thousands of species have been described.

Cardioceras (Fig. 11.31.2), *Harpoceras,* and *Kossmatia* are common

---

Figure 11.31 (*opposite*). Ammonitida (Ammonitina or Typical Ammonites).

1a, 1b. Side and ventral views of a young specimen of *Prionotropis woolgari*, 2/X, Cretaceous, western interior. 2a, 2b. Side view (2/3X) and suture of *Cardioceras cordiforme*, Jurassic, western interior. 3. Side view of a fragment of *Douvilleiceras mammillatum*, 2/3X, Cretaceous, Texas. 4. Side view of *Dufreynoya justinae*, 2/3X, Cretaceous, Texas. 5a, 5b, 5c. Side and apertural views (2/3X) and suture of *Mortoniceras shoshonense*, Cretaceous, Wyoming. 6a, 6b. Side view (2/3X) and suture of *Haresiceras placentiforme*, Cretaceous, Wyoming.

(1 after Meek, 1876. 2a after Whitfield and Hovey, 1906. 2b after Reeside, 1919. 3, 4 after Scott, 1939. 5 after Reeside, 1927a. 6 after Reeside, 1927b.)

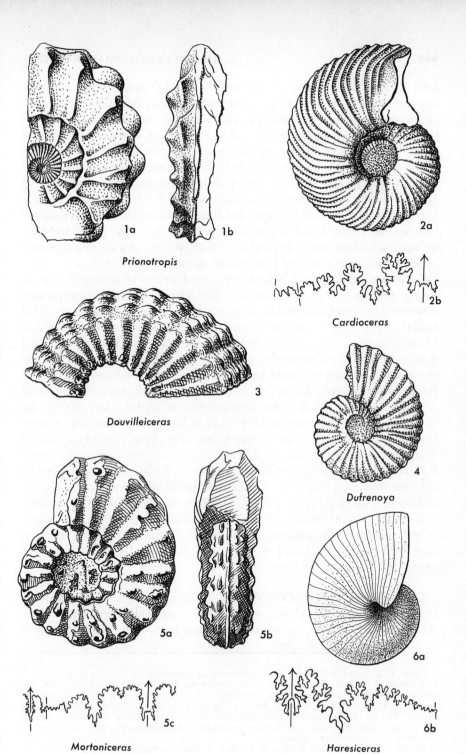

1a **1b**

Prionotropis

2a

2b

Cardioceras

3

Douvilleiceras

4

Dufrenoya

5a **5b**

5c

Mortoniceras

6a

6b

Haresiceras

Jurassic Genera. *Douvilleiceras, Mortoniceras,* and *Oxytropidoceras* are common Lower Cretaceous Genera on the Gulf Coast. In the Upper Cretaceous, *Acanthoceras* is a rather well-known Genus in the western interior of Canada and the United States as well as on the Gulf Coast. *Prionocyclus* is a well-known Upper Cretaceous Genus in the western interior. *Parapachydiscus* (Fig. 11.14.3) is widespread in Upper Cretaceous deposits and is particularly well known from specimens about 2 feet (60 cm) in diameter in Baja California and Southern California; except for a specimen 3 feet (90 cm) in diameter from the Cretaceous of the western interior, *Parapachydiscus* includes the largest coiled ammonoids in North America. All of the foregoing Genera have rather normal ammonitic sutures and are distinguished in large part on the basis of external ornamentation.

Contrasted with them, however, are several strains of ammonites whose sutures resemble those of ceratites at first glance. These are the **pseudoceratites.** They are derivatives of animals whose conchs bear normally frilled saddles; but the saddles of pseudoceratites become progressively simpler and smoother until no serrations are present. Lobes, too, may lose much sutural detail, although the character of serrations in the lobes is apt to reveal the ammonitine ancestry of some pseudoceratites; minor sutural indentations frequently are roundly lobate instead of being angularly serrate. Pseudoceratitic modifications affected the Ammonitina at several times during the Cretaceous; thus, *Engonoceras* (Fig. 11.32.3) bridges the boundary between the Lower and Upper Cretaceous but *Sphenodiscus* (Fig. 11.32.4) only occurs near the top of the Cretaceous. *Placenticeras* has a very compressed conch with an elaborate suture in which saddles on the flanks of conchs are simpler than are those near the venter or near the umbilicus (Fig. 11.32.1). Finally, *Indoceras* (Fig. 11.32.6), from the Middle East, not only develops pseudoceratitic sutures, but the number of saddles and lobes increases more than in any other cephalopod—there being about 75 in an adult suture. *Indoceras* seems to have been the last ammonite to evolve and was one of the last to become extinct at the end of the Cretaceous.

ORIGIN OF THE AMMONOIDS.   Paleontologists have proposed two incompatible theories to explain the origin of ammonoids from the nautiloids. According to one view, the ammonoids arose from an involute descendant

---

Figure 11.32 (opposite). Ammonitida (Pseudoceratitic Ammonitina).
  1. Suture of *Placenticeras placenta*, 1 1/3X, Cretaceous, New Jersey. 2a, 2b. Apertural and side views of *Placenticeras meeki*, 2/3X, Cretaceous, western interior. 3. Suture of *Engonoceras subjectum*, 1X, Cretaceous, Texas. 4. Suture of *Sphenodiscus beecheri*, 1/2X, Cretaceous, New Jersey. 5a, 5b, 5c. Suture and apertural and side views (1/3X) of *Metoicoceras whitei*, Cretaceous, Texas and Utah. 6. Suture of *Indoceras baluchistanensis*, the last Genus of ammonites, 1X, Cretaceous, India.
  (1, 3-5 after Hyatta, 1903. 2 after Meek, 1876. 6 after Noetling, 1895.)

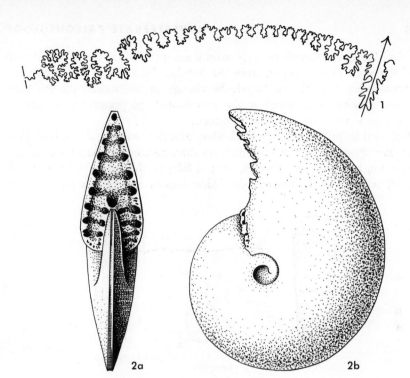

Placenticeras

2a 2b

1

3

Egonoceras

5a

4

Sphenodiscus

6

Indoceras

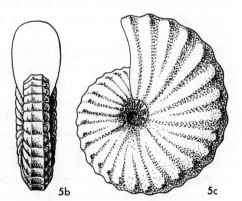

5b 5c

Metoicoceras

of some late gyroceraconic or early nautiliconic nautiloid in about the Silurian or Devonian. The transition from the Subclass Nautiloidea to the Subclass Ammonoidea was effected largely by change in the sutural pattern from straight to sinuous, although it also necessitated the presence of or change from a subcentral to a ventral siphuncle.

Opposed to this hypothesis is the view that the ammonoids evolved from *Bactrites* or one of its relatives which are characterized by a ventral siphuncle and a single, adapically directed, ventral lobe in the suture. The bactritids are all orthoceracones, whereas the oldest known ammonoids are all coiled

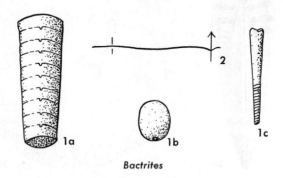

Bactrites

Figure 11.33. Bactritid Cephalopods.
1. *Bactrites arkonensis,* Devonian, Ontario. 1a, ventral side of an internal mold showing ventral lobe of sutures, 3X. 1b, cross section showing ventral siphuncle, 3X. 1c, nearly complete conch, 2/3X.   2. Suture of *Bactrites schlotheimii,* Devonian, Germany.
(After Miller, 1938.)

tightly enough to have impressed zones. Intermediate changes in shape are not known, but sutures can be arranged in a morphologic series leading from *Lobobactrites* (Lower Devonian) through *Bactrites* to *Mimoceras* and *Anarcestes.* The bactritids range from Ordovician to Late Permian, so the ammonoids might have arisen from a form more primitive than even *Lobobactrites.*

Bactritids are placed among the Nautiloidea by some specialists and among the Ammonoidea by other specialists, depending upon whether they think that the ventral siphuncle is a definitive character or is merely a recurrent aberration which affected straight-shelled nautiloids from time to time.

GEOLOGIC HISTORY OF THE AMMONOIDS. The ammonoids appeared in the Lower Devonian as both coiled and uncoiled forms. Sutural development progressed quickly through sinuous stages to the goniatitic stage, which latter was attained before the end of the Devonian. In the meantime, one aberrant group with a dorsal siphuncle (clymeniids) arose and became extinct. During the remainder of the Paleozoic the goniatites dominated cephalopod evolution. The principal sutural pattern of the Goniatitida was goniatitic, but ceratitic sutures arose more than once, and sutures of one group of goniatites even reached the ammonitic pattern.

While the true goniatites flourished, a less spectacular Paleozoic offshoot of the goniatites, the prolecanitines, evolved steadily into conchs with a ceratitic suture. The Ceratitina arose from this one stock during the Permian and went into such an explosive radiation during the Triassic that the Triassic is called the Age of Ceratites. In its most advanced and latest stage, the suture of ceratites attained the ammonitic pattern.

Aside from the Ceratitina, the only ammonoids which survived into the Mesozoic were a few descendants of the prolecanitines.

Toward the end of the Triassic the ceratites went into a disastrous decline and then became extinct just before the end of the Triassic Period. Their decline is analogous to, but more precipitous than, the extinction of goniatites at the end of the Permian, or the extinction of anarcestines and clymeniids at the end of the Devonian. Nevertheless, ammonoids survived after the Triassic because the Ammonitida arose from Early Triassic ceratites with a typical ceratitic suture and evolved into forms with completely ammonitic sutures. The first Ammonitida had rounded or leaflike sutures; these are the Phylloceratina, which are rather characteristic of the Jurassic. They never were very important, compared to other ammonoids, but they gave off two very important descendant groups in the Early Jurassic. Of these, the Lytoceratina were not impressive until almost the end of the Cretaceous when they erupted (for at least the second time) into an amazing array of uncoiled forms, the habits, cause, and purpose of which are enigmatic. From time to time the Lytoceratina and (more commonly) the Phylloceratina gave off lineages of ammonites with closely coiled conchs and elaborate sutures; these are the true ammonites or Ammonitina. The final modification of ammonites was the smoothing out of saddles to form pseudoceratites immediately preceding the extinction of the group.

Figure 11.34 shows that at least three groups of ammonoids had ceratitic sutures, and at least three had ammonitic sutures. In neither case was the genetic relationship among the three members of any group having a similar sutural pattern closer than the level of Suborder. In the older purely morphologic classifications, however, the ammonoids were divided into three groups having the same sutural pattern, irrespective of discontinuities in their ranges and lack of demonstrable kinship.

Not long before the end of the Cretaceous the ammonites declined and then vanished abruptly in what is possibly the most striking faunal change in geologic history. There seems to be no alteration in their construction which would indicate a precarious existence. Moreover, the forms which vanished so suddenly had been in existence for several millions of years.

Various hypotheses account for the disappearance of ammonoids by assuming that they became unadaptable, that emergence of lands affected them in some way, that the climate changed, that predators overtook them, that disease ravaged them, or that racial senility brought about their death. Some or all of these factors may have contributed to their decline, but it is hard to support any single suggestion with evidence, except in the case of finding conchs in the visceral regions of fossil marine reptiles. On the other

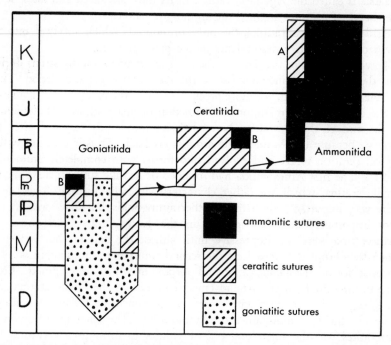

Figure 11.34. Ranges of Sutural Pattern of Ammonoids.
The three main kinds of ammonoid sutures are indicated by different shading in each of the three great Orders. Arrows indicate probable evolutionary descent. A indicates pseudoceratites. B indicates pseudoammonites.

hand, lytoceratine evolution seems to have been directed toward diminution in the size of the phragmocone relative to the size of the living chamber. Apparently many of the ammonoids were changing habits rapidly toward the end of the Cretaceous; hence an explanation of their disappearance should be sought in connection with changes in conchs and adaptations.

SUBCLASS 3.   COLEOIDEA

Except for three species of *Nautilus,* all the living cephalopods are referable to the Coleoidea. This Subclass includes about 200 species of squids, octopods, and sepiids, of which the squids are by far the most abundant. All members of the Subclass are characterized by the presence of two gills; hence, the group sometimes is referred to as the Dibranchia instead of as the Coleoidea. Generally, the Coleoidea also are typified by reduction or absence of a shell; but if a shell is present, it is almost invariably internal. Finally, coleoids are characterized by the number of arms and the nature of suckers and retractile hooks which may be present on the arms. Most coleoids have ten arms, of which eight **sessile arm**s are of the same size and two **tentacular arms** are much longer. Tentacular arms usually bear lanceolate paddles at the ends of circular shafts, the whole being wonderfully retractile. An octopus, as is well known from its name, only has eight arms. These arms seem to be homologous with sessile arms. Tentacular arms arise from a different position than do the sessile arms.

Coleoids were important rock-makers during the Mesozoic, whence about 400 species of belemnites have been described. The Subclass ranges from Upper Mississippian to Recent and may be at its peak of abundance now.

Fundamentally, coleoid shells consist of an internal, rigid, axial rod which serves the same function as the notochord or spinal column in vertebrates— that is, it enables muscles to act in couples against this axis and thereby to increase the power and effectiveness of muscular movements. The basic coleoid shell consisted of a **phragmocone** with a thick sheath (**guard**) around it and a hoodlike extension (**proostracum**) in front of it (Fig. 11.35.4). Reduction of some of the three skeletal elements or improvement of others enables recognition of four Orders of the Subclass Coleoidea.

    Subclass 3. Coleoidea
      Order a. Belemnitida
      Order b. Sepiida
      Order c. Teuthida
      Order d. Octopodida

Probable evolutionary patterns of Orders within the Subclass are shown in Figure 11.40.

KEY TO ORDERS OF COLEOIDEA

  I. Shell present
    A. Guard prominent .... Belemnitida
    B. Guard obscure
      1. Phragmocone prominent .... Sepiida
      2. Phragmocone obscure .... Teuthida
  II. Shell absent .... Octopodida

Order a.   Belemnitida

Belemnites are among the fossils noted earliest by man, and an ancient impression persisted for centuries that these objects were the hard points at the tips of thunderbolts. Their calcareous guard makes them unusually durable; hence, they are apt to be locally prolific as a residue from readily weathered sediments.

Phragmocones of belemnites resemble very much the conchs of orthoceraconic nautiloids. They are straight and camerate, but the siphuncle which traverses the septa of belemnitoid phragmocones is near the ventral margin instead of being subcentral (Fig. 11.35.1c). As in the case of living chambers of orthoceracones, a belemnitoid phragmocone terminates anteriorly in a space somewhat larger than the camerae. Each phragmocone is contained within a thin sheath, the **conotheca,** which is analogous to (and possibly homologous with) the external shells of nautiloids. When a proostracum is present, it is merely a dorsal outgrowth of the conotheca which extends anteriorly from the phragmocone.

A guard is a one- to many-layered cigar-shaped mass of calcareous material which invests the phragmocone with a thin veneer close to the aperture but which extends as a solid rod some distance posteriorly from the phragmocone and terminates in a point, the **apex.** The guard is composed of crystals of calcite which radiate from a subcentral axis lying posterior to the apex of the phragmocone. When guards are broken transversely the radiating crystalline structure is readily apparent (Fig. 11.35.3b). Cross sections of guards belonging to different groups can be characterized externally by subcircular or subquadrate shapes and by the presence or absence of one or more **furrows.** Furrows are deep grooves, one of which may lie on the ventral surface, or furrows may incise each of the two lateral surfaces. The proportionate length of the phragmocone to the guard is useful in identifying belemnites. For instance, Triassic belemnites have proportionately longer phragmocones than do Jurassic or Cretaceous belemnites.

Eobelemnites, the oldest belemnite, is an Upper Mississippian Genus from Oklahoma and Utah which has a short guard and a proostracum of unknown proportions (Fig. 11.40.1). The only other Paleozoic belemnoid was reported from the Permian of the island of Timor.

Among the Mesozoic Genera, *Aulacoceras* (Triassic and Jurassic) is characterized by the presence of two lateral furrows; *Atactrites* (Triassic and Jurassic) has no furrows (Fig. 11.35.2); *Pachyteuthis* (Jurassic) has no furrows but has a quadrate cross section (Figs. 11.35.3 and 11.40.2); and *Belemnitella* (Cretaceous) has long slender guards with a short ventral furrow (Fig. 11.35.1).

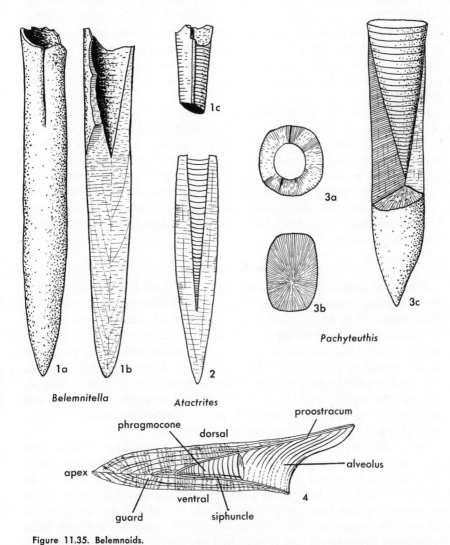

Belemnitella

Atactrites

Pachyteuthis

Figure 11.35. Belemnoids.

1. *Belemnitella americana*, 2/3X, Cretaceous, Atlantic Coast. 1a, ventral side with ventral fissure. 1b, broken longitudinal section. 1c, dorsal side of phragmocone. 2. Longitudinal section of *Atactrites clavatulus*, 1 1/3X, Triassic, Nevada. 3. *Pachyteuthis densus*, 2/3X, Jurassic, western interior. 3a, broken section across the alveolus. 3b, broken section across the shell behind the alveolus. 3c, partially broken longitudinal section revealing phragmocone. 4. Schematic longitudinal section of a belemnite conch in probable living positions, about 2/3X.

(1 after Whitfield, 1892. 2 after Smith, 1914. 3a after Meek, 1876. 3c after Whitfield and Hovey, 1906. 4 after Woodward, 1880.)

At the start of their Mesozoic flare in the Triassic, eight Genera of belemnoids are known. Belemnites become abundant in the Cretaceous of New Jersey and in the Jurassic (Sundance) of the western interior of Canada and of the United States. They are even more common in Europe than in North America. The only belemnite possibly to have survived into the Tertiary is *Vasseuria,* from the Eocene of France. Forty-five Genera of belemnoids are known.

It is likely that the belemnoids evolved from some mid-Paleozoic orthoceraconic ancestor when the phragmocone was reinforced with a guard and the conch was enveloped within the body to produce an internal skeleton. Presumably the guard would change the buoyancy of the conch and the animal would be oriented horizontally instead of tending to hang suspended in the water. Weighing down the outside of the phragmocone is a somewhat external solution to buoyancy control analogous to the internal solution used by nautiloids with their cameral and siphuncular deposits on the interior of their phragmocones.

Order b.   Sepiida

Sepiids are notable because of their ability to eject black to gray ink (sepia) into the water to obscure their presence and to irritate pursuers chemically. The presence of an ink sac is not peculiar to the sepiids, because some teuthids and octopods also have an ink sac. Sepiids bear a characteristic internal shell which is called the cuttlebone in common parlance and which should be reason enough to restrict the name cuttlefish to the sepiids. Unfortunately, the word cuttlefish often is applied loosely to any groups which have an ink sac—the sepiids, teuthids, and octopods. Sepiids mostly inhabit shallow water and seem to prefer a benthonic or near-benthonic existence. Twenty-nine Genera of fossil and living sepiids are known.

Specifically, sepiids are dorsoventrally flattened, squidlike animals with fins along the lateral margins of the body and with an obscurely chambered internal shell, the **sepium** (Fig. 11.36.2). Ten arms are present, of which eight are short and two are long. From a paleontologic standpoint, only the sepium is important; and fortunately it retains evidence of the derivation of the Order. The sepium consists primarily of the phragmocone, although some guard and proostracum are present in early forms. A sepium consists of aragonite, mineralogically. Two different evolutionary strains of sepiids are recognized—depending upon whether septa in the phragmocone tend to be normally transverse or are oblique to the long axis.

TRUE SEPIIDS.   In this, the common strain of sepiids, septa are oblique to the long axis of the phragmocone. Moreover, septa become increasingly

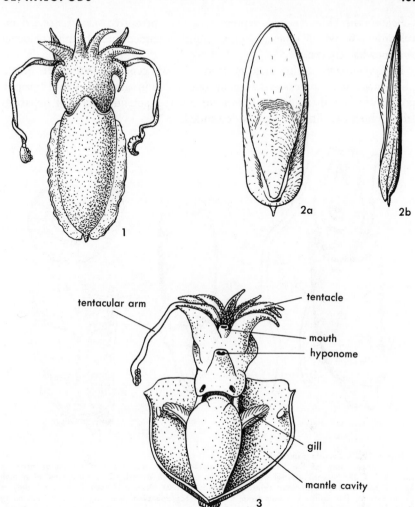

Figure 11.36. Sepiida.
1. Dorsal view of *Sepia orbignyana,* 1/2X, Recent. 2a, 2b. Ventral and lateral views of the sepium of *Sepia officinalis,* 1/2X, Recent. 3. Ventral view of *Sepia elegans,* 1X, Recent. The mantle has been laid open to reveal the two gills. Only one tentacular arm is shown.
(After Jatta, 1896.)

close in later forms until they are almost in contact and even start to become joined by interseptal skeletal tissue. No siphuncle is present.

Voltzia, the oldest of all Sepiida, comes from the Upper Jurassic of Cuba. It has a small phragmocone and a rather long proostracum, but no guard is known.

Belemnosis (Fig. 11.40.6) represents a very primitive stage in sepiid development in which septa are only slightly inclined and the phragmocone is somewhat curved.

In *Spirulirostra* (Fig. 11.40.7) from the Miocene the curvature of the phragmocone is increased to about one volution and the guard projects posteriorly in a sharp point. This seems to be a potential point of departure from which two lines of sepiids descended.

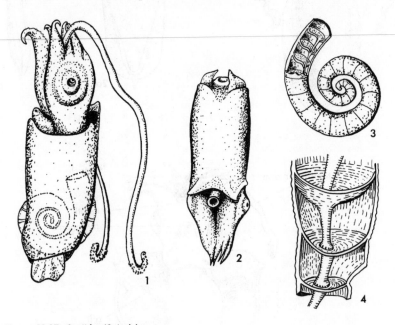

Figure 11.37. Sepiida (*Spirula*).
1. Schematic view of the left side of a female *Spirula australis* with tentacular arms extended, 1 1/3X, Recent. Internal portions of the conch are dotted.   2. Ventral view of a male *Spirula spirula* with tentacular arms contracted, 1 1/3X, Recent. Conch is exposed only at posterior end. This figure is drawn from a rare photograph of a swimming specimen ascending. 3. Conch of *Spirula* sp. with several chambers cut away to show the endogastric siphuncle, 2X, Recent.   4. Portions of four chambers showing details of the siphuncle, 5X, Recent.
   (1, 3, 4 after Huxley and Pelseneer, 1885. 2 after Bruun, 1943.)

Spirulirostrina (Fig. 11.40.8) became less curved and less pointed and the inclined septa of the phragmocone began to be accentuated.

This strain culminated in *Sepia* (Fig. 11.40.9) in which the siphuncle is lost and the skeleton consists mainly of septa and a pointed remnant of the guard. *Sepia* (Tertiary and Recent) is the type example of the Sepiida. Its shells are the familiar cuttlebones which are placed in bird cages.

SPIRULIDS. In the other strain of Sepiida, represented by *Spirula*, the phragmocone consists of a loosely coiled conch in which the siphuncle is persistent and also lies along the inner or concave side of curvature (Figs. 11.37.3, 4; 11.40.10).

It is probable that *Spirula* (Pliocene to Recent) arose from a Genus such as *Spirulirostra* by loss of the guard and all trace of the proostracum. The conch of *Spirula* consists of a loosely coiled spire with about two to three volutions. Walls of camerae may be slightly expanded between septa so that the external appearance of the conch is beadlike. From its orientation within the body of complete individuals, it is demonstrable that the conch of *Spirula* truly is endogastric—a feature which would be suggested as well by the position of the siphuncle on the concave margin of the conch. *Spirula* is of exceptional interest to biologists because it is the only living dibranchiate cephalopod which has coiled, camerate, aragonitic conchs with siphuncles. Its conch is almost entirely internal, there being only a small portion of the conch exposed at a gap in the mantle (Fig. 11.37.1). Thus, this Genus represents an imperfect stage in the process of enveloping the conch in the body; complete investing is apparent in *Sepia* and the squids.

In life *Spirula* tends to hang suspended from its buoyant posterior end and moves up and down by ejecting water fore and aft through its tubular movable funnel (Fig. 11.37.2). It can move laterally in short dashes, however. Although the bare conchs commonly have drifted all over the world, even into polar seas, complete fleshy specimens are among the rarest of animals. Only about 200 complete specimens are known and these were collected mostly by one Danish vessel, the "Dana," in the 1920-1930 decade. The three known species seem to live only in tropical and subtropical waters and to prefer a depth of about 200 meters (about 600 ft) near continental margins.

Order c. Teuthida

This Order comprises some of the most dramatic creatures in creation, including the classic examples of the coleoids, the squids. As with the Sepiida, the Teuthida bear ten arms, two of which are long tentacular arms. Internally, however, the axial skeleton of a living squid differs notably from that of a living sepiid because the squid bears only a **pen,** which is the proostracum without guard or phragmacone (Fig. 11.38.1b). Pens consist of flexible conchiolin and rarely are preserved. The 94 Genera of living and fossil teuthids make this Order about as large as all other coleoids combined. Teuthids range from Jurassic to Recent.

Most of our understanding of the locomotion of cephalopods has been obtained from observations upon squids. Their normal method of jet propulsion is backward through the water at very considerable speed—rivaling that of the fishes upon which they prey. They also can leap forward or make sharp turns, all by directing their funnel in the proper opposed direction. Squids are the favorite food of many fish; hence, there is much interplay of hunter and hunted between fish and squids. When a squid is desperately trying to evade its hunter, it may leap more than 12 feet (4 m) above the surface of the water. Moreover, members of the "Kon-tiki" voyage reported seeing squids travel through the air a distance of 150 to 180 feet (50 to 60 m). It also has been reported that squids, while airborne, make a popping noise as they manipulate their empty mantle cavities.

Of greatest interest of all cephalopods, however, is the giant squid, *Architeuthis,* from the North Atlantic (Fig. 11.38.6a, 6b). It is the most ponderous known invertebrate, living or extinct. Several huge specimens of this awesome creature have been studied, particularly near the Newfoundland Banks off the northeast coast of North America. So far, the largest specimen yet measured had a body 20 feet long with tentacular arms extending another 35 feet, the whole animal being 55 feet (18.3 m) long. The oblong eyes, for instance, measure about 7 by 9 inches (18 by 23 cm). *Architeuthis* is a favorite food of sperm whales, but apparently the giant squids put up violent struggles, some of which have been witnessed. Suckers on giant squids bear a circular horny rim with a sharp saw-toothed edge (Fig. 11.38.6a); hence, the skin of sperm whales may be scarred with circular furrows which are relics of encounters with *Architeuthis.* Several species of giant squids are known, and possibly three Genera qualify for the name of giant squid.

The most primitive teuthids, *Belemnoteuthis* and *Acanthoteuthis,* occur with other but more specialized teuthids in the famous Solenhofen limestone (Jurassic) of Germany. These squids differ from other Teuthida in retaining a considerable portion of the phragmocone and even a trace of the guard (Fig. 11.40.3). No wonder, then, that sometimes they are grouped with the Belemnitida, with which they are transitional. Specimens retaining impressions of soft parts around the shell reveal the eight sessile tentacles and in some cases even show clawlike hooks 7.5 millimeters long on the tentacles. *Acanthoteuthis* has hooks on the arms. Moreover the long proostracum of the teuthids is well developed in *Acanthoteuthis,* whereas it is rudimentary in *Belemnoteuthis.*

Teuthida rarely are discovered as fossils because the pen is composed of conchiolin with only small amounts of calcium carbonate. In Recent seas, nevertheless, true squids abound and various Genera are differentiated on the nature of stabilizing fins, tentacles, and eyes. In North America *Loligo* (Fig. 11.38.1, 2) dominates cephalopod faunas on the North Atlantic Coast and *Ommastrephes* (Fig. 11.38.3) is the principal Genus on southern coasts. Although they live at the same time, *Ommastrephes* (Fig. 11.40.4) retains a small cup-shaped posterior termination and therefore seems to be somewhat more primitive than Genera such as *Loligopsis* which lack the cup (Fig. 11.40.5). None of these squids has hooks on the arms. On the other hand,

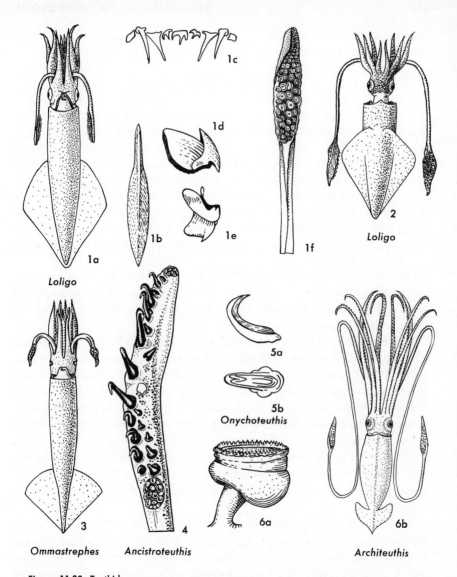

Figure 11.38. Teuthida.
1. *Loligo pealei*, Recent. 1a, ventral view of a female, 1/5X. 1b, gladius, 1/5X. 1c, a row of radular teeth, 15X. 1d, upper mandible, 1X. 1e, lower mandible, 1X. 1f, tentacular arm of a large male bearing suckers, 1/2X. 2. Dorsal view of *Loligo vulgaris*, 1/3X, Recent. 3. *Ommastrephes illecebrosus*, 1/3X, Recent. 4. Spine-bearing tentacular arm of *Ancistroteuthis lichtensteini*, slightly enlarged, Recent. 5a, 5b. Side and top views of a spine of *Onychoteuthis banksii*, 4X, Recent. 6. *Architeuthis princeps*, the giant squid, Recent. 6a, a single sucker with its spinose rim, 2/3X. 6b, dorsal view of a reconstruction, 1/92X.

(1, 3, 5, 6 after Verrill, 1882. 2 after Bartsch, 1917. 4 after Jatta, 1896.)

Onychoteuthis and its relatives constitute a Family of living squids in which some or all arms bear hooks as well as suckers (Fig. 11.38.4, 5).

Order d.   Octopodida

Octopods, paradoxically, both repel and attract human interest. Because they are a gourmet's delight, they are sought avidly by people along many shores. But, being enormously strong and possessed of a sinister demeanor, the octopods have earned a reputation for being dangerous, although naturalists constantly stress the timidity and retiring nature of these animals. Nevertheless, popular literature abounds with horror stories varying from attacks by large octopods upon man, to attacks of gigantic octopods upon ships. In this regard it is appropriate to mention that the largest octopus for which authentic measurements are available is a species on the north Pacific Coast of North America which reaches a diameter of 28 feet (8.5 m) when the arms are extended.

Octopods crawl about the bottom of the ocean in rocky places or swim about using their funnels. In a few forms a fleshy membrane connects the arms and assists in swimming in the same way that the umbrella of the jellyfish does (Fig. 11.39.1).

Lack of a shell in Octopodida would render the possibility of their fossilization remote, if it were not for the fact that females of *Argonauta,* for instance, secrete a calcareous brood pouch. This structure resembles involute ammonite conchs to a remarkable degree in shape and ornamentation (Fig. 11.39.4). It has a flattened to grooved venter bordered by nodes, and the flanks are covered with close-set transverse ribs. It differs from true conchs, however, in the absence of any trace of septa or siphuncle. Moreover, the brood pouch is not secreted by the mantle, as were the conchs of other cephalopods, but it is secreted by special glands on two of the arms. Mineralogically, the brood pouch is entirely calcitic, whereas conchs of ammonites are largely aragonitic.

The first octopods appeared in the Late Cretaceous as the unique Genus *Palaeoctopus,* from Lebanon (Fig. 11.39.3). This specimen has an ink sac, two triangular fins, a partial umbrella, a single row of suckers on each arm, and is about 15 centimeters long. Octopods quite naturally comprise a rare element in extinct faunas although brood pouches of *Argonauta* have been reported from Miocene and Pliocene strata. Twenty-five Genera of octopods are known, of which only two are represented by fossils and only one of the Genera is extinct.

Unlike the other coleoids, there is almost no evidence bearing on the origin of the Octopodida. They are dibranchiates but they have only eight

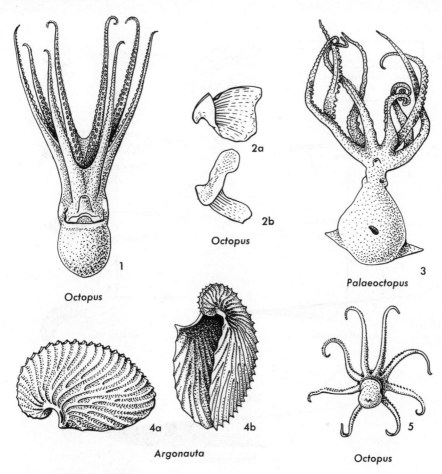

Figure 11.39. Octopodida.
1. Ventral view of *Octopus piscatorum* showing the hyponome and the web between the arms, 1/2X, Recent. 2a, 2b. Upper and lower mandibles of *Octopus bairdii*, 2X, Recent. 3. *Palaeoctopus newboldi*, the oldest known octopode, 1/2X, Cretaceous, Lebanon. 4a, 4b. Side and oblique apertural views of the brood chamber of *Argonauta argo*, 2/3X, Recent. 5. A young *Octopus macropus*, 2/3X, Recent.
(1, 2 after Verrill, 1882. 3 after Woodward, 1896. 5 after Jatta, 1896.)

arms, whereas the other coleoids have ten arms. It has been presumed by some authorities, therefore, that the Octopodida evolved from some other coleoids by complete loss of the conch and by reduction in number of arms. On the other hand, it is also possible that the Octopodida evolved from the tetrabranchiate cephalopods by reduction in the number of gills and by loss of the conch. In this latter case, the eight arms of the Octopodida would be

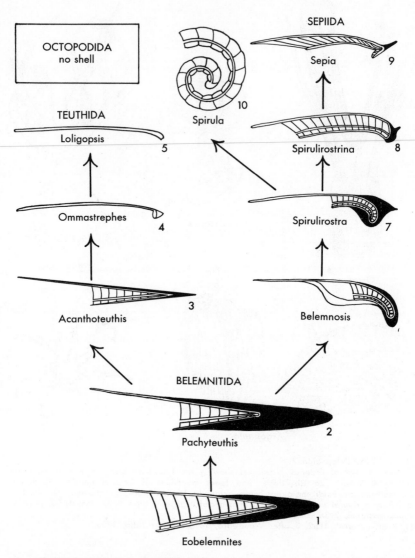

Figure 11.40. Modifications of Coleoid Conchs.
Illustrations are somewhat schematic and are drawn to various scales. Arrows indicate probable lines of descent of the Orders of coleoids, except that the origin of the Octopodida is unknown.
(After Roger, 1948; Lang, 1896; Dunbar, 1924; and Flower, 1945.)

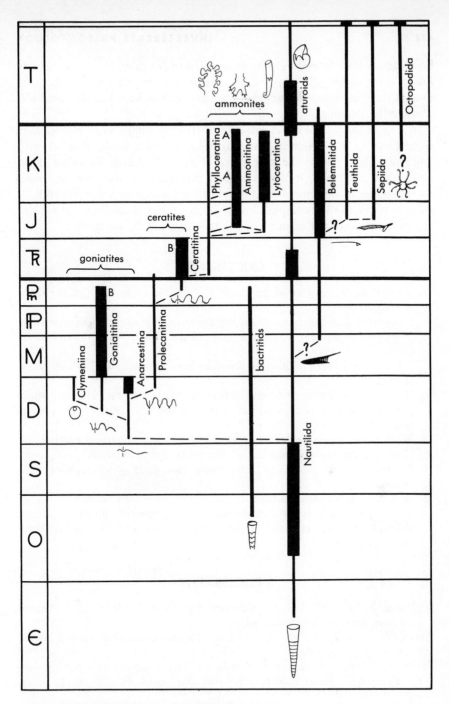

Figure 11.41. Geologic Range of Cephalopods.
Probable lines of evolution are indicated by dashed lines. Specialized sutures are indicated by block letters, of which A refers to pseudoceratites and B refers to pseudoammonites.
(After Kummel, 1952; Arkell, 1950; Wright, 1952; Miller and Furnish, 1957.)

homologous with the eight groups of tentacles in *Nautilus*. Of course, nobody knows how many gills or tentacles were present in the ammonoids, even though these cephalopods commonly are assumed to have had the same soft anatomy as *Nautilus*.

In spite of the lack of direct evidence, there may still be some evolutionary significance to the astonishing similarity of argonaut brood pouches with ammonite shells and to the appearance of octopods during the reign of the ammonites. Moreover, it has even been hypothesized that the enigmatic disappearance of ammonoids at the end of the Cretaceous is due not to their extinction, but to their complete loss of shells. In fact, according to this view, the ammonites are not extinct, even today—they are the octopods.

QUESTIONS

1. What is the significance of the shape of *Vermetus* compared with the shape of *Helicoceras*?
2. From what ancestral forms could the ammonoids presumably have arrived?
3. What theories account for disappearance of the ammonoids at the end of the Cretaceous?
4. What bearing does evolution of *Scaphites* have on the Law of Irreversibility of Evolution?
5. How can one decide whether a suture is referable to the true ammonites (Ammonitina) or is a pseudoammonitic suture? Or ceratitic? Or pseudo-ceratitic?
6. What habits might be indicated by breviconic and decollated conchs?
7. How can one explain uncoiling of nautiloids and ammonoids?
8. What effect does mineralogic composition have upon preservation of cephalopods?
9. Why are cephalopods particularly suited to ontogenetic studies?
10. Why are relatively fewer Ammonitina than Lytoceratina illustrated herein, although the Ammonitina are represented by many more Genera and thousands more species?

BIBLIOGRAPHY

Anderson, F. M., 1938, Lower Cretaceous deposits in California and Oregon: Geol. Soc. America Spec. Paper 16.

Arkell, W. J., 1950, A classification of the Jurassic ammonites: Jour. Paleont., v. 24, no. 3, pp. 354–364.

Barrande, J., 1860, Troncature Normale ou Periodique de la Coquille dans Certains Céphalopodes Paléozoïques: Bull. Soc. Géol. France, ser. 2, v. 17, pp. 573–600.

Bartsch, P., 1917, Pirates of the deep—stories of the squid and octopus: Smithsonian Inst., Ann. Rept. (1916), pp. 347–375.

Berry, E. W., 1922, An American Spirulirostra: Amer. Jour. Sci., ser. 5, v. 3, pp. 327–334.

Bisat, W. S., 1924, The Carboniferous goniatites of the north of England and their zones: Proc. Yorkshire Geol. Soc., n. ser., v. 20, pt. 1, pp. 40–124.

———, 1933, The faunal stratigraphy and goniatite phylogeny of the Carboniferous of western Europe, with notes on the connecting links with North America: Internat. Geol. Congr., Rept., XVI sess., v. 1, pp. 529–537.

Bruun, A. F., 1943, The biology of *Spirula spirula* (L.): Carlsberg's Fdn., Dana-Report 24.

———, 1955, New light on the biology of *Spirula,* a mesopelagic cephalopod. Essays in the natural sciences in honor of Captain Allan Hancock: Los Angeles, Univ. Southern California Press, pp. 61–72.

Cobban, W. A., 1951, Scaphitoid cephalopods of the Colorado group: U. S. Geol. Survey Prof. Paper 239.

Dean, B., 1901, Notes on living Nautilus: Amer. Midland Naturalist, v. 35, pp. 819–837.

Diener, C., 1922, A critical phase in the history of ammonites: Amer. Jour. Sci., ser. 5, v. 4, pp. 120–126.

Dunbar, C. O., 1924, Phases of cephalopod adaptation *in* Thorpe, R. M. (ed.), Organic adaptation to environment: New Haven, Yale Univ. Press, pp. 187–223.

Fischer, A. G., 1951, A new belemnoid from the Triassic of Nevada: Amer. Jour. Sci., v. 249, pp. 385–393.

Flower, R. H., 1941, Development of the mixochoanites: Jour. Paleont., v. 15, no. 5, pp. 523–548.

———, 1945, A belemnite from a Mississippian boulder of the Caney shale: Jour. Paleont., v. 19, no. 5, pp. 490–503.

———, 1946, Ordovician cephalopods of the Cincinnati region: Bull. Amer. Paleont., v. 29, no. 116 (especially pp. 13–90 on nautiloid morphology).

———, 1954, Cambrian cephalopods: New Mexico St. Bur. Mines Min. Res., Bull. 40.

———, and Kummel, B., Jr., 1950, A classification of the Nautiloidea: Jour. Paleont., v. 24, no. 5, pp. 604–616.

Foerste, A. F., 1924, Notes on American Paleozoic cephalopods: Denison Univ. Bull., Jour. Sci. Labs., v. 20, pp. 193–268.

———, 1926, Actinosiphonate, trochoceroid and other cephalopods: Denison Univ. Bull., Jour. Sci. Labs., v. 21, pp. 285–383.

———, 1928, A restudy of American orthoconic Silurian cephalopods: Denison Univ. Bull., Jour. Sci. Labs., v. 23, pp. 236–320.

Foord, A. H., 1891, Mandibles of fossil nautiloids *in* Catalogue of the fossil cephalopoda, pt. II: London, British Mus. (Nat. Hist.), pp. 360–377.

———, and Crick, G. C., 1897, Catalogue of the fossil Cephalopoda, pt. 3: London, British Mus. (Nat. Hist.).

Frech, F., 1915, Loses und geschlossenes Gehäuse der tetrabranchiaten Cephalopoden: Centralblatt Mineral. Geol. Paläont., pp. 593–606.

Furnish, W. M., and Unklesbay, A. G., 1940, Diagrammatic representation of ammonoid sutures: Jour. Paleont., v. 14, no. 6, pp. 598–602.

Griepenkerl, O., 1889, Die Versteinerungen der Sinonen Kreide von Koenigslutter im Herzogthum Braunschweig: Palaeont. Abh., v. 4, pt. 5.

Griffin, L. E., 1900, The anatomy of Nautilus pompilius: Nat. Acad. Sci., v. 8, mem. 5, pp. 103–231.

Haas, O., 1942, Recurrence of morphologic types and evolutionary cycles in Mesozoic ammonites: Jour. Paleont., v. 16, no. 5, pp. 643–650.

Hall, J., 1843, Paleontology of New York: Natural History of New York, v. 1.

Hauer, F. R., von, 1860, Nachträge zur Kenntniss der Cephalopoden-Fauna der Hallstätter Schichten: Sitz. Akad. Wiss. Wien, Math.-natur. Cl., v. 41, pp. 113–150.

Huxley, T. H., and Pelseneer, P., 1895, Report on the specimen of the Genus *Spirula* collected by H. M. S. "Challenger": Report on the scientific results of the exploring voyage of H. M. S. "Challenger," Summary of the results with appendices, pt. 2, Zoology, pt. 83.

Hyatt, A., 1887, On primitive forms of cephalopods: Amer. Naturalist, v. 21, pp. 64–66.

——, 1889, Genesis of the Arietidae: Smithsonian Inst. Contr. Knowledge, v. 26, art. 2.

——, 1894, Phylogeny of an acquired characteristic: Proc. Amer. Phil. Soc., v. 32, no. 143, pp. 349–647 (especially pp. 349-424).

——, 1903, Pseudoceratites of the Cretaceous: U. S. Geol. Survey, Mon. 44.

Imlay, R. W., 1953, Callovian (Jurassic) ammonites from the United States and Alaska: U. S. Geol. Survey Prof. Paper 249–B, pp. 41–108.

Jatta, G., 1896, I Cephalopodi viventi nel Golfo di Napoli: Fauna und Flora des Golfes von Neapel, Mon. 23 (Berlin).

Jeletzky, J. A., 1955, Evolution of Santonian and Campanian *Belemnitella* and paleontological systematics: exemplified by *Belemnitella praecursor* Stolley: Jour. Paleont., v. 29, no. 3, pp. 478–509.

Kobayashi, T., 1935, On the phylogeny of the primitive nautiloids, with descriptions of *Plectronoceras liaotungense,* n. sp., and *Iddingsia* (?) *shantungensis,* n. sp.: Japanese Jour. Geol. Geog., v. 12, pp. 17–26.

Kummel, B., Jr., 1952, A classification of the Triassic ammonoids: Jour. Paleont., v. 26, no. 5, pp. 847–853.

——, and Lloyd, R. M., 1955, Experiments on relative streamlining of coiled cephalopod shells: Jour. Paleont., v. 29, no. 1, pp. 159–170.

Lindström, G., 1890, The Ascoceratidae and the Lituitidae of the Upper Silurian formation of Gotland: Kongl. Svenska Vetensk.-Akad. Handlingar, v. 23, no. 12.

Meek, F. B., 1876, A report on the invertebrate Cretaceous and Tertiary fossils of the Upper Missouri country: U. S. Geol. Survey Terr. (Hayden), v. 9.

——, and Hayden, F. V., 1865, Palaeontology of the Upper Missouri: Smithsonian Inst. Contr. Knowledge, v. 14, art. 5.

Miller, A. K., 1938, Devonian ammonoids of America: Geol. Soc. America Spec. Paper 14.

——, 1947, Tertiary nautiloids of the Americas: Geol. Soc. America, Mem. 23 (especially pp. 3–24).

————, and Collinson, C., 1951, Lower Mississippian ammonoids of Missouri: Jour. Paleont., v. 25, no. 4, pp. 454–487.

————, and Downs, R. H., 1948, A cephalopod fauna from the type section of the Pennsylvanian "Winslow formation" of Arkansas: Jour. Paleont., v. 22, no. 6, pp. 672–680.

————, Downs, R. H., and Youngquist, W., 1949, Some Mississippian cephalopods from central and western United States: Jour. Paleont., v. 23, no. 6, pp. 600–612.

————, Dunbar, C. O., and Condra, G. E., 1933, The nautiloid cephalopods of the Pennsylvanian System in the Mid-continent region: Nebraska Geol. Survey, Bull. 9, ser. 2, (especially pp. 15–38).

————, and Furnish, W. M., 1940a, Permian ammonoids of the Guadalupe Mountain region and adjacent areas: Geol. Soc. America Spec. Paper 26.

————, and Furnish, W. M., 1940b, Studies of Carboniferous ammonoids: pts. 1–4: Jour. Paleont., v. 14, no. 4, pp. 356–377.

————, and Furnish, W. M., 1940c, Studies of Carboniferous ammonoids: pts. 5–7: Jour. Paleont., v. 14, no. 6, pp. 521–543.

————, and Furnish, W. M., 1954, The classification of the Paleozoic ammonoids: Jour. Paleont., v. 28, no. 5, pp. 685–692.

————, and Youngquist, W., 1948, The cephalopod fauna of the Mississippian Barnett formation of Central Texas: Jour. Paleont., v. 22, no. 6, pp. 649–671.

Moore, R. C., and Sylvester-Bradley, P. C., 1957, Taxonomy and nomenclature of aptychi: Treatise on invertebrate paleontology, pt. L, pp. L465–L471.

Müller-Stoll, Hanns, 1936, Beiträge zur Anatomie der Belemnoidea: Nova Acta Leopoldina, n.f., v. 4, no. 20, pp. 159–226.

Naef, A., 1922, Die fossilen Tintenfische: Jena, Gustav Fischer, 322 pp.

Noetling, F., 1895, The fauna of the Kellaways of Mazár Drik: Mem. Geol. Survey India, Palaeontologia Indica, ser. 16, v. 1, pt. 1.

Plummer, F. B., and Scott, G., 1937, Upper Paleozoic ammonites in Texas: Univ. Texas Bull. 3701, The geology of Texas, v. 3, pt. 1 (especially pp. 34–47).

Reeside, J. B., 1919, Some American Jurassic ammonites of the Genera Quenstedticeras, Cardioceras, and Amoeboceras. Family Cardioceratidae: U. S. Geol. Survey Prof. Paper 118.

————, 1927a, Cephalopods from the lower part of the Cody shale of Oregon Basin, Wyoming: U. S. Geol. Survey Prof. Paper 150-A, pp. 1–19.

————, 1927b, Cephalopods of the Eagle sandstone and related formations in the western interior of the United States: U. S. Geol. Survey Prof. Paper 151.

Roger, J., 1948, Découverte d'une coquille de Sepia (*S.* cf. *vindobonensis* Schloenbach) dans le Vindobonien supérieur de Saubrigues (Landes) et histoire paléontologique des Sepiidae: Bull. Soc. Géol. France, ser. 5, v. 17, pp. 225–232.

Salfeld, H., 1913, Über Artbildung bei Ammoniten: Zeitschr. Deutsch. Geol. Ges., Monatsber., v. 65, pp. 437–440.

Schevill, W. E., 1950, An Upper Jurassic sepioid from Cuba: Jour. Paleont., v. 24, no. 1, pp. 99–101.

Schindewolf, O. H., 1954, On the development, evolution, and terminology of ammonoid suture line: Bull. Mus. Comp. Zool. (Harvard), v. 112, no. 3, pp. 217–237.

Schmidt, M., 1929, Anaptychen von Lytoceras cornu copiae Young u. Bird: Neues Jahrb. Min. Geol. Paläont. Abh., B.-B. 61, Abt. B, pp. 399–432.

Scott, G., 1939, Cephalopods from the Cretaceous Trinity group of the south-central United States: Univ. Texas Pub. 3945, pp. 969–1106.

Smith, J. P., 1903, The Carboniferous ammonoids of America: U. S. Geol. Survey, Mon. 42.

———, 1914, The Middle Triassic marine invertebrate faunas of North America: U. S. Geol. Survey Prof. Paper 83.

———, 1927, Upper Triassic marine invertebrate faunas of North America: U. S. Geol. Survey Prof. Paper, 141.

———, 1932, Lower Triassic ammonoids of North America: U. S. Geol. Survey Prof. Paper 167.

Spath, L. F., 1923–1930, A monograph of the Ammonoidea of the Gault, v. I: Palaeontographical Soc. (London) (especially pp. iii–vi, 3–13).

———, 1933, The evolution of the Cephalopoda: Cambridge Phil. Soc., Biol. Revs., v. 8, no. 4, pp. 418–462.

Stenzel, H. B., 1948, Ecology of living nautiloids: Rep. Comm. Treatise Mar. Ecol. Paleoecol. no. 8 (1947–1948): Washington, D. C., Nat. Res. Council, pp. 84–90.

Stephenson, L. W., 1941, The larger invertebrate fossils of the Navarro group of Texas: Univ. Texas Pub. 4101.

Swinnerton, H. H., and Trueman, A. E., 1917, The morphology and development of the ammonite septum: Geol. Soc. London Quart. Jour., v. 73, pp. 26–58.

Tchernow, A., 1907, The Artinskian stage. Ammonoides of the Jaiva, Kosva, and Tchoussovaia basins: Bull. Soc. Imp. Naturalistes Moscow, n. ser., v. 20, pp. 270–401. (In Russian with French abstract.)

Trauth, F., 1927, Aptychenstudien. I. Über die Aptychen im Allgemeinen: Annal. Naturhist. Mus. Wien, v. 41, pp. 171–259.

Trueman, A. E., 1920, The ammonite siphuncle: Geol. Mag., v. 57, pp. 26–32.

———, 1941, The ammonite body-chamber, with special reference to the buoyancy and mode of life of the living ammonite: Geol. Soc. London Quart. Jour., v. 96, pp. 339–383.

Verrill, A. E., 1882, Report on the cephalopods of the northwestern coast of America: U. S. Fish. Comm. Rep. (1879), pt. VII, pp. 211–455.

Wedekind, R., 1916, Über Lobus, Suturallobus und Inzision: Centralblatt für Mineral., Geol. u Paläont. (1916), no. 8, pp. 185–195.

Whitfield, R. P., 1892, Gastropoda and Cephalopoda of the Raritan clays and greensand marls of New Jersey: U. S. Geol. Survey, Mon. 18.

———, and Honey, E. O., 1906, Remarks on and descriptions of Jurassic fossils of the Black Hills: Bull. Amer. Mus. Nat. Hist., v. 22, pp. 389–402.

Woodward, H., 1896, On a fossil octopus . . . from the Cretaceous of the Lebanon Geol. Soc. London Quart. Jour., v. 52, pp. 229–234.

Woodward, S. P., 1866 (1880), A manual of the Mollusca: 2nd ed., London, Virtue Bros., 542 pp., ill. (4th ed., 1880).

Wright, C. W., 1952, A classification of the Cretaceous ammonites: Jour. Paleont., v. 26, no. 2, pp. 213–222.

Wright, T., 1878, Monograph on the Lias ammonites of the British Isles, pt. I: Palaeontographical Soc. (London).

Youngquist, W., 1949, The cephalopod fauna of the White Pine shale of Nevada: Jour. Paleont., v. 23, no. 3, pp. 276–305.

Chapter 12

TRILOBITES AND CHELICERATES

PHYLUM XIII. ARTHROPODA

It is a widespread belief of biologists that arthropods rival the Protozoa and Nemathelminthes in abundance and exceed all other creatures in diversity of bodily form, adaptation, and habit. The insects alone constitute the most numerous megascopic creatures on the face of the earth and are so diversely constructed that entomologists are apt to restrict themselves to the study of one Order (such as beetles, or flies, or moths and butterflies) rather than to try to struggle with the voluminous literature on the Class Insecta in general. Moreover, members of any one group of the other living arthropods such as lobsters, crabs, crayfish, spiders, barnacles, centipedes, and scorpions may be hopelessly remote from the attentions of specialists in some closely allied group. Extreme specialization by students of living arthropods has been fostered because of the important position of the Arthropoda in dietary and medical matters. Paleontologists are interested in arthropods because of the evolutionary significance of fossil forms, as well as for the stratigraphic value of a few groups. Of all the fossil arthropods, however, trilobites have been the most attractive to geologists in general and to laymen interested in geology. Ostracodes, however, rival trilobites for their value in applied paleontology because they can be used in micropaleontology in the same manner as foraminifers.

Arthropoda are characterized by the presence of an external skeleton **(exoskeleton)** and by a fundamentally segmented body bearing paired appendages on most segments. In most arthropods the segmentation of the body is reflected in the axial exoskeleton as a series of joints separating articulating segments **(somites)**. Moreover, that portion of the exoskeleton which surrounds the appendages is also divided by joints into movable segments so that the animal can move about—hence Arthropoda, meaning "jointed feet." The exoskeleton consists of chitin, although extensive calcification of some forms during life has rendered the chitin quite rigid, except

484

at the joints. Bodies of most arthropods can be differentiated into a **head, thorax,** and **abdomen,** for which special names are given in different groups, depending upon the amount of fusion of somites into unified regions. Somites of the head, for instance, are fused together in all Arthropoda, although other somites more or less retain their articulating potentiality. Bristlelike hairs, the **setae,** fringe many regions of the body, particularly the limbs; and limbs of some groups terminate in pincerlike claws.

Subaqueous arthropods breathe by means of gills which may be borne on the limbs or confined to a special gill chamber. Air-breathers, on the other hand, tend to develop tubular processes (**tracheae**) which ramify through the tissues and communicate with the exterior through special pores which enable exchange of carbon dioxide and oxygen. The nervous system of arthropods is highly organized, with special sensory devices on the head in the form of antennae and antennules, as well as in simple and compound eyes. The double nerve cord centers in a brain and bears pairs of ganglia in most somites. Sexes are separate and eggs either hatch internally or externally. In many forms there is a remarkable **metamorphosis** in which the body of a caterpillar, for instance, is antecedent to that of a moth or a butterfly. In some degenerate forms, on the other hand, all trace of arthropodan segmentation is lost and the affinities of the adult creature are obscure.

Understanding the relationship among various Arthropoda is assisted by knowing something about the larval development of some marine forms. All Crustacea are characterized by the presence in their early developmental history of a larval **nauplius** stage about 1 millimeter in diameter (Fig. 12.7.5). When the first nauplius was discovered in 1785 it was not realized that it represented a larval stage; hence, for a short time thereafter species were described under the assumption that nauplius was a Genus. A nauplius larva consists of an ovate body bearing three pairs of appendages and a single median eye spot. Each of the anterior pair of appendages consists of a single unsegmented axis bearing two setae at its tip. It becomes the antennule in an adult crustacean. The second pair of appendages consists of a large ray and a small ray, each of which bears several setae. This **biramous** appendage is the principal swimming organ in the larval stage but becomes the antenna in the adult. The third or posterior pair of appendages is biramous and bears setae but is smaller than the second pair. It helps the larva to swim but becomes a mandible in the adult. Further growth of the larva entails adding thoracic segments and increasing the number of biramous cephalic appendages to five pairs; at this stage the larva is called a **metanauplius.** Other stages are recognized but are not pertinent to general considerations. It will be noted, however, that the first pair of appendages is fundamentally uniramous and that the others are biramous. Moreover, the biramous appendages are strictly locomotor in function in the larvae, even though they may take on some other function in adulthood.

Growth of many Arthropoda poses serious problems because the soft body is encased within an essentially unexpandable exoskeleton. From time to time some arthropods such as the Crustacea find it necessary to shed the exoskeleton and to grow a new one. This operation of molting or **ecdysis** is exemplified by blue crabs, which, when they have cast off their overly tight exoskeletons, are "soft-shelled crabs" (and are a prized delicacy, not only to people but to many marine predators). For a matter of a day or so the soft shell is covered only by a paper-thin chitinous membrane, inside of which the soft body expands in anticipation of acquiring a new suit of armor. It is known that ecdysis commences at the nauplius stage and continues during most of the life of various arthropods, commonly involving half a dozen molts. Each molted carapace is referred to as an **instar**. It is thought by some biologists that the addition of every new somite may require a new molt, in which case, for instance, most trilobites would have molted 10 to 15 or more times. Obviously, animals which molt are more apt to leave fossilized remains than are animals which do not molt. Moreover, ecdysis brings about some rather considerable changes in the appearance of molts of trilobites; hence, it is not surprising that different molt stages of the same species sometimes have been given separate generic and specific names. Strangely, however, molt stages in most instances are not known to reflect the supposed phylogeny of most arthropods, even though the molted exoskeletons represent ideal material for examination of young stages. Perhaps adaptations of young animals overshadow phylogenetic features or crowd them back out of the developmental stages represented by molting.

Arthropods are rather generally conceded to have arisen from the Annelida by coalescence of several anterior somites into a head, by development of jointed appendages, by improvement of the nervous system, and by reduction in the number of functions carried on individually by each segment. As in the case of the annelid worms, new somites are added to the body just anterior to the anal segment. Unlike the annelids, however, segmentation in Arthropoda merely affects the exoskeleton instead of also dividing the internal organs into successive metameres.

CLASSIFICATION. So diversified are the Arthropoda, and so specialized are the interests of students of arthropods, that great difference of opinion exists as to how many large taxa should be recognized and what taxonomic level should be assigned the taxa. Recent tendencies are to elevate former Classes to the level of Subphyla or even Phyla. No matter how desirable the proliferation of systematic groups may be, it poses grievous problems to a student entering upon the study of Arthropoda. Comprehending the nuances of elaborate classifications of Arthropoda requires a degree of familiarity not normally attained without special training in zoology and paleontology. Moreover, the effort thus expended would be all out of proportion to the value of the knowledge to a paleontologist. Accordingly, the classification of Arthropoda used herein is a simplification of most current ones rather than a definitive classification. Arthropoda are treated as a homogeneous Phylum and the main groups are treated as Classes.

Phylum XIII. Arthropoda

Class A. Onychophora
Class B. Trilobitae
Class C. Chelicerata
Class D. Crustacea
Class E. Insecta
Class F. Myriapoda

Class A. Onychophora

The Class Onychophora is so aberrant that some systematists have made it the basis of a separate Phylum or Subphylum. Recent onychophorans have a wormlike shape with at least 14 pairs of stumpy appendages bearing tiny

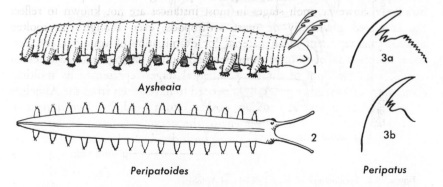

Aysheaia

Peripatoides

Peripatus

Figure 12.1. Onychophora.
1. *Aysheaia pedunculata*, 1 1/2X, Middle Cambrian, British Columbia. 2. Dorsal view of *Peripatoides* sp., 3X, Recent. 3. Mandibles of *Peripatus* sp., 50X, Recent.
(1 after Hutchinson, 1931. 2, 3 after Bouvier, 1905.)

claws. There is no segmentation of the body, but the supposed relationship of the Onychophora to the Arthropoda is shown in details of the embryology and in the presence of tracheae. On the other hand, the close resemblance of the Onychophora to the Annelida is revealed by the nature of the nephridia and the reproductive apparatus. Certain ciliated organs are present in this Class, as in the annelid worms and in more primitive Phyla, but are absent in the arthropods. It is possible that the Onychophora are transitional between the Annelida and the higher Arthropoda.

Peripatoides is a living example of the Class (Fig. 12.1.2). It is strictly terrestrial. The only fossils referred to the Class have been questioned. Of these, *Aysheaia,* from the Burgess shale (Middle Cambrian) is the best known.

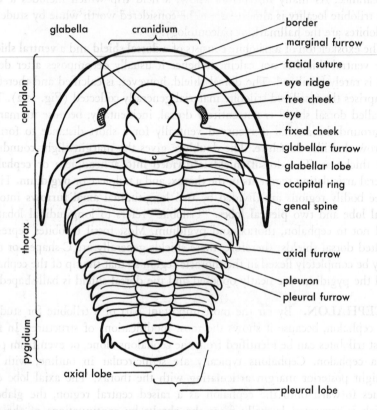

Figure 12.2. Terminology of Dorsal Shield of Trilobites.
(After Howell, *et al.,* 1947 and Warburg, 1925.)

Aysheaia was a marine animal and therefore probably lacked tracheae. Moreover, only ten pairs of appendages are present, but these bear six claws, whereas appendages of Recent onychophorans bear only two claws. *Aysheaia* may represent a very primitive onychophoran which is closer to the annelids than to the arthropods, although being intermediate between the two groups.

Onychophorans bear chitinous mandibles (Fig. 12.1.3) which might be preserved as fossils, although none has been reported as yet.

Class B.   Trilobitae

Of all fossils, trilobites seem to be especially interesting because they are among the earliest of animals, were the first so-called "rulers of the world," have been extinct a long time, and still resemble living arthropods in general appearance. As many instructors know, a field trip which includes a visit to a trilobite locality is almost sure to be considered worth while by students. Trilobites are the hallmark of paleontology.

The exoskeleton of a trilobite consists of a **dorsal shield** and a **ventral shield.** The ventral shield is not calcified; hence it usually decomposes after death and is rarely fossilized. The dorsal shield, however, is calcified and therefore comprises the fossilized trilobite material generally collected (Fig. 12.2). The so-called dorsal shield is not entirely dorsal, incidentally, because its margin all around the animal is recurved ventrally for a short distance to form a narrow shelflike **doublure.** The doublure gives the margin slight roundness and thickness. The dorsal shield is divided into a headpiece or **cephalon,** several articulating segments in the **thorax,** and a tailpiece or **pygidium.** These three bodily regions are divided by two longitudinal **axial furrows** into an **axial lobe** and two **pleural lobes.** "Trilobite" refers to longitudinal lobation and not to cephalon, thorax, and pygidium. Most fossil trilobites represent molted dorsal shields; therefore, these shields generally are C-shaped or they may be completely flexed in the thoracic region so that the tip of the cephalon and the pygidium are neatly opposed and the dorsal shield is ball-shaped.

CEPHALON.   By far the most important part of a trilobite for study is the cephalon, because it shows the most modifications of structures. In fact, most trilobites can be identified from the cephalons alone, or even from parts of a cephalon. Cephalons typically are semicircular in outline, with the straight posterior margin articulating with the thorax. The axial lobe continues forward onto the cephalon as a raised central region, the **glabella,** which is separated laterally from the **cheeks** by continuations of the two longitudinal axial furrows and is separated anteriorly from the **brim** by the **preglabellar furrow.** The cheeks and brim are continuous surfaces around the glabella. A **marginal furrow** follows a course parallel to the margin of the cephalon and just inside it, thus delimiting the intervening region as the **border.** A pair of **eyes** generally lies on the cheeks and may be connected with the glabellum by a **facial ridge.** In most trilobites the cephalon bears two **facial sutures,** each of which passes lengthwise close to the axial side of an eye. Thus, the cheeks are divided into outer or **free cheeks** which may become detached from the remainder of the cephalon and **fixed cheeks** which always remain firmly united with the glabella. A glabella and two fixed cheeks together constitute a **cranidium.**

The only visible segmentation on the cephalon is confined to the glabella. In all cases a narrow posterior part of a glabella is set off from the rest of the glabellum as the **occipital ring,** by the **occipital furrow.** In many trilobites the occipital furrow and the posterior part of the marginal furrow make a continuous groove across the cephalon. Anterior to the occipital furrow there may be three **glabellar furrows,** or three pairs of glabellar furrows in cases wherein medial portions of furrows disappear and only the lateral portions remain. The three normal glabellar furrows and the occipital furrow divide the glabella into five segments, of which the occipital ring already has been mentioned; the anterior segment is the **frontal lobe** and the other three are **glabellar lobes.** Glabellar furrows exhibit a distinct tendency with the passage of time to diminish in strength, starting at the anterior end and then shifting posteriorly; commonly the occipital furrow is retained, but even it may eventually disappear. Loss of glabellar furrows is interpreted as evolutionary advance, being in accord with supposed improvement in cephalization of anterior somites of arthropods. Considerable confusion exists as to exactly which furrow or lobe of one trilobite is homologous with a corresponding feature of another trilobite. For instance, a fourth pair of glabellar furrows has been reported in the group of furrows anterior to the occipital furrow in a few trilobites. Moreover, a pair of posterior-lateral lobes may be isolated from the rest of the glabellar lobes as so-called **occipital lobes,** but occipital lobes may not be homologous in all trilobites (compare *Phillipsia* or *Ditomopyge* with *Flexicalymene* or *Eurekia*). Finally, a few trilobites (*Ditomopyge,* for instance) have a **preoccipital lobe** of uncertain derivation which is located between the occipital lobes and anterior to the occipital ring.

Several modifications of the glabellar outline are noteworthy. In some trilobites such as *Elrathia* the glabella tapers anteriorly, but in the majority of Genera there is a strong tendency for the anterior portion to be expanded laterally. In *Zacanthoides* the axial furrows are parallel and in *Paradoxides* the frontal portion of the glabella is much wider than the posterior portion. Various other shapes are known, such as the sinuous sides of the glabella of *Griffithides* and the teardrop-shaped glabella of *Cryptolithus. Isotelus* has lost every trace of its glabella, so it has a perfectly smooth cephalon as well as a smooth pygidium. Glabellae with primitive outlines may appear far later in one strain than outlines of advanced shape may appear in a closely related strain; therefore, it is apparent that rates of evolution and directions of modification of glabellar outlines are irregular and complex.

It will be remembered that the dorsal cephalic shield continues around onto the ventral surface as a doublure. The surface of the doublure may resemble that of the dorsal shield or it may be ornamented with distinctive striae. The cephalic doublure is a semicircular rim around the curved anterior and lateral margins. Attached more or less securely to the central part of the doublure is a movable flap of skeletal tissue, the **hypostome,** which covered the mouth as an upper lip in life (Fig. 12.4.1). The hypostome generally consists of a large centrally swollen area surrounded by a depressed border. Anterior lateral regions may be expanded into winglike processes, and the midposterior region may be indented rather deeply. In many trilobites a pair of tiny raised nodes called **maculae** (sing. **macula**) lie just behind the raised central portion of the hypostome (Fig. 12.6.4).

THORAX. The thorax is the least significant portion of a trilobite, possibly because most of its modification took place early in the history of the Class. A thorax consists of segments separated by joints or **articular furrows.** The central raised portion of a thoracic segment is the **axial ring** and the two lateral portions are the **pleura** (sing. **pleuron**). Pleura may be smooth, or grooved parallel to the articular furrow by a false joint or **pleural furrow,** or equipped with a **pleural ridge** or with **punctae** in place of the pleural furrow. The lateral or outer portions of the pleura terminate in angular edges which give the thoracic margin a distinctly saw-toothed or spinose appearance. In very primitive trilobites the inner pleural areas are narrow and the outer pleural areas consist of long spines. Moreover, posterior thoracic segments of primitive trilobites are less broad than are the anterior segments, so the trilobites may taper notably from anterior to posterior. During the passage of time the breadth of the posterior thoracic segments increased until all thoracic segments were about equally broad; moreover, the inner pleural areas expanded laterally, whereas the length of spines on the outer pleural areas decreased. At the end of these changes the thorax had acquired more or less parallel sides and the broad inner pleural areas had become fringed only with short blunt spines of the outer pleurae.

Articulation of thoracic segments improved with the passage of time. The calcified segments of primitive trilobites essentially abut one against the other and are united by a U-shaped band of flexible chitin along the base of the articular furrows. Upon death the chitin decomposed and the thoracic segments could be disassociated easily by currents. This explains the paucity of complete specimens of many Early Cambrian trilobites. A famous locality in the Marble Mountains in the Mojave Desert in eastern California, for instance, yielded only half a dozen specimens retaining articulated thoracic segments in a single collection of 1150 specimens. Improvement in articulation of thoracic segments came about quickly, however, for the segments of many Middle Cambrian and of almost all later trilobites retain their articulation. This is because their articular furrows become interlocked by a slight enrolling of the adjacent margins.

A final phenomenon affecting the thorax is change in the number of segments. Trilobites can be divided into two great groups on the basis of how many thoracic segments are present. A few Cambrian forms such as *Agnostus* and *Eodiscus* have only 2 or 3 thoracic segments, respectively (Fig. 12.10). All other Cambrian and later trilobites have at least 6 thoracic segments, and most of them have from 9 to 15. The number is rather constant for adult molts of a species. Although the number increases in some evolutionary strains, decrease in the number of thoracic segments is the dominant trend. New segments are added posteriorly at the junction of the thorax and the pygidium. From studies of molt stages it appears that a new segment first appears as the most anterior segment fused to the pygidium, but in a later molt stage the segment will have become a freely articulated part of the thorax and the pygidium will have lost one segment.

PYGIDIUM. A pygidium consists of a number of somites which have fused into a rigid plate by calcification of articular furrows. Some pygidia represent only half a dozen somites, but others represent 15 or 20. The number is rather constant in a single species. Just as in the thorax, the axial lobe continues onto the pygidium, but usually does not cross to the posterior margin. Pleura resemble thoracic pleura in having pleural furrows and false articular furrows. False articular furrows may extend to the lateral margins of the pygidium or may not reach it. Pleural furrows normally do not reach the margin. In cases wherein neither set of furrows reaches the margin, a smooth **marginal flange** is produced. Ordinarily, pleural furrows diminish in strength and disappear from a pygidium before false articular furrows do, but in a few cases the reverse is true. Some care is needed in order to determine whether the obvious **ribs** on the pleura of pygidia represent entire somites or halves of pleura between two different sorts of furrows. In some cases it is not possible to decide which part of a pleuron is homologous with a rib. Differentiation of ribs or of true pleura is desirable because the number of somites in the axial lobe of pygidia may be different from the number in the pleural lobes. Thus, pygidia of *Dikelocephalus* (Upper Cambrian) may have five axial somites and ten pleural ribs (Fig. 12.11.8b), and pygidia of *Phacops* (Devonian) may have ten axial somites and six pleural somites (Fig. 12.14.1). In some Genera such as *Isotelus* (Ordovician), almost every vestige of segmentation has been lost from both the axial and pleural lobes so that the pygidia are nearly smoothly convex shields (Fig. 12.12.3).

Pygidia vary from the normal outline of a semiellipse to attenuated V-shaped and quadrate outlines. Margins may be entire, indented posteriorly, or equipped with spines in line with pleura so that margins resemble the thorax closely. Still other pygidia have smooth marginal flanges bearing several curved spinose processes not in line with pleura; or just a pair of large, curved, posterior spines; or perhaps just a single, elongate, caudal spine. Quadrate pygidia tend to have very broad marginal flanges.

Pygidia arose from forms such as *Paedeumias* in which there is no fusion of posterior somites, but in which the body merely tapers posteriorly or even bears a string of narrow **post-thoracic segments** which resemble the tail on a kite (Fig. 12.9.7). It seems that the dominant trend in pygidial evolution was for increase in size until the pygidium became about the same size as the cephalon. On the other hand, pygidia in a few cases decreased in size. Details of pygidial construction, shape, and size are considered by some paleontologists to be as valuable in study of trilobites as are facial sutures.

EYES. Eyes of trilobites are unusually interesting, not only because of their morphologic features and their value in interpreting habits of trilobites, but because it was through the eyes of trilobites that creatures first looked out on the face of the earth. Arthropods in general have **simple** or **compound** eyes. In a simple eye the single lens consists of a tiny, thickened, transparent node of the exoskeleton, beneath which are a few sensory and pigmented cells. Compound eyes, on the other hand, typically consist of a large number (up to about 25,000 in some insects) of separate visual bodies (**ommatidia**), each of which consists of an outer, lens-bearing refractive medium and a deeper sensory or perceptive region (Fig. 12.3.4). Individual ommatidia are separated by intervening pigmented regions so that each ommotidium receives its own impulses. Moreover, curvature of the eye surface causes each ommatidium to be directed in a different direction over the field of vision. Compound eyes are especially sensitive to changes of movement in an object under observation.

Closely associated with normal compound eyes are facial ridges, one of which connects each eye or false eye with the anterior inner part of the frontal lobe of the glabella. Facial ridges are strongly developed in primitive trilobites, such as *Mesonacis* (Fig. 12.8), but are lost progressively in more advanced Genera. Lower and Middle Cambrian trilobites, many of which seem at first glance to be equipped with large and impressive eyes on the dorsal surface, actually are blind, and their false eyes are nothing but extensions of the facial ridges. The oldest trilobite with dorsal eyes may be *Eurycare* from the Upper Cambrian of Sweden.

In addition to the primarily blind trilobites, another category of trilobites has become blind secondarily by progressive reduction in the size of the eyes. Variations in eye size are common among trilobites, and several strains have become blind. The free cheeks of blind trilobites commonly are narrow marginal slivers, although this is not always the case. It does seem that marginal retraction of free cheeks can accompany blindness in some strains. Secondarily blind trilobites commonly are adapted for a burrowing existence, as is also indicated by their smoothly streamlined surfaces. Trilobites of the

Family Trinucleidae bear testimony to the course of progressive blindness, for larval molts bear eye spots, but adult molts lack any trace of eyes.

Simple eyes (also called **ocelli,** sing. **ocellus**) have been identified in a few trilobites, but are not common. In *Eoharpes* (Ordovician) one or two large ocelli lie at the ends of the facial ridges. Perhaps tiny ocelli will be discovered in more trilobites as detailed studies increase. Ocelli could occur at unex-

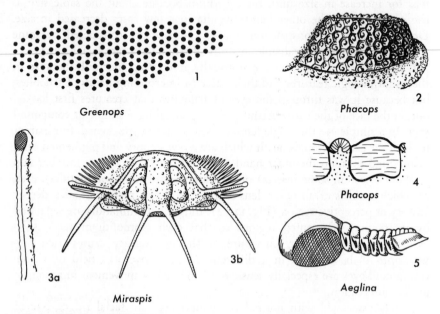

Figure 12.3. Eyes of Trilobites.
1. Pattern of 206 lenses in *Greenops boothi,* enlarged. 2. Aggregate eye of *Phacops rana,* 4X, Devonian, eastern United States. 3. *Miraspis mira,* Ordovician, Czechoslovakia. 3a, eye stalk with lenses and median suture, 6X. 3b, dorsal view of cephalon, 1 1/2X. 4. Vertical section of eye of *Phacops rana* showing lens (radiating lines) surmounting ommatidial cavity (stippled) surrounded by sclera (dashed), enlarged. 5. Side view of *Aeglina prisca,* 4X, Ordovician, Czechoslovakia.
(1, 4 after Clarke, 1888. 2 after Hall and Clarke, 1888. 3 after Barrande, 1852. 5 after Barrande, 1872.)

pected places on cephalons and be confused with the tubercles which commonly stud the surfaces of trilobites.

Compound eyes are the obvious eyes of trilobites (Fig. 12.3). If the surface of a compound eye is covered by a continuous, smooth, transparent cornea, beneath which the separate lenses are located, the eye is a truly compound or **holochroal eye.** These are the most common eyes seen in trilobites, as well as in most arthropods. In a few Genera, such as *Phacops* and *Greenops* (Fig. 12.3.1, 2, 4), however, the separate ommatidia are recessed below the general eye surface so that the lenses lie in **lensal pits** and are separated by a cribwork of intervening frames. In this latter case the cornea consists of small discrete units and each lens is covered with its own separate cornea; these are not truly compound eyes but are **aggregate eyes** or **schizochroal eyes.** Lensal pits are circular in most eyes and in all early stages, but become hexagonal in some eyes or in some late ontogenetic stages. In *Phacops rana* the ommatidia are arranged in two obliquely intersecting rows. From 8 to 11 rows occur in vertical succession, and each aggregate eye contains from 33 to 88 ommatidia. About 65 to 80 ommatidia are present in most specimens. From theoretical considerations, it generally is supposed that ocelli are primitive eyes and that compound eyes evolved from them, after which aggregate eyes evolved from compound eyes. Not much paleontologic evidence bears on this subject as yet, and stratigraphic evidence is contradictory. The oldest ocelli are known from Early Ordovician trilobites, whereas the first compound eyes occur in Late Cambrian forms, and the first aggregate eyes are Devonian. The foregoing occurrences lead us to believe that eyes are of very ancient origin and that the evidence from fossils represents stages much too late to reveal the evolutionary history.

Eyes are wonderfully adaptable among trilobites—possibly being the most sensitive indices of their habits. Eyes on the anterior margin of the cephalon, or eyes extending around the anterior margin from dorsal to ventral, are thought to indicate an active swimmer, whereas large eyes on the ventral side of the cephalon indicate a surface-dweller. Most trilobite eyes are located midway on the free cheeks and occupy slightly raised curved areas. The compound or aggregate lens system enables the kind of vision that would be useful to a creature whether it crawled over the bottom or swam about occasionally. A rather startling modification produces eyes at the tips of long stalks above their normal sites, as in *Miraspis* (Fig. 12.3.3). Presumably the stalk-eyed trilobites were half-buried grovelers in the surficial sediment. Burrowing habit is thought to be indicated by blind trilobites, which, like *Isotelus* and *Bumastus,* have smooth dorsal surfaces with suppressed lobation. Various evolutionary trends have been detected in the eyes, such as shifting from ventral to dorsal in position or increasing or diminishing in size.

Aeglina had the largest eyes of any trilobite. In species of this Genus the compound eyes are two huge orbs on the margin of the cephalon, and together comprise more than half of the whole cephalon (Fig. 12.3.5). Probably the strangest place for eyes, however, is on the hypostome (Fig. 12.6.4). Several functional eye spots have been detected on the posterior surfaces of maculae on hypostomes. In all, 136 species belonging to 39 Genera are known to have had hypostomes, and eye spots had been found on hypostomes of 36 species of these by Lindström as early as 1901. Interestingly, some larval Recent crustaceans bear eye spots on their hypostomes, although no eyes are present adjacent to the mouths of adults.

SUTURES. As normally applied to trilobites, the word suture implies an uncalcified seam of chitin in the exoskeleton of the cephalon. Sutures of trilobites resemble seams because the chitin decomposes either after the death of the animal or after the molting of the carapace. In a way, sutures are analogous to articular furrows in the thorax, because both consist of uncalcified chitin. It follows, therefore, that sutures may have served primarily to impart flexibility to the broad cephalon. It has even been hypothesized by some paleontologists that sutures are not only analogous to articular furrows but are homologous with these furrows; and therefore the two free cheeks may represent aberrant remnants of a former segment. Direct evidence to support this theory has not been forthcoming.

It generally is conceded that ecdysis of trilobites was facilitated by the splitting of the cephalon along sutures. Thus, the soft tissues, being tapered posteriorly, were able to wriggle out of the anterior end of the ruptured carapace. It will be noted that the visual surfaces of eyes would be freed at an early stage of molting and accordingly would receive a minimum of rough usage and would be nonfunctioning for only a short time when sight is a major factor of survival. Sutures therefore seem to have served at least two functions, splitting being an adaptation of the earlier service of flexibility. Although free cheeks may have hung on to the rest of the molted cephalon for a time by shreds of chitin remaining in the sutures, decomposition of that chitin eventually could release the free cheeks. No wonder, then, that isolated free cheeks abound in some strata or that cranidia in the same beds commonly lack free cheeks. Of course, in cases wherein free cheeks are not completely outlined by sutures, they remain attached to the rest of the cephalon and may even fall back into the positions they occupied in life. Molted carapaces, therefore, commonly are so complete and natural-appearing that a person usually is puzzled as to whether the carapaces really are molts or possibly represent dead adults.

The most obvious sutures, and the only ones which normally can be seen, are **facial sutures** on the dorsal side of the cephalon (Fig. 12.4.1b). The anterior limbs of the facial sutures generally commence at the margin just anterior to the eyes and extend back along the axial sides of the faceted portion of the eye, separating the light-sensitive area on the free cheek from a mere raised skeletal area (**palpebral lobe**) on the fixed cheek against which the eye abuts. The posterior limb of the facial suture follows one of three courses, but its path is constant for adults of a species. In **opisthoparian** trilobites (Figs. 12.11; 12.13), the posterior limb continues posteriorly from the eye and intersects the posterior margin of the cephalon at some point between the lateral margin of the glabella and the genal angle.

In **proparian** trilobites (Fig. 12.14), the posterior limb diverges laterally from the eye and intersects the lateral margin of the cephalon at some point anterior to the genal angle.

The third or intermediate group, for which no formal name has been accepted, is characterized by *Flexicalymene* (Fig. 12.12.2a), in which the posterior limb of the facial suture passes precisely through the genal angle. The intermediate calymenoid condition once was thought to represent a transition from opisthoparian to proparian sutures. This hypothesis was supported for a long time by the complete dominance of Cambrian faunas by opisthoparian trilobites, whereas post-Cambrian faunas supposedly contained the first proparians as well as the later opisthoparians. It is known

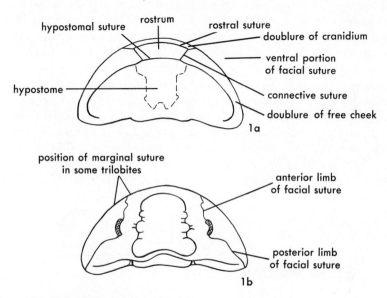

Figure 12.4. Terminology of Sutures of Trilobites. 1a, ventral view. 1b, dorsal view. (After Warburg, 1925.)

now, however, that opisthoparians range from Early Cambrian to Permian, and proparians range from Medial Cambrian to Mississippian; hence, proparians such as *Burlingia* (Fig. 12.14.5) do occur early enough to be ancestral to typical post-Cambrian proparians. It was also known for a long time that the posterior limbs of facial sutures tend to move closer to the genal angle as time passes; hence, opisthoparians could have given rise to proparians through a form such as the calymenoids. On the other hand, proparians might have been ancestral, even though the majority of examples seem to indicate that opisthoparians were ancestral. Recent studies indicate that proparian sutures occur in early molts of species in at least five Genera whose adult forms have opisthoparian sutures. From the present state of our knowledge it seems that similar patterns of facial sutures may have arisen along different courses and that opisthoparian and proparian sutures may not indicate genetic relationship.

In addition to the facial sutures, other cephalic sutures are present on many trilobites, but they are almost or entirely hidden in a dorsal view. It is necessary, therefore, to study the doublure and its structures in order to locate the other sutures (Fig. 12.4). In the first place, the entire doublure may be separated from the rest of the dorsal shield by a **marginal suture** which, as the name implies, lies along the outline of the cephalon. *Paedeumias* is an example of a trilobite with a marginal suture, and *Paedeumias* even bears its hypostome on the doublure (Fig. 12.5.1). Hypostomes may be separated from doublures of some trilobites by a **hypostomal suture** or may remain attached to doublures along a hypostomal furrow. In the former case, isolated hypostomes may occur scattered through sediments. Incidentally, some hypostomes have been mistaken for early molt stages, and, indeed, the resemblance of the two can be great. In the third kind of ventral suture a sector of the doublure at the anterior margin becomes separated from the lateral portions of the doublure by a pair of transverse **connective sutures.** At the same time the intervening sector becomes separated from the dorsal shield by a **rostral suture** which may or may not be continuous with the marginal suture; the resulting isolated piece is the **rostrum.** Considerable

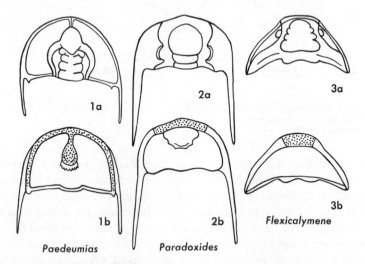

Figure 12.5. Sutures of Trilobites.
Cephalons are arranged in a morphologic series to show progressive reduction in size of the rostrum and loss of the connective sutures. Dorsal views are in the upper row and ventral views are in the lower row. Ventral posterior details have not been proved in all cases. Rostra are stippled. Illustrations are rather schematic and are not drawn to the same scale.

difference of opinion exists as to the homologies of rostral and marginal sutures, as well as to whether connective sutures are merely ventral extensions of facial sutures extending across the doublure or are special sutures. Kjer and Warburg both supported a hypothesis of Barrande that the two connective sutures such as are present in *Paradoxides* and *Calymene* moved closer together until they obliterated the rostrum and fused into a **median suture,** as in *Isotelus.* Then, by a slight additional loss, the median suture disappeared, as in *Dalmanitina.* Convincing phylogenetic series have not been assembled in support of this hypothesis, although isolated morphologic stages such as are shown in Figure 12.5 can be selected to illustrate it.

APPENDAGES. Trilobites had been known from dorsal shields alone since 1698, long before the first unquestioned trace of the ventral shield or of appendages was discovered in 1825. Biologists had eagerly awaited the discovery of ventral structures and paleontologists had earnestly sought suitably preserved material. Interest in appendages of trilobites flourished with only slight encouragement because appendages are the key to unraveling affinities of most groups of the higher Arthropoda, and trilobites have universally been recognized as the most abundant, primitive, arthropodan fossils. A few insignificant appendages of trilobites had been reported before an assiduous collector traced a single loose specimen of *Triarthus becki* to its outcrop in the Utica shale (Ordovician) in New York in 1892 and discovered thereby one of the most important beds of fossils in the world. In order to collect

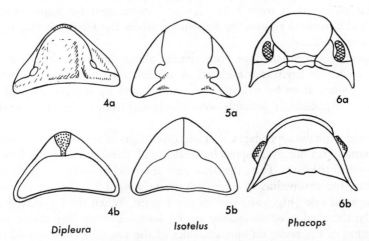

1. *Paedeumias transitans,* slightly deformed, Lower Cambrian, widespread. 2. *Paradoxides harlani,* Middle Cambrian, eastern United States. 3. *Flexicalymene meeki,* Ordovician, east-central United States. 4. *Dipleura dekayi,* Devonian, New York. 5. *Isotelus gigas,* Ordovician, New York. 6. *Phacops cristata,* Devonian, New York.

(1 after Walcott, 1910. 2 after Walcott, 1884. 3 after Meek, 1873. 4, 6 after Hall and Clarke, 1888. 5 after Hall, 1847. Suggested in part by Warburg, 1925 and Stubblefield, 1935.)

from a layer only 10 millimeters thick, tons of black shale have been quarried in the search for pyritized specimens which preserve the ventral anatomy. From a collection of 500 specimens, C. E. Beecher prepared 50 specimens by rubbing away the matrix with fine abrasive and rubber erasers. In this fashion he revealed for the first time the appendages of three Genera of trilobites. Since his work, other less prolific localities over the world have provided material from which the ventral anatomy of about two dozen species has been determined.

Details of the organization of trilobite appendages are quite as significant as biologists and paleontologists had hoped that they would be. The cephalon bears five pairs of appendages, arrayed alongside a subcentral mouth (Fig. 12.6.6). Each member of the anterior pair of appendages, the **antennule,** consists of a single strand. The next four pairs are biramous, segmented, walking limbs which resemble very closely the biramous walking limbs of the thorax. Great significance is attached to the correspondence in number between the five cephalic appendages and the usual five segments of the glabella. Of particular interest is the lack of any mouth parts on a trilobite. Cephalic appendages of some higher arthropods seem to have been modified into mandibles and maxillae; hence, the discovery of true locomotor limbs around the mouths of very primitive arthropods (trilobites) supports the hypothesis that mouth parts of arthropods evolved from legs. If, as seems probable, trilobites either raked food particles toward their mouths with their limbs, or scooped up food between the hypostome and mouth when they stepped backward, it must have been very convenient for some forms to have had a patch of eyes on the hypostome where the food-gathering operations were centered.

Appendages seem to have been similar along the whole length of the thorax. This in itself is considered as a primitive character from which higher groups arose by reduction in number and by specialization of appendages. Appendages probably were eliminated from the posterior somites first.

As with cephalic appendages, thoracic appendages of trilobites are biramous. The same terminology adopted by students of Crustacea is applied to appendages of trilobites. Thus, the basal unit of a trilobite limb is a single large segment, the **coxopodite.** It commonly bears a rigid knucklelike extension on the axial side (Fig. 12.6.1) of its pivot point. When the leg moved posteriorly, the axial node necessarily swung forward. According to one view, oscillation of the nodes on opposite sides of the ventral midline could have been used to advantage by the animal to move food forward to the mouth.

Springing from the coxopodite are two rami of the appendage. The ventral ramus or **endopodite,** which lay next to the ventral midline, consisted of six segments in a row (Fig. 12.6.1, 3). Endopodites seem to have been smooth, except for tiny claws on the tip of the last segment. It is reasonably certain

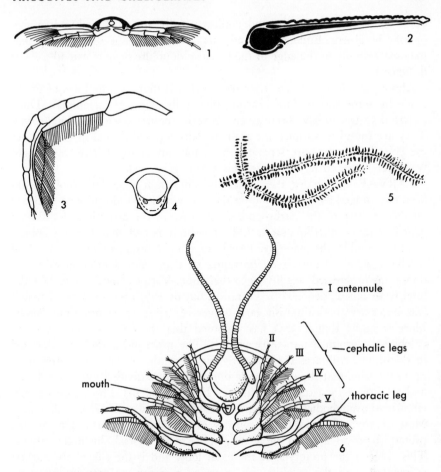

Figure 12.6. Anatomy of Trilobites.
1. Transverse section of a thorax with appendages. 2. Longitudinal section showing alimentary canal and dorsal heart. 3. A thoracic limb showing the two rami. 4. Ventral surface of a hypostome with two maculae (stippled) which may have been eye spots. 5. Tracks of a small arthropod, probably a trilobite, 1X, Cambrian, Arizona. 6. Ventral view of the cephalon and first thoracic segment of *Triarthus becki* with attached appendages, 1 1/3X, Ordovician, New York.
(1-3, 6 after Raymond, 1920. 4 after Warburg, 1925. 5 after White, 1877.)

that endopodites were used for crawling. On the dorsal side of the endopodite, between it and the ventral surface (farther away from the ventral midline, that is), lay a many-segmented slender ramus bearing numerous fine threads projecting ventrally from it like teeth in a comb. This ramus, the **exopodite,** presumably was used for swimming. If the pendant comblike structures bore blood vessels, the endopodite also could have served for respiration. Among higher arthropods, for instance, exopodites may be the primary swimming organs or they may be modified into gills; in both of these cases, however, the endopodites usually are much reduced in size or may be absent. Endopodites and exopodites are about equally long and may extend only to the edge of the thoracic doublure or may extend a short distance beyond it.

Almost certain proof that trilobites crawled is found in the form of tracks made by some sort of limb-bearing, bilaterally symmetrical animal. These chevronlike tracks have been given "generic" names, such as *Climaticnites*. They are found in various fine-grained Paleozoic sediments. In a few cases the paired footprints are separated by a median groove where the ancient wanderer seems to have dragged his telson (Fig. 12.6.5).

LARVAE. Seach for the earliest possible molt stages of trilobites has been encouraged by the expectation that early molts would provide evidence on the ancestry of the Arthropoda as well as on the evolution of different genetic strains of trilobites. It has even been hoped that larval trilobites would resemble the nauplius larval stage of Crustacea. The first larval trilobites were recognized by Barrande in 1849, and description of larval stages has progressed steadily since that time. Various larval stages of trilobites were called "degrees" by Barrande, but by 1895 Beecher decided that it was necessary to distinguish early stages of trilobites as **protaspid larvae.** More recently, Raw (1925) has proposed that the various molt stages of trilobites be grouped into three periods. The **protaspid period,** as restricted in definition, embraces the distinctly larval conditions from the first molt up to the time that the early single dorsal shield is divided into a headpiece and a tailpiece by a transverse suture (Fig. 12.7.1a, 1b). Protaspids are sub-circular to ovate bodies ranging from about 0.4 to 1.0 millimeter in diameter. Most of the protaspid molts consists of cephalic structures. During the protaspid period a **larval ridge** may traverse the dorsal shield lengthwise. This ridge is the prototype of the axial lobe, and is the site of the earliest segmentation of the trilobite, for traces of five somites may be borne on the larval ridge. Ultimately the larval ridge becomes the glabella when the next period is entered. The **meraspid period** begins with the separation of the primordial pygidium from the protaspis and continues through the youth of the trilobite while successive somites are added to the thorax and to the pygidium (Fig. 12.7.1c–1g). Meraspid molts, therefore, span the indefinite boundary between the larval and postlarval stages. The **holaspid period** refers to molts in the adult condition and is defined as those stages in which individuals contain the adult number of thoracic segments (Fig. 12.7.1h, 1i).

It is recognized that protaspid molts resemble nauplius larvae in size and in five-fold segmentation of the cephalic regions. Starting from these basic relationships, Beecher attempted a reconstruction of a complete protaspis based in part upon some philosophical considerations of the homologies of crustacean limbs (Fig. 12.7.5). On the ventral surface of a reconstructed protaspis he located a uniramous pair of antennules, followed by four pairs of biramous appendages. The second pair he assumed were somewhat larger than the others and served as major swimming organs, because this is the condition existing with respect to the pair in a nauplius which become antennae. Earliest nauplius larvae have only three pairs of cephalic ap-

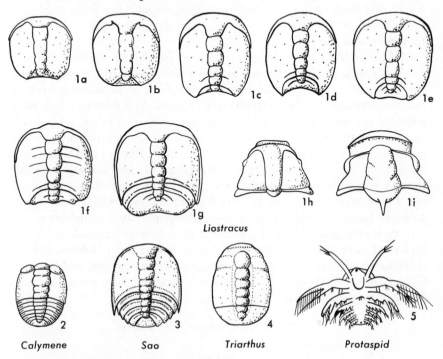

Liostracus

Calymene   Sao   Triarthus   Protaspid

Figure 12.7. Early Molt Stages of Trilobites.
1. *Liostracus linnarssoni*, Cambrian, Sweden. 1a, 1b, protaspid period, 33X. 1c-1g, meraspid period, 33X. 1h, cranidium of young individual, 24X. 1i, cranidium of adult, 3X. 2. Late meraspid period of *Calymene senaria* with eye lobes, Silurian, New York. 3. Late meraspid period of *Sao hirsuta*, 20X, Cambrian, Czechoslovakia. 4. Meraspid period of *Triarthus becki*, 30X, Ordovician, New York. 5. Reconstruction of nauplius-like protaspid stage of *Triarthus becki*.
(1, 2 after Warburg, 1925. 3-5 after Beecher, 1895.)

pendages and there is no segmentation of the trunk region. By the time that five cephalic appendages are present in a crustacean larva, the trunk is distinctly segmented and the larva is in the metanauplius stage. From these considerations it appears that segmentation in a trilobite larva occurs at a distinctly earlier stage than it does in a crustacean larva. Thus, the protaspid period can be correlated with the nauplius stages, and the early meraspid period approximately corresponds to the metanauplius stage. These would be the expected relationships if trilobites are ancestral to the crustaceans. In general, differences between protaspids and nauplius stages are thought to have arisen because of subsequent adaptations on the part of the crustacean larva.

Additional detail is known of the changes involved in larvae of trilobites, but most of it concerns individual differences in form and plan which need not be described. In any case, different larval stages differ from each other rather strikingly. Compare, for instance, corresponding stages of *Liostracus, Calymene,* and *Sao* (Fig. 12.7.1g, 2, 3).

CLASSIFICATION. Cephalic sutures are peculiar to trilobites; therefore much attention has been devoted to their description in the hope that they would provide especially valuable aids to identifying and classifying trilobites and to understanding their evolutionary changes. As a matter of fact, more attention has been devoted to the nature of sutures than to any other single character of trilobites. In spite of the most carefully discriminated sutural distinctions, it is now rather apparent that sutures alone are no philosopher's stone, from the use of which the relationships of trilobites will be made clear. A recent authority has made the plaintive observation that paleontologists have been mesmerized by sutural detail and now will have to use all anatomic features in order to carry on the taxonomic study of trilobites.

In view of a general lack of agreement as to how to subdivide the Class, no formal subdivisions are recognized herein among the Trilobitae. Instead, characteristics of several of the common groups are described and common Genera are cited. About 50 Families of trilobites have been recognized, and 2525 generic names are on record.

KEY TO MAJOR GROUPS OF TRILOBITES

I. Two or three thoracic segments
    A. Transverse furrows on axial lobe of
        pygidium .... Eodiscids
    B. No transverse furrows on axial lobe
        of pygidium .... Agnostids
II. Five or more thoracic segments
    A. No pygidium .... Mesonacids
    B. Pygidium present
        1. Opisthoparian facial suture .... Opisthoparians
        2. Proparian facial suture .... Proparians

Mesonacids. This group includes the oldest trilobites and therefore the first abundant faunas of the geologic record. The whole group is typified by *Mesonacis* (which is the prior name for *Olenellus*). Cephalons are semicircular and may or may not bear genal spines, as well as small intergenal spines projecting from the posterior border (Figs. 12.8, 12.9). The glabella is tapered or parallel-sided and usually bears four or five glabellar furrows or pairs of glabellar furrows. The occipital ring is always prominent. Facial ridges normally are very strong and continue posteriorly as raised kidney-shaped areas which simulate eyes to a remarkable degree, but which are not known to have borne visual organs. In short, all mesonacid trilobites were blind. No facial sutures, or, therefore, free cheeks are present.

The thorax consists of 15 somites which taper posteriorly until the fifteenth segment is reached; this segment consists largely of the axial lobe because pleura are reduced essentially to posteriorly curved spines. The fifteenth

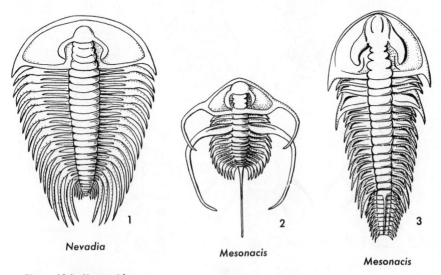

Nevadia

Mesonacis

Mesonacis

Figure 12.8. Mesonacids.
1. *Nevadia weeksi,* 1/2X, Lower Cambrian, Nevada. 2. *Mesonacis fremonti,* 1X, Lower Cambrian, Nevada. 3. *Mesonacis vermontana,* 2/3X, Lower Cambrian, Vermont. (After Walcott, 1910.)

segment, incidentally, can be identified because it bears a large, dorsally directed spine. Another very characteristic feature of mesonacids is the expansion of the third thoracic segment into a segment which is distinctly wider and broader than any others in the thorax. The V-shaped mesonacid thorax apparently represents a primitive condition, whereas the posterior pleura of higher trilobites widened until the entire thorax was essentially parallel-sided.

No pygidium is present in any mesonacid. Instead, there was a series of narrow **post-thoracic segments** which were about as wide as the axial lobe of the thorax but had very narrow pleura with short spines. As many as 47 post-thoracic segments have been counted in mesonacids, but even then there was no evidence as to how the body of the animal terminated. Specimens of mesonacids showing articulated thoracic segments are uncommon, and speci-

mens with post-thoracic segments are exceedingly rare. In some instances the
fifteenth thoracic segment was interpreted as the pygidium and its spine was
thought to be a telson or caudal spine, but these were misapprehensions.
The post-thoracic segments resemble to a remarkable degree a nereid worm
appended to the thorax of a mesonacid. It is not difficult, therefore, to pre-
empt this appearance as additional evidence that arthropods evolved from

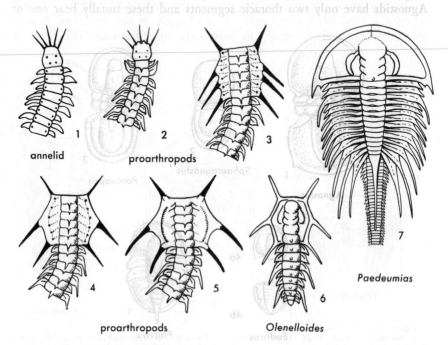

Figure 12.9.   Annelid Ancestry of Trilobites.
1. Generalized view of the anterior segments of a polychaete annelid worm. 2. Proarthropod
with axial and pleural spines. 3. Early arthropod with head consisting of six segments.
4, 5. Successive stages in coalescence of head segments. 6. Dorsal view of *Olenelloides
armatus*, 6X, Cambrian, Scotland. 7. *Paedeumias robsonensis* with post-thoracic segments
reminiscent of an annelid worm, 1/3X, Lower Cambrian, British Columbia.
(1-5 after Raw, 1953. 6 after Raw, 1957. 7 after Raymond, 1920.)

annelids and that the mesonacids occupied an intermediate position on the
evolutionary path. Stages in the supposed evolutionary series are depicted in
Figure 12.9.

   Mesonacis [*Olenellus*] is the best-known Genus. The oldest Genus of
trilobites, however, is *Nevadia*, with its tapering body. *Paedeumias* is another common Genus and is characterized by a small rostral suture between
the glabella and the anterior margin of the cephalon (Figs. 12.5.1, 12.9.7).
All of the seven known Genera of mesonacids are Lower Cambrian. Meson-

acids are widespread. Specimens can be collected in considerable quantities from Lower Cambrian strata in California, Nevada, and Pennsylvania.

Agnostids. Although agnostids (together with the next group, the eodiscids) are the smallest of the trilobites, they are very useful in stratigraphic work and are interesting from an evolutionary point of view. They range in size from 2 or 3 millimeters up to about 1 centimeter in length. Agnostids have only two thoracic segments and these usually bear one or

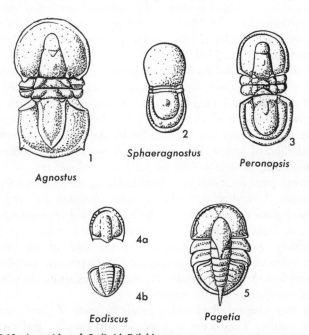

Figure 12.10. Agnostid and Eodiscid Trilobites.
1. *Agnostus interstrictus*, 4X, Cambrian, Nevada, Utah. 2. *Sphaeragnostus similaris*, 6X, Ordovician, Czechoslovakia. 3. *Peronopsis montis*, 3X, Cambrian, British Columbia. 4a, 4b. Cephalon and pygidium of *Eodiscus bellimarginatus*, 1 1/2X, Cambrian, Newfoundland. 5. *Pagetia clytia*, 8X, Cambrian, Idaho and Utah.
(1 after White, 1877. 2 after Kobayashi, 1939. 3 after Matthew, 1899. 4, 5 after Kobayashi, 1944.)

two nodes on the axial lobe (Fig. 12.10.1–3). The cephalon and pygidium are semicircular to quadrate and generally are exactly the same size and shape. Although the axial lobe commonly is delimited by axial furrows, no eyes or facial sutures are visible on the potential cephalon, and no series of transverse furrows subdivides the axial lobe of the potential pygidium into segments. It is not surprising, therefore, that there have been differences of opinion as to which end of an agnostid is anterior. The consensus is that terminal spines on one shield probably point posteriorly as in most other trilobites; that effacement of surficial details is most common on anterior regions as in other trilobites; and that articular facets sometimes seen on axial rings are on the anterior margins of the thoracic segments. Kobayashi (1939) has suggested a useful rule-of-thumb method for orienting most agnostids. His system is based upon division of the axial lobe in one or both of the two (cephalic and pygidial) shields by a transverse furrow. If the portion of the axial lobe nearest the thorax is larger than the distal portion, then that shield is the cephalon; but if the proximal portion is smaller than the distal portion, then the shield is the pygidium. In addition, many agnostids have a pair of basal lobes at the posterior-lateral margins of the glabella; these may be occipital lobes.

Agnostus is the typical Genus of the group. All together, however, 38 Genera and 286 species (including synonyms) had been described by 1939. Species of *Peronopsis* and *Pseudagnostus* are common in North America. The first agnostids appeared in the Early Cambrian of the eastern United States where three Genera are known. By Medial Cambrian there was an explosive radiation of agnostids over the entire world. They declined in the Late Cambrian and became extinct in the Late Ordovician.

Two different interpretations have been made of the evolutionary position of the agnostids. According to one view these creatures are very primitive trilobites which gave rise to higher forms by increased segmentation and by development of facial sutures. According to the other view, agnostids represent extremely specialized arthropods at the end of an evolutionary sequence of trilobites in which segmentation and eyes, and possibly sutures also, have been lost. A rather considerable literature exists on the phylogenetic position and significance of the agnostids.

Agnostids comprise excellent index fossils in spite of their controversial morphologic nature. They seem to have evolved rapidly, and Genera and species are widespread, although agnostids do not seem to have been particularly well adapted for swimming. If they were burrowers they probably would have preferred one kind of bottom in which to live, but their remains occur with more or less equal abundance in various kinds of clastic and carbonate sediments. It has been suggested by Howell and Resser (1934), therefore, that agnostids may have clung to floating seaweeds and have been pseudoplanktonic, thereby attaining widespread distribution and also being entombed in dissimilar sediments.

Eodiscids. Eodiscids are so similar to agnostids in size and appearance that some care is needed in order to tell them apart. Eodiscid trilobites are characterized by the possession of two or three thoracic somites and by cephalons and pygidia of very similar construction. An ornamental internal or external border of nodes or crenulations is present on the cephalon, and a variable number of segments (5 to 14) is present in the axial lobe of the pygidium (Fig. 12.10.4, 5). Eodiscid dorsal shields usually are disassociated; hence, thoracic segments may be rare. Axial rings on the thoracic segments of eodiscids lack the paired nodes which characterize many agnostids. Moreover, the glabellae of agnostids are prominently bilobed, whereas those of the eodiscids are only faintly furrowed transversely, if at all. The largest eodiscids, when complete, are only about 2 centimeters long.

Two subdivisions of eodiscids are recognized. The blind forms, typified by *Eodiscus* (Middle Cambrian), lack not only eyes, but also facial sutures (Fig. 12.10.4). A large spine extends backward from the occipital ring in this Genus. *Eodiscus* has three thoracic segments. The other group, characterized by *Pagetia* (Middle Cambrian), bears tiny eyes near the lateral margins of the cephalon and the eyes are associated with small free cheeks and proparian sutures (Fig. 12.10.5).

Eodiscids are known from Lower and Middle Cambrian strata in many parts of the world. Five Genera and 12 species have been reported from North America, and the total for the world comprises 15 Genera and 46 species. Early Cambrian eodiscids belong to the Atlantic faunal realm, but by Medial Cambrian time the eodiscids had migrated into the Indo-Pacific faunal realm. So far, however, eodiscids have not been collected in Africa or in western and central Asia.

Opisthoparians. Practically all Middle and Upper Cambrian trilobites and the majority of post-Cambrian trilobites have opisthoparian sutures (Figs. 12.11–12.13). Authorities do not agree at this time upon subdivisions of the group, except that it contains about a score of Families.

As soon as the mesonacids became extinct at the end of the Early Cambrian, the opisthoparians appeared as the dominant form of Medial and Late Cambrian life. Moreover, opisthoparians far outstripped the mesonacids in numbers and diversity. Thoraxes tend to remain articulated; therefore rather complete specimens can be collected. Evolution of cephalons can be traced primarily in changes of the shape of glabellae and in the number of glabellar furrows. Eyes of Cambrian opisthoparians are usually distinct and do not vary much in position or in size.

Pygidia of opisthoparians are usually interesting because they not only appear for the first time in normal trilobites (that is, other than in agnostids and eosdiscids), but they are subject to extensive modification. The number of segments in axial and pleural lobes of pygidia begins to vary disharmonically early in their evolution; when pygidial spines are present on the margin their positions may either be coordinated with segments or they may be located according to another plan. In some forms the axial lobe becomes notably elevated, and in others the pleural lobes expand laterally. Pygidia of Late Cambrian opisthoparians in particular had wide pleural lobes in conjunction with wide brims of cephalons. *Dikelocephalus* (Fig. 12.11.8) is

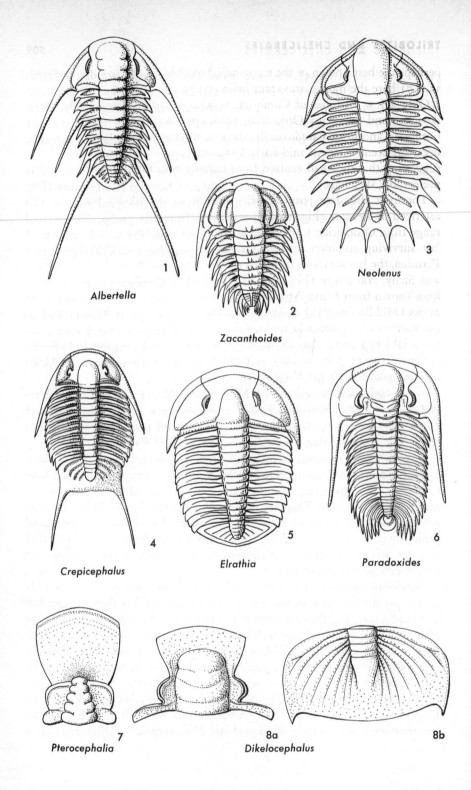

1 Albertella

2 Zacanthoides

3 Neolenus

4 Crepicephalus

5 Elrathia

6 Paradoxides

7 Pterocephalia

8a 8b Dikelocephalus

perhaps the best known of the scoop-tailed trilobites, but *Pterocephalia* (Fig. 12.11.7) bore the most extravagant brim on the cephalon.

Only a few Families of Cambrian opisthoparians survived into the Ordovician, and not many Ordovician opisthoparians are known to have had Cambrian ancestors. Paradoxically, the second group of opisthoparians burst upon the scene at about mid-Early Ordovician time in wonderful diversity, suggesting that they had evolved from unknown ancestors with largely non-preservable skeletons.

The most abundant post-Cambrian opisthoparians are the proetids, characterized by *Proetus* (Fig. 12.12.5) and about 64 additional Genera. Proetids range from Ordovician to Permian and have the distinction of including the last surviving trilobites. Fifteen Genera of proetids are known from the Permian, the last survivors of which seem to have made their stand in Timor and Sicily. *Anisopyge* (Fig. 12.12.7), which is the youngest Genus of trilobites known from North America, occurs not uncommonly in the Guadalupe Series (Middle Permian) of Texas. During the later part of proetid evolution the number of segments in the pygidium tended to increase (particularly in the axial lobe) and a smooth marginal flange arose on the pygidium.

Flexicalymene (Fig. 12.12.2) and about a dozen related Genera comprise another group with generalized form which is especially common in Ordovician and Silurian rocks in eastern North America. *Flexicalymene* is referred to the opisthoparians somewhat doubtfully, however, because the posterior limb of the facial suture passes through the genal angle instead of occupying a distinctly opisthoparian or proparian position.

In addition to the foregoing opisthoparians with orthodox appearances, several groups became noteworthy and easily recognizable because of anatomic peculiarities or even monstrosities. Among the aberrant forms are *Bumastus* and *Isotelus* (Fig. 12.12.1, 3), both of which lost almost every vestige of sculpture on the cephalons and pygidia and also lost their eyes. These Genera usually have been interpreted as burrowers and mud-grubbers.

Trinucleid trilobites have prominently three-lobed cephalons; hence the name of the typical Genus, *Trinucleus*. In addition, only six thoracic segments are present, the pygidium is very small, and the adults were blind (although small eyes present in young forms). In North America the typical trinucleids are represented by *Cryptolithus,* which is common in sediments in the Ordovician of the northern Appalachian geosyncline and

Figure 12.11 (opposite). Cambrian Opisthoparians.
1. *Albertella helenae,* 1 1/2X, Montana.   2. *Zacanthoides idahoensis,* 4X, Idaho.   3. *Neolenus pugio,* 1 1/2X, Utah.   4. *Crepicephalus iowensis,* 2/3, Wisconsin.   5. *Elrathia kingi,* 1X, Utah.   6. *Paradoxides harlani,* 1/5X, Massachusetts.   7. Cranidium of *Pterocephalia laticeps,* 1X, Nevada.   8a, 8b. Cranidium and pygidium of *Dikelocephalus minnesotensis,* 1/3X, Wisconsin and Minnesota.
(1-3 after Walcott, 1905. 4 after Walcott, 1916. 5 after White, 1877. 6 after Walcott, 1884. 7 after Hall and Whitfield, 1877. 8 after Hall, 1863.)

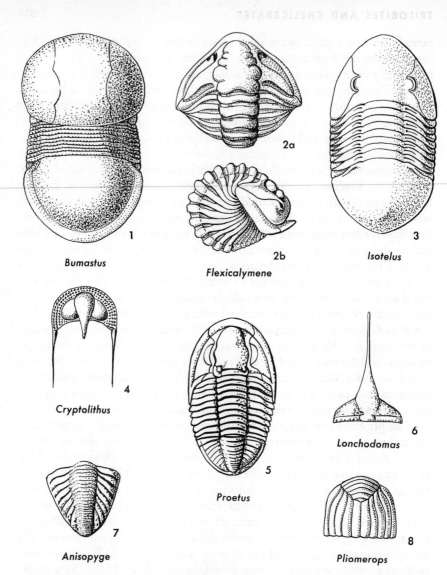

Figure 12.12. Post-Cambrian Opisthoparians.
1. *Bumastus barriensis*, 1X, Silurian, eastern United States.   2a, 2b. Dorsal and side views of an enrolled *Flexicalymene meeki*, 1X, Ordovician, Ohio.   3. *Isotelus gigas*, 1X, Ordovician, eastern United States.   4. Cephalon of *Cryptolithus tesselatus*, 1X, eastern United States and Canada. 5. *Proetus nevadae*, 1 3/4X, Devonian, Nevada. 6. Cephalon of *Lonchodomas halli*, 2X, Ordovician, New York and Ontario. 7. Pygidium of *Anisopyge perannulata*, 2X, Permian, Texas. One of the last trilobites known from North America. 8. Pygidium of *Pliomerops canadensis*, 1X, Ordovician, New York and Ontario.
(1 after Hall, 1852. 2 after Meek, 1873. 3, 4 after Hall, 1847. 5 after Merriam, 1940. 6, 8 after Raymond, 1906. 7 after Girty, 1908.)

extends west into the midcontinent (Fig. 12.12.4). Even small fragments of the cephalon of *Cryptolithus* can be identified because the cephalic border is extensively pitted and resembles a lacy ruff or frill. The 13 Genera of trinucleids locally are abundant in Ordovician strata of Europe and North America, but only 2 or 3 Genera are common to both continents. Two Genera are known from Manchukuo. Rapidity of evolution enables the trinucleids to be useful in correlations.

A close relative of the trinucleids, *Lonchodomas,* lacks a lacy frill but bears a remarkably long median spine like a medieval jousting lance on the front of the cephalic border (Fig. 12.12.6). Reconciliation of the value of this spine in a blind trilobite should provide a philosophically inclined person with ample material for thought. *Lonchodomas* also is peculiar in having only five thoracic segments, whereas other normal trilobites (both opistho-parian and proparian) have six or more. The Genus occurs in Ordovician strata of Europe and North America.

The several remaining groups of opisthoparians resemble each other in the distinct and sometimes astonishing spinosity of the later members of each group. In the first rank, *Lichas* and *Arctinurus* represent a group of about 40 Genera in which the glabellae consist basically of six lobes instead of the usual five. Most of the evolution of the lichadids took place in Europe through the Ordovician and Devonian, but populations migrated into North America in the Medial Silurian and Early Devonian. A typical glabella of advanced forms not only lacks the third and fourth lateral glabellar furrows but is divided by two longitudinal furrows into three lengthwise lobes instead of preserving the basic pattern of five transverse furrows. Pygidia bear about three pairs of rather broad pleural ribs which are produced into points around the margin. A striking feature of the lichadids such as *Echinolichas* (Fig. 12.13.5) and *Gaspelichas* (Fig. 12.13.6) is their tendency to become spinose immediately prior to their extinction at the end of the Devonian.

In addition to the lichadids, *Acidaspis* and its relatives also became exces-sively spinose (Fig. 12.13.2). Acidaspids differ from lichadids principally in having smaller pygidia, but acidaspids also may be even more spinose than the lichadids are, so that pleura of pygidia may be produced into long spines. Acidaspids range from Ordovician to Devonian.

Spinosity of different kinds is also present in the so-called odontopleurids, which range from Ordovician to Devonian. About 16 Genera are included in the Family. In one case, very complicated pygidia such as those of *Dicanthaspis* even bear secondary spines on the major pygidial spines (Fig. 12.13.3). Cephalons of *Dicanthaspis* and *Miraspis* (Fig. 12.3.3) bore a mar-ginal fringe of long straight spines like teeth of a comb. The cephalon of *Dicranurus* (Fig. 12.13.7) bore a remarkable, forked, recurved spine which resembled the horns of a bighorn sheep.

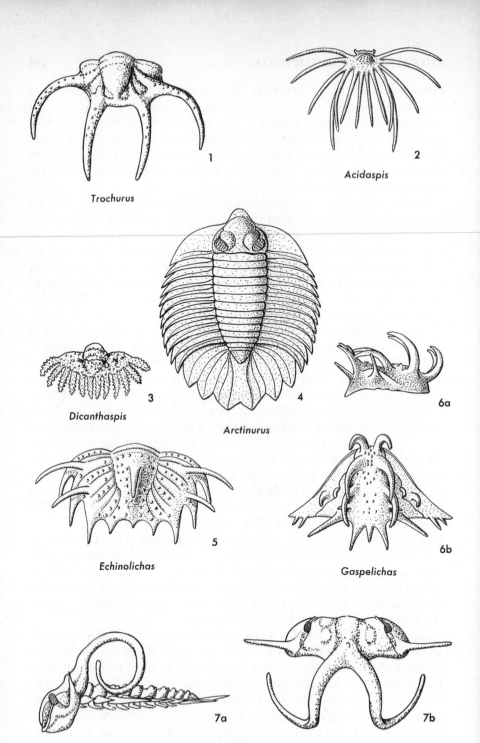

1

Trochurus

2

Acidaspis

3

Dicanthaspis

4

Arctinurus

6a

5

Echinolichas

6b

Gaspelichas

7a

7b

Dicranurus

Proparians. As in the case of the opisthoparians, those trilobites which are characterized by a proparian sutural trace are not known to constitute a close-knit genetic group. Only half a dozen Families are referred to the proparians with confidence. *Burlingia* (Fig. 12.14.5), from the Middle Cambrian, is the oldest accepted proparian trilobite and is the only known Cambrian Genus. Other Genera range from Ordovician to Mississippian. (Specialists seem to be agreed that *Pagetia* [Fig. 12.10.5], which has proparian sutures, is an eodiscid and is therefore quite unrelated to the true proparians).

The most important proparian Family, the phacopids, is characterized in American faunas by *Phacops* and *Dalmanites* (Fig. 12.14.1, 3). Phacopids range from Early Ordovician into Early Mississippian, but their greatest flare was during the Devonian. The phacopids are one of the two or three Families of trilobites which survived beyond the Devonian (the only other important Family being the proetids among the opisthoparians). *Dalmanites* is well known because of the prominent terminal spine on the pygidium, which has been likened to the telson of the Recent horseshoe crab, *Limulus*. This articulated spine is used in *Limulus* as a lever which is drawn down sharply and thereby drives the animal backward. In *Dalmanites,* however, the spine is rigidly fastened to the pygidium and probably was too fragile to be used as a trigger for propulsion. *Dalmanites,* therefore, seems to have been a bottom-dweller.

Trimerus (Fig. 12.14.2) is one of about ten Genera in a Family which is characterized by loss of most of the sculpture from the cephalon, thus converging upon the character of *Isotelus* among the opisthoparians.

Encrinurus (Fig. 12.14.7) characterizes another group of about 18 Genera. This Genus resembles the proetids somewhat in having discordant numbers of axial and pleural segments in the pygidium.

Finally, some of the proparians also were subject to spinosity. **Cheirurids** are spinose trilobites which fill a position among proparians parallel to that of the lichadids and other spinose forms among opisthoparians. Fifteen of the 19 Genera of cheirurids became extinct by the end of the Ordovician and only 2 Genera lasted until the end of the Devonian when the whole group became extinct. *Ceraurus* is a well-known Ordovician Genus (Fig. 12.14.4) and *Cheirurus* is common in the Silurian (Fig. 12.14.8, 9). Spinosity among cheirurids principally affects the pygidium, although genal spines usually

Figure 12.13 (*opposite*). Spinose Opisthoparians.
1. Pygidium of *Trochurus phylactainodes*, 1X, Silurian, Illinois. 2. Pygidium of *Acidaspis romingeri*, 1X, Devonian, Michigan. 3. Pygidium of *Dicanthaspis secretus*, 9X, Ordovician, Virginia. 4. *Arctinurus boltoni*, 1/4X, Silurian, New York. 5. Pygidium of *Echinolichas eriopsis*, 3X, Devonian, New York. 6a, 6b. Side view of cranidium and dorsal view of cephalon of *Gaspelichas forillonia*, 1/3X, Devonian, Quebec. 7a, 7b. Side view and dorsal view of cephalon of *Dicranurus monstrosus*, 1X, Devonian, Czechoslovakia.
(1 after Weller, 1907. 2, 5 after Hall and Clarke, 1888. 3, 7 after Whittington, 1956. 4 after Hall, 1852. 6 after Clarke, 1908.)

are present and thoracic pleura may be rather spinose. Pygidia normally have only three or four segments and may be difficult to differentiate from the thorax. Two geographic races seem to have arisen among even the earliest cheirurids, for Genera such as *Cheirurus* which bear spines of subequal length on all pygidial pleura are almost confined to southern Europe. On the other hand, Genera such as *Ceraurus* with extra long spines on the first pygidial pleura are confined to northern Europe and North America. Unlike most other trilobites, evolution of cheirurids can be traced in modifications in length and slope of the pleural furrows and variations in the number of punctae in the pleural furrows. In addition, some cheirurids evolved into blind forms.

Of all the spinose trilobites, however, the proparian Genus *Deiphon* from the Silurian of Europe is one of the most bizarre (Fig. 12.14.6). Its cephalon is reduced to a swollen glabella with eye-bearing spines for fixed cheeks. Thoracic pleura are merely long spines and the pygidium is reduced to a pair of spines. Presumably *Deiphon* was a planktonic trilobite.

Adaptations of Trilobites. Spines are singularly represented in the evolution of most trilobites. Mesonacids not only bore genal spines, but the pleura terminated in spines. Later on pygidia became well established and also tended to become spinose in some groups. Chief among the spinose trilobites, of course, are the lichadids, acidaspids, and cheirurids, which are characterized by truly extravagant spinosity. Each of these three groups arose in the Ordovician and became extinct at the end of the Devonian, during which interval there was a distinct tendency for increase in spinosity in each strain. Paleontologists dicovered long ago that extinction followed upon culmination of spinosity and concluded that spines indicated the onset of racial old age. Moreover, the parallelism among the three groups of spiny trilobites mentioned above was looked upon by some naturalists as being the result of orthogenesis.

In succeeding years biologists have tended to explain spinosity in trilobites in relation to adaptation to environment. The general adaptive trends among trilobites seem to have led from crawling to swimming and then to planktonic existence. Thus, the mesonacids with no pygidia, and the other

---

Figure 12.14 (opposite). Proparians.
1. *Phacops rana*, 2/3X, Devonian, New York. 2. *Trimerus delphinocephalus*, 2/3X, Silurian, New York. 3. *Dalmanites limulurus*, 1X, Silurian, New York. 4. *Ceraurus pleurexanthemus*, 1X, Ordovician, New York. 5. *Burlingia hectori*, 6X, Middle Cambrian, British Columbia. 6. *Deiphon forbesi*, 2X, Silurian, Czechoslovakia. 7. Pygidium of *Encrinurus ornatus*, 1X, Silurian, central and eastern United States. 8. Pygidium of *Cheirurus welleri*, 1X, Silurian, north-central and eastern United States. 9. Cephalon of *Cheirurus niagarensis*, 1X, Silurian, north-central and eastern United States.
(1, 2 after Hall and Clarke, 1888. 3, 7 after Hall, 1852. 4 after Raymond and Barton, 1913. 5 after Walcott, 1908. 6 after Barrande, 1872. 8 after Weller, 1907. 9 after Raymond, 1916.)

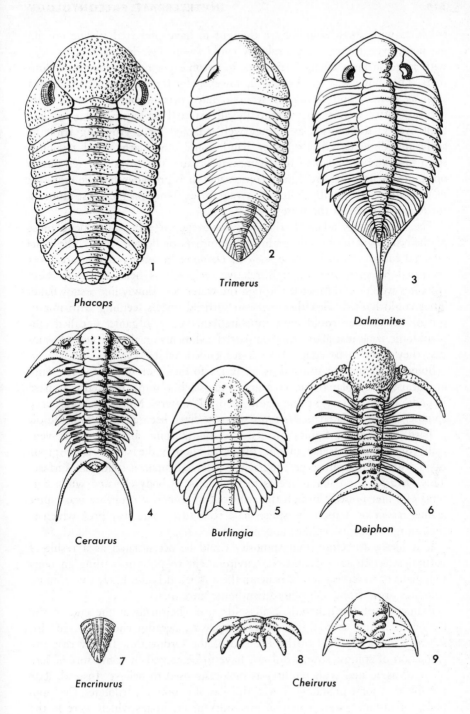

1   *Phacops*

2   *Trimerus*

3   *Dalmanites*

4   *Ceraurus*

5   *Burlingia*

6   *Deiphon*

7   *Encrinurus*

8, 9   *Cheirurus*

trilobites with small pygidia, are thought to have preferred to live on the sea floor, even though they probably could swim. Development of pygidia with large surfaces enabled trilobites to become potentially effective swimmers. The ability was only potential, however, for some large-tailed trilobites such as *Isotelus* and *Bumastus* seem to have become burrowers. At least the two latter Genera lost essentially all external sculpture and even lost their eyes in some cases, as if they were adapted for a groveling habit in surficial sediments. On the other hand, some other large-tailed trilobites seem to have been adapted for swimming because their eyes are well developed and their bodies are lightly constructed. It is probable that the majority of trilobites were equally suited to a vagrant existence on the substratum or for journeys through the water.

The most highly adapted trilobites, however, probably could spend most of their time in the pelagic realm as swimmers or floaters. Thus, the best-adapted forms would be those such as *Deiphon* in which surface area was increased by spinosity although relative weight was held constant; these trilobites would tend to settle through the water very slowly like a snowflake. They could have dwelt either in clean surficial waters teeming with microorganisms, or they could have inhabited that oozy, organic, so-called epiplanktonic zone just above the compacted sediments on the sea floor. In any case they seem to be adapted for a suspended habit.

Spinosity cannot be utilized as an index to depth of water, for not only are near-surface planktonic creatures spinose, but some markedly spinose isopods (Fig. 13.12.5) come from bathyal waters. Moreover, one very spinose trilobite related to *Miraspis* seems to have been adapted to a life on a hard substratum. Spines on its cephalic margins all were bent ventrally until their tips lay in one plane, as though the spines were props upon which the creature perched when it landed upon a solid, flat surface. This *Miraspis*-like trilobite seems to have kept its body elevated while currents of water passed through the cribwork of spines. It probably was either a filter-feeder or it used the spines as a weir to ensnare tiny prey which it then caught with its cephalic appendages.

It is likely, therefore, that spinosity could be accentuated as a result of natural selection in a planktonic environment to prevent settling in oozy sediments or to serve as props beneath the animal. It is also likely that spinose trilobites arose from nonspinose benthonic ancestors.

Extinction of the lichadids, acidaspids, and cheirurids at the end of the Devonian is not as coordinated as it appears, because cheirurids, for instance, had mostly died off by the end of the Ordovician. In any case the extinction of spinose strains did not have to be caused by some sort of loss of vigor associated with senility, as biologists used to believe. Instead, it is possible that some predators cleared the seas of planktonic trilobites. Cephalopods, for instance, were potential predatory invertebrates which were in the ascendancy during the Paleozoic and were particularly vigorous toward the end of the Devonian when the natutiloids were still abundant and the ammonoids were just embarking upon their evolutionary burst.

But more effective carnivores were the sharks and fish which experienced their most rapid rise while the trilobites rapidly declined. Bony fish with

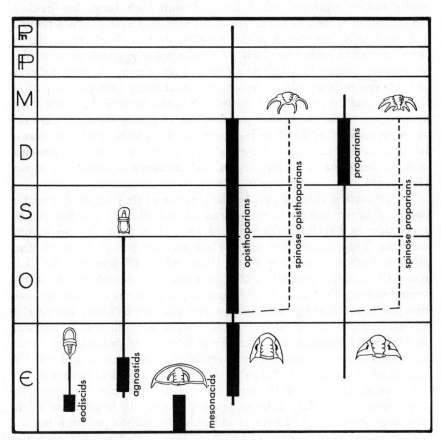

Figure 12.15. Geologic Range of Trilobites.
Ranges of spinose strains are shown by dotted lines.
(After Whittington, 1954.)

good jaws and teeth were well established by the end of the Devonian; hence they may have reduced the trilobites to their benthonic and burrowing habits and have caused the extinction of the ultraspinose strains.

GEOLOGIC HISTORY. Details of the history of trilobites are interwoven above with the discussion of the different groups. In addition, the ranges of the major groups are shown in Figure 12.15.

Class C.   Chelicerata

The Chelicerata comprise the scorpions, spiders, mites, and the extinct eurypterids. Primitive and ancient members of the Class seem to have been mostly marine organisms which breathed with **book lungs,** but modern representatives of the Chelicerata are mostly terrestrial animals which breathe with book gills. Respiration in the most highly specialized chelicerates is either assisted or carried on solely by tubular **tracheae** which permeate the body tissues. Bodies of Chelicerata are divided into a composite cephalothorax and into one or two posterior regions, the latter being analogous to part of the thorax and the pygidium of trilobites. It cannot be proved that the three body regions of the chelicerates are composed of exactly the same segments as are represented in the three body regions of trilobites or of crustaceans; hence, it is customary to name the body regions of chelicerates the **prosoma** or head, **mesosoma** or thoracic region, and **metasoma** or abdominal region (Fig. 12.18).

The prosoma is characterized by the presence of six pairs of appendages instead of by five pairs as in the crustaceans and trilobites. The first pair of appendages in a chelicerate is a pair of small claws borne on two stumpy segments. These appendages, called **chelicerae,** are one of the most characteristic features of members of the Class and are the source of the Class name, Chelicerata. Chelicerae are so short that they are only visible on the ventral surface of the animals. Chelicerae are homologous with the biramous first pair of cephalic legs in Trilobitae and with the biramous antennae of Crustacea. Moreover, no appendages function as antennules or as antennae in Chelicerata. Posterior to the chelicerae is a pair of **pedipalps** which are homologous with the second pair of cephalic legs in trilobites and with the mandibles of crustaceans. Pedipalps may be very large and equipped with conspicuous claws. It will be found upon comparison, however, that these claws occupy an entirely different position than do the large chelae on the first large thoracic legs of lobsters and crabs. Behind the pedipalps but still on the prosoma are four pairs of **walking legs,** each of which bears a tiny claw at its tip. Two pairs of the walking legs of chelicerates are homologous with the two pairs of posterior cephalic appendages of trilobites, but the two remaining pairs of legs of a chelicerate seem to be represented by thoracic legs in trilobites.

The mesosoma contains six or seven segments. In some groups these segments may tend to fuse together. If book lungs are present, then the apertures to the gill chambers will open in pairs through the ventral surfaces of the anterior segments. Also, the genital pore is located centrally on the ventral surface of the first segment of the mesosoma. If appendages of trilobites and chelicerates correspond as suggested above, then the genital segment of chelicerates seems to be homologous with the third thoracic segment of trilobites which is so enlarged among mesonacids. If appendages are present on the mesosoma they are small to rudimentary. Usually they are lacking.

The metasoma also contains six segments, but never bears appendages. Inasmuch as the anal opening is located in the last segment, the metasoma cannot be homologous with the pygidium of trilobites, although it seems to correspond with the abdomen of crustaceans. The metasoma is terminated by a spine (**telson**), by a stinger, or by fan-shaped uropods such as are present among the Crustacea.

CLASSIFICATION. The Chelicerata can be divided into two Sub-classes according to whether the animals are primarily aquatic or terrestrial. Within each of these Subclasses a few Orders are discussed below. All of the Orders of Merostomata are included in the classification because most of them are represented by significant fossil remains, but only a few Orders of Arachnoida are discussed because of the great diversity of these forms and their insignificant representation as fossils.

KEY TO SUBCLASSES AND ORDERS OF CHELICERATES

I. Respiration by book gills .... Subclass Merostomata
    A. 12 thoracic segments
       1. Walking legs unmodified .... Order Aglaspida
       2. Walking legs modified .... Order Eurypterida
    B. Fewer than 12 thoracic segments
       1. Thoracic with shield .... Order Xiphosurida
       2. No thoracic shield; seven
          pairs of appendages .... Order Pycnogonida
II. Respiration by book lungs or tracheae .... Subclass Arachnoida
    A. Body unsegmented .... Order Acarida
    B. Body segmented
       1. Pedipalps with claws .... Order Scorpionida
       2. Pedipalps clawless
         a. Pedipalps spinose .... Order Pedipalpida
         b. Pedipalps not spinose
           (1) Waist constricted .... Order Araneida
           (2) Waist not constricted .... Order Phalangida

SUBCLASS 1. MEROSTOMATA

The Merostomata are characterized by the presence of book gills which may either be exposed or covered by greatly modified appendages. All mero-stomes are aquatic but fresh-water as well as marine representatives may be included. In addition to described and named hard parts, trails of supposed merostomes have been called *Merostomichnites*.

Order a.   Aglaspida

The aglaspids comprise an Order of very primitive chelicerates which is restricted to the midcontinent of the United States. Only 11 Genera and 23 species are known, but the group is important because of its early occurrence and evolutionary significance.

Aglaspid carapaces are composed of chitino-phosphatic material. They resemble the carapaces of trilobites and eurypterids so much that some care

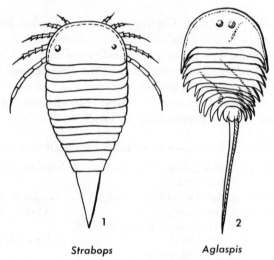

Strabops   Aglaspis

Figure 12.16. Aglaspids.
1. Reconstruction of *Strabops thacheri*, 1/3X, Cambrian, Missouri.   2. *Aglaspis spinifer*, 2/3X, Cambrian, Wisconsin.
(1 after Clarke and Ruedemann, 1912. 2 after Raasch, 1939.)

may be needed to tell them apart. Unlike trilobites, however, the aglaspids lack the two dorsal furrows which set off the axial lobe from the two pleural lobes. Instead, the trilobation of an aglaspid is very faint and consists only of slight changes in convexity. The cephalothorax is a flat shield devoid of furrows, facial sutures, or glabella. It does bear two compound eyes, however. Behind the cephalothorax the trunk consists merely of a tapering succession of 12 segments ending in a prominent telson. Some tendency toward fusion of segments is seen in one Family. Aglaspids range in size from 1 inch (26 mm) to possibly 6 feet (2 m) in length. The maximum size is unknown because segments of the trunk have not been discovered in articulation with the largest head shields.

The appendages consist of six pairs of uniramous limbs, of which the anterior pair is chelicerate and the rest are tapering walking legs.

The oldest aglaspids occur in the Middle Cambrian of the Midwest and the youngest discovered so far is a single specimen from the Upper Ordovician of Ohio. Practically all of the other aglaspids occur in Upper Cambrian sandy sediments of Wisconsin and Missouri. *Aglaspis* and *Strabops* are two well-known Genera (Fig. 12.16).

The Aglaspida are all associated with marine invertebrates and were surely marine organisms. They retain many trilobitan features but also are distinctly allied with the rest of the Chelicerata. It appears, therefore, that the evolution of the Chelicerata was so far advanced by Medial Cambrian time that we must search for the origins of the Subclass in Precambrian strata.

Order b. Xiphosurida

This is a small Order, but is among the most interesting of arthropods because it contains *Limulus,* a veritable living fossil and one of the most primitive of all chelicerates. Xiphosurida are characterized by having the carapace divided into as few as three pieces, but the divisions are unlike those of other chelicerates (Fig. 12.17). The cephalothorax is a large shield of rather trilobitan aspect, which, although it retains faintly trilobate division, lacks any trace of facial sutures. Two kinds of eyes are present, of which the compound eyes are large and prominent. In addition to them there are two simple eyes or ocelli located close together between and slightly anterior to the compound eyes. A pair of ventral eyes is present just anterior to the chelicerae in *Limulus.* Thus, as in many other chelicerates, at least four eyes are present on the dorsal surface and two more may be present somewhere else on the dorsal or ventral surface. Posterior to the cephalothorax is a second large shield which consists of some or all of the six to nine trunk segments fused together but retaining the trace of earlier segmentation. This shield sometimes is referred to as the abdomen, but it may not be entirely homologous with the abdomen of other arthopods such as Crustacea. It tapers sharply and is succeeded by a single long spine, the telson.

The appendages are well known because they can be studied in *Limulus.* As is usual in Chelicerata, no antennules or antennae are present. The chelicerae are short and the four pairs of walking legs are reasonably short—only barely extending as far out as the margin of the carapace. All of the locomotor appendages bear distinct claws. The appendages lie in a deep excavation on the ventral surface of the cephalothorax. In fact, the cephalothorax is really very thin and light, in spite of its seemingly ponderous construction. Appendages beneath the so-called abdominal shield are highly modified, consisting merely of elongate plates, at the end of each of which is a book of platelike gills. From this it can be appreciated that the gills of Xiphosurida hang freely in the water. It is this feature of the gills which helps to impart such extraordinary interest to the group, including *Limulus,* because all other living Chelicerata have internal gills or have lost every vestige of gills. The Xiphosurida, therefore, represent the ancestral condition from which higher Chelicerata are thought to have evolved.

The oldest xiphosurans have been reported from the Early Ordovician of Tennessee. These primitive forms are characterized by having some of the segments of the trunk free instead of being fused into a solid shield. Thus, all segments are free in *Neolimulus* (Silurian of England) and some are free in *Hemiaspis* (Silurian, Fig. 12.17.3). By Pennsylvanian time all segments of the trunk were fused, as in *Euproöps* from Illinois (Fig. 12.17.2). *Limulus* itself ranges from Triassic to Recent and is the only Recent Genus in the Order (Fig. 12.17.1).

Limulus is represented today by five species which are distributed along the eastern coast of North America and the eastern coast of Asia. These animals inhabit shallow water and may be stranded on the shore in great numbers after storms, as at Cape Hatteras, Virginia. Common names are the king crab and the horseshoe crab. *Limulus* burrows along in the surficial sediments with its carapace about half buried. Progress is effected by active scraping of the feet and flapping of the gill structures, in addition to which the animals arch up the body so that only the anterior rim of the cephalothorax and the tip of the telson touch the sediment. Then the carapace is thrust into the sediment when the body is straightened and the spine serves as an anchor post. Locomotion on the bottom is accompanied by humping along. Limuloids also can swim freely by use of their legs, although such journeys usually are short. Small limuloids in captivity seem to delight in diving off a submerged rock and swimming about on their backs until they land upside down on the floor of the aquarium. They then right themselves by performing a sort of backward somersault, assisted by the long telson.

Food of *Limulus* consists of worms and of soft molluscs which are abraded away by being rubbed vigorously between the raspy bases of some of the limbs near the mouth, particularly the pedipalps. The minute particles then are swallowed.

Molting is very significant, for the carapace splits around the anterior margin of the cephalothorax and the soft animal simply crawls out frontwards. Surely this is analogous to the process practiced by most trilobites.

Figure 12.17 (opposite). Xiphosurans.

1. *Limulus polyphemus,* Recent. 1a, ventral surface, 1X. 1b, newly hatched larva in the so-called trilobite stage, 6X. 1c, young specimen after first molt, 4X?. 1d, a one-year-old specimen, 1X. 2. *Euproöps thompsoni,* 1 1/3X, Pennsylvanian, Illinois. 3. *Hemiaspis limuloides,* 1X, Silurian, England. 4. *Belinurus lacoei,* 1 1/3X, Pennsylvanian, Illinois.

(1a after Clarke and Ruedemann, 1912. 1b, 1c, 1d after Lockwood, 1870. 2 after Raymond, 1944. 3 after Woodward, 1865b. 4 after Packard, 1886.)

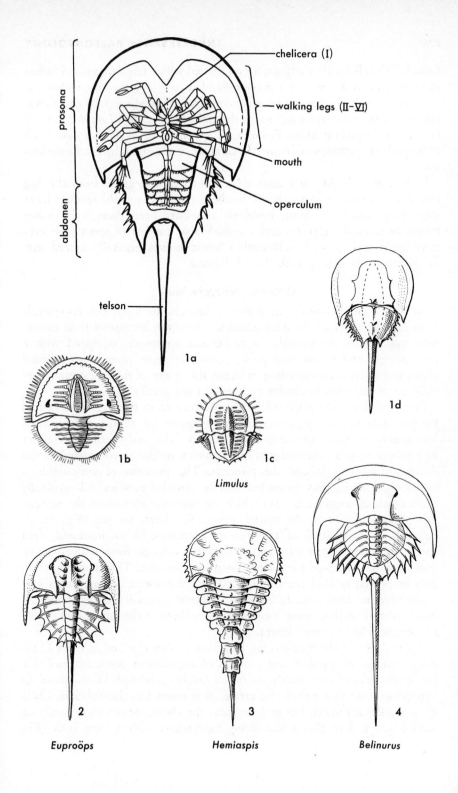

chelicera (I)

walking legs (II–VI)

prosoma

mouth

abdomen

operculum

telson

1a

1b

1c

Limulus

1d

2

Euproöps

3

Hemiaspis

4

Belinurus

Limuloids swell up after ecdysis, for an animal which left a carapace 8 inches (20 cm) long was reported to have expanded to a length of 9.5 inches (24 cm) after a molt. In this regard it is noteworthy that when crabs and *Limulus* were kept in the same aquarium the crabs ate the dead *Limulus* but did not eat the molted carapaces. From this it appears to be likely that most fossil arthropods are represented by molted carapaces rather than by dead individuals.

During growth the early molt stage just after emergence from the egg resembles trilobites very much and has been referred to as the trilobite-larva stage (Fig. 12.17.1b). Adult limuloids also have been thought by many people to resemble trilobites and a considerable amount of speculation centered upon their possible relationship before it was generally agreed that the Xiphosurida belong with the Chelicerata.

Order c.   Eurypterida

Of all of the Paleozoic invertebrates brought to light, the eurypterids seem to have acquired the most dreadful reputation because of their malevolent appearance. Scorpionlike in proportion, commonly equipped with a cruel stinger and a capacious poison gland, in some cases bearing brutal claws, and in one case exceeding in length the height of the tallest man, they truly merit our awe. Creatures such as this are gratifyingly extinct.

Eurypterids are characterized by the presence of 12 free segments behind the prosoma, but the segments are only vaguely (if at all) differentiated into mesosoma and metasoma (Fig. 12.18.1). The body terminates either in a telson or in a subcircular tailpiece, which might be considered as the thirteenth segment behind the prosoma. The prosoma of eurypterids is rather quadrate in most forms but may be rounded anteriorly. It generally bears a pair of large lateral eyes which are variously located on the margin, near the margin, or on the central area of the dorsal surface (Fig. 12.19). Assuming that position of eyes reflects adaptation to environment, then species with dorsal eyes were bottom-dwellers, whereas those with marginal eyes were well adapted for a free-swimming existence. The lateral eyes can only be proved to have been compound in a few forms because facets generally have not been seen. In addition to lateral eyes, eurypterids commonly bear a pair of ocelli in some median position between the lateral eyes. Ocelli are absent in only a few Genera.

Appendages on the prosoma are like those in *Limulus* and in other Chelicerata insofar as number and position of appendages are concerned, but the appendages of eurypterids are rather notably modified. Of the usual six appendages, the first pair is chelicerate, as is normal in the Subclass. Chelicerae usually are short, but in *Pterygotus* the chelicerae are enormously extended and end in chelae resembling nutcrackers with spinose jaws (Fig.

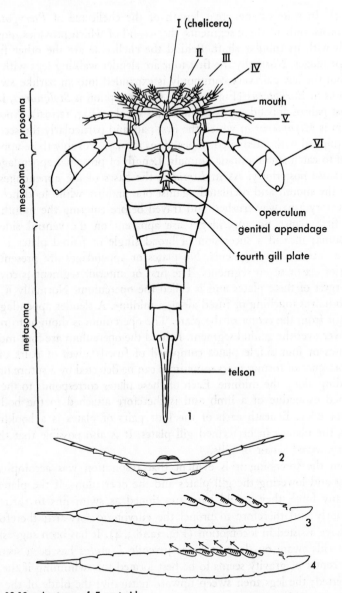

Figure 12.18. Anatomy of Eurypterids.
1. Ventral surface with appendages. 2. Anterior view of eurypterid depicted as swimming on its back. 3. Side view of swimming individual with its gill covers elevated. 4. Side view as in 3, but gill covers have shut, expelling water posteriorly (arrows) and propelling animal anteriorly.
(1 after Clarke and Reudemann, 1912. 2, 3, 4 after Störmer, 1934.)

12.19.3). In spite of the great length of the chelicerae of *Pterygotus*, they still consist only of three segments, the second of which provides most of the length with its tubular shaft. Behind the chelicerae are the other five pairs of appendages. Normally the first four are slender walking legs with pointed tips, but the last pair very commonly is expanded into an oarlike swimming organ as in *Eurypterus* (Fig. 12.19.4). One exception is *Stylonurus*, in which the last pair of appendages is pointed and slender (Fig. 12.19.6). Another exception is *Mixopterus* in which the first pair and particularly the second pair are equipped with attenuated spines (Fig. 12.19.5). Possibly these appendages served to catch small aquatic animals. Length of prosomal appendages tends to increase posteriorly. As in *Limulus,* the bases of the appendages cluster about the mouth and oscillated against one another while food held in the masticatory area was crushed and frayed before entering the mouth.

At first glance no appendages are apparent on the ventral side of the mesosoma; instead a succession of broad single or paired plates is present on the anterior five segments. No plates or appendages are present on the posterior six or seven segments. The first or anterior segment is covered by the largest of these plates and is called the **operculum.** Normally it consists of two halves touching or fused along a midline. A slender appendage hangs pendant from the center of the plate. The operculum is thought to represent the cover over the genital segment. Behind the operculum are four more pairs of plates or four single plates composed of fused halves of pairs of plates. The presence of former pairs sometimes can be detected by a suture or groove extending along the midline. Each of these plates corresponds to the greatly flattened exopodite of a limb and is therefore attached to the body at its anterior edge. Beneath each of the four pairs of plates is a booklike gill; hence, the plates can be termed **gill plates.** It is also possible that the operculum covered a pair of gills.

From the foregoing it is evident that respiration was accomplished by raising and lowering the gill plates and the operculum. If the plates closed with any force, they would have functioned as swim fins to thrust water posteriorly and therefore to propel the eurypterid forward; therefore they may have assisted in locomotion (Fig. 12.18.3, 4). It has been suggested that eurypterids swam on their backs as juvenile *Limulus* has been seen to do. Their center of gravity seems to be best located for swimming if the animal is inverted; the legs then sweep upward naturally; the blade of the last appendage would scoop water best; the anterior curvature of the carapace

---

Figure 12.19 (opposite) Eurypterids.
   Mixopterus is 1/8X and is from Norway. *Pterygotus* is 1/40X. All others are 1/4X. All except *Mixopterus* are from New York.
   (5 after Störmer, 1934. Others after Clarke and Reudemann, 1912.)

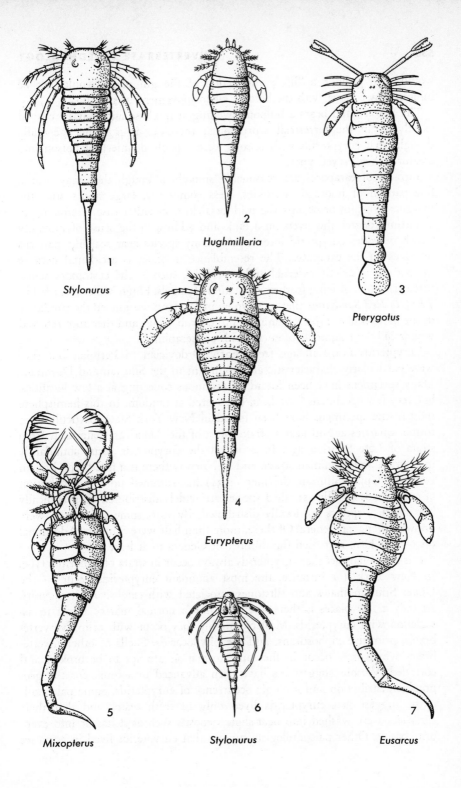

1 Stylonurus

Hughmilleria
2

Pterygotus
3

4
Eurypterus

5
Mixopterus

Stylonurus
6

Eusarcus
7

would then provide a "lift"; and action of the gill plates would not be inhibited by contact with the bottom when movement was begun.

The telson often bears a bulbous swelling at the base and may be curved exactly as in the terrestrial scorpionids; therefore it is rather generally thought that eurypterids with telsons were capable of injecting poison into creatures they preyed upon.

Surfaces of carapaces are reasonably smooth, although they may bear a fine pattern of nodes or wrinkles. Less commonly, large nodes stud the margins of plates or occupy the middorsal line, in either case resembling to a startling degree the rivets on a tank and adding to the sense of unreality which pervades eurypterid lore. Lastly, many species bear scalelike patterns in zones on the carapaces. The resemblance to scales is accidental because the pattern is strictly external and superficial, such as the customary sculptured rendition of wing feathers on statues of angels. Hugh Miller recorded in *The Old Red Sandstone* that quarrymen in Scotland recognized the similarity of the pattern of eurypterid carapaces to cherub wings and therefore referred whimsically to fragments of eurypterids as "seraphim"!

Eurypterids range in age from Early Ordovician to Permian but they were particularly characteristic and abundant in the Silurian and Devonian. Many specimens have been found by assiduous collecting at a few localities, but very few specimens have been discovered at random. In this hemisphere most of the specimens have been found in New York State, particularly in former quarries at and near Buffalo. Most of the American material is from strata of Late Silurian age. In Scotland the eurypterids occur abundantly in Silurian and Devonian strata, and in Norway there is a fine fauna known from the Upper Silurian. Störmer (1934) has summed up the distribution of eurypterids as follows: allied species are widely distributed geographically but identical species are locally distributed. By 1916, some 160 species were known among 14 Genera. Of these, more than half were Silurian. Additional discoveries have increased the number of Genera to at least 19.

It is a peculiar fact that eurypterids always occur in strata of abnormal type. In New York, for instance, the most abundant eurypterids occur in the Upper Silurian shales and siltstones associated with extensive salt deposits. At only a few places is there anything like a normal marine fauna in association with eurypterids. Most commonly they occur with primitive vertebrates, primitive xiphosurans, and the phyllocarids. Shells of other invertebrates which may occur in the same formation are apt to be broken and corroded. Various suggestions have been advanced to account for the geographic distribution and geologic occurrence of eurypterids. Some paleontologists suggest that eurypterids lived only in fresh water and that their carapaces were washed into near-shore deposits such as deltas or into evaporite basins. Other paleontologists suggest that eurypterids lived in estuaries and invaded rivers periodically. Where corals and brachiopods occur in nearby association with eurypterids, it has been proposed that the eurypterids were caught in a lagoon behind a bioherm or reef. In any case it seems certain that eurypterids did not constitute part of the normal marine fauna of their time. Continued interest in the ecology of eurypterids is assured because the problem bears on the origin of vertebrates, and on the origin of scorpionids and the other terrestrial chelicerates.

Order d. Pycnogonida

The pycnogonids are represented in Recent seas by a few very aberrant crablike creatures which rarely are seen because they are abundant only in

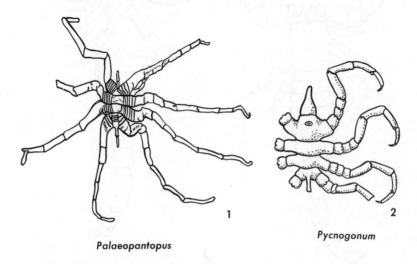

1

2

Pycnogonum

Palaeopantopus

Figure 12.20. Pycnogonids.
1. Dorsal impression of *Palaeopantopus maucheri*, 2/3X, Devonian, Germany. 2. Ventral view of *Pycnogonum littorale* with appendages shown only on right side, 1X, Recent.
(1 after Broili, 1929. 2 after Hedgpeth, 1947.)

deep water. The body is much reduced in size and the appendages are long and are either very tenuous or much too massive to seem to belong to the tiny body. Moreover, the presence of seven pairs of appendages distinguishes these animals from all other aquatic chelicerates. A supposed fossil pycnogonid has been reported from the Devonian of Germany, but other reports are lacking (Fig. 12.20).

SUBCLASS 2. ARACHNOIDA

As considered herein, the Arachnoida comprise the air-breathing chelicerates such as scorpions, spiders, tarantulas, and ticks. Respiration of arachnoids is by book lungs or tracheae. Otherwise they retain the general structure and appendages of the Merostomata.

Order a. Scorpionida

Scorpionids are characterized by the presence of chelae on the first two appendages (chelicerae and pedipalps, Fig. 12.21), whereas eurypterids bear chelae only on the first pair. It is the second pair of appendages which

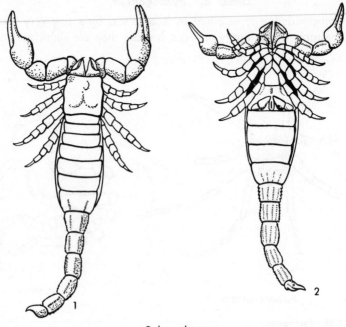

Palaeophonus

Figure 12.21. Scorpions.
1. Dorsal view of *Palaeophonus nuncius*, 1/10X, Silurian, Sweden. 2. Ventral view of *Palaeophonus hunteri*, 1/6X, Silurian, Scotland.
(After Pocock, 1901.)

bear the large and prominent chelae, for the chelicerae are as diminutive as in most of the Chelicerata. The remaining four pairs of appendages end in minute movable claws. In addition to the stinging spine on the tail, there are 12 segments behind the prosoma, none of which bears any trace of appendages. Mesosoma and metasoma are not readily differentiated, although each consists of six segments.

Respiration is by book lungs which are located in pairs beneath the third to sixth segments of the mesosoma. Their position is indicated by the presence of small slits, the **stigmata,** which are the external apertures of the lung chambers. The operculum of scorpionids is much smaller than it is in euryp-terids.

Compound eyes are not known among scorpionids, but several pairs of ocelli may be present. They are located in two general areas; thus, one or two pairs of **median eyes** may lie subcentrally on the cephalothorax, and two to five pairs of **lateral eyes** may be distributed near the margin. The number and position of ocelli is diagnostic of Genera and species. Eyesight of scorpions is poor but efficient tactile and chemical senses are provided through minute hairs which protrude from the body.

The oldest known scorpionid is *Palaeophonus,* which occurs in the late Silurian of Europe (Fig. 12.21.1, 2). It has long been considered as a veritable missing link because it bridges the gap between the eurypterids and the scorpionids. *Palaeophonus* is a scorpionid in all respects except that it lacks stigmata; hence, some specialists assume that it had book gills and led an aquatic existence. On the other hand, it has been pointed out that stigmata are hard to see and that *Palaeophonus* is truly scorpionid in all other respects; hence, it probably was a true scorpion. Although the generic name means "ancient murderer," these primitive scorpionids did not rival their marine cousins, the eurypterids, in size, for *Palaeophonus* was only 0.5 to 2.5 inches (1 to 6 cm) in length. A few Carboniferous scorpionids also have been reported.

Order b.   Pedipalpida

This Order comprises the tarantula and other species belonging to about a score of other Genera. The chelicerae have lost the third or terminal seg-ment which consists of claws, but the pedipalps are prominent and bear spines and claws (Fig. 12.22.5). Prey caught between the spinose inner edges of the pedipalps is punctured when hugged between them. Unlike most other arachnids, the Pedipalpida use only three pairs of appendages for walking. The Order has been reported from strata as old as the Pennsyl-vanian.

Order c.   Araneida

Araneids are the spiders. They are characterized by the presence of spin-nerets and by constriction of the body into two portions by the narrow waist. As in the Pedipalpida the chelicerae retain only two segments and therefore do not bear claws. The orifice for the poison gland is, however, borne on the end of the second segment. Unlike the Pedipalpida, however, the pedipalps of araneids lack large claws—in fact all five ambulatory ap-

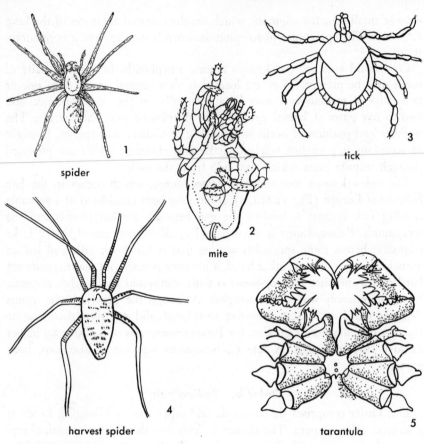

spider

tick

mite

harvest spider

tarantula

Figure 12.22.   Arachnoids.
1. *Segestria secessa*, 2X, Miocene, Colorado.   2. Ventral view of *Protocarus crani*, the oldest mite, 75X, Devonian, Scotland.   3. Dorsal view of a tick, *Amblyomma* sp., showing the festoon of abdominal segments, enlarged, Recent.   4. Dorsal view of *Eotrogulus fayoli*, the oldest of the phalangids, 1 1/3X, Pennsylvanian, France.   5. Dorsal view of the prosoma of *Tarantula palmata* showing the spinose pedipalps, enlarged, Recent.
(1 after Scudder, 1890.   2 after Hirst, 1923.   3 after Raw, 1957.   4 after Thévenin, 1901.   5 after Störmer, 1934.)

pendages of spiders are similar (Fig. 12.22.1). Eyesight of most spiders is poor but a few spiders have very keen sight. Almost all spiders breathe with tracheae in addition to which some have two and some have four pairs of book lungs which communicate exteriorly through stigmata.

The oldest spiders occur in the Middle Devonian of Scotland. Of the 250 species of fossil spiders, about 180 have been reported in amber from Cenozoic strata in northern Europe. Numerous spiders also have been reported from the Florissant shale (Miocene) of Colorado.

Order d. Phalangida

The Order Phalangida is introduced mainly to illustrate the presence of spiderlike arachnoids without a constricted waist. Spinnerets are generally absent. All of the Phalangida breathe by means of tracheae and lack book lungs. The phalangids are known under the common names of harvest spiders and daddy-long-legs. The Order has been reported from the Pennsylvanian (Fig. 12.22.4).

Order e. Acarida

The Acarida include the ticks and mites which are characterized by the presence of unsegmented bodies. Most of the members of the Order are modified for a parasitic or sucking existence. Thus, in the ticks the chelicerae are represented by an elongate piercing organ. Other limbs may be more or less normally arachnoid in number or position. A festoon of abdominal segments surrounds the main part of the body (Fig. 12.22.3). Ticks are notoriously prolific—one female being able to lay as many as 20,000 eggs. The seasonal disappearance of ticks is due to the long periods of development between the larval stages, during which times of growth the animals remain in the soil or hidden among rocks and vegetation. In recent years ticks have become a major nuisance to man because they are the carriers of diseases such as tularemia and Rocky Mountain spotted fever. The Order goes back to the Middle Devonian, but the fossil record is very sparse. A mite (Fig. 12.22.2) is known from the Rhynie chert in the Old Red Sandstone of Scotland.

GEOLOGIC RANGE OF CHELICERATA. Chelicerates probably descended from some trilobitan ancestor, but no known trilobite seems to be the veritable stem from which the chelate arthropods arose. It seems probable, therefore, that the Chelicerata arose during Precambrian time when the trilobites themselves were undergoing their principal diversification. Subsequent ranges of some chelicerates are shown in Figure 12.23. Xiphosurans seem to have given rise to both the pycnogonids and the eurypterids among the Merostomata. The Arachnoida seem to have arisen from the Eurypterida, at least in the case of the scorpions, but known fossil forms are not primitive enough to indicate the nature of intermediate steps among the other Orders. Most fossil chelicerates have been collected from nonmarine deposits and therefore are sporadically represented in the geologic record. Only the eurypterids might be considered to have any significant geologic record.

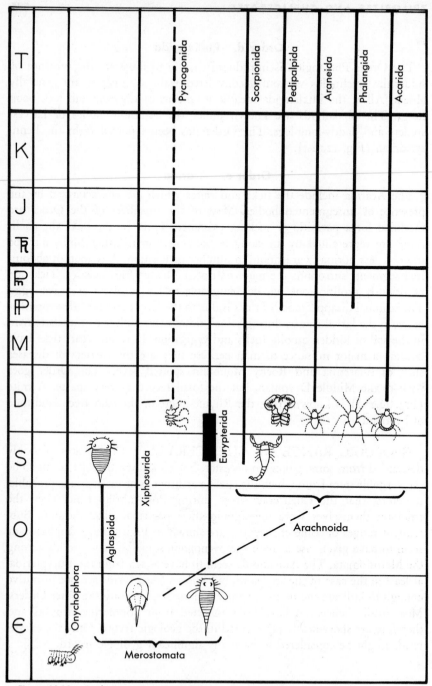

Figure 12.23. Geologic Ranges of Chelicerata and Onychophora.
(In part after Snodgrass, 1938.)

QUESTIONS

1. What is the principal disadvantage of identifying arthropods by their molt stages?
2. What intermediate stages connect the merostomes and arachnoids?
3. How does spinosity of trilobites give credence to orthogenesis? How else can the spinosity be explained? How might spinose but blind trilobites evolve?
4. How do facial sutures assist in classification of trilobites? What are the taxonomic limitations of facial sutures?
5. Why did the two races of cheirurids persist?
6. What is peculiar about the geologic occurrence of eurypterids?
7. Why should species of eurypterids be restricted in their geographic distribution, yet similar species evolve over extensive regions?
8. What limits the effective use of arachnoids in correlation?
9. Why might agnostids and mesonacids be removed from taxonomic association with the other trilobites?
10. Why were biologists so eager to know the nature of appendages of trilobites?

BIBLIOGRAPHY

Barrande, J., 1852, 1872, Systeme Silurien du Centre de la Bohème: Prague, pt. I, v. 1, pls. Suppl., 1872.

Barton, D. C., 1915, A revision of the Cheirurinae with notes on their evolution: Washington Univ. (St. Louis) Studies, v. 3, pt. 1, no. 1.

Beecher, C. E., 1895, The larval stages of trilobites: Amer. Geol., v. 16, pp. 166–197.

Bouvier, E.-L., 1905, Monographie des onychophores: Annales Sci. Nat. (Zool.), ser. 9, v. 2.

Broili, F., 1928, Crustaceenfunde aus dem rheinischen Unterdevon: Akad. Wiss. (München), Sitzungb. Math.-Natur. Abt., pt. 3, pp. 197–204.

———, 1929, Beobachtungen an neuen Arthropodenfunden aus den Hunsrücks-chiefern: Sitz. bayer. Akad. Wiss. (München), Math.-Natur. Abt., pt. 3, pp. 253–280.

Carpenter, F. M., 1951, Studies on Carboniferous insects from Commentry, France: pt. II. The Megasecoptera: Jour. Paleont., v. 25, no. 3, pp. 331–355.

Caster, K. E., and Macke, W. B., 1952, An aglaspid merostome from the Upper Ordovician of Ohio: Jour. Paleont., v. 26, no. 5, pp. 753–757.

Clarke, J. M., 1889, The structure and development of the visual area in the trilobite, *Phacops rana,* Green: Jour. Morph., v. 2, pp. 253–270.

———, 1908, Early Devonic history of New York and eastern North America: New York State Mus., Mem. 9.

———, and Ruedemann, R., 1912, The Eurypterida of New York: New York State Mus., Mem. 14, v. 1, 2.

Delo, D. M., 1935, Locomotive habits of some trilobites: Amer. Midland Naturalist, v. 16, no. 3, pp. 406–409.

———, 1940, Phacopid trilobites of North America: Geol. Soc. America Spec. Paper 29.

Garstang, W., 1940, Störmer on the appendages of trilobites: Annals Mag. Nat. Hist., ser. 11, v. 6, pp. 59–66.

Girty, G. H., 1908, The Guadalupe fauna: U. S. Geol. Survey Prof. Paper 58.

Hall, J., 1847, Palaeontology of New York, v. 1: Natural History of New York, pt. 6.

———, 1852, Palaeontology of New York, v. 2: Natural History of New York, pt. 6.

———, 1863, Preliminary notice of the fauna of the Potsdam sandstone: Univ. State New York, St. Cab. Nat. Hist., 16th Ann. Rept., append. D, pp. 119–209.

———, and Clarke, J. M., 1888, Palaeontology: New York Geol. Survey, v. 7.

———, and Whitfield, R. P., 1877, Paleontology: U. S. Geol. Expl. 40th Parallel, v. 4, pt. 2, pp. 199–302.

Hedgpeth, J. W., 1947, On the evolutionary significance of the Pycnogonida: Smithsonian Misc. Coll., v. 106, no. 18.

Hirst, S., 1923, On some arachnid remains from the Old Red Sandstone (Rhynie Chert bed, Aberdeenshire): Annals Mag. Nat. Hist., ser. 9, v. 12, pp. 455–474.

Howell, B. F., *et al.,* 1947, Terminology for describing Cambrian trilobites: Jour. Paleont., v. 21, no. 1, pp. 72–76.

———, and Resser, C. E., 1934, Habitats of the agnostian trilobites (abstract): Geol. Soc. America, Proc. (1933), pp. 360, 361.

Kobayashi, T., 1939, On the agnostids (pt. I): Jour. Fac. Sci., Imp. Univ. Tokyo, ser. 2, v. 5, pt. 5, pp. 69–198.

———, 1944, On the eodiscids: Jour. Fac. Sci., Imp. Univ. Tokyo, sec. 2, v. 7, pt. 1, pp. 1–74.

Lindström, G., 1901, Researches on the visual organs of the trilobites: Kongl. Svenska Vetensk.-Akad. Handl., n. ser., v. 34, no. 8.

Lochman, Christina, 1956, The evolution of some Upper Cambrian and Lower Ordovician trilobite Families: Jour. Paleont., v. 30, no. 3, pp. 445–462.

———, and Wilson, J. L., 1958, Cambrian biostratigraphy in North America: Jour. Paleont., v. 32, no. 2, pp. 312–350.

Matthew, G. F., 1899, Studies on Cambrian faunas, no. 3: Trans. Roy. Soc. Canada, ser. 2, v. 5, sec. 4, pp. 39–66.

Meek, F. B., 1873, Descriptions of invertebrate fossils of the Silurian and Devonian Systems: Ohio Geol. Survey, v. 1, pt. 2, pp. 1–246.

Merriam, C. W., 1940, Devonian stratigraphy and paleontology of the Roberts Mountains region, Nevada: Geol. Soc. America Special Paper 25.

O'Connell, M., 1916, The habitat of the Eurypterida: Bull. Buffalo Soc. Nat. Sci., v. 11, no. 3.

Packard, A. S., 1886, On the Carboniferous xiphosurous fauna of North America: Mem. Nat. Acad. Sci., v. 3, pt. 2, pp. 141–157.

Palmer, A. R., 1957, Ontogenetic development of two olenellid trilobites: Jour. Paleont., v. 31, no. 1, pp. 105–128.

Petrunkevitch, A., 1949, A study of Paleozoic Arachnida: Trans. Connecticut Acad. Arts Sci., v. 37, pp. 69–315.

———, 1953, Paleozoic and Mesozoic Arachnida of Europe: Geol. Soc. America, Mem. 53.

Phleger, F. B., 1936, Lichadian trilobites: Jour. Paleont., v. 10, no. 7, pp. 593–615.

Pocock, R. I., 1901, The Scottish Silurian scorpion: Quart. Jour. Micro. Sci., n. ser., v. 44, pp. 291–311.

———, 1911, A monograph of the terrestrial Carboniferous Arachnida of Great Britain: Palaeontographical Soc. (London).

Raasch, G. O., 1939, Cambrian Merostomata: Geol. Soc. America Spec. Paper 19.

Rasetti, F., 1952, Revision of the North American trilobites of the Family Eodiscidae: Jour. Paleont., v. 26, no. 3, pp. 434–451.

Raw, F., 1925, The development of *Leptoplastus salteri* (Callaway), and of other trilobites (Olenidae, Ptychoparidae, Conocoryphidae, Paradoxidae, Phacopidae, and Mesonacidae): Geol. Soc. London Quart. Jour., v. 81, pp. 223–324.

———, 1953, The external morphology of the trilobite and its significance: Jour. Paleont., v. 27, no. 1, pp. 82–129.

———, 1957, Origin of chelicerates: Jour. Paleont., v. 31, no. 1, pp. 139–192.

Raymond, P. E., 1906, The trilobites of the Chazy limestone: Annals Carnegie Mus., v. 3, pp. 328–386.

———, 1916, New and old Silurian trilobites from southeastern Wisconsin, with notes on the genera of the Illaenidae: Bull. Mus. Comp. Zool. (Harvard), v. 60, no. 1, pp. 1–41.

———, 1920, The appendages, anatomy, and relationships of trilobites: Mem. Connecticut Acad. Arts Sci., v. 7.

———, 1944, Late Paleozoic xiphosurans: Bull. Mus. Comp. Zool. (Harvard), v. 94, no. 10, pp. 475–508.

———, and Barton, D. C., 1913, A revision of the American species of Ceraurus: Bull. Mus. Comp. Zool. (Harvard), v. 54, no. 20, pp. 525–546.

Reed, F. R. C., 1898, Blind trilobites: Geol. Mag., n. ser., dec. 4, v. 5, pp. 439–447, 493–506, 552–559.

Snodgrass, R. E., 1938, Evolution of the Annelida, Onychophora, and Arthropoda: Smithsonian Misc. Coll., v. 97, no. 6.

Stoff, H. von, and Rack, H., 1911, Ueber die Lebensweise der Trilobiten: Freunde, Sitz. Gesell. Naturforsch, Berlin, no. 2, pp. 130–146.

Störmer, L., 1934, Merostomata from the Downtownian sandstone of Ringerike, Norway: Oslo, Skr. Norske Vidensk.-Akad. Mat.-Naturvid. Kl. (1933), v. 2, no. 10.

———, 1944, On the relationships and phylogeny of fossil and Recent Arachnomorpha: Oslo, Skr. Norske Vidensk.-Akad. Mat.-Naturvid. Kl., no. 5.

———, 1951, Studies on trilobite morphology, pt. III: Norsk Geol. Tidsskrift, v. 29, pp. 108–158.

Stubblefield, C. J., 1936, Cephalic sutures and their bearing on current classifications of trilobites: Cambridge Phil. Soc., Biol. Revs., v. 11, no. 4, pp. 407–440.

Swinnerton, H. H., 1919, The facial suture of trilobites: Geol. Mag., dec. 6, v. 6, pp. 103–110.

Thévenin, A., 1901, Sur la Découverte d'Arachnides dans le Terrain Houiller de Commentry: Bull. Soc. Géol. France, ser. 4, v. 1, pp. 605–611.

Ulrich, E. O., and Resser, C. E., 1933, The Cambrian of the Upper Mississippi Valley: Bull. Milwaukee Public Mus., v. 12, no. 2, pp. 123–306.

Walcott, C. D., 1884, On the Cambrian faunas of North America: U. S. Geol. Survey, Bull. 10.

——, 1908, Cambrian trilobites: Smithsonian Misc. Coll., v. 53, no. 2, pp. 13–52.

——, 1910, Olenellus and other Genera of the Mesonacidae: Smithsonian Misc. Coll., v. 53, no. 6.

——, 1916, Cambrian trilobites: Smithsonian Misc. Coll., v. 64, no. 3.

Warburg, E., 1925, The trilobites of the Leptaena limestone in Dalarne with a discussion of the zoological position and the classification of the Trilobita: Univ. Upsala, Bull. Geol. Inst., v. 17, pp. 1–446.

Weller, J. M., 1937, Evolutionary tendencies in American Carboniferous trilobites: Jour. Paleont., v. 11, no. 4, pp. 337–346.

——, 1952, Analysis of trilobite generic nomenclature and its implications regarding progress in paleontology: Jour. Paleont., v. 26, no. 2, pp. 137–147.

Weller, Stuart, 1907, The paleontology of the Niagaran limestone in the Chicago area: Bull. Chicago Acad. Sci., v. 4, pt. 2, pp. 163–281.

White, C. A., 1877, Report upon the invertebrate fossils, etc.: U. S. Geog. Surveys West of 100th Meridian (Wheeler), v. 4, pt. 1.

Whittington, H. B., 1941, The Trinucleidae—with special reference to North American Genera and species: Jour. Paleont., v. 15, no. 1, pp. 21–41.

——, 1954, Arthropoda: Trilobita *in* Status of invertebrate paleontology, 1953: Bull. Mus. Comp. Zool. (Harvard), v. 112, no. 3, pp. 193–200.

——, 1956, Silicified Middle Ordovician trilobites: the Odontopleuridae: Bull. Mus. Comp. Zool. (Harvard), v. 114, no. 5, pp. 156–288.

Wilson, J. L., 1954, Late Cambrian and Early Ordovician trilobites from the Marathon Uplift, Texas: Jour. Paleont., v. 28, no. 3, pp. 249–285.

Woodward, H., 1865, On a new Genus of Eurypterida from the lower Ludlow rock of Leintwardine, Shropshire: Geol. Soc. London Quart. Jour., v. 21, pp. 490–492.

Chapter 13

CRUSTACEANS AND INSECTS

PHYLUM XIII. ARTHROPODA (Continued)

Class D. Crustacea

Crustacea are dominantly marine arthropods although members of several groups inhabit fresh water and a few are terrestrial. Even most of the terrestrial arthropods, however, must spend their early developmental life in water. A characteristic feature of Crustacea is the presence of leaflike or comblike gills or branchiae which are either attached to the thoracic appendages or lie near them on the thoracic segments. It is rather commonly (but not universally) thought that Crustacea inherited their branchial plan from the trilobites whose exopodites functioned as gills. Gills are not present in all Crustacea; in fact, respiration takes place over the entire body surface of some small forms. Another feature that characterizes Crustacea is the general trend toward fusion of some thoracic segments with the head shield. This trend reaches its culmination in the lobsters and crabs. In conjunction with fusion of segments are the tendencies for reduction in number and for consistency in the number of segments in advanced groups. Thus, the number of segments in many primitive arthropods is variable, but the number is fixed in the lobsters and crabs.

Appendages of simple forms tend to be biramous, whereas those of higher arthropods may be uniramous. Only the antennules are consistently uniramous throughout the Class. It follows that differentiation of Subclasses of Crustacea is based upon nature of appendages and of segmentation.

In his highly readable account of the Crustacea, Smith (1923) has likened them to the Insecta in that each is the most prolific group of arthropods in its particular environment and each has exploited the potentialities of its environment to the utmost—except that Crustacea never developed any tendency toward social behavior.

SUBCLASS 1.   BRANCHIOPODA

Branchiopods consist of a diverse group of small, more or less shrimplike animals, in which the bodies mostly are enclosed in carapaces (Fig. 13.1). Body segments bear leaflike appendages, but abdominal segments lack appendages. Different Orders of Recent branchiopods sometimes are referred

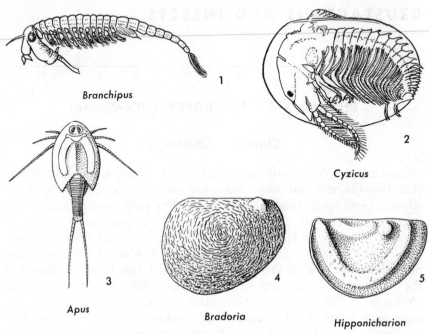

Figure 13.1. Branchiopods.
1. *Branchipus* sp., a form without a carapace, enlarged, Recent. 2. *Cyzicus* sp., with the left valve removed to show the leaflike gill-bearing appendages, enlarged, Recent. 3. *Apus* sp., showing a form with a single carapace, 1X, Recent. 4. Right valve of *Bradoria robusta*, 6X, Cambrian, Nova Scotia. 5. Right valve of *Hipponicharion confluens*, 12X, Cambrian, Nova Scotia.
(1-3 after Packard, 1883.   4, 5 after Ulrich and Bassler, 1931.)

to as fairy shrimps and as water fleas. Of the four known Orders of Branchiopoda, the Order of any paleontologic importance is referred to as the conchostracans by most specialists.

Conchostracan branchiopods consist of a segmented body with as many as about two dozen pairs of appendages. Even the antennae are used for swimming. The carapace seems at first glance to be bivalved, but it really consists of two flaps which are mirror images of one another and which are continuous across the dorsal region. Carapaces generally are less than 2 centimeters long and about half that high. Appendages and body segments have not been found; hence, paleontologic information is confined to what can be gleaned from the carapaces. Zoologists, on the other hand, largely concentrate their studies on the appendages and soft anatomy of Recent forms; therefore, it is doubtful that paleontologic and zoologic generic names refer to concepts of equal magnitude or can be used with confidence in both sciences. We are indebted to Kobayashi (1954) and his students for assembling most of our knowledge of fossil branchiopods.

Carapaces of branchiopods consist of a thin sheet of only slightly calcified chitin; therefore, the carapaces become flattened and slightly wrinkled when they are buried in sediments. Unlike ostracodes, which shed their carapaces at each ecdysis, a branchiopod retains its carapace and sheds only the exoskeleton of the body proper. The result is that carapaces of branchiopods are marked by a series of concentric ridges, each one delineating the thickening of the rim of the carapace at a time of molting. These concentric ridges are quite characteristic of the Subclass. The depressed bands (**intervales**) between adjacent ridges bear various sorts of ornamentation ranging from granules to pits, nodes, transverse ridges, and polygonal or reticulate ornamentation (Fig. 13.2.11–14). Kobayashi listed 20 general types of sculpture on carapaces and showed that more than one type may occur on a single carapace. More work needs to be done in order to establish the sequence in which different ornamentation evolves, but at the present it seems that basic ornamentation may consist of spots, striae, or polygons. Spots tend to increase in size and to be arranged in various subsidiary bands. Striae become stronger, passing into parallel radial grooves and then subdividing into branching or dendritic patterns. Polygons become more regular and finally are succeeded by reticulations. These details, plus ratios of length to breadth of carapaces, enable the differentiation of Genera and species of branchiopods.

It is customary, however, to divide the fossil conchostracan branchiopods into two groups on the basis of whether or not the carapace is crossed by a few, strong, radial ridges (**carinae**). The commonest group, which contains all living and most fossil forms, is typified by *Cyzicus* (Fig. 13.1.2) and about 15 allied Genera including about 250 species. (For many years this Genus was known as *Estheria* until the name was found to have been used earlier for a Genus of insects; nevertheless, most conchostracan branchiopods still are commonly called estherians, after the old name *Estheria*.) The other group, with 2 strong carinae, is typified by *Leaia* (Fig. 13.2.4, 5) and another 15 Genera, with some 50 species.

The two groups reached the acme of their development in the Late Paleozoic and Triassic and then reached another but lesser pinnacle of development during the Cretaceous. Inexplicably, no Tertiary conchostracans have been reported, but Recent conchostracans are abundant. In the United States

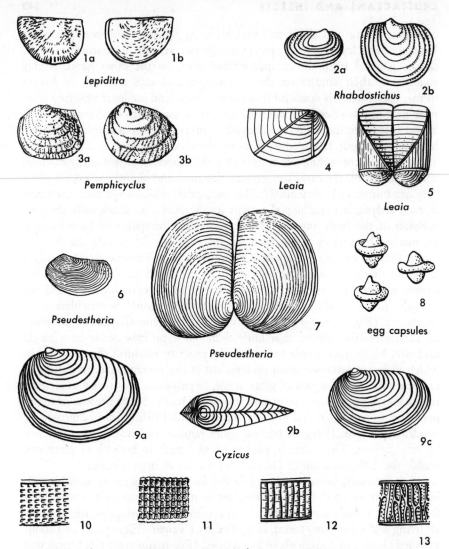

ornamentation

Figure 13.2 Branchiopods.

1a, 1b. Two valves of *Lepiditta alata*, 12X, Cambrian, New Brunswick. 2a, 2b. Two specimens of *Rhabdostichus buchoti*, enlarged, Siluro-Devonian, France. 3a, 3b. Two specimens of *Pemphicyclus ortoni*, 6X, Pennsylvanian, Ohio. 4. *Leaia tricarinata*, 6X, Pennsylvanian, Illinois. 5. *Leaia williamsoniana*, 7X, Pennsylvanian, England. 6. *Pseudestheria multicostata*, 5X, Triassic, Virginia. 7. *Pseudestheria emmonsi*, 4X, Triassic, Virginia. 8. Three egg capsules, greatly enlarged, Recent. 9. *Cyzicus tetracerus*, 2X, Recent. 9a, 9b, side and dorsal views of a female. 9c, side view of a female. 10-13. Portions of intervales showing variations in ornamentation in four species of branchiopods; greatly enlarged.

(1, 2, 4, 8, 10-13 after Kobayashi, 1954. 3 after Raymond, 1946. 5-7 after Jones, 1862. 9 after Daday, 1914.)

estherians occur in the nonmarine shales of Pennsylvanian cyclothems in Indiana and Illinois and in the Newark series (Upper Triassic) of the Atlantic seaboard. Estherians have been used to zone the Upper Carboniferous strata of western Europe and of the Donetz Basin in Russia.

The foregoing association of estherians with terrestrial deposits is characteristic of branchiopods. Only a few branchiopods have been found in marine sediments, but they occur commonly in fresh-water and in brackish-water deposits. Living representatives are predominantly nonmarine also. Branchiopods produce minute top-shaped egg capsules which have been identified in sediments (Fig. 13.2.8). When ponds dry up the egg capsules

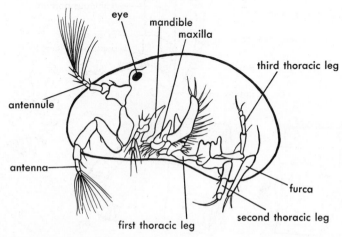

Figure 13.3   Appendages of an Ostracode.
(After Bassler and Kellett, 1934; and Kesling, 1956.)

function as resting stages and can be blown about by the wind. This may explain their erratic environmental and geographic distribution and their ability to populate areas on both sides of an intervening ocean.

SUBCLASS 2.   OSTRACODA

Ostracodes are characterized by the presence of a bivalved **carapace** which covers an only vaguely segmented body. Carapaces are mostly from 0.5 to 4 millimeters in length, although a few as long as 25 millimeters have been reported. Of the total of seven pairs of appendages with which the animals swim, two pairs (antennules and the biramous antennae) are located on the cephalic region (Fig. 13.3). Zoologic differentiation of living ostracodes depends largely upon details of construction of the appendages, but the only traces of appendages which have been reported on fossil ostracodes were discovered on one specimen from the Carboniferous of France. Paleontolo-

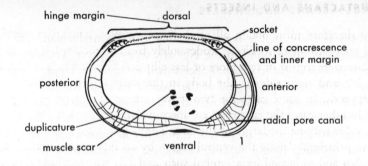

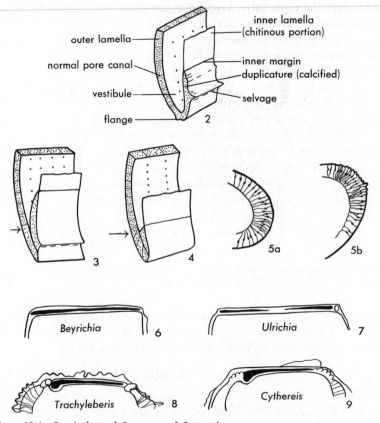

Figure 13.4. Terminology of Carapaces of Ostracodes.

1. Interior of left valve of *Cythere* sp., greatly enlarged. 2. Oblique cut-away diagram of the contact margin of a monolamellar shell, greatly enlarged. 3. Bilamellar shell in which the inner margin extends above the line of concrescence. 4. Bilamellar shell in which the inner margin coincides with the line of concrescence. 5a, 5b. Tangential sections of shell margins showing radial pore canals, greatly enlarged. 6-9. Hinge lines of four species of ostracodes showing increasing complexity in dentition, greatly enlarged. 6. *Beyrichia fittsi*, 25X, Devonian, Oklahoma. 7. *Ulrichia bituberculata*, 55X, Carboniferous, Scotland. 8. *Trachyleberis scabrocuneata*, 35X, Recent. 9. *Cythereis ciliata*, probably 35X, Cretaceous, Europe.

(1-4 after Bradley, 1941. 5 after Alexander, 1933. 6, 7 after Levinson, 1950. 9 after Sylvester-Bradley, 1948.)

gists therefore must obtain all of their information about the morphology and relationships of fossil ostracodes solely from studies of the carapaces.

Carapaces consist of two more or less elliptical **valves** which are located on the left and right sides of the body in the same positions as the valves of pelecypods. In some cases the two valves are mirror images of each other, but in other cases the carapaces are inequivalved and either the right or the left valve may be the larger of the two. The larger valve encloses the smaller valve principally along the ventral region by an increment referred to as the **overlap** and indicated by a symbol such as L/R, which means that the left valve overlaps the right valve. Overlap is consistent for a particular species. The two valves are in contact dorsally along a rather straight **hinge margin** (Fig. 13.4.1). Valves are composed of a calcareous central layer embedded in a thin chitinous sheath which not only covers the inner and outer surfaces of a carapace, but extends across the hinge margin and holds the valves together in much the same way that a ligament does in pelecypods. When an ostracode molts, the carapace is shed and is preserved with the two valves in opposition if it is entombed rapidly. Reworked carapaces commonly consist of isolated valves because the chitinous outer layer has decomposed and the valves have become separated.

Although carapaces commonly are straight along the hinge margin, the **contact margin** is continuously curved around the remainder of the periphery. Contact margins can be divided rather arbitrarily into **anterior border, ventral border,** and **posterior border.** Great importance is attached to the profile of curvature of the anterior and posterior borders of a carapace, not only for purposes of identification, but also for orienting the valves as to anterior and posterior. Outlines vary between bean-shaped and banana-shaped; therefore ratios of length to breadth and to height also are useful in delimiting species.

Muscles which close the two valves and which operate some of the appendages are attached at about the center of each valve (Fig. 13.4.1). Adductor muscles, which close the valves, produce the largest muscle scars. Size, position, and distribution of muscle scars are not only characteristic of various taxonomic groups, but also may be helpful in determining orientation of valves. For instance, muscle scars of almost all living ostracodes are concentrated in the anterior halves of the valves. Muscle scars may be located at the site of a large pit, as seen on the exterior of the valves. Muscle scars and eye spots can be confused on carapaces. The position of each of the paired eyes is indicated by a small tubercle or by a thin place in the substance of the shell.

Orientation of ostracode carapaces has been a singularly vexatious problem. Among living ostracodes, the greatest width of the valves is commonly posterior, whereas the greatest height is commonly anterior. Orientation of many Mesozoic and of most Cenozoic ostracodes presents no problem because the carapaces can be compared with those of closely allied Recent species in which soft anatomy is preserved and in which orientation by shape can be verified. On the other hand, orientation of carapaces of Paleozoic ostracodes is a subject for controversy because of considerable variation in shape, outline, and internal morphologic features. Moreover, two features which indicate opposite orientations may be combined in one carapace. In general, the contact margin with the greater radius of curvature (more blunt end, that is), is more or less arbitrarily said to be posterior. When determining relative curvature of ends it is important not to confuse height with degree of angularity because the less elevated end may be the more bluntly rounded.

Surfaces range from glossy smoothness to being minutely pitted, in addition to which there may be various kinds of ornamentation in the form of large pits, nodes, welts, ribs, spines, and frills. Peculiar ornamentation offers the most ready method of identifying some ostracodes and enables some to serve as useful guide fossils in micropaleontology.

Increasing attention is being devoted to interiors of valves as study of ostracodes progresses. It has been demonstrated that ostracodes with similar external characteristics can be assigned to different Families on the basis of dentition of the hinge margin. The earliest ostracodes of the Paleozoic have a long groove along the hinge margin in one valve and a corresponding ridge in the opposite valve (Fig. 13.4.7). In slightly more advanced types the groove is divided into anterior and posterior portions. Moreover, a tooth or socket may be present at the anterior end of the hinge margin (Fig. 13.4.8). Next, a tooth or socket may appear at the posterior end of the hinge margin. If additional complications are introduced, they invariably seem to arise first at the anterior position before appearing posteriorly; hence, the more diverse dentition denotes the anterior direction. Hinge margins of many Mesozoic and Cenozoic ostracodes are very elaborately denticulate or crenulate (Fig. 13.4.8, 9). Dentition of the most advanced type, however, is secondarily simplified until only a single tooth or socket may occupy the positions formerly occupied by clusters of teeth or sockets.

Microstructure of the two kinds of contact margins also can be helpful in taxonomic studies of ostracodes. In the simplest kind the outer shell bends around at the contact margin and doubles back on itself to form a U-shaped edge, leaving a space (**vestibule**) between the **outer lamella** and the **inner lamella**; these are **monolamellar** contact margins (Fig 13.4.2). The other kind of contact margin seemingly was derived from the monolamellar kind as the lamellae moved closer together until they came in contact along the margin. In these latter **bilamellar** contact margins the lamellae look as though they had been pinched together to form a marginal band, the inner edge of

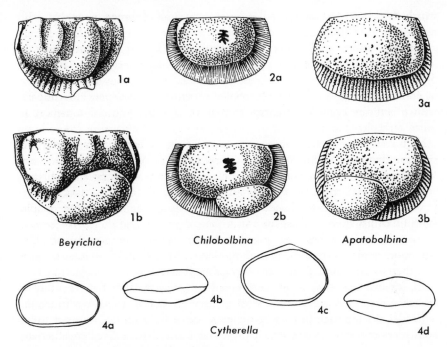

Figure 13.5. Dimorphism in Ostracodes.
1a, 1b. Male and female valves of *Beyrichia moodeyi*, 18X, Silurian, Pennsylvania. 2a, 2b. Male and female valves of *Chilobolbina dentifera*, 17X, Ordovician, Esthonia. 3a, 3b. Male and female valves of *Apatobolibina granifera*, 16X, Silurian, Pennsylvania. 4. *Cytherella fredericksburgensis*, 25X, Cretaceous, Gulf Coast. 4a, 4b, side and dorsal views of a male. 4c, 4d, side and dorsal views of a female.
(1-3 after Swartz, 1936. 4 after Alexander, 1932.)

which appears on many valves as the **line of concrescence** (Fig. 13.4.3, 4). If the inner lamella projects freely above the line of concrescence, the actual innermost edge is called the **inner margin.** Ostracode valves are traversed by microscopic **pores,** each of which bore a sensitive bristle in life. Most of the shell is traversed at right angles to the surface by **normal pores,** but the contact margin, when transparent, reveals the presence of **radial pores** which add to the laciness of its appearance in many cases (Fig. 13.4.5).

Ostracodes reproduce sexually by union of male and female sex cells and also reproduce parthenogenetically through fertile eggs produced by the female alone and hatched out only as females. In the former case there commonly are observable differences between the carapaces of males and females. Sexual dimorphism of ostracodes, when present, may be manifested by variations in shape, size, and proportions of carapaces. Differences may be slight (Fig. 13.5.4) or the differences can be strikingly apparent (Fig. 13.5.1–3). Sexual dimorphism is particularly obvious in various Paleozoic ostracodes, in which case the presumed females bear some sort of **brood pouch** or **frill** near one end of the ventral border (Fig. 13.5.1–3). So-called pouches vary in appearance from simple frills somewhat like the lateral keels on an ocean liner to globular or melonlike swellings. Brood pouches may be so large that they obscure the normal appearance of a valve, or they may not be present in some molts. Obviously, the presence or absence of brood pouches, coupled with other dimorphic differences, can make identifications of some ostracodes difficult.

Frills and pouches are commonly assumed to have had some reproductive function, but this assumption is not a certainty. According to one hypothesis supported by observations upon a living species, males swim near the surface and females rise from their bottom-dwelling habitat to the surface during reproductive periods. Frills and pouches therefore might serve the double function of providing ballast for a benthonic existence and shelter for larvae. In fact, it has even been suggested that extravagant development of frills and pouches may have impaired locomotion or copulation of some ostracodes and thereby contributed to their extinction. It has also been suggested that frills, for instance, may have been merely adaptive features for a benthonic existence on a soft substratum without serving any reproductive function. This idea is supported in part by the presence of frills on what appear to be both sexes of some species which presumably could have lived together on an oozy sea floor.

Although most arthropods pass through a series of molt stages, the study of molted carapaces (**instars**) has attained particular significance in connection with ostracodes. For one thing, ostracodes are prolific animals with relatively short life spans, so they are apt to be represented by myriad instars in one stratum. Moreover, ostracodes are valuable stratigraphic markers whose identifications over a period of years have been based upon increasingly fine discrimination of differences.

Ostracode eggs hatch as nauplius larvae which very shortly are encased within their first, minute carapaces. Thereafter, a single animal casts off its first carapace and, eventually, a succession of other instars as it grows to

Figure 13.6 (opposite).   Paleozoic Ostracodes.
1. *Eurychilina reticulata*, 17X, Ordovician, Minnesota.   2. *Aechmina cuspidata*, 19X, Devonian, Maryland.   3. *Euprimitia sanctipauli*, 50X, Ordovician, Minnesota.   4. *Hollina spiculosa*, 22X, Devonian, Kentucky.   5. *Leperditia fabulites*, 3X, Ordovician, Minnesota.   6. *Bassleratia typa*, 35X, Ordovician, Ontario.   7. *Ceratopsis chambersi*, 25X, Ordovician, Minnesota.   8. *Bollia burgeneri*, 17X, Devonian, Pennsylvania.   9. *Dicranella bicornis*, 20X, Ordovician, Minnesota. 10a, 10b. Side and end views of *Glyptopleura varicostata*, 32X, Mississippian, Illinois.   11a, 11b. End and side views of *Amphissites exiguus*, 32X, Mississippian, Illinois.   12. *Hollinella radiata*, 27X, Mississippian, Illinois.   13. *Paraparchites cyclopeus*, 17X, Pennsylvanian, Midcontinent.   14. *Bairdia beedei*, 15X, Pennsylvanian, Midcontinent.   15. *Knightina harltoni*, 40X, Pennsylvanian, Midcontinent.   16. *Kirkbya symmetrica*, 40X, Mississippian, Illinois.   17. *Kellettina montosa*, 30X, Pennsylvanian, Midcontinent.
(1–4, 6–9 after Swartz, 1933.   5 after Bassler and Kellett, 1934.   10–13, 16 after Cooper, 1941. 14, 15 after Payne, 1937.   17 after Cooper, 1941.)

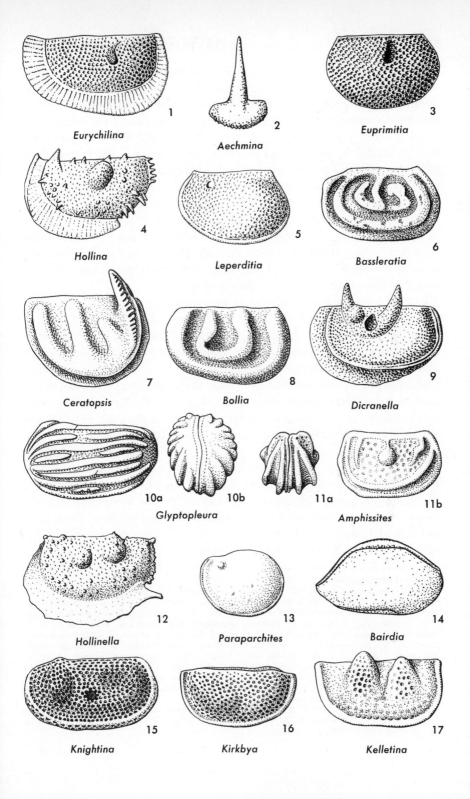

1 Eurychilina

2 Aechmina

3 Euprimitia

4 Hollina

5 Leperditia

6 Bassleratia

7 Ceratopsis

8 Bollia

9 Dicranella

10a 10b Glyptopleura

11a 11b Amphissites

12 Hollinella

13 Paraparchites

14 Bairdia

15 Knightina

16 Kirkbya

17 Kelletina

maturity. Various species probably molt from five to eight times before they reach maturity and become sexually active. It appears from somewhat tentative data on growth dynamics that the bodily volume of ostracodès is doubled between successive instars; hence ostracodes grow unusually vigorously compared to some other arthropods such as lobsters and crabs. Any parameter such as length, height, or thickness increases in a consistent fashion in a particular species; therefore ostracodes lend themselves particularly well to biometric studies. In addition, external ornamentation which may be present varies slightly from instar to instar as growth proceeds. In fact, variation in dimensions and ornamentation among instars of different ages in one species may be as great as or greater than differences among instars of the same age in two different species. Accordingly, the precise differentiation of some species of ostracodes is becoming increasingly dependent upon statistical studies of the complete sequences of instars.

It is probable that more species of fossil ostracodes have been described than are truly represented by the diverse carapaces which have been collected so far. Major reasons for the excess of names and for the difficulty of identifying species of ostracodes include variation among instars, sexual dimorphism, dietary differences which affect construction of valves, parasitism (commonly by microscopic worms) which alters shapes of valves, and deformation of carapaces during compaction of sediments. Nevertheless, many paleontologists have discovered that the advantages in the study of ostracodes far outweigh the disadvantages; hence increasing attention is being devoted to this Subclass.

Ostracodes first appeared in the Early Ordovician and quickly rose to a prominence which they have maintained into the Recent. Although most ostracodes are marine, others inhabit fresh water and some even may live in hot springs or sulfurous waters. By habit they swarm about the bottom or on vegetation by a combination of crawling and swimming, but they also may swim freely at various depths in open water. Fresh-water forms gen-

---

Figure 13.7 (opposite). Mesozoic and Cenozoic Ostracodes.
1. Rv *Paracypris dentonensis*, 35X, Cretaceous, Gulf Coast. 2 Rv. *Cythereis fredericksburgensis*, 35X, Cretaceous, Gulf Coast. 3. Rv *Cythereis worthensis*, 70X, Cretaceous, Gulf Coast. 4. Lv *Cytheropteron acutolobatum*, 70X, Cretaceous, Gulf Coast. 5. Rv *Loxoconcha claibornensis*, 120X, Eocene, Gulf Coast. 6. Rv *Cythereis lemnicata*, 30X, Paleocene, Gulf Coast. 7. Rv *Cytheridea ruginosa*, 40X, Paleocene, Gulf Coast. 8. Rv *Cytheridea ehlersi*, 45X, Eocene, Gulf Coast. 9. Rv *Haplocytheridea wallacei*, 45X, Eocene, Gulf Coast. 10. Lv *Cytherelloidea alabamensis*, 50X, Oligocene, Atlantic Coast. 11a, 11b. Exterior and interior of Lv of *Eucythere byramensis*, 65X, Oligocene, Gulf Coast. 12a, 12b. Rv and dorsal view of *Cythereis americana*, 30X, Miocene, Florida. 13a, 13b. Rv and dorsal view of *Cythereis exanthemata*, 25X, Miocene, Florida. 14. Rv *Hemicythere jollaensis*, 40X, Pliocene, California. 15. Lv *Cythereis pennata*, 40X, Pliocene, California.
(1-4 after Alexander, 1929. 5, 9 after Stephenson, 1946. 6, 7 after Alexander, 1934. 8 after Howe and Chambers, 1935. 10 after Sexton, 1951. 11 after Howe and Law, 1936. 14, 15 after LeRoy, 1943.)

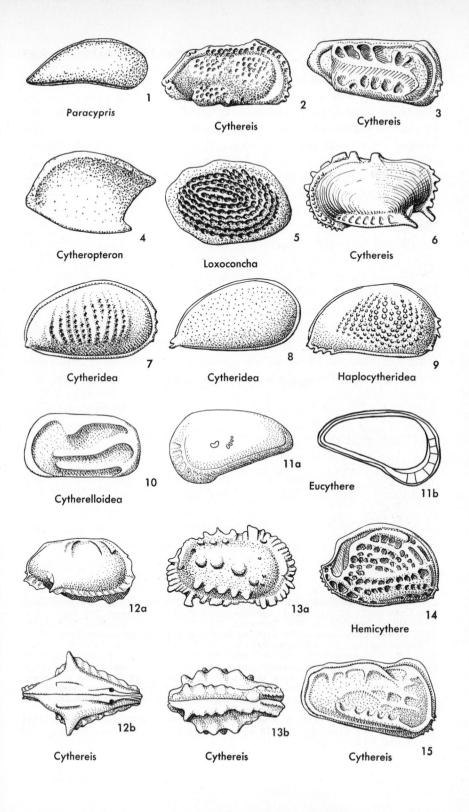

1 Paracypris

2 Cythereis

3 Cythereis

4 Cytheropteron

5 Loxoconcha

6 Cythereis

7 Cytheridea

8 Cytheridea

9 Haplocytheridea

10 Cytherelloidea

11a

Eucythere 11b

12a

13a

14 Hemicythere

12b Cythereis

13b Cythereis

15 Cythereis

erally are characterized by smooth or monotonous surface features, outlines of valves, details of structures on the hinge line, and by muscle scars.

Study of fossil ostracodes has been enhanced by their usefulness in commercial micropaleontologic work. In Paleozoic rocks, for instance, smaller foraminifers are very rare throughout, and even fusulinids are not common before the Early Pennsylvanian. Ostracodes, however, become increasingly abundant through the Paleozoic; hence they can be almost as useful for correlation of Paleozoic strata as smaller foraminifers are for Cretaceous and Cenozoic strata. Accordingly, about 3400 species belonging to about 300 Genera had been described from the Paleozoic alone by 1942 (Fig. 13.6). Numerous additional Genera and species have been described from the Mesozoic and Cenozoic, particularly on the Gulf Coast of the United States and in Europe (Fig. 13.7). On the other hand, strata in the Tertiary basins of the Pacific Coast do not contain many ostracodes, although Quaternary representatives are common. Fresh-water ostracodes occur in association with branchiopods in the nonmarine members of cyclothems in the midcontinent, in terrestrial sediments of the western interior, and in some Pleistocene lake beds of various countries (Fig. 13.8).

SUBCLASS 3.   COPEPODA

Copepods are tiny crustaceans with a segmented body and five pairs (rarely six) of appendages which are used in swimming. No appendages are present on the abdomen. Antennae may be biramous. No separate carapace is present, although some thoracic segments fuse with cephalic segments. Of the free-swimming copepods, *Cyclops,* one of the water fleas, is the best known. It and similar forms constitute a major element of the planktonic life in the oceans and in fresh water. Other copepods are parasitic upon fish. No fossil copepods have been reported.

SUBCLASS 4.   CIRRIPEDIA

The name of the Cirripedia, or barnacles, refers to the curly tufts of appendages which can be projected from the open end of the exoskeleton. Barnacles are the most aberrant of all of the arthropods; in fact, most barnacles do not resemble other arthropods at all from external appearances. Of the two principal kinds of living barnacles, the gooseneck barnacles, *Lepas* and *Scalpellum,* bear almond-shaped crowns of calcareous plates on a stalk (Fig. 13.9). These **pedunculate** barnacles are pelagic, in that they incrust all sorts of floating objects. For some reason lepadid barnacles have been involved in mysticism, it once being generally believed that they grew on trees and then fell to the ground where they metamorphosed into geese. The other and better-known group of **sessile** barnacles is characterized by

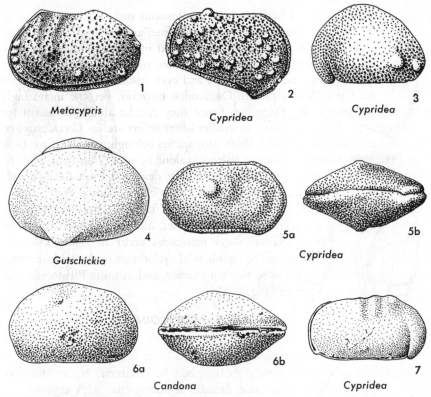

Figure 13.8. Fresh-Water Ostracodes.
1. *Metacypris angularis,* 35X, Cretaceous, Rocky Mountains. 2. *Cypridea wyomingensis,* 35X, Cretaceous, Rocky Mountains. 3. *Cypridea longispina,* 35X, Cretaceous, Rocky Mountains. 4. *Gutschickia deltoidea,* 25X, Pennsylvanian, Midcontinent. 5a, 5b. Side and dorsal views of *Cypridea arvadensis,* 30X, Cretaceous, Rocky Mountains. 6a, 6b. Side and dorsal views of *Candona pagei,* 25X, Eocene, Rocky Mountains. 7. *Cypridea bisulcata,* 30X, Eocene, Rocky Mountains.
(1 after Peck, 1941. 2, 3, 5 after Peck, 1951. 4 after Scott, 1944. 6, 7 after Swain, 1949.)

Balanus, the acorn barnacle (Fig. 13.11). It has a volcano-shaped form and predominantly incrusts hard surfaces on the sea floor, although it also incrusts various floating objects, even whales. It is notorious that barnacles foul the bottom of ships; crusts an inch or two thick are composed of forests of lepadid and balanid barnacles, together with tubicolous worms and bryozoans. Most barnacles inhabit shallow water, but they also are represented in the deep sea at 12,000 feet (4000 m). Some even have been found in globigerine ooze. Barnacles reveal a distinct tendency to become parasitic. Thus, one Genus, *Sacculina,* has achieved dubious zoologic fame by infesting crabs and casting off every visible vestige of arthropodan ancestry. In the adult form it is merely a sac of tissue with rootlets, but its larvae pass through

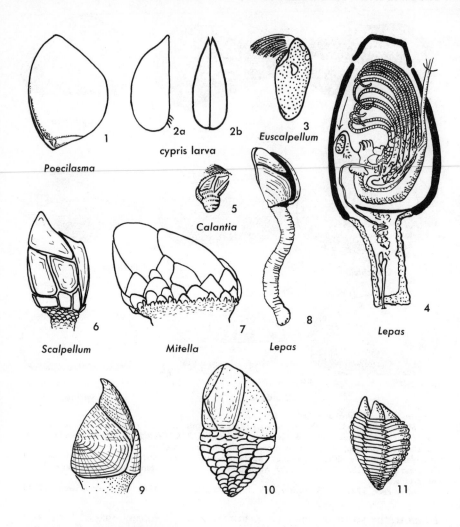

Figure 13.9. Lepadid Barnacles.

1. Interior of scutum of *Poecilasma inequilaterale*, 1X, Recent. 2a, 2b. Side and dorsal views of cypris larva of *Lepas* just before becoming attached, 15X, Recent. 3. Early attached stage of *Euscalpellum* sp., enlarged, Recent. 4. Cut-away view of female *Lepas* sp. with site of male individual indicated by arrow, enlarged, Recent. 5. Male of *Calantia* sp., greatly enlarged, Recent. 6. Capitulum of *Scalpellum* sp., showing sparse latera, 1 1/2X, Recent. 7. Capitulum of *Mitella* sp., showing numerous latera, 2X, Recent. 8. *Lepas hilli*, 1/2X, Recent, world-wide. 9. *Praelepas* sp., the oldest barnacle, 6X, Pennsylvanian, Russia. 10. Capitulum and armored peduncle of *Archaeolepas* sp., 2X, Jurassic, Germany. 11. *Stramentum flabellum*, 1X, Cretaceous, England.

(1, 6-8 after Pilsbry, 1907. 2-5 after Withers, 1928. 9 after Withers, 1935. 10 after Withers, 1928. 11 after Woodward, 1928.)

a nauplius stage, and it has a faintly segmented body prior to entering the tissues of its host; therefore *Sacculina* is allied with the Crustacea.

Orientation of barnacles is obscure from the outside, surprising from the inside, and confusing for purposes of description. In the first place, its exoskeleton resembles that of no other arthropod. Moreover, the body is hidden from view, except for the tips of feet, and even these rarely are visible because the animal withdraws its appendages and closes off its aperture when it is out of water. If a barnacle is dissected, however, one finds that the body is lying dorsal side down and is attached to one side of the exoskeleton by the anterior end (Fig. 13.9.8). Thus, as an approximation, the base or stalk is dorsal, the aperture is ventral, and one side of the circular balanid skeleton or one keel of the compressed lepadid skeleton is anterior. It is not surprising, therefore, that specialists in the study of barnacles prefer to ignore the common terms of orientation and to use special names for each plate in an exoskeleton.

Understanding orientation of barnacles is assisted by knowledge of early developmental stages. After the nauplius stage, barnacles pass into another free-swimming larval stage, the **cypris,** in which a bivalved carapace like that of an ostracode is present (Fig. 13.9.2). The cypris attaches itself to a suitable substratum with its disc-shaped antennae. The larval eyes and anterior appendages begin to be obliterated, at the same time that a cirripedian skeleton begins to take form beneath the bivalved carapace. Soon thereafter, the young barnacle casts off the cyproid carapace and starts its adult growth as a blind rather headless arthropod with six pairs of appendages (Fig. 13.9.3).

Lepadid Barnacles. As typified by *Lepas,* which is a very simple lepadid, the animal consists of a **peduncle** or stalk, surmounted by a crown or **capitulum** usually consisting of five calcareous plates—a median keel plate (**carina**), two side plates (**scuta**), and two terminal plates (**terga**) (Fig. 13.9.8). All of these plates are held together by flexible chitinous bands, and the aperture passes between the terga at the summit. A scutum may resemble a single valve of a pelecypod so closely that the two probably have been confused by collectors (Fig. 13.9.1). In other lepadid barnacles a capitulum may consist of more plates than the 3 to 5 plates present in *Lepas,* in which case the extra plates generally are termed **latera.** Thus, *Scalpellum* has 12 to 15 large plates including latera, plus a zone of tiny scaly plates at the top of the peduncle (Fig. 13.9.6). *Mitella* has 18 or more irregularly overlapping large plates which gradually decrease in size downward and merge with a zone of small latera (Fig. 13.9.7).

The oldest lepadid barnacle, and indeed the oldest barnacle yet discovered, is *Praelepas* from the Pennsylvanian of Russia. It is a rather simply constructed capitulum which resembles *Lepas* itself and probably was borne on an unarmored peduncle in life (Fig. 13.9.9). *Archaeolepas* (Fig. 13.9.10) and *Stramentum* (Fig. 13.9.11) from the Jurassic and Cretaceous of Europe consist of a large number of small subequal plates (**latera**) on the peduncle surmounted by the few large plates of the capitulum. *Stramentum* seems to represent the culmination in increase of number of plates from the Paleozoic types, after which the peduncle was clearly differentiated from the capitulum and decrease in number of plates became the dominant evolutionary trend. *Scalpellum* and *Lepas* represent later stages in the evolutionary series.

Lepadid barnacles apparently range from the Pennsylvanian to the Recent. Among Recent forms, 56 species belonging to 13 Genera and Subgenera had been reported in American waters alone by 1907.

Balanid Barnacles.   These are the common conical barnacles which visitors to the seashore observe incrusting rocks in the intertidal zone. They consist of a **wall,** the individual plates of which are rigidly locked together, and of an **operculum** of four movable plates. It appears that two pairs of the opercular plates, the **scuta** and **terga,** are homologous with corresponding plates in the capitulum of a gooseneck barnacle. The scuta and terga are united by a chitinous band, the **opercular membrane,** which also binds them to the wall. During ecdysis, the opercular membrane is shed along with the chitinous cuticle over the appendages, but the wall and opercular plates are retained permanently.

Plates in the wall are called **compartments.** One of the compartments can be proved to be homologous with the carina of a lepadid barnacle, and another compartment on the opposite side corresponds to the rostrum. In generalized balanids there are eight compartments in the wall; hence, three compartments on either flank between the carina and the rostrum are not present in lepadid barnacles. Balanids are characterized in large part by the number of compartments which are retained in the wall while reduction in number of compartments takes place (Fig. 13.10.1-3). Reduction is accomplished in two ways—either by elimination of compartments or by fusion of two or more of these plates. Inasmuch as the eight original compartments overlap each other in characteristic ways, and their surfaces are differently ornamented, it is possible to recognize each compartment and to decide whether a particular compartment is missing or merely is fused to an adjacent plate. The Genera *Octomeris* and *Catophragmus,* for instance, retain eight compartments, whereas two compartments are fused to a third in *Balanus* to make a total of six. *Tetraclita* has only four compartments because two are fused to a third and two more are eliminated.

The wall rests upon a **basis,** which may be thin and chitinous or may be partly calcareous.

Balanid barnacles are thought to have been derived from lepadid ancestors with eight main compartments. Thus, the Recent *Catophragmus* exemplifies a generalized and potentially intermediate ancestor between the lepadids and forms such as *Balanus*. *Catophragmus* has bands of small latera near the

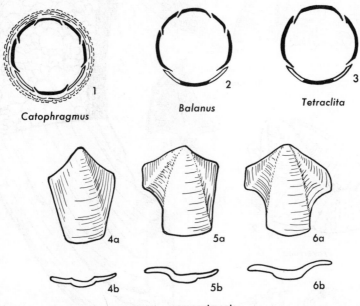

Catophragmus   *Balanus*   *Tetraclita*

compartments

Figure 13.10.   Compartments of Sessile Barnacles.
1-3. Schematic cross sections of balanoid barnacles. 4a, 4b. Surface and cross section of a compartment with two radii. 5a, 5b. Surface and cross section of a compartment with an ala on the left and a radius on the right. 6a, 6b. Surface and cross section of a compartment with two alae.
(1-3, 4a, 5a, 6a after Pilsbry, 1916.)

base of the wall, somewhat like the lepadid, *Mitella* (Fig. 13.9.7). Unfortunately, the paleontologic record provides very little material bearing on the subject of ancestry of balanids.

One of the most peculiar of all balanids is a giant species which is a common index fossil of the Upper Miocene of California (Fig. 13.11.4). Specimens become almost a foot long and 3 inches in diameter (30 cm by 8 cm). They are filled with large blisterlike vesicles which are convex upward. The outer wall is minutely vesicular as in many other balanids. These skeletons converge to a remarkable degree upon the structure of the rudistoid pelecypods—so much so, in fact, that they were at first thought to be the only known post-Cretaceous rudistoids. Paleontologists refer to this fossil barnacle as *Tamiosoma gregaria,* but zoologists call it *Balanus gregarius*.

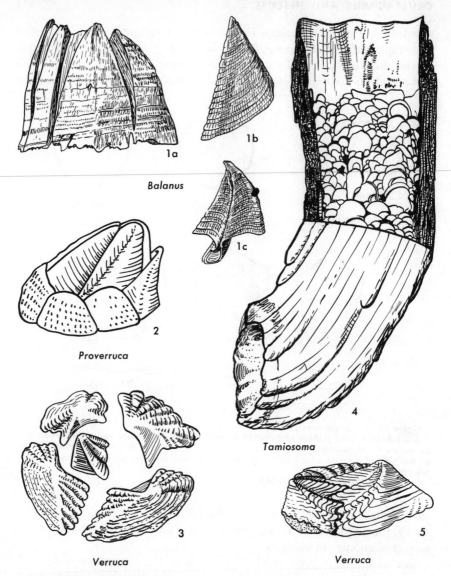

Figure 13.11. Balanoid Barnacles.
1. *Balanus concavus chesapeakensis*, 2/3X, Miocene, Maryland. 1a, side view. 1b, exterior of scutum. 1c, exterior of tergum. 2. Oblique side view of *Proverruca vinculum*, the oldest sessile barnacle, 15X, Cretaceous, England. 3. Four compartments and a tergum of *Verruca pusilla*, 8X, Cretaceous, Holland. 4. Cut-away view of *Tamiosoma gregaria*, 2/3X, Miocene, California. 5. Side view of an asymmetrical barnacle, *Verruca alba*, 7X, Recent.
(1, 4, 5, after Pilsbry, 1916. 2, 3 after Withers, 1935.)

Only it and *Balanus laevis coquimhensis* from the Pleistocene of Chile and the Recent of western South American coastal waters have the same vesicular filling.

Verruca (Fig. 13.11.3, 5) and its relatives resemble *Balanus* but the plates are asymmetrically distributed.

Recent species of balanid barnacles were referable to 24 Genera and 223 species in 1916. Some of the species had been reported as fossils. Rather oddly, however, not many studies have been published yet upon either lepadid or balanid barnacles, in spite of the fact that remains of barnacles are rather abundant in near-shore Cenozoic sediments, and skeletons of barnacles retain considerable evidence of their evolutionary modification.

Balanids occur as early as the Mesozoic and then range through the Cenozoic. Supposed Paleozoic Genera of balanids seem to be questionable.

SUBCLASS 5. MALACOSTRACA

All of the commonly encountered Crustacea, such as lobsters, crabs, shrimps, and crayfish, are malacostracans. Most of these animals are marine, but some, such as the crayfish, inhabit fresh water, and a few are even terrestrial.

Malacostraca are characterized by the fusion of the cephalic carapace with some of the thoracic segments to form a **cephalothorax** (Fig. 13.12.7). The entire carapace is molted periodically, along with the covering of all of the appendages. Inasmuch as ecdysis of lobsters is known better than that of any other arthropod, it serves to illustrate the process which probably took place when extinct arthropods molted. As the lobster grows, the number of cells increases but the volume of the carapace remains the same except for a slight expansion due to flexibility along joints. The soft tissue therefore is compressed in order to accommodate the new cells. By the time that additional adjustment of the flesh to the rigid armor is impossible, a new, thin, chitinous envelope or cuticle has been secreted between the flesh and the old shell. Then, as ecdysis becomes imminent, decalcification of parts of the cephalothorax and joints takes place. Decalcification provides additional flexibility during withdrawal of soft parts from the shell. Ecdysis begins with transverse splitting of the carapace along the dorsal suture between the thorax and abdomen, after which the soft animal first backs out of the front part of the carapace and then climbs forward out of the abdominal portion. It is apparent that advantage is taken of natural taper of the carapace so that withdrawal is always in the expanding direction. At the time of molting the platelike skeletal divisions among muscles also are shed because these partitions really are infolded portions of the carapace. Once having molted, a lobster quickly takes in fluid and allows preformed cells to expand even beyond their normal size, as if in anticipation of a future necessity to lose water as new cells are formed. A lobster observed by Herrick came out of a shell 11.25 inches (28.6 cm) long and was 12 inches (30.5 cm) long shortly thereafter. At the end of four days when the carapace had begun to harden perceptibly, it was 12.5 inches (31.8 cm) long.

For a period of about six weeks after molting a lobster leads a retiring existence while it adds calcium carbonate to its carapace. A lobster is a great delicacy for some fish during its soft-shelled stages, just as the blue crab is highly prized by people during its soft-shelled stages. A lobster 10.5 inches (26.7 cm) long will have molted about 25 times, will be about 5 years old, and will weigh 1.75 pounds. Incidentally, the name of the Subclass, Malacostraca, was derived from two Greek words meaning "soft" and "shell."

In addition to the presence of a cephalothorax, Malacostraca are characterized by the presence of 19 recognizable segments in the body, not counting stalked eyes and the terminal segment, both of which may be considerably modified. The head consists of 5 segments, the thorax of 8, and the abdomen of 6, all of which segments can be characterized by the modifications of the paired appendages they inherited from a generalized ancestral form. Thus, the appendages of the head consist of an anterior pair of uniramous **antennules,** a pair of biramous **antennae,** a pair of heavy biramous **mandibles** for chewing, and two pairs of lighter biramous **maxillae** to assist in chewing. These five pairs of cephalic appendages often are represented as simple specializations of the ancestral trilobitan plan of ventral appendages which mostly served locomotor functions. Considerable difference of opinion exists as to which pair of crustacean limbs is homologous with a particular pair of trilobitan or of other arthropodan limbs on the respective head regions.

Behind the head, the paired appendages on the eight thoracic segments commonly are modified to serve two functions. As many as four anterior pairs are articulated in such a way that they help in handling food near the mouth, yet they also resemble locomotor appendages; therefore, they are given the compound name of **maxillipedes** (jaw-feet). At least the posterior four pairs of appendages on the thorax serve strictly as walking **legs.** It is the walking legs which are the commonly seen appendages of lobsters and crabs. Abdominal appendages normally are insignificant, biramous swimmerets, except for the posterior pair. Both rami of the last pair are much expanded circular plates (**uropods**) which spread out to make the four parts of the effective tail fans of lobsters and crayfish. A lobster, for instance, propels itself backward at high speed by swinging the uropods down and forward in a violent muscular spasm.

Respiration is carried on by one or more rows of gills which lie at the base of the legs or on the thoracic segments in an elongate gill chamber where the thorax is overlapped by the external carapace of the cephalothorax. Another special structure is the **gastric mill.** This consists of chitinous masticatory devices located within the anterior part of the digestive track, but internally from the external chewing feet such as the mandibles. Gastric mills are molted along with the exoskeleton.

Only a few of the most important groups with fossil representatives are considered below, although this procedure does not do justice to the great zoologic importance of Crustacea.

The oldest malacostracans have been collected from the Devonian of New York and Germany. *Acanthotelson* (Fig. 13.12.2) is a Pennsylvanian form which is potentially able to be ancestral to the later Malacostraca.

Phyllocarids. Phyllocarids are shrimplike animals which depart radically from all other Malacostraca by having a variable number—up to 20—of body segments, the extra segment being in the abdomen. This numerical difference is considered to be great enough by some naturalists to warrant separating the phyllocarids from the rest of the Malacostraca. Thoracic limbs are leaflike—a feature which is the source of the name phyllocarid (leaf shrimp). The group is represented by *Nebalia,* which is a Recent Genus (Fig. 13.12.9), and possibly by several extinct forms which existed as early as the Cambrian. *Echinocaris* (Fig. 13.12.8) is a characteristic Paleozoic Genus. According to zoologic considerations, *Nebalia* and its relatives represent transitional forms between the ostracodes and branchiopods on the one hand, and the malacostracans on the other hand.

Isopods. Isopods are rather small dorsoventrally flattened crustaceans (Fig. 13.12.5). Carapaces are lacking, thoracic appendages and antennules usually are uniramous, and abdominal appendages usually are biramous. Isopods (equal feet) are so named because the thoracic appendages are all the same. The largest living isopod is about 11 inches (28 cm) long and the smallest are microscopic. They abound at various depths in the oceans where they are major scavengers, but marine isopods are almost never seen by laymen. Instead, the most widely known living isopod is *Armadillidium,* which is the common pill bug or wood louse of gardens. This strange fellow is one of the few terrestrial Crustacea, sharing this distinction principally with a few land crabs. Fresh-water forms of isopods also are known.

Isopods have been reported from rocks as old as the Devonian, and several Mesozoic species are known, such as *Cyclosphaeroma* (Jurassic) from England (Fig. 13.12.3). At least 28 fossil species have been described, most of which are from the Tertiary of Europe where isopods have been found abundantly at a few localities. Two species are known from North America, both from the Cretaceous.

Amphipods. Amphipods resemble the isopods but are compressed laterally instead of dorsoventrally. Only one or two thoracic segments are fused with the head in this group of shrimplike animals, whereas all thoracic segments are fused with the head in the true shrimps belonging to the decapods. Two kinds of thoracic appendages are present, of which the anterior ones bear small claws and the posterior ones do not—hence amphipod, meaning "both kinds of feet." Many marine amphipods are known, in addition to which several fresh-water species have been reported. Among the latter are the well shrimp and the gammarid shrimp such as *Gammarus*. Another common amphipod is the tiny terrestrial sand hopper, which occurs on most sandy beaches where it dwells in windrows of seaweed and skits about noses and ears of sun bathers.

Decapods. Crustacea with ten legs are typified by lobsters, crabs, shrimps, and prawns. One decapod, the Japanese giant crab, *Macrocheira,* is the largest arthropod ever to live. It becomes as great as 11 feet (3.6 m) in diameter as measured to the tips of opposite legs. It is the well-known canned crab of commerce. Among the decapods there has been a dominant trend toward development of uniramous appendages by suppression of the exopodite. Moreover, there is a trend toward increased reflexing of the abdomen forward and ventrally. Thus, in lobsters, crayfish, shrimps, and prawns, the abdomen extends in a gentle arc posteriorly and ends in a fan-shaped tail; in hermit crabs the abdomen is slightly reflexed; and in common crabs the abdomen is so completely reflexed that it is closely appressed against the ventral surface of the thorax (Fig. 13.12.10). The abdomen of crabs also is reduced in size and tends to lack the uropods. Shape of the carapace, such as circular, quadrate, or triangular, is useful in identification of crabs.

Decapod crustaceans can be differentiated into groups on the basis of variation in construction of legs. All groups reveal a distinct tendency toward development of pincers (**chelae**) on one or more pairs of legs; legs which bear chelae are **chelipedes.** In a lobster, for instance, the anterior pair of legs consists of huge claw-bearing chelipedes, whereas the other four pairs of legs lack chelae. In shrimps and prawns, on the other hand, two or three pairs of legs bear chelae and three or two pairs, respectively, lack them. A few un-

---

Figure 13.12 (opposite). Malacostracans.
1. *Palaeocaris typus*, 1 1/3X, Pennsylvanian, Illinois. 2. *Acanthotelson stimsoni*, 2/3X, Pennsylvanian, Illinois. 3. *Cyclosphaeroma trilobatum*, 2/3X, Jurassic, England. 4. *Nahecaris stürtzi*, 1/3X, Devonian, Germany. 5. *Dendrotion hanseni*, 11X, Recent. 6. *Mesothyra oceani*, 1/4X, Devonian, New York. 7. *Anthrapalaemon gracilis*, 3X, Pennsylvanian, Illinois. 8. *Echinocaris socialis*, 1/2X, Devonian, New York. 9. *Nebalia* sp., 5X, Recent. 10. Ventral view of a spider crab with two appendages attached, about 1X, Recent.
(1 after Packard, 1885b. 2 after Packard, 1885a. 3 after Woodward, 1898. 4 after Broili, 1929. 5 after Menzies, 1956. 6 after Broili, 1928. 7 after Packard, 1885c. 8 after Hall and Clarke, 1888. 9 after Packard, 1883. 10 after Rathbun, 1925.)

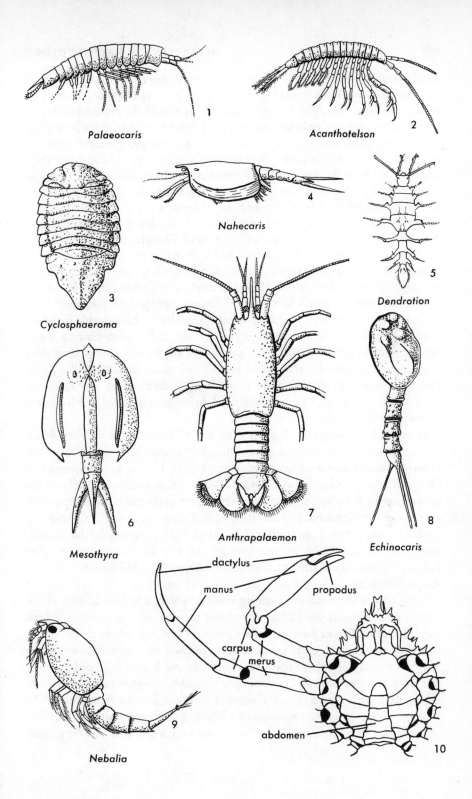

Palaeocaris

Acanthotelson

Cyclosphaeroma

Nahecaris

Dendrotion

Mesothyra

Anthrapalaemon

Echinocaris

Nebalia

dactylus

manus

propodus

carpus

merus

abdomen

usual decapod crustaceans bear one large chela on one appendage and a small chela on the matching appendage of the same pair, as in fiddler crabs. One chela of a certain decapod is larger than all the rest of the animal combined. Chelae are useful, not only for catching food and for defense, but for digging, hammering, and climbing. The coco crab, for instance, climbs trees for coconuts, pounds a hole in one by knocking out an "eye" of the inner shell, and then feeds on the meat inside. Other kinds of crabs inhabit empty shells, holes, or hollow stems of plants, and may even close off the entrance to their particular residence by using one or both chelae as a neatly fitting door.

In view of the remarkable adaptability of chelipedes, it is likely that they may become the most stratigraphically useful of all malacostracan remains. A cheliped is the huskiest part of a crab and is therefore the part most likely to occur as a fossil. A cheliped consists of three short segments culminating in the large chela or claw proper (Fig. 13.12.10). The chela consists of a main portion, the **manus,** which bears a fixed finger or **propod** on the lower edge. Opposed to this and operated by powerful muscles is the movable finger or **dactyl.** The dactyl has a smooth upper surface and a tooth-bearing lower surface which opposes teeth on the propod. A **sulcus** and **pits** bearing setae may occupy the lateral surfaces, and a variety of spines may clothe the dactyl and manus. Recent work by Menzies (1951) indicates that species of the common crab, *Cancer,* can be recognized from dactyls alone in Pleistocene deposits of California.

More fossil decapods are known than are all other kinds of fossil Malacostraca combined. The oldest decapodlike crustaceans are reported from the Pennsylvanian (as *Anthrapalaemon,* Fig. 13.12.7), but the first unquestioned decapods occur in the Triassic. Decapods are rather common locally in the Jurassic, as at Solenhofen, Germany. They were particularly abundant, however, from the Cretaceous to the Recent, and they occur as fossils in many lands. A compilation from Rathbun (1935) of fossil decapods on the Atlantic and Gulf Coastal Plains reveals that species are distributed according to time as follows: Cretaceous 72, Eocene 53, Oligocene 5, Miocene 27, Pliocene 5, and Pleistocene 14.

Some decapods manifest a **homing instinct** which is unique among all invertebrates. In recent years adult lobsters off the coast of California have been banded like birds and then transported to new grounds where it was hoped that they might inaugurate new colonies. Instead, they swam back to their former haunts! Lindberg (1955) reported that one lobster returned 30 miles in two or three months and crossed deep channels. Another moved 100 miles in 100 days, and one record of a 200-mile homing journey is reported. The geologic and zoologic implications of a homing instinct are diverse, but it is probable that an active homing instinct would keep a group of lobsters isolated and thereby increase the differentiation of local populations. If isolation persisted over a long enough period of time, it would serve to create numerous local species and to inhibit the use of such creatures for purposes of paleontologic correlation. Distribution of decapods is governed in part by their sensitivity to changes in temperature; hence, a homing instinct would further increase the provinciality of decapod faunas. Perhaps it should not be surprising to find a strong homing instinct in Crustacea, inasmuch as the homing instinct in arthropods such as bees is well known.

Fresh-Water Malacostraca. In the course of populating different aqueous environments, the Malacostraca have invaded rivers, lakes, and even the innermost recesses of caves. It is concluded that the marine forms gave rise to the fresh-water forms because the overwhelming majority of all Malacostraca are marine, and marine forms occur earlier in the geologic record than fresh-water forms do. It also seems to be likely that fresh-water strains arose on more than one occasion. For instance, both the crabs and the crayfish occur in fresh water, yet neither of these groups seems to have given rise to the other. Moreover, there is a distinction at the generic and even Family level between crayfish of the northern hemisphere and crayfish of the southern hemisphere, which suggests that they did not have a common ancestor. Most of the fresh-water decapods have been referred to six Families. Crayfish are able to inhabit water which is decidedly cooler than that which the river crabs and prawns can tolerate; therefore, the river crabs and prawns are restricted to tropical and subtropical streams. Thus, fresh-water Malacostraca are distributed in three climate zones with the river crabs and prawns in the middle. River crabs, however, are much more aggressive than are crayfish; hence, the two groups are mutually exclusive. They may exist in the same region but not in the same body of water. It appears that the crabs are able to drive the crayfish ever farther away from the tropics.

The geologic record of fresh-water malacostracans is, expectedly, much less complete than is the record of marine forms, but there is still a significant record of the fresh-water forms. The oldest known fresh-water crayfish have been reported from the Early Cretaceous of Australasia; by Medial Cretaceous time there were unquestioned occurrences of fresh-water crayfish in that region. Crayfish then spread quickly to Central America and over most of the world, except Africa, which is almost devoid of crayfish. The effectiveness with which crayfish have been distributed is demonstrated by the presence of at least 67 species of the common Genus of crayfish, *Cambarus,* in the central and eastern United States alone.

The oldest fresh-water crabs have been reported from the Late Cretaceous. They appeared first and almost simultaneously in India and in the southern portion of North America.

Geologists, paleontologists, and zoogeographers all have been concerned with a problem which arises from the stratigraphic and geographic distribution of fresh-water Malacostraca. That is, how did fresh-water decapods such as *Cambarus* get on opposite sides of the Atlantic Ocean? No fresh-water decapod has a resting stage; therefore they cannot be transported while inactive. Nor has any decapod egg or larva been found adhering to birds. Nor is any one of them able to survive even for a short time in salt water, much less drift or swim thousands of miles. In an effort to allow for individual terrestrial migrations over short distances, and thereby ultimately to reach distant lands, some scientists have postulated an elaborate system of land bridges connecting different continents. In this way the distribution of creatures such as fresh-water decapods can be explained. On the other hand, considerable geologic and geophysical evidence suggests that there have not been land bridges across the major oceans. Many biologists think that fresh-water decapods might have survived the trip across an ocean on some floating object, even though the probability that the event would take place is extremely small.

Class E. Insecta

Insects may be the most diverse creatures on the face of the earth and definitely are the most abundant form of animal life seen by man. Only protozoans and worms exceed them in numbers, but both of the former groups are inconspicuous. According to one authority, 83,780 species of insects had been described in the United States up to 1946, but only 1370 common names have been recognized, even by specialists. Peterson (1948) was informed by entomologists in the U. S. Department of Agriculture that 662,298 species of living insects have been described and given scientific names, but this figure does not include subspecies and varieties (except among some ants). New species of insects are being described at the rate of about 6000 per year, which is probably faster than all other animals combined are being described. Even so, only a minor portion of the total number of living species of insects probably has been discovered.

Insects typically are terrestrial or aerial, but many, such as the mosquito, pass their early developmental stages in water. Only a few, such as water beetles, are distinctly aquatic. Insects breathe by means of tracheae. Their other most obvious character is the presence of three pairs of locomotor appendages on the thorax.

Bodies of insects are divided into **head, thorax,** and **abdomen.** The head may bear simple or compound eyes, or both. Much difference of opinion has been expressed by entomologists as to exactly how many segments are represented in the head of an insect, but most specialists recognize five or six segments. Only four pairs of appendages generally are present on the head.

These appendages comprise one pair of antennae, one pair of mandibles, and two pairs of maxillae. More difference of opinion exists among entomologists as to the homologies of these appendages with the appendages of other arthropods. It is apparent that there has been some reduction in number of appendages, but there is not widespread agreement as to which pair of appendages is missing and which pairs may not serve their former functions.

The most remarkable changes in insects relate to their manner of growth. Although the adults of most living insects do not molt, they surely were derived from creatures which did molt. In a very few cases among living insects, the adult emerges from the egg fully developed. Nevertheless, it is thought that the adult form of primitive insects arose by a gradual succession of molts in which each successive stage more nearly approached the adult form. **Incomplete metamorphosis** was introduced when the number of molt stages was reduced and rather more extensive changes transpired between molt stages than had taken place previously. Changes could be reflected in the nature of appendages or in the construction of the head. The form characterizing each of the stages during metamorphosis is a **nymph.** Nymphal stages are known from the Carboniferous.

Most living insects pass through a **complete metamorphosis** in which radical morphologic changes affect the larva during a long resting period and only one ecdysis occurs between the early form, the **pupa,** and the finished adult, the **imago.** The occurrence of complete metamorphosis among insects is well known through the changes of caterpillars during their pupal resting stage in cocoons into a butterfly or a moth as an imago. Complete metamorphosis is known to have taken place in insects as long ago as the Early Permian. Present data indicate that 5 per cent of the Early Permian insects went through complete metamorphosis, whereas 88 per cent of the Recent insects do.

The heads of insects are modified by the development of structures associated with the operation of the mouth parts. In some very primitive forms the mouth parts are recessed within flaps of chitin to form a pouched head. Primitive features of this sort are present in the living springtails and their relatives, the ancestors of which are known from the Middle Devonian of Scotland and are the oldest insects yet discovered. In another primitive group, represented by the living silverfish, the mouth parts are operated by muscles attached to internal chitinous supports in the head. From this latter group arose the higher insects in which the inward growths of the head eventually coalesced to produce a capsule (**tentorium**) about the cephalic ganglion. In neither of these two primitive groups (springtails and silverfish) is there any wings; hence they stand apart from the other insects and comprise the wingless insects or Apterygota.

Contrasted with the Apterygota are the winged insects or Pterygota. Wings are borne on the dorsal sides of the second and third thoracic appendages, whereas legs of insects are borne on the ventral sides of all three thoracic appendages. One or two pairs of wings may be present, or wings may be missing in some forms or at some stages in their development. It is a peculiarity of insects that wings are special outgrowths from the body wall, whereas in other flying creatures (pterosaurs, bats, and birds) wings are modified legs. Entomologists disagree as to whether wings arose from wingless forms or wings were aborted to produce wingless forms. The idea that the Pterygota arose from the Apterygota seems to be supported by more paleontologic evidence at present. For instance, the oldest Apterygota are known from the Medial Devonian, but the oldest Pterygota do not appear until the Pennsylvanian. Unfortunately, the developmental stages in the evolution of size of wings have not been discovered in fossils. It does seem, however, that an extra, small, winglike **prothoracic flap** was present on the first thoracic segment of many Late Paleozoic winged insects (Fig. 13.13.1). The prothoracic flaps bore veins and hairs such as the other two pairs of wings do, but there is no living or fossil insect known in which a third pair of wings, such as could be derived from prothoracic flaps, is present.

Almost immediately after the appearance of the first wings, there was rapid evolution of wing posture and venation. Wings of the most ancient insects were held upward or projected out stiffly away from the body, whereas the wings of later insects could be folded back over the posterior region of the body. The former insects are the Paleopterica; the latter, the Neopterica. Paleopterica are represented by several groups in Carboniferous rocks and are still known from the living mayflies and dragonflies. Neopterica lived as early as the Early Pennsylvanian and today comprise about 97 per cent of all insect species. It has been shown that the neopterous insects had a great advantage over the paleopterous insects because the Neopterica could fold back their wings and hide among vegetation. This feature acquired great survival value in the Mesozoic when pterosaurs and birds both arose. Perhaps the numerous, long, slender, partly projecting teeth of *Ctenochasma* and even the strong but erratically placed teeth of *Rhamphorhynchus* (two Jurassic pterosaurs) were adapted for catching air-borne insects.

Figure 13.13 (opposite). Insects.
1. *Mischoptera* sp., 1/2X, Pennsylvanian, France. 2. *Cacalydus* sp., a cicadalike form, 4X, Miocene, Colorado. 3. Left side of *Prodryas* sp., a butterfly, 1 1/3X, Miocene, Colorado. 4. *Aegialia* sp., a beetle, 8X, Eocene, Wyoming. 5. *Sackenia* sp., a flylike form, 3X, Oligocene, Colorado. 6. *Liometopum* sp., an ant, 3X, Oligocene, Colorado. 7. *Tyrbula* sp., a grasshopper, 1 1/3X, Miocene, Colorado. 8. *Anthracoblattina* sp., a cockroach, 1 1/3X, Pennsylvanian, Germany. 9. *Inocellia* sp., a lacewing, 4X, Miocene, Colorado. 10. Wing of *Aeschna* sp., a dragonfly, 2X, Miocene, Colorado.
(1 after Carpenter, 1951. 2, 4-10 after Scudder, 1890. 3 after Scudder, 1889.)

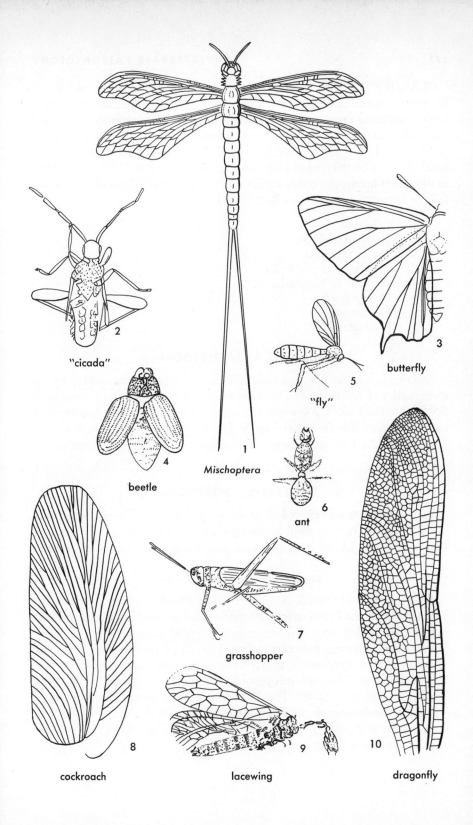

"cicada"

beetle

1

Mischoptera

"fly"

5

butterfly

3

6

ant

7

grasshopper

8

cockroach

9

lacewing

10

dragonfly

CLASSIFICATION. Living insects are grouped into about 25 Orders. In addition, some 44 Orders of extinct insects have been described, but many Orders are based upon a single peculiar feature or upon incompletely known material. About 13,000 species of fossil insects have been described from approximately half a million specimens. Naturally, this great wealth of material can only be referred to a few large groups in a general text. The classification used herein is a much simplified version of current classifications and follows a pattern suggested by Ross (1957).

> Class E. Insecta
> Subclass 1. Apterygota
> Subclass 2. Pterygota
> Superorder a. Paleopterica
> Superorder b. Neopterica
> Orthopteroids
> Hemipteroids
> Neuropteroids

SUBCLASS 1. APTERYGOTA

Apterygota are the wingless insects, such as are represented today by the springtails and silverfish. The Subclass ranges from the Medial Devonian of Scotland to the Recent. *Rhyniella,* the oldest known insect, was discovered in 1926 in chips of flint from a bed in the Old Red Sandstone in Scotland. The head capsule, a few appendages, and incomplete abdominal segments are known.

SUBCLASS 2. PTERYGOTA

To this Subclass are referred all of the winged insects, although some, such as the fleas, may have evolved into wingless forms secondarily. This group is known from the Lower Pennsylvanian. Two Superorders can be recognized.

Superorder a.   Paleopterica

All winged insects which carry their wings straight out from their bodies are included in the Paleopterica. Dragonflies and mayflies are common living representatives, but several other groups of equal rank are known. These latter Orders represent paleopterous anticipations of roaches, flies, bugs, and so forth, but are not known to have been the actual ancestors of the later comparable groups. Instead, it is possible that insects participated in two great parallel evolutionary series. The Paleopterica arose in the Early Pennsylvanian but only one of the five Orders of Paleopterica survived into the Triassic and that group is still living. *Mischoptera* (Fig. 13.13.1) is typical of the Carboniferous Paleopterica.

Superorder b.　Neopterica

Neopterica are the insects whose wings can be folded back over the body. Growth involves increasingly profound metamorphosis. Identifications depend to a large extent upon differentiation in the venation of the wings. The Neopterica appear shortly after the Paleopterica in the Early Pennsylvanian and are the dominant living insects. Ordinarily the group is divided into a score or more of Orders, several of which are so large and diverse that a single Order can occupy the attention of a specialist for his entire professional lifetime. The neopterous Orders are discussed below in three general groups based largely upon progressive complexity of the life histories.

Orthopteroids. These strictly terrestrial insects are typified by the cockroaches, grasshoppers, and termites. Development of orthopteroids takes place gradually through a succession of nymphs. Specialists recognize at least five Orders of orthopteroids. Orthopteroids are known from as early as the Pennsylvanian when cockroaches were abundant and large. The greatest of these Carboniferous swamp dwellers reached a length of 4 inches (10 cm).

Hemipteroids. Hemipteroids are the lice, thrips, aphids, and scale insects, the principal characteristic of which is modification of the mouth parts for sucking, piercing, and biting functions. Many hemipteroids are notorious pests which prey upon plants and animals alike. Nymphs of hemipteroids are distinctly different from the adults; for instance, nymphs generally lack the three ocelli (eye spots) which are characteristic of the adults, and wings are present only in the last two or three molt stages. Specialists recognize at least 5 Orders of hemipteroids. The oldest members lived in the Early Permian and the group is extremely abundant today.

Neuropteroids. Most insects belong to the neuropteroids, including beetles, bees, flies, fleas, ants, butterflies, and moths. Metamorphosis is complete among the neuropteroids, and three dissimilar bodily forms (larva, pupa, and imago) may be involved in the developmental history of a species. Specialists ordinarily divide the neuropteroids into at least 10 Orders, based primarily upon changes in the number, nature, size, and venation of the wings. Thus, the flies and mosquitoes (Fig. 13.13.5), for instance, only have two wings (Order Dipterida), and fleas have become secondarily wingless. Beetles (Order Coleopterida) retain the anterior pair of wings but that pair is modified into hard chitinous covers (**elytra**) which fold over the hind pair of wings as a durable cover (Fig. 13.13.4). In lacewings (Order Neuropterida) the venation becomes elaborately subdivided (Fig. 13.13.9), but in scorpionflies the venation becomes secondarily simplified. In bees and ants (Order Hymenopterida) the fore wings are larger than the hind wings and the mouth parts are used for biting (Fig. 13.13.6). Wings of butterflies and moths (Order

Lepidopterida) are subequal and mouth parts are used for sucking (Fig. 13.13.3).

Neuropteroids are known in rocks as old as the Early Permian when scorpionflies and ant lions existed. Of the other groups (Orders), beetles are known from the Late Permian; bees, ants, flies, mosquitoes, butterflies, and moths are known from the Jurassic; and fleas are known from the Early Tertiary.

GEOLOGIC OCCURRENCE. The oldest insects of any sort are the wingless forms from the Medial Devonian. The oldest known winged insects lived during the Early Pennsylvanian, but it is almost certain that Mississippian species will be found because the Pennsylvanian species are rather far advanced.

Wings of ancient insects may be readily confused with plant remains because of similar venation. Completely veined leaves are not known before the Cretaceous, however, so any Paleozoic fossil which seems to have leaflike venation is presumably referable to the insects and not to the plants.

Insects evolved very rapidly during the Pennsylvanian and Permian, producing ancient forerunners of many later adaptive trends. In North America the best Permian collections have been made in Kansas and Oklahoma. Insect populations changed radically at the end of the Paleozoic or in Triassic time. The next extensive faunas (from the Jurassic of Solenhofen, Germany) show dominance of neopterous forms. Unfortunately, only a few extensive insect populations are known from the Cretaceous when flowering plants were becoming perfected and widespread. By Tertiary time, however, several fine collecting localities were established. In North America the Green River lake beds (Eocene) of Wyoming and Colorado and the volcanic ash beds in the Florissant shale (Miocene) of Colorado are both excellent sources of fossil insects. In Europe the best Tertiary insects by far have come from lumps of amber in Oligocene sediments on the Baltic Plain in northern Germany. Possibly over 100,000 specimens of insects have been collected in amber from those deposits. More recently, abundant remains of Late Pleistocene insects have been discovered in the fine screenings from the famous asphalt pits at Rancho La Brea in Los Angeles, California.

ORIGIN OF FLYING INSECTS. It is generally agreed that insect wings are outgrowths from the dorsal side of the body wall. It also has been rather widely held that insects developed the power of flight as a perfection of the ability to soar through the air; but there has been some difference of opinion as to whether insects soared from plant to plant or whether they leaped out of the water and planed through the air for short distances.

One hypothesis held that insects originated from trilobites in coordination with the adaptation to flight. Thus, according to Handlirsch, wings are modifications of the pleura of trilobites and winged insects arose directly from these primitive aquatic ancestors. Moreover, wingless insects must have been derived from winged forms if Handlirsch's hypothesis is tenable.

Some biologists prefer a hypothesis by Hansen that insects arose from a crustacean rather than from a trilobite. Certainly Crustacea are much closer to insects in general advancement of organization than are trilobites. For instance, mouth parts are similar and compound eyes are similar.

According to still another hypothesis, by Versluys, the insects and myriapods both descended from a common terrestrial tracheate ancestor among the Onychophora. Moreover, the trilobites and crustaceans both supposedly

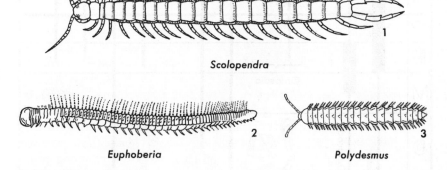

Scolopendra

Euphoberia   *Polydesmus*

Figure 13.14. Myriapods.
1. *Scolopendra polymorpha*, a chilopod, 1X, Recent. 2. *Euphoberia armigera*, 2/3X, Pennsylvanian, Illinois. 3. *Polydesmus erythropygus*, a diplopod, 1X, Recent.
(1, 3 after Wood, 1869. 2 after Meek and Worthen, 1868.)

descended from the same ancestor. Versluys' hypothesis is almost diametrically opposed to most other proposals because it requires the aquatic arthropods to be descended from terrestrial ancestors.

The discovery of wingless insects in the Devonian reinforces the argument that the Pterygota arose from the Apterygota. Wings may be thought of as flat lobes which grew out from the body wall of a flightless insect. The lobes presumably would have contained tracheal tubes from the time of their origin and these tubes would have been modified into veins in later stages of wing development. Thus, lateral lobes would have enabled early forms to plane from object to object very much as flying squirrels glide from tree to tree. In this regard, a few Recent roaches glide from plant to plant in the same manner. No large plants are known from deposits older than the Late Devonian, so the evolution of flying insects could have received its first great impetus

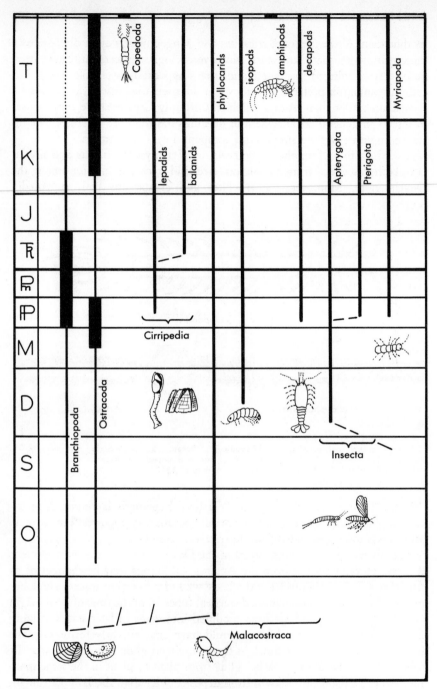

Figure 13.15. Geologic Distribution of Crustacea, Insecta, and Myriapoda.
(Evolutionary pattern after Snodgrass, 1938.)

at that time. Primitive plants are recorded from the Middle Devonian in association with the first insects, but it does not seem probable that insects could have glided far by soaring down from a primitive plant which was only a few centimeters tall.

Class F.   Myriapoda

Elongate terrestrial arthropods which bear numerous segments and appendages along the length of the body comprise the myriapods. Various myriapods are known as centipedes and millipedes. Their differentiation is based upon the number of segments, the position of the genital opening, and whether each segment bears one pair or two pairs of appendages (Fig. 13.14). Some myriapods have antennae and some forms bear poisonous claws. Thousands of living species are known but only a few fossil forms have been described. The oldest of the fossils is Pennsylvanian.

QUESTIONS

1. How, and in what groups of crustaceans, is dimorphism important?
2. What appendages bear the "claws" in lobsters, crabs, *Limulus, Pterygotus,* scorpions?
3. What theories account for the development of flight in insects?
4. What has the evolutionary ascendancy of insects to do with their metamorphoses?
5. What paleontologic evidence bears on the ancestry of arthropods?
6. Trace the evolution of barnacles. How does their embryology suggest the ancestry of the entire group?
7. In what unique way can branchiopods be distributed geographically? What other invertebrates can be spread by the same means?
8. Trace the geographic distribution of fresh-water crustaceans. How does competition affect their distribution? What do these things have to do with paleogeography and evolution?
9. What is the relationship between abundance and stratigraphic usefulness of ostracodes, decapods, branchiopods, and isopods?
10. What is the bearing between the ecology and habits of Recent lobsters and crayfish and usefulness of trilobites and eurypterids for stratigraphic correlation?

BIBLIOGRAPHY

Alexander, C. I., 1929, Ostracoda of the Cretaceous of North Texas: Univ. Texas Bull. 2907.

———, 1932, Sexual dimorphism in fossil Ostracoda: Amer. Midland Naturalist, v. 13, no. 5, pp. 302–311.

———, 1933, Shell structure of the ostracode Genus Cytheropteron, and fossil species from the Cretaceous of Texas: Jour. Paleont., v. 7, no. 2, pp. 181–214.

———, 1934, Ostracoda of the Midway (Eocene) of Texas: Jour. Paleont., v. 8, no. 2, pp. 206–237.

Bassler, R. S., and Kellett, B., 1934, Bibliographic index of Paleozoic Ostracoda: Geol. Soc. America Spec. Paper 1.

Bock, W., 1953, American Triassic estherids: Jour. Paleont., v. 27, no. 1, pp. 62–76.

Brues, C. T., Melander, A. L., and Carpenter, F. M., 1954, Classification of insects: Bull. Mus. Comp. Zool. (Harvard), v. 108.

Carpenter, F. M., 1951, Studies on Carboniferous insects from Commentry, France: pt. II. The Megasecoptera: Jour. Paleont., v. 25, no. 3, pp. 336–355.

———, 1953, The evolution of insects: Amer. Scientist, v. 41, no. 2, pp. 256–270.

Carter, J., 1889, On fossil isopods, with a description of a new species: Geol. Mag., n. ser., dec. 3, v. 6, pp. 193–196.

Cooper, C. L., 1941, Chester ostracodes of Illinois: Illinois Geol. Survey, Rept. Inv. 77.

———, 1942, Occurrence and stratigraphic distribution of Paleozoic ostracodes: Jour. Paleont., v. 16, no. 6, pp. 764–776.

———, 1946, Pennsylvanian ostracodes of Illinois: Illinois Geol. Survey, Bull. 70.

Daday, E. de Deés, 1914, Monographie Systématique des Phyllopodes Conchostracés: Annales Sci. Nat., Zool., ser. 9, v. 20, pp. 37–330.

Forbes, W. T. M., 1943, The origin of wings and venational types in insects: Amer. Midland Naturalist, v. 29, no. 2, pp. 381–405.

Herrick, F. H., 1896, The American lobster: a study of its habits and development: Bull. U. S. Fish. Comm., v. 15 (1895), pp. 1–252.

Howe, H. V., et al., 1935, Ostracoda of the Arca zone of the Choctawhatchee Miocene of Florida: Florida Dept. Cons., Bull. 13.

———, and Chambers, J., 1935, Louisiana Jackson Eocene Ostracoda: Louisiana Geol. Survey, Bull. 5.

———, and Laurencich, Laura, 1958, Introduction to the study of Cretaceous Ostracoda: Baton Rouge, Louisiana State Univ. Press, 536 pp.

———, and Law, J., 1936, Louisiana Vicksburg Oligocene Ostracoda: Louisiana Geol. Survey, Bull. 7.

Hutchinson, G. E., 1931, Restudy of some Burgess shale fossils: Proc. U. S. Nat. Mus., v. 78, art. 11.

Jones, T. R., 1862, A monograph of the fossil Estheriae: Palaeontographical Soc. (London).

Kesling, R. V., 1951, Terminology of ostracod carapaces: Univ. Michigan, Contr. Mus. Paleont., v. 9, no. 4.

———, 1952, A study of Ctenoloculina cicatricosa (Warthin): Univ. Michigan, Contr. Mus. Paleont., v. 9, no. 8.

———, 1956, The ostracod—a neglected little crustacean: Turtox News, v. 34, nos. 4, 5, 6.

Kobayashi, T., 1954, Fossil estherians and allied fossils: Jour. Fac. Sci. Imp. Univ. Tokyo, sec. 2, v. 9, pt. 1, pp. 1–192.

Levinson, S. A., 1950, The hingement of Paleozoic Ostracoda and its bearing on orientation: Jour. Paleont., v. 24, no. 1, pp. 63–75.

Lindberg, R. G., 1955, Growth, population dynamics, and field behavior in the spiny lobster, Panulirus interruptus (Randall): Univ. California Pubs. in Zool., v. 59, no. 6, pp. 157–248 (especially pp. 181–188 on movements).

Lockwood, S., 1871, The Horse foot crab: Amer. Naturalist, v. 4, no. 5, pp. 257–274.

Meek, F. B., and Worthen, A. H., 1868, Palaeontology of Illinois: Illinois Geol. Survey, vol. 3, pp. 289–565.

Menzies, R. J., 1951, Pleistocene Brachyura from the Los Angeles area: Cancridae: Jour. Paleont., v. 25, no. 2, pp. 165–170.

———, 1956, New bathyal Isopoda from the Caribbean with observations on their nutrition: Mus. Comp. Zool. (Harvard), Breviora, no. 63.

Ortmann, A. E., 1902, The geographical distribution of freshwater decapods and its bearing upon ancient geography: Proc. Amer. Phil Soc., v. 41, pp. 267–400.

Packard, A. S., Jr., 1883, A monograph of the phyllopod Crustacea of North America, with remarks on the Order Phyllocarida: U. S. Geol. Geog. Survey Terr., Wyoming and Idaho (1878), pt. 2, pp. 295–592.

———, 1885a, On the Syncarida, etc.: Nat. Acad. Sci., v. 3, Mem. 15, pp. 123–128.

———, 1885b, On the Gampsonychidae, etc.: Nat. Acad. Sci., v. 3, Mem. 15, pp. 129–133.

———, 1885c, On the Anthracaridae, etc.: Nat. Acad. Sci., v. 3, Mem. 15, pp. 135–139.

Payne, K. A., 1937, Pennsylvanian Ostracoda from Sullivan County, Indiana: Jour. Paleont., v. 11, no. 4, pp. 276–288.

Peck, R. E., 1941, Lower Cretaceous Rocky Mountain nonmarine microfossils: Jour. Paleont., v. 15, no. 3, pp. 285–304.

———, 1951, Nonmarine ostracodes—the Subfamily Cyprideinae in the Rocky Mountain area: Jour. Paleont., v. 25, no. 3, pp. 307–320.

Peterson, Alvah, 1948, Larvae of insects, pt. 1, Lepidoptera and plant infesting Hymenoptera: Columbus, Ohio State Univ. Press.

Pilsbry, H. A., 1907, The barnacles (Cirripedia) contained in the collections of the U. S. National Museum: Smithsonian Inst., U. S. Nat. Mus., Bull. 60.

———, 1916, The sessile barnacles (Cirripedia) contained in the collections of the U. S. National Museum; including a monograph of the American species: Smithsonian Inst., U. S. Nat. Mus., Bull. 93.

Rathbun, M. J., 1925, The spider crabs of America: U. S. Nat. Mus., Bull. 129.

———, 1935, Fossil Crustacea of the Atlantic and Gulf Coastal Plain: Geol. Soc. America Spec. Paper 2.

Raw, Frank, 1955, The Malacostraca: their origin, relationships and phylogeny: Annals Mag. Nat. Hist., ser. 12, v. 8, pp. 731–756.

Raymond, P. E., 1946, The Genera of fossil Conchostraca—an Order of bivalved Crustacea: Bull. Mus. Comp. Zool. (Harvard), v. 96, no. 3, pp. 217–307.

Ross, H. H., 1957, The evolution of the insects: Ward's Nat. Sci. Bull., v. 30, no. 2, pp. 23–26.

Sailer, R. I., *et al.,* 1955, Common names of insects approved by the entomological Society of America: Bull. Entom. Soc. America, v. 1, no. 4.

Scott, H. W., 1944, Permian and Pennsylvanian fresh-water ostracodes: Jour. Paleont., v. 18, no. 2, pp. 141–147.

———, and Borger, H. D., 1941, Pennsylvanian ostracodes from Lawrence County, Illinois: Jour. Paleont., v. 15, no. 4, pp. 354–358.

———, and Summerson, C. H., 1943, Non-marine Ostracoda from the Lower Pennsylvanian in the southern Appalachians, and their bearing on inter-continental correlation: Amer. Jour. Sci., v. 241, pp. 653–675.

Scourfield, D. J., 1940, The oldest known fossil insect (Rhyniella praecursor Hirst & Maulik)—further details from additional specimens: Proc. Linnean Soc. London, 152nd sess., pt. 2, pp. 113–131.

Scudder, S. H., 1889, The fossil butterflies of Florissant: U. S. Geol. Survey, 8th Ann. Rept., pp. 439–474.

———, 1890, The fossil insects of North America: New York, Macmillan and Company, 2 vols., ill.

Sexton, J. V., 1951, The ostracode *Cytherelloidea* in North America: Jour. Paleont., v. 25, no. 6, pp. 808–816.

Smith, G., 1923, Crustacea *in* The Cambridge natural history: London, Macmillan and Co., Ltd., vol. 4, pp. 3–17, 55–217.

Snodgrass, R. E., 1938, Evolution of the Annelida, Onychophora, and Arthropoda: Smithsonian Misc. Coll., v. 97, no. 6.

Stephenson, M. B., 1936, Shell structure of the ostracode Genus *Cytheridea*: Jour. Paleont., v. 10, no. 8, pp. 695–703.

———, 1946, Weches Eocene Ostracoda from Smithville, Texas: Jour. Paleont., v. 20, no. 47, pp. 297–344.

Swain, F. M., 1949, Early Tertiary Ostracoda from the western interior United States: Jour. Paleont., v. 23, no. 2, pp. 172–181.

Swartz, F. K., 1936, Revision of the Primitiidae and Beyrichiidae, with new Ostracoda from the Lower Devonian of Pennsylvania: Jour. Paleont., v. 10, no. 7, pp. 541–586.

Sylvester-Bradley, P. C., 1941, The shell structure of the Ostracoda and its application to their palaeontological investigation: Annals Mag. Nat. Hist., ser. 11, v. 8, pp. 1–33.

———, 1948, The ostracode Genus *Cythereis*: Jour. Paleont., v. 22, no. 6, pp. 792–797.

Tillyard, R. J., 1931, The evolution of the Class Insecta: Papers and Proc. Roy Soc. Tasmania (1930), pp. 1–89.

Ulrich, E. O., and Bassler, R. S., 1931, Cambrian bivalved Crustacea of the Order Conchostraco: Proc. U. S. Nat. Mus., v. 78, Art. 4.

Withers, T. H., 1928, Catalogue of fossil Cirripedia, Triassic and Jurassic: London, British Mus. (Nat. Hist.), v. 1.

———, 1935, Catalogue of fossil Cirripedia, Cretaceous: London, British Mus. (Nat. Hist.), v. 2.

Wood, H. C., Jr., 1869, The Myriapoda of North America: Trans. Amer. Phil. Soc., n. ser., v. 13, pp. 137–248.

Woodward, H., 1898, On the discovery of *Cyclosphaeroma* in the Purbeck beds of Aysesbury: Geol. Mag., n. ser., dec. 4, v. 5, pp. 385–388.

Chapter 14

ATTACHED ECHINODERMS

PHYLUM XIV.   ECHINODERMA

Spiny-skinned animals, as the name Echinoderma implies, characteristically are equipped with some sort of protruding, skeletal barbs, but not all echinoderms are truly spinose—their skeletons may merely be globular arrangements of hard plates. Members of the Phylum can be rather loosely characterized as invertebrates with **pentameral** (five-rayed) **symmetry** and a skeleton consisting of calcareous plates. Echinoids and starfish include well-known living examples of the Phylum, but several other groups are of equal systematic importance, even though they bear only remote resemblance to echinoids and starfish. Perhaps half of the important taxa such as cystoids and blastoids are extinct, and crinoids are largely known as fossils. All three of the foregoing Classes are represented by animals of unusual morphology which are familiar to students of historical geology. Inasmuch as no one Class can be said to represent the whole Phylum adequately, a general appreciation of the diversity of the Echinoderma must be obtained through reference to several Classes.

Differences among various echinoderms are understood best by comparing posture with orientation and nature of the digestive track. Crinoids, cystoids, and blastoids (Fig. 14.1.1–4) lived dorsal side down and were commonly attached to the substratum by a stem. Edrioasteroids (Fig. 14.1.5) were discoidal animals which lived attached to a shell or other hard surface; they cannot be said to have had definite dorsal or ventral surfaces, but only oral and aboral surfaces. Starfish and ophiuroids (Fig. 14.1.10, 11) lived ventral side down, whereas holothuroids (Fig. 14.1.9) lived on their sides; none of the three groups was attached to the substratum. Among the living echinoids, the sand dollars (Fig. 14.1.6) either live on sandy bottoms or are inserted obliquely into the sand; sea urchins (Fig. 14.1.8) wedge themselves into niches on rocky headlands, but heart urchins (Fig. 14.1.7) bury themselves in the sand. All echinoids normally live ventral side down and do not move about very much.

The configurations of the digestive systems of some of the foregoing echinoderms are shown in Figure 14.2.7–12.

A zoologic description of the Echinoderma not only must take into account the pentameral symmetry and calcareous skeleton mentioned above, but must also take note that echinoderms possess a **water vascular system** which is unique to this Phylum and which is accorded fundamental importance in classifications. A water vascular system consists of an elaborate network of tubes which resembles a blood vascular system, but opens freely

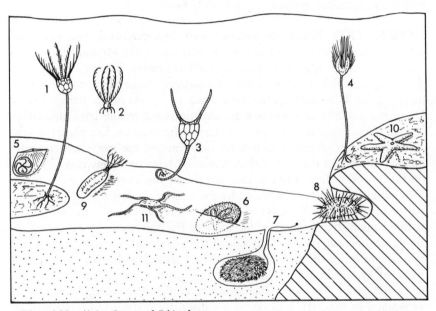

Figure 14.1. Major Groups of Echinoderms.
1. Attached crinoid. 2. Free-living crinoid. 3. Cystoid. 4. Blastoid. 5. Edrioasteroid. 6. Sand dollar. 7. Heart urchin. 8. Sea urchin. 9. Holothurian. 10. Starfish. 11. Ophiuroid.

into the surrounding sea water through a special **hydropore** or through a special perforated plate, the **madreporite.** Water vascular systems assist in locomotion and respiration and possibly also in ridding echinoderms of some waste products or even of excess water. One comparative anatomist has observed that the flow of water is consistently out of the madreporite rather than both ways; moreover, he concludes that water vascular systems may be modifications of one of the nephridial ducts of echinoderms.

Echinoderms have a large body cavity, very highly organized nervous system, and strictly solitary growth habit. No true blood vascular system is present, but a **lacunar system** of noncirculatory fluid-filled sinuses extends down each ray and seems to serve as a means of transporting nourishment through the body.

Reproductive organs may occupy much of the interior of an echinoid, but they are represented by minute organs out on the slender arms of crinoids.

Methods of obtaining food differ radically, and even digestive systems of echinoderms are most diversified. Echinoderms may be detritus-feeders, filter-feeders, or voracious predators, but they function to a large extent as scavengers. Starfish, for instance, seek their food, but crinoids rely upon currents to bring their food to them. Again, starfish have relatively large stomachs, whereas stomachs of crinoids are relatively small.

SYMMETRY. When echinoderms were first described they were considered, together with the coelenterates, to comprise the Phylum Radiata because both groups seemed to exhibit radial symmetry. It is now recognized that all corals are fundamentally symmetrical bilaterally and that echinoderms are bilaterally symmetrical also; but pentameral, tetrameral, or hexameral patterns of symmetry are superimposed on the basic bilaterality in each of the foregoing groups. In a starfish, for instance, five planes of symmetry can be recognized which bisect one arm and the space between arms on the other side of the central disc. A starfish, however, bears its madreporite on the upper surface between two arms, and the animal normally moves forward in the direction projected by the arm on the left side of the madreporite. In effect, then, there is one anterior-posterior plane of symmetry which is based upon the direction of locomotion. But this arrangement leaves the single madreporite on the right side of the plane with nothing to balance it symmetrically on the left side; therefore a second and more fundamental plane of symmetry can be drawn which passes through the madreporite and the opposite arm. An analogous situation is evident among humans (and vertebrates in general), because we are distinctly symmetrical bilaterally, yet we have only one heart and it is on the left side of our anterior-posterior plane of symmetry.

The fundamental bilateral symmetry of echinoderms also is manifested by the early larval forms; but a larva subsequently undergoes a metamorphosis involving resorption of digestive organs, after which the animal is reorganized into a new larval form with pentameral symmetry. It is the latter larva which develops into an adult animal.

SKELETON. Echinoderm skeletons are essentially exoskeletons in that they are boxlike containers around the soft internal viscera. Skeletons consist of separate plates called **ossicles,** which may be flexibly articulated, rigidly interlocked, or merely distributed as isolated bodies through the flesh. Most ossicles are blocky, but some are spiniform, others are fibrous, and others are

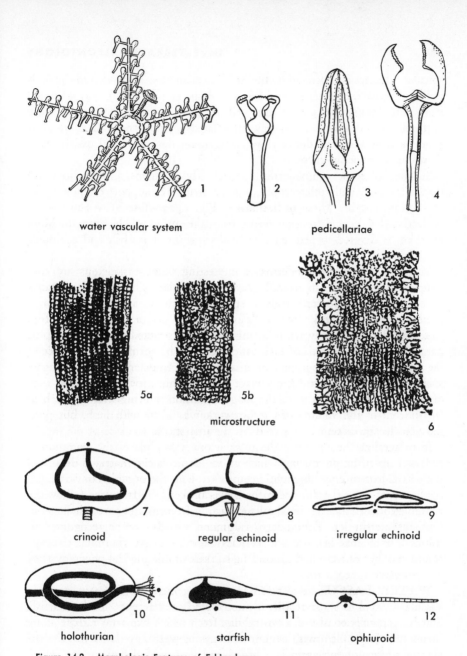

water vascular system

pedicellariae

5a   5b

microstructure

6

crinoid   regular echinoid   irregular echinoid

holothurian   starfish   ophiuroid

Figure 14.2. Morphologic Features of Echinoderms.
1. Schematic diagram of the water vascular system of a starfish, about 1X, Recent. 2-4. Pedicellariae of echinoids at 70X, 27X, and 160X, Recent. 5a, 5b. Longitudinal and transverse sections of spicules in a plate of *Strongylocentrotus*, 70X, Recent. 6. Longitudinal section of a pillar of *Dendraster*, 45X, Pleistocene, California. 7-12. Schematic vertical sections of various echinoderms to show relationship between digestive track and body outline. The mouth region is indicated by a dot in each case.

(1 after Coe, 1912. 2-4 after Durham, 1955. 7-12 partly after Cuenot, 1891; Lang, 1896; Pratt, 1948; and Storer and Usinger, 1957.)

spicular. Ossicles are secreted by the mesoderm and are suspended in the flesh itself, being covered externally in life by a fleshy ciliated sheath and separated from neighboring plates by a thin veil of soft tissue. Ossicles are therefore parts of an endoskeleton. Loosely articulated echinoderms fall apart after death because the flesh decomposes, whereupon the individual ossicles may be scattered by ocean currents.

Surfaces of some echinoderms (particularly echinoids and starfish) are thickly covered with microscopic, jawlike structures supported upon stalks of varying lengths. These **pedicellariae** (Fig. 14.2.2–4) seem to function as protective devices and to clean refuse from the surface of the animals. More attention is devoted to pedicellariae in discussions of starfish and echinoids in Chapter 15.

Microstructure of echinoderms is interesting because skeletons are constructed in conformity to crystallographic orientation. The skeletal substance is composed of microscopic rods or spicules which are arranged in a three-dimensional latticework like a "monkey gym" of a playground (Fig. 14.2.5, 6). All of the boxwork of a single ossicle is secreted in crystallographic parallelism, but the C-axis of each ossicle tends to be normal to the surface of the test. Similar crystallographic orientation has been determined for elongate spinose plates such as stud the surface of sea urchins, for the C-axis of each of those plates coincides with the long dimension. During life, as much as 60 per cent of the volume of the boxwork was filled with flesh, but post-mortem decomposition leaves voids in the interstices.

If mineralization of echinoderm skeletons takes place, the commonest process is calcification, during which an inorganic calcite matrix is deposited with its C-axis in crystallographic continuity with the organic boxwork. Accordingly, if a fossil echinoderm ossicle is broken, the fractures follow the rhombic form characteristic of calcite, passing from matrix through skeleton without interruption. Echinoderm fragments usually can be recognized in lithified sediments because the ossicles produce large, rhombic, cleavage fragments in a fine-grained ground mass, thus simulating the phenocrysts of a porphyritic igneous rock.

WATER VASCULAR SYSTEM. Arrangement of tubes in a water vascular system is most readily demonstrated by reference to the starfish. Starfish generally consist of a **central disc** from which five **arms** radiate along imaginary lines called **rays,** leaving interrays between any two arms. On the ventral surface of each arm is a broad and deep **ambulacral groove** which is filled with fleshy **tube feet** about 1 millimeter in diameter. The hollow tube feet project down vertically from the roof of the ambulacral groove in pairs, and the position of each pair is denoted in the skeleton by a pair of closely spaced **pores.** A radial canal extends along the axis of each arm and connects the tube feet with a **water ring** which encircles the mouth at the central disc

(Fig. 14.2.1). In turn, the water ring communicates through a single S-shaped **stone canal** with the madreporite or **sieve plate** lying on the dorsal surface in the interray just to the right of the anterior arm. Sea water has free access to the water vascular system through the madreporite. Solid particles are kept out of the system by the straining action of the minute perforations in the madreporite.

Starfish utilize muscular contraction and a marvelous arrangement of valves and pressure domes (**ampullae**) to increase or decrease pressure in the water vascular system. When the pressure within the water vascular system is greater than the hydrostatic pressure of the ocean, the delicate concave membrane on the tip of a tube foot is forced outward and flattened against a solid object. Then, if pressure is decreased in the water vascular system by muscular action, the hydrostatic pressure of the ocean creates a suction by the tube foot quite like that obtained in a suction cup or "plumbers' friend." The concerted and coordinated action of many tube feet enables a starfish or echinoid to hold fast to solid objects and to move slowly along surfaces, even if inverted. And all the time that locomotion is being effected, the water vascular system is also serving as the respiratory apparatus.

REPRODUCTION. Echinoderms reproduce sexually, and sexes normally are separate, except that a few instances of lateral budding are known among holothrians. Various kinds of larvae are of great significance in echinoderm studies because the different larvae share features which presumably were present in the adult stages of ancestral echinoderms. A **dipleurula stage** has been proposed as a strictly hypothetical evolutionary stage from which all echinoderms might have evolved. The dipleurula actually seems to have counterparts among fossil echinoderms, as will be seen in a later section (Fig. 14.3.3).

Echinoderms retain remarkable powers of regeneration of damaged tissue and may also possess the startling capacity of **self-mutilation,** whereby they can cast off an arm or, in the case of holothurians, even eviscerate themselves

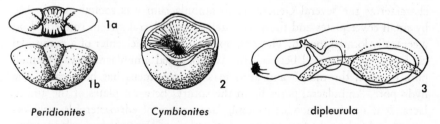

Peridionites   Cymbionites   dipleurula

Figure 14.3. Primitive Echinoderms.
1a, 1b. Top and side views of *Peridionites navicula*, 3X, Cambrian, Australia. 2. Oblique view of *Cymbionites craticula*, 2X, Cambrian, Australia. 3. Schematic side view of the hypothetical dipleurula stage of echinoderms, enlarged.
(1, 2 after Whitehouse, 1941. 3 after Walcott, 1911.)

when disturbed—after which they grow entirely new organs to replace those which have been lost.

CLASSIFICATION. Two Subphyla of Echinoderma are recognized, of which the attached forms are referred to the Pelmatozoa and the free-living echinoderms are referred to the Eleutherozoa. It has long been thought that the attached forms were ancestral to the free-living echinoderms, in spite of the fact that all Recent echinoderms which are attached pass through an unattached larval stage. Whitehouse (1941) has proposed that some problematic, Middle Cambrian, nonattached echinoderms in Australia represent adults in a primitive state which corresponds to the larval stage of advanced echinoderms (Fig. 14.3.1, 2). He referred these peculiar bodies to two other Subphyla (not treated herein) and suggested that both Pelmatozoa and Eleutherozoa were derived from them.

Subphylum I.   Pelmatozoa

The Subphylum Pelmatozoa consists of echinoderms which typically are attached to the substratum by a stem, although a few forms have attained nonattached habits and others attach part of the body surface to the substratum without intervention of a stem. It is customary to refer to the body of a stemmed echinoderm as a **calyx.**

Class A.   Edrioasteroida

Edrioasteroids are discoidal, circular, or more or less pentagonal echinoderms, most of which are less than 5 centimeters in diameter and 1 centimeter thick. Their most characteristic feature is the presence of five radiating ambulacral areas which may be either straight or recurved at their tips. In most cases four ambulacra curve counterclockwise and one (the right posterior) curves clockwise, but variations on the plan and number of rays characterize the several Genera. Each ambulacrum was roofed over in life by small cover plates and the whole stellate ambulacral system converged on a centrally located mouth. The anal opening was in the center of a pyramidal circlet of plates located between the two opposed ambulacral rays. A small pore between the mouth and anus in some specimens has been called the hydropore. Ambulacral pores lie in the sutures between plates of the ambulacra. It is not known whether ambulacral pores of edrioasteroids were occupied in life by tube feet or opened directly into the water vascular system. Randomly distributed interambulacral plates occupy the areas between ambulacra. These plates are either pentagonal or are scalelike. They overlap up toward the mouth instead of down like shingles on a roof.

In life some edrioasteroids were attached by the rarely observed aboral
surface or were unattached. They
range in age from Early Cambrian
to Late Mississippian, but were never
common and are rarely important
in stratigraphic studies. Their chief
value lies in their position akin to
both pelmatozoans and eleuthero-
zoans. The consensus now is that they
were ancestral to the Eleutherozoa,
but their unique morphology makes
any hypothesis concerning their evolutionary position difficult to support.

Isorophus is a characteristic edrioasteroid Genus which lived during
the Ordovician when edrioasteroids
seem to have reached their greatest
diversity (Fig. 14.4). *Edrioaster* is the type Genus.

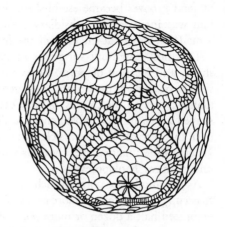

Figure 14.4. Edrioasteroida.
Dorsal view of *Isorophus cincinnatiensis*, 3X,
Ordovician, midcontinent.
(After Meek, 1873.)

Class B. Cystoidea

Cystoids constitute an extinct group of pelmatozoan echinoderms which
is characterized by the presence of more or less abundant pores on the surface of the calyx.

Calyces vary in shape from biscuitlike and somewhat pliable sacs of ossicles
to globular and vaselike calyces. The former cystoids rested directly upon
the substratum, but the latter commonly were supported by a stem. Stemless
cystoids were succeeded by stem-bearing forms. Ossicles of primitive cystoids
were randomly distributed, but ossicles were inserted in orderly rows in many
other cystoids.

Cystoids all seem to have been filter-feeders. In their least specialized condition there is no indication of food-gathering apparatus, but it is possible
that cilia on the exterior surface of the calyx created currents of water which
washed particles of food toward the mouth. In somewhat more specialized
cystoids the surfaces of the plates near the mouth were indented to form
food grooves along which ciliated tissue presumably was concentrated.

Primitive cystoids had three food grooves arranged in the plan of an inverted Y. One food groove extended anteriorly in the plane occupied by the
mouth and periproct, and the other two food grooves diverged laterally and
posteriorly. The number of five food grooves was attained when the two
posterior food grooves each branched once. After the basic pentameral pattern

of food grooves became established, the food-gathering efficiency of the system was increased by subsidiary branching and by the addition of simple arms (**brachioles**) at the ends of the food grooves.

The most important variations in cystoids, however, involve the number, shape, and location of pores. Pores may be distributed at random over the surface of a calyx, may conform to general patterns, may be confined to particular zones on the calyces, or may even be concentrated in small diamond-shaped areas. In their most general condition, pores are random perforations over the surface of each ossicle (Fig. 14.5.1a); pores of this sort are barely visible to the unaided eye. Cystoids with haphazard distribution of pores are said to have **haplopores.**

As the number of pores in each plate decreased, the remaining pores tended to occupy the bottoms of more or less sinuous grooves on each ossicle. Grooves embraced half a dozen or more pores at one stage, but eventually the pattern seems to have been stabilized with only two pores in each elliptical depression. This latter condition defines **diplopores** (Fig. 14.5.1e, 2). Some plates bear several diplopores but most plates of advanced Genera bear only one diplopore. Specialization is thought to be recorded not only in a decrease in the number of diplopores, but in the restriction of diplopores to particular areas such as the margins of food grooves. Food grooves arose concurrently with the development of diplopores among the cystoids. Finally, some echinoderms, which appear on other grounds to be cystoids, do not have pores; hence their systematic position is controversial.

Diplopore-bearing cystoids contain some anomalous features which have led to the "Diplopore Paradox." In many Recent echinoderms such as starfish and echinoids it can be observed that tube feet pass through plates of the test in a pair of pores. What could be more probable than that tube feet must have been present on cystoids with haplopores and that paired tube feet were established because diplopores evolved from haplopores? Unfortunately, outer surfaces of cystoid plates seem either to have been covered with a thin veneer of calcareous **epistereom,** or the ossicles were sheathed in a hard epidermis. No matter which is correct, the diplopores apparently did not communicate with the outside. It follows, therefore, that if diplopores could not have accommodated tube feet, they may not even have been part of the water vascular system. It has been suggested that diplopores may have been involved in operation of the lacunar system, but it is no more probable that blind alleys in ossicles could have served the lacunar system than that they could have served a water vascular system. Here, then, is a strange and unsolved contradiction. The function of diplopores is as yet undetermined, but it is possible that these structures originally served one function and subsequently served another function in descendant groups. Similar instances are known in the Animal Kingdom, as for instance in the transition of gill slits into the Eustachian tubes of higher mammals.

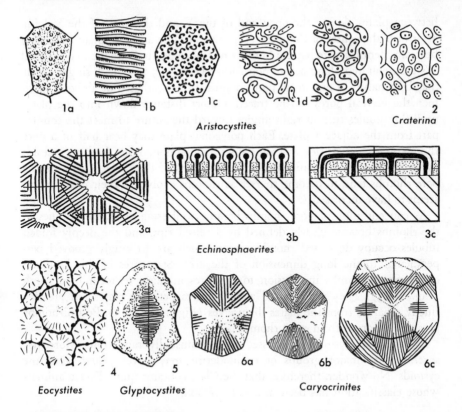

Figure 14.5. Pores of Cystoids.
1. *Aristocystites bohemicus,* Ordovician, Czechoslovakia. 1a, internal surface of a plate showing pattern of simple haplopores, 2X. 1b, cross section of a plate showing sinuous canals, 2X. 1c, surface of a plate in which most haplopores are united within a groove, 2X. 1d, 1e, two successive stages in which diplopores are perfected, 4X. 2. Diplopores in *Craterina bohemica,* 2X, Ordovician, Czechoslovakia. 3. *Echinosphaerites infaustus,* Ordovician, Czechoslovakia. 3a, surfaces of several plates showing horizontal ridges associated with canals, 3X. 3b, vertical cross section parallel to the edge of a plate, 8X. 3c, vertical section along a canal and across the suture between two plates, 8X. 4. Part of the surface of *Eocystites longidactylus,* about 2X, Cambrian, Nevada. 5. A pectinirhomb of *Glyptocystites* sp., 2X, Ordovician, Russia. 6. *Caryocrinites ornatus,* Silurian, widespread. 6a, 6b, inner surfaces of two plates, 1 1/3X. 6c, internal mold of a calyx showing pore rhombs, 1X.
(1-3 after Barrande, 1887. 4 after Walcott, 1886. 5 after Schmidt, 1874. 6 after Hall, 1852.)

A second pattern of pores arose among cystoids at the same time that haplopores were evolving into diplopores, but the two patterns do not occur on the same cystoids. Pores of the second kind became concentrated in diamond-shaped patterns called **pore rhombs** (Fig. 14.5.3, 5, 6). Pore rhombs consist of groups of nearly straight to U-shaped tubules in which the opposite ends of a tubule open on adjacent plates of a test, but the tubules are buried within the substance of the plates. Surfaces of unweathered plates of some cystoids contain rows of pores in V-shaped patterns, with the suture between plates closing the open end of the V and the apex of the V lying at or near the center of the plate (Fig. 14.7.1). The adjacent plate invariably bears an identical pore pattern but as a mirror image because the two opposed V's are separated along a common suture (Fig. 14.5.3a, 6c). A single ossicle may bear halves of one to six pore rhombs. In a weathered or abraded specimen the vertical pores can be traced a short distance down into the plates until the tubules turn at right angles toward the suture to meet the counter part from the adjacent plate. Each polygonal plate may bear half of a pore rhomb on each of its sides, or some sides may be nonporous. In some cystoids the pore rhombs are confined to certain regions of the calyx. All in all, the pore rhombs tend to become sparser as rhombs evolve, so their effectiveness seems to have increased.

As concentration of pore rhombs became well established, the outlines of the rhombs became clearly defined by a raised rim, and the deeply folded tubules occupy depressed rhombic areas which are strikingly grooved perpendicular to the long dimension of the area. Structures of this kind are called **pectinirhombs** in allusion to their resemblance to teeth in a comb (Fig. 14.5.5). They are inserted along sutures between plates but are distinctly separate from the plates themselves (Fig. 14.7.3, 4, 5). Pectinirhombs presumably arose from pore rhombs.

Evolution of cystoids progressed at an unusually rapid rate. Moreover, several other major groups of echinoderms may have sprung from the cystoids. No wonder, therefore, that the Class contains quite diverse animals whose classification has been in a state of flux.

Order 1. Diploporida

Cystoids which either have diplopores or haplopores make up this heterogeneous Order.

Aristocystites, from the Middle Ordovician of Czechoslovakia, is probably the most primitive cystoid yet discovered. In fact, it is reasonably similar to the hypothetical dipleurula stage mentioned above. *Aristocystites* had a pear-shaped, rather flexible test about 8 centimeters long which was constructed of smooth, more or less hexagonal, irregularly distributed ossicles. The mouth was a slot at the broad end of the test and the anal opening occupied the center of a pyramidal cluster of plates (the **periproct**) which was also located well toward the oral end. Two perforations have been discovered in the space between the mouth and the periproct. Of these two, a slit nearest the mouth is thought to be the hydropore at the entrance of the water vascular system, whereas a tiny hole near the periproct is thought to be the gonopore whence the sex products were discharged. No stem is present, but the plates at the aboral end generally comprise a crude circlet. Arms and food grooves are absent. Several pores traverse each plate of *Aristocystites*

and are arranged at random, although here and there a curved groove indents the surface and connects two pores. *Aristocystites* has haplopores.

Advances in evolution of food grooves are well illustrated by *Glyptosphaerites,* a spherical cystoid from the Middle Ordovician of Europe. In this
Genus the five grooves are not only incised into the plates of the test but
their food-gathering ability was increased by lateral grooves (Fig. 14.6.4).

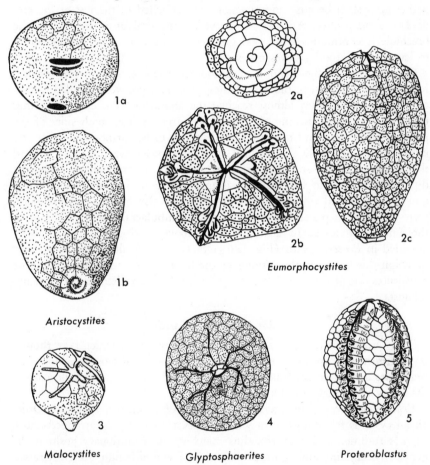

Eumorphocystites

Aristocystites

Malocystites   *Glyptosphaerites*   *Proteroblastus*

Figure 14.6. Cystoids (Diploporida.)
   1. *Aristocystites bohemicus,* 3/4X, Ordovician, Czechoslovakia. 1a, summit view showing
slitlike mouth underlain by probable hydropore, small gonopore, and ovate anal opening.
1b, oblique side view with impression of gastropod at place of attachment. 2. *Eumorphocystites
multiporatus,* Ordovician, Oklahoma. 2a, 2b, basal and summit views, 1 1/2X. 2c, side view,
1X. 3. Oblique side view of *Malocystites murchisoni,* 1X, Ordovician, southeastern Canada. 4.
Summit of *Glyptosphaerites leuchtenbergi,* 2/3X, Ordovician, Russia. 5. *Proteroblastus schmidti,*
1 1/2X, Ordovician, Russia.
   (1 after Barrande, 1887. 2 after Branson and Peck, 1940. 3 after Billings, 1858. 4 after
Volborth, 1846. 5 after Mortensen, 1935.)

Moreover, the grooves in *Glyptosphaerites* pass across an **oral circlet** of plates surrounding the mouth and extend about one-third of the way across the test. *Aristocystites* has no oral circlet; and although immediate forms such as *Sphaeronites* have an oral circlet, the food grooves do not pass beyond it to rest upon other plates in the test as they do in *Glyptosphaerites*. *Glyptosphaerites* represents one other notable improvement of the food-gathering system because one brachiole was attached to the test at the end of each food groove. An incised groove on the oral or inner face of the brachiole is continuous with food grooves on the test and therefore serves to lengthen the food grooves materially.

Continuation of the trend toward more efficient food-gathering devices followed two courses. In the first of these the main grooves extended farther over the test until they almost reached the aboral or stem end. The other tendency was for branching of short lateral grooves from both sides of the main food grooves, and for each lateral groove to be surmounted at its end by a slender brachiole. As changes in food grooves were leading toward definite localization and depression of the rays as **ambulacral areas,** the diplopores tended to become increasingly sparse in **interambulacral areas** and to be crowded up against the food grooves. Eventually the diplopores were confined to plates of special shape (**adambulacral plates**) adjacent to the ambulacral areas. In fact, the food grooves and pores are so closely adjoined in *Proteroblastus* (Fig. 14.6.5) that it is difficult to decide whether to assign this Genus to the cystoids or the blastoids. *Proteroblastus* therefore constitutes one of the "missing links" which have been discovered by paleontologists.

Order 2.   Rhombiferida

This Order mostly consists of stem-bearing cystoids in which pore rhombs or pectinirhombs are present instead of haplopores or diplopores. Moreover, brachioles are better developed, and incised food grooves are less developed, than they are among the Diploporida.

Echinosphaerites (Fig. 14.7.2) is a Genus of primitive, spherical, Ordovician cystoids from Europe in which plates are irregularly arranged and a stem is rudimentary or absent, thus matching in evolutionary position the genus *Aristocystites* among the Diploporida. The oral region is slightly raised into a triangular platform with very short food grooves, from the outer corner of which the brachioles arise. Pore rhombs are present over all of the test.

Evolution progressed from *Echinosphaerites* by decrease in the number of plates, development of a stem, improvement in the cyclical arrangement of plates, increase in number of arms, and restriction of pore rhombs to aboral portions of the test. *Caryocrinites,* a Silurian Genus, is a classical example

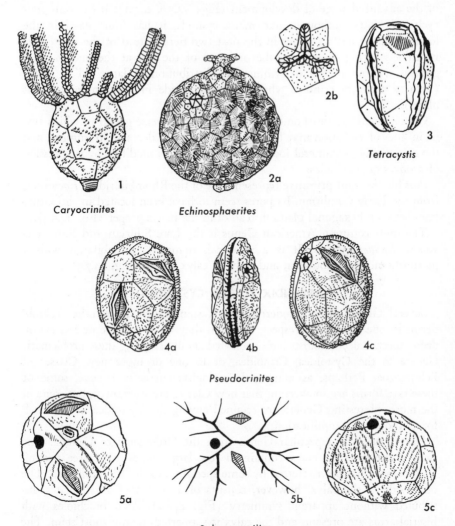

Tetracystis

Caryocrinites

Echinosphaerites

Pseudocrinites

Sphaerocystites

Figure 14.7. Cystoids (Rhombiferida).
1. Caryocrinites ornatus, 1X, Silurian, midcontinent, New York, Ontario. 2. *Echinosphaerites aurantium*, Ordovician, Russia. 2a, side view, 2/3X. 2b, food grooves surmounting oral circlet, 1 1/3X. 3. Side view of *Tetracystis fenestratus*, 2X, Silurian, Tennessee. 4a, 4b, 4c. Views of the antanal, lateral, and anal sides of *Pseudocrinites abnormalis*, 1X, Devonian, West Virginia. 5a, 5b, 5c. Summit, schematic pattern of food grooves with pectinirhombs and mouth, and side view of *Sphaerocystites multifasciatus*, 2X, Silurian, Maryland and West Virginia.
(1 after Springer, 1926. 2 after Volborth, 1846. 3-5 after Schuchert, 1904.)

of the advanced stage of development (Figs. 14.5.6, 14.7.1). It has only four cycles of plates; although, like many cystoids, it has four plates in the lowest cycle, it has six plates in the next two tiers instead of the usual five. Brachioles spring up around the oral end of the test at the end of food grooves without regard to symmetrical distribution of large calical plates (such as occur in crinoids wherein arms coincide in position with radial plates).

Cystoids with pectinirhombs constitute a very diverse group in which two main lines of evolution may be seen. Pectinirhombs decrease in number, and the primitively pentameral food-gathering system is modified by suppression of grooves or brachioles.

Possibly the most primitive representative of the Rhombiferida is *Eocystites,* from the Early Cambrian. Its pores seem to have been located in the suture lines between hexagonal plates instead of in the plates proper (Fig. 14.5.4).

The most common American Genus is the Late Silurian and Early Devonian *Sphaerocystites*. It is a spherical, stemmed, rhombiferan with 3 pectinirhombs, 4 ambulacra, and only 18 calyx plates (Fig. 14.7.5).

APPENDIX TO THE CYSTOIDEA

Several Genera of echinoderms depart significantly from other echinoderms in one or another respect, although they retain a more or less cystoidean aspect. Paleontologists have vacillated about assigning these problematic Genera to the Cystoidea, Crinoidea, or to one or more new Classes of Pelmatozoa. Perhaps, as many paleontologists currently believe, some of these rare forms are so aberrant that new Classes are warranted, but some of the more interesting Genera are retained among the Cystoidea in this book for purposes of simplification.

Pleurocystites is a peculiar Genus from the Ordovician of Canada. One side of the flattened calyx contains a few large plates and three pectinirhombs, so it has been referred by some specialists to the Rhombiferida. The other side of the calyx, however, consists of a swarm of small plates distributed without apparent symmetry (Fig. 14.8.2). Two brachioles with biserial arms are present, and the calyx is supported upon a short stem. The mouth is a slit between the brachioles.

Another rarely encountered Genus of doubtful assignment is *Comarocystites* from the Middle Ordovician of Canada (Fig. 14.8.4). It is characterized by irregularly arranged large plates like a primitive cystoid, but the pores only pass part way through the plates. Arms are uniserial as in primitive crinoids, but the periproct is rather cystoidean in appearance. A stem is present.

Enopleura (Fig. 14.8.3) is a most perplexing organism which may belong with the Cystoidea. Its calyx is flattened and presents two different patterns of plates on the two sides, somewhat as in the case of *Pleurocystites*. Two short arms remind one of brachioles of cystoids, also, but there is no apparent pore pattern of any kind. The probable posterior end of the animal terminates in a stem or stalk, but it does not closely resemble the stems of echinoderms. *Enopleura* is principally noteworthy, however, because the distribu-

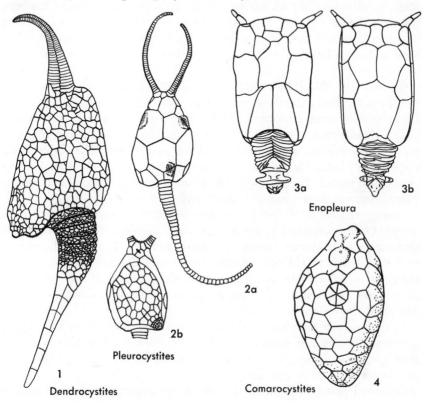

Figure 14.8. Carpoid Cystoids.
1. Reconstruction of *Dendrocystites sedgwicki*, 1X, Ordovician, Czechoslovakia and Russia. 2a, 2b. Antanal and anal sides of *Pleurocystites filitextus*, 2/3X, Ordovician, southeastern Canada. 3a, 3b. Two sides of *Enopleura popei*, 1 1/2X, Ordovician, Ohio. 4. Side view of *Comarocystites punctatus*, 1 1/2X, Ordovician, southeastern Canada and Michigan.
(1 after Barrande, 1887. 2 after Kirk, 1911, and Billings, 1858. 3 after Caster, 1952. 4 after Foerste, 1916.)

tion of ossicles on the calyx is strikingly similar to the pattern of scutes on the plastrons of some very primitive vertebrates. Inasmuch as some embryologists have suggested that the echinoderms might have been involved in the ascendancy of the vertebrates, *Enopleura* may some day be recognized as being pertinent to the evolution of the Chordata.

One of the most anomalous organisms in the Animal Kingdom is *Den-*

drocystites, from the Ordovician of eastern Europe and Canada (Fig. 14.8.1). It is a flattened sac of irregular calcareous plates from which a stem projects at one end and a single armlike structure with several plates in each tier arises from the other. No pores are present. A star-shaped periproct such as occurs in cystoids is located near the stem end (an uncystoidean arrangement, incidentally) but no distinct mouth, hydropore, or gonopore has been discovered! One wonders how these grotesquely Gothic animals existed at all rather than why they became extinct. The single arm may have served in some unknown fashion for feeding and possibly for other functions.

GEOLOGIC SIGNIFICANCE. The oldest cystoids probably are *Eocystites* from the Early Cambrian of western North America. Members of the Genus usually occur as isolated, radially sculptured plates. *Eocystites* is possibly a rhombiferan cystoid. The last surviving cystoid was also a rhombiferan, *Strobilocystites,* from the Late Devonian of Iowa. The Diploporida range from Medial Ordovician (*Aristocystites*) to Early Devonian (*Carpocystites* in Europe). Niagaran (Middle Silurian) strata in central and eastern North America have produced many diploporitan species.

Among rhombiferan cystoids, *Echinosphaerites* is locally abundant in Middle Ordovician strata in the Appalachians. *Caryocrinites* is a widespread Ordovician and Silurian Genus of cystoids which is known in Europe as well as in Niagaran (Middle Silurian) strata near Chicago and the Niagara Gorge of New York. *Sphaerocystites* is locally so abundant that 5000 specimens were collected from a single quarry in Upper Silurian strata in Maryland.

In spite of any inference to the contrary in the above remarks, cystoids are normally very rare fossils. Their local abundance presumably is due to their gregarious nature. They must have grown in localized "gardens" just as crinoids do even to this day.

Columnal plates from stems of cystoids are apparently identical in size and shape with columnal plates of some crinoids and blastoids, so cystoids may be represented by columnals more commonly than has been realized.

Class C. Blastoidea

Blastoids are stem-bearing echinoderms in which pentameral symmetry reached a high state of perfection and calyx plates are reduced to about the minimum number for any echinoderms. Blastoids lived from the Ordovician to the Permian but their Mississippian flare was as spectacular as their representation at other times was meager.

A typical blastoid had a globular to pentagonal calyx about an inch or less in diameter which was supported upon a root-bearing stem. Columnal plates seemingly cannot be differentiated from other pelmatozoan stem plates; hence many "crinoid plates" reported in Paleozoic faunas are probably blastoid plates. Numerous slender brachioles arose from five long ambulacral areas and resembled bristles in a shaving brush. Fossilized blastoids almost always are devoid of stems and brachioles. Their denuded calyces are important components of strata in many places in the eastern United States. They are less commonly known in Europe, southeastern Asia, and Australia.

Blastoid calyces consist of three cycles of plates, of which the lowest cycle contains only three **basal plates** (abbreviated BB) but the other two tiers contain five plates each. If viewed from below as in Figure 14.12.6b, the basal plates produce a pentameral figure divided by three sutures so that two of the resulting plates have the same shape and the smaller one is differently shaped. Presumably the ancestral form had five basals, but no blastoids have been found with that number. In the commonest blastoids the base of the calyx is convex or pointed and the scar (**cicatrix**) where the stem was attached to the basals is clearly visible; but in a few Genera of blastoids the basals are depressed and the stem is attached within a recess. Stems seem to have been lacking in only a few blastoids.

The next higher cycle of plates above the basals consists of large plates which are deeply slotted from their upper ends to form two-tined, forked, or horseshoe-shaped plates called **radial plates** (RR). Finally, the tips of the radials are truncated laterally and the resulting space is occupied by triangular or elongate **deltoid plates.** Within any Genus, differences in proportion of the plates, particularly in length of deltoids and depth of the slot in the radials, are used for recognizing different species. Some importance is also attached to the lateral profile of the calyx when making specific differentiation.

In addition to the 13 prominent plates comprising the calyces of most blastoids, numerous small plates fill in the **ambulacra** of the 5 forked radial plates and surround the mouth. Almost no attention needs to be given to the ambulacra in cursory examination because details of size and shape are sufficient for most identifications, but a little extra study of ambulacra reveals how diverse and paradoxical the blastoids are. Most, if not all, of an ambulacrum is occupied by a single **lancet plate,** which may lie above an **underlancet plate** (Fig. 14.9.1). The lancet plate is covered by a double row of tiny **side plates** (Fig. 14.9.1, 2) and even, rarely, by flanking **outer side plates.** All of these exposed plates are flush with the ambulacral surface, but are crossed by a median, longitudinal, zigzag groove sharply incised into the lancet plate. Lateral grooves cross most of the width of the side plates before continuing up the inner faces of the numerous brachioles. In view of the identical situation observable in arms of living crinoids, it is apparent that the grooves of blastoids were ciliated **food grooves** in life. Moreover, excep-

tionally well-preserved specimens retain tiny plates which roofed over the food grooves on the brachioles and on the ambulacra in the same way that arms of Recent crinoids are constructed. The whole food-gathering system led to the summit of the calyx where a star-shaped plate was perforated by the mouth opening.

Ambulacra of some Genera also seem to have borne openings of the water vascular system as pores along both margins of each ambulacrum. These pores lay in a linear series in two narrow, elongate **hydrospire plates,** one on each side of the lancet plate. If the side plates extended over the hydrospire plates, a notch in the margin of each side plate was superimposed over the

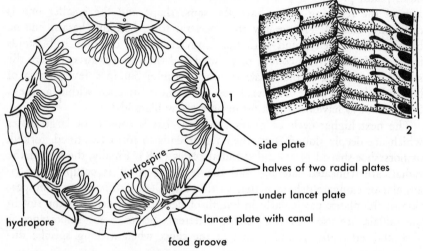

side plate

halves of two radial plates

under lancet plate

hydropore

lancet plate with canal

food groove

Figure 14.9. Water Vascular System of Pentremites.
1. Cross section of a calyx of *Pentremites pyriformis*, 3X, Mississippian, midcontinent. 2. Portion of the exterior of an ambulacrum with some side plates and outer side plates removed on the left side, 9X.
(1 after Wachsmuth and Springer, 1879. 2 after Etheridge and Carpenter, 1886.)

underlying water pore and provided communication of the water vascular system with the surrounding sea water. Inner ends of each row of pores opened into a **hydrospire** (Fig. 14.9.1) which was a thin calcified membrance pleated into several folds extending lengthwise beneath a margin of each ambulacrum. Each ambulacrum served two hydrospires. In addition to opening through the water pores, the hydrospires communicated externally through large porelike **spiracles** around the mouth.

In unspecialized Genera such as *Cryptoblastus* (Fig. 14.10.3), each of the ten hydrospires opened through its own spiracle at the summit, but in more advanced Genera pairs of spiracles from adjacent ambulacra were located closer and closer together until they first merged into five partially divided

openings and ultimately were represented by five simple round pores, each of which served two hydrospires, as in *Orbitremites* (Fig. 14.10.4). Spiracles either coalesced over the tops of intervening deltoids, or the deltoid plates themselves were each perforated either by two spiracles or eventually by one spiracle. The exceptionally large posterior spiracle is divided by inner partitions and contains three instead of two orifices.

Considerable difference of opinion has existed as to the function of the various openings in blastoids. Although everyone seems to agree that the mouth is properly identified, the third opening in the large posterior spiracle has been variously called the anus and the genital pore. Even more confusion exists with regard to the hydrospires. They seem indubitably to pertain to the water vascular system, but the direction of circulation of water is not

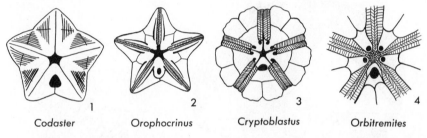

1	2	3	4
Codaster	Orophocrinus	Cryptoblastus	Orbitremites

Figure 14.10. Summits of Blastoids.
1. *Codaster pyramidatus*, with hydrospires crossing the radial-detailed suture and lying parallel to the food grooves, 4X, Devonian, Kentucky. 2. *Orophocrinus stelliformis*, in which paired slits alongside each ambulacrum function as hydropores and spiracles, 3X, Mississippian, midcontinent. 3. *Cryptoblastus melo*, in which spiracles are paired and hydropores are minute perforations along the margins of the ambulacra, 5X, Mississippian, midcontinent. 4. *Orbitremites norwoodi*, showing fused spiracles, about 4X, Mississippian, midcontinent.
(1, 3, 4 after Etheridge and Carpenter, 1886. 2 after Meek and Worthen, 1873.)

known. Water pores along the margins of the ambulacra have been said to be incurrent, whereas spiracles have been thought of as excurrent, but many well-preserved blastoids reveal no trace of water pores. In those cases the spiracles have been assumed to contain cilia which beat in opposite directions and thus served to circulate water in both directions. The calcified hydrospires themselves were probably rigid, so circulation created by bellows action is not likely. Indeed, hydrospires have not been found in all blastoids, even though they are peculiarly blastoidean features. According to majority opinion, hydrospires and spiracles served a double function of respiration and reproduction. Whatever they were, it seems probable that they would not create an excurrent stream of water so strong as to wash away food particles settling onto the tips of the brachioles. It is also likely that circulation of water through spiracles was the same in blastoids with water pores as in those without water pores; therefore, it is not probable that "water pores" were open to the outside but that they must have communicated with tube feet or some other fleshy organs inherited from cystoids and operated by the water vascular system. Then, although the hypothetical organs disappeared in the course of blastoidean evolution, the spiracles continued to operate as before. Surely this "paradox of the blastoids" will yield to future research.

EVOLUTION OF BLASTOIDS. *Asteroblastus* is an Ordovician echinoderm from Russia which seems to be only slightly more advanced than *Proteroblastus*—indeed, *Asteroblastus* may also be a cystoid because diplopores are present on a single terminal plate at the oral end of each

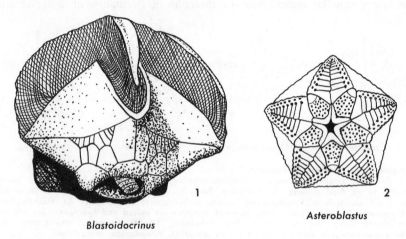

Blastoidocrinus

Asteroblastus

Figure 14.11. Blastoids (Protoblastoidea).
1. Oblique side view of *Blastoidocrinus carchariadens*, 2 1/2X, Ordovician, New York. 2. Summit of *Asteroblastus stellatus*, 1X, Ordovician, Russia.
(1 after Hudson, 1907. 2 after Schmidt, 1874.)

interambulacral ray (Fig. 14.11.2). Its calyx contains numerous irregularly arranged plates. Ambulacral areas, however, are blastoidean in construction, with side plates, brachioles, and pinnate food grooves.

Blastoidocrinus, from the Middle Ordovician of New York, California, and Russia, is perhaps the most primitive undoubted blastoid (Fig. 14.11.1). It has 80 or 90 plates in the dorsal region of the calyx but the oral half consists mostly of triangular deltoid plates so large that they have been mistaken for teeth of sharks. Margins of each ambulacral area are lined by as many as 50 slender brachioles which are kept apart by a series of wing plates which extend lengthwise down the midline of each ambulacral area. Hydrospires open through elongate slits in the base of each deltoid plate.

In addition to the foregoing primitive blastoids, the remaining more orthodox blastoids can be divided into two groups on the basis of presence or absence of hydrospires. Those without hydrospires occur very rarely in Ordovician and Silurian strata of North America and Europe. *Stephanocrinus* is the best-known example. Possibly this group should not be classed as blastoids.

Practically all blastoids belong in the remaining group which is charac-

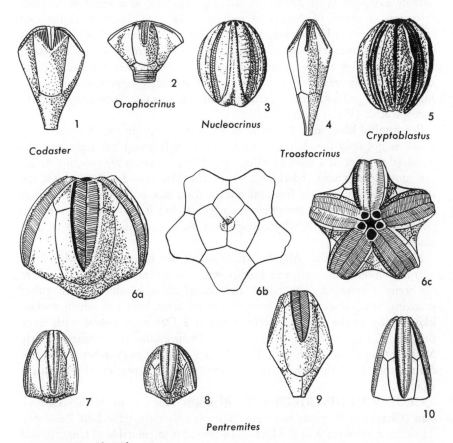

Figure 14.12. Blastoids.
1. *Codaster pyramidatus*, 3X, Devonian, Kentucky, Ohio, New York. 2. *Orophocrinus stelliformis*, 1X, Mississippian, midcontinent. 3. *Nucleocrinus verneuili*, 2/3X, Devonian, midcontinent. 4. *Troostocrinus reinwardti*, 1 1/2X, Silurian, Tennessee, Kentucky. 5. *Cryptoblastus melo*, 2X, Mississippian, midcontinent. 6a, 6b, 6c. Anterior, apical, and basal views of *Pentremites sulcatus*, 1X, Mississippian, midcontinent and Alabama. 7. *Pentremites conoideus*, 1X, Mississippian, midcontinent and Montana. 8. *Pentremites godoni*, 1X, Mississippian, widespread in United States. 9. *Pentremites pyriformis*, 1X, Mississippian, midcontinent. 10. *Pentremites angustus*, 1X, Lower Pennsylvanian, Arkansas.
(1 after Etheridge and Carpenter, 1886. 2 after Meek and Worthen, 1873. 3 after Springer, 1926. 4 after Wood, 1909. 5 after Cline, 1937. 6-9 after Galloway and Kaska, 1957. 10 after Hambach, 1903.)

terized by the presence of 13 calical plates, hydrospires, and 5 equal ambulacral areas. Within this category one can recognize three different fundamental shapes, which, however, probably do not represent consistent genetic groups.

Truncate Blastoids. The truncate oral surface of these blastoids bears short and proportionately wide ambulacral areas. The aboral region may be notably elongate, as in *Troostocrinus* (Fig. 14.12.4), as a result of upward extension of basals, of descent of radials, or of a combination of the two trends. *Codaster,* which ranges from Silurian to Mississippian, characterizes the shape of truncate blastoids (Fig. 14.12.1), but *Codaster* is a primitive form without spiracles and without hydrospires in the posterior interray (Fig. 14.10.1). *Orophocrinus* is a common truncate Mississippian Genus (Fig. 14.12.2). Long slits alongside each ambulacrum function as both hydrospires and spiracles (Fig. 14.10.2).

Pentremitid Blastoids. *Pentremites,* from Mississippian and Pennsylvanian strata, is not only the characteristic Genus of this group but represents the standard concept of a blastoid (Fig. 14.12.6–10). *Pentremites* contains by far the most species and individuals of all the blastoids. In *Pentremites* ten spiracles have fused into five and one of these not only contains openings for two hydrospires, as the other spiracles do, but it also contains the supposed anal opening. Each hydrospire may be folded into as many as nine plates.

Melonlike Blastoids. All of these blastoids are barrel-shaped with long, narrow, ambulacral areas and usually with an indented aboral area where the stem is fastened. The raised ambulacral areas, combined with either grooving or narrow ridges in interambulacral areas, lend a decidedly melonlike ribbing to the calyces. *Nucleocrinus* is a Devonian Genus with large deltoids and ten spiracles (Fig. 14.12.3). *Orbitremites* is a common Early Mississippian Genus with only five spiracles (Fig. 14.10.4), whereas *Cryptoblastus,* of about the same age, has five pairs of spiracles (Fig. 14.10.3; 14.12.5).

GEOLOGIC DISTRIBUTION. Blastoids range from Medial Ordovician (Chazy) to Permian, but were common only during the Late Paleozoic. Their local abundance in the Devonian Period is attributable to truncate and melonlike forms. Then the blastoids attained explosive abundance and diversity in the Mississippian when all three shapes were represented. Melonlike blastoids reached the acme of their development in Early Mississippian seas of the midwestern United States. By Late Mississippian time the melonlike forms became rare and the pentremitid shape became dominant. *Pentremites* seems to have been peculiarly North American in distribution. Upper Mississippian strata in the midwestern and Appalachian regions abound with species of *Pentremites,* but species of *Pentremites* are only rarely encountered in the western states. At the end of the Mississippian Period, *Pentremites* and the few other Genera of blastoids almost became extinct. *Pentremites* persisted as a relict fauna in an isolated harbor of refuge in northwestern Arkansas and northeastern Oklahoma on the northern shore of the Ouachita geosyncline. There *Pentremites* persisted into Early Pennsylvanian (Morrow) time and is even abundant locally, as at "Acorn Cut" south of Fayetteville, Arkansas. Perhaps, needless to say, the "acorns" in Acorn Cut comprise a species of *Pentremites* (Fig. 14.12.10), which some residents also refer to as fossil hickory nuts. But *Pentremites* was also driven from this refuge, for uplift of the region during the Ouachita Disturbance caused the retreat of the Morrow seas and consequent migration of blastoids to unknown refuges. Almost no blastoids are reported from Pennsylvanian and Permian strata anywhere, until the Class experienced one last spectacular burst of diversity in the Late Permian of the East Indies (Timor), Australia, and Russia. Among the 16 Genera so far reported from the island of Timor, several are characterized by the presence of unusual keels, knobs, and protuberances. Then, after their last expansion, the entire Class died out, no blastoid having survived beyond the Permian Period.

Class D.   Crinoidea

Crinoids were among the first fossils ever noticed by mankind and they seem continually to have excited the imagination of observant people down through the years. Their star-shaped or discoidal stem plates occur in rocks of many ages, so it is no wonder that the "star-stones" or *asterias,* as they were called in ancient times, have been collected alike by medieval metaphysicists and by twentieth-century picnickers. In days of unashamed mysticism it was thought that star-stones were dreadful bodies which originated by force of starlight or as natural "ferments" in the earth. Nowadays it is widely believed by youngsters in the Midwest that the perforated stem plates are Indian beads. Nor does the appeal of crinoids seem to be less when students learn about the systematic position of crinoids and about the vast gardens of crinoids which flourished on Paleozoic sea floors.

After having been known as fossils for almost 2000 years, crinoids were recognized in 1592 as the living "feather stars," and were separated in systematics from the true starfish. Since that time oceanographers have discovered crinoids so abundantly in Recent marine gardens that the ship "Fish Hawk" was able to dredge more than 10,000 specimens of *Antedon* from 876 feet of water in a single haul off Martha's Vineyard, Massachusetts, in 1881 (Verrill, 1882); and tons of specimens were piled on the deck of the "Albatross" several times on its scientific cruise in 1906 (A. H. Clark, 1915).

Recent crinoids live from near the low tide level down into abyssal depths, but most of them live in water so deep as to make it unlikely that their bodies can be washed ashore. The most abundant shallow-water crinoids in Recent seas occur off southeast Asia. Contrariwise, most crinoids are inhabitants of deep water in American and European seas. If it were not for local occurrences of free-living crinoids such as *Antedon* in the Bay of Naples, occidental laymen generally would know nothing of the existence of this important Class of echinoderms.

MORPHOLOGY. Bodies of most crinoids consist of three parts: the stem, the calyx, and the arms, but a few lack the stem at some time in their lives, or never have a stem.

Stems and Roots. Stems consist of a linear series of discoidal plates (**columnals**) which are mostly circular or ovate in plan view, but sometimes are pentagonal. A central canal passes lengthwise down the stem, so each columnal bears an axial perforation, the **lumen,** which varies in outline from circular to pentagonal, or even to being elaborately lobed as in a cinquefoil. Inasmuch as columnals are of mesodermal origin, they are not only covered in life by flesh on their periphery, but a thin fleshy layer between adjacent plates allows flexibility of the stem. **Articular surfaces** of stems, therefore, bear radiating ridges (**crenellae**) which interlock like teeth on gears to hold adjacent plates in articulation. **Peripheral surfaces** of columnals commonly bear circular scars, each of which marks the site of attachment of a slender, movable, fingerlike or branched prong, the **cirrus.** In stemless forms the cirri are located in clusters around the base of the calyx and clutch the substratum on which the crinoid rests. Most columnal plates are less than 1 centimeter in diameter and are about 2 or 3 millimeters thick, but some are as large as 3 centimeters in diameter. One incomplete stem was traced along a quarry floor in Indiana for 70 feet, but it is likely that a stem 5 feet long is a reasonably long one.

Columnals are almost the despair of field geologists because they are widespread, yet are of almost no practical value. Indeed, crinoid columnals probably are not distinct from columnals of cystoids and blastoids. On the other hand, there are a few characteristic columnals, such as the elliptical or square plates of *Platycrinites* with a strong lengthwise ridge on the articular surface and a tendency to form stems twisted like a strand of rope. In addition, the so-called pentacrinid stem plates of the Mesozoic are characterized by chevron-shaped groups of crenellae on the points of the star-shaped plates.

Stems are terminated at their lower ends in a variety of ways. Probably the most common method is for that end to bear a branching system of roots which resembles roots of plants so much as to lend credence to the former assignment of crinoids to the Vegetable Kingdom (Fig. 14.13.1). Other crinoids, however, such as *Myelodactylus,* coiled up the end of the stem like a watch spring or a snake and may have relied for attachment upon entangling some support in the loops of the stem. *Scyphocrinites* had a bulbous float as large as an apple (Fig. 14.13.3), which was partitioned into compartments in accord with principles of good marine engineering so as seemingly to insure against sinking if the hull were punctured. The end of the stem of *Ancyrocrinus* was enlarged into a heavy spinose grapple (Fig. 14.13.2).

New stem plates originate just beneath the calyx in crinoids with homogeneously shaped columnals, but in stems with alternating large and small columnals, the small plates are introduced between previously established

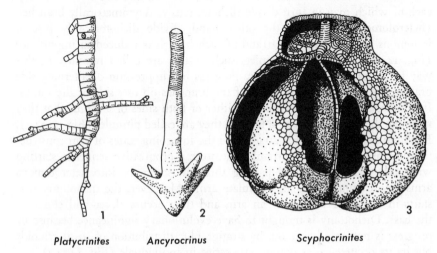

Platycrinites   *Ancyrocrinus*   *Scyphocrinites*

Figure 14.13. Crinoid Roots.
1. Common branched root of *Platycrinites* sp., 2/3X. 2. Grapnel of *Ancyrocrinus spinosus*, 1/2X, Devonian, New York. 3. Schematic cut-away diagram of the float of *Scyphocrinites* [*Camarocrinus*] sp., 2/3X, Devonian and Silurian, widespread.
(1 after Wachsmuth and Springer, 1897. 2 after Kirk, 1911. 3 after Springer, 1917.)

large ones; moreover, more than one cycle of secondary insertions of small plates may take place.

From an evolutionary point of view, the most primitive columnals consist of a spiral ring of separate wedges, each ossicle of which abuts against its neighbors along sutures. In the course of time the oblique rows of segments became aligned in horizontal rows and more firmly united until the sutures vanished and the commonly encountered, monolithic, ringlike construction of columnal plates was attained.

Arms. The efficiency of the food-gathering mechanism of crinoids was improved over that of the cystoids as the arms extended farther from the mouth and lateral branches were added to the main strand (**ramus**) of the arms. Crinoids sway on their stalks or swim about by graceful grasping motions of the flexible arms. In doing so they also obtain their microscopic food particles, which enter a groove on one side of the arm and are washed toward the mouth by cilia. The grove is roofed over by tiny **cover plates** which can be raised to admit the food particles (Fig. 14.14.4b, 7a).

Details of construction of arms and of branching of arms are valuable in classifying crinoids. Of the three general kinds of arms which are recognized, the simplest are the atypical **unbranched** arms. Two typical complex kinds are distinguished according to whether the arms branch symmetrically or asymmetrically. In symmetrically branched (**isotomous**) arms (Fig. 14.14.3b), the ramus of the arm divides dichotomously (that is, into two equal strands), each of which may in turn divide dichotomously. Asymmetrically branched (**heterotomous**) arms, on the other hand, divide dichotomously just as isotomous arms do, but one strand of each branch is reduced in importance (Fig. 14.14.3c). Subsidiary armlets such as this are called **ramules.** In this way heterotomous branching may progress by suppression of alternate side branches or by suppression of all of the branches on one side of the ramus. If ramules are so closely packed on either or both sides of a ramus that they resemble the lateral vanes on a feather, they are called **pinnules** (Fig. 14.14.2). Evolutionary significance is attached to the foregoing states of arm construction because they almost certainly constitute a progressive sequence starting with unbranched arms and passing through isotomous into heterotomous arms before culminating in pinnulate arms. Moreover, the dichotomy first starts in the outer reaches of an arm and then occurs closer and closer to the base. Dichotomy is thought to have evolutionary significance because its progress is not only borne out by stratigraphic distribution of fossil crinoids but by its occurrence as ontogenetic series in individuals (Fig. 14.14.3).

Actual dichotomy occurs at special plates called **axillaries** which have a flat base, two vertical sides, and two sloping upper sides analogous to the pitch of a roof. Lower portions of arms customarily consist of two square plates (**brachials**) surmounted by an axillary plate. Each new branch above an

---

Figure 14.14 (*opposite*). Crinoid Arms.
1. Uniserial arm consisting of a primibrachial plate and two rows of quadrate secundibrachial plates, 1X. 2. Pinnulate arm. 3. Ontogenetic series illustrating change from uniserial to biserial arms in one species, 3X. 3a, very young stage. 3b, young stage. 3c, mature stage. 4. Netlike arms of species of *Crotalocrinites*, Silurian, Europe. 4a, side view of complete calyx, 1/2X. 4b, small portion of a network showing food grooves and cover plates, 3X. 5. Ventral view of *Petalocrinus mirabilis*, 1X, Silurian, Iowa. 6. Calyx of *Eretmocrinus remibrachiatus* with paddlelike arms, 2/3X, Mississippian, Missouri and Iowa. 7. Three brachial plates of *Cyathocrinus* sp., 3X, Silurian, Europe. 7a, cover plates closed over food groove. 7b, cover plates removed. 8. Portion of a uniserial radial trunk of *Eucladocrinus multibrachiatus*, 2X, Mississippian, Iowa and Missouri. 8a, uniserial lower surface. 8b, upper surface with food grooves on the true arms and cover plates on the radial trunk. 9. Biserial lower surface and true arms of a radial trunk of *Ctenocrinus nobilissimus*, 5X, Devonian, New York.
(1 after Moore and Plummer, 1939. 2 after Bather, 1890. 3 after Kirk, 1937. 4, 5 after Springer, 1926. 6, 8, 9 after Wachsmuth and Springer, 1897. 7 after Bather, 1892.)

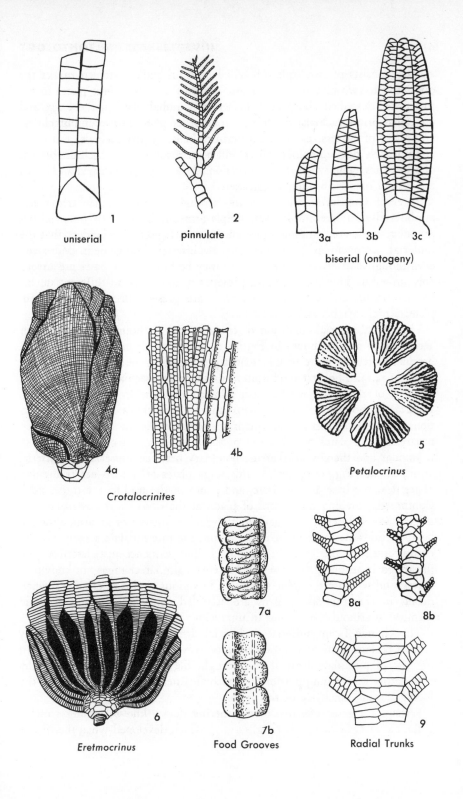

1
uniserial

2
pinnulate

3a 3b 3c
biserial (ontogeny)

4a
4b
Crotalocrinites

5
Petalocrinus

6
Eretmocrinus

7a
7b
Food Grooves

8a
8b

9
Radial Trunks

axillary consists of two square brachials and an axillary, which marks the division into two new branches again, and so forth. The three plates in the first order described above are attached to a radial plate in the calyx and are called **primibrachials;** the three second-order plates are **secundibrachials;** and plates of successive orders are **tertibrachials, quadribrachials,** and other appropriately devised names. There will be occasion to refer back to patterns of arm plates again when the construction of the calyx is discussed and when the system of classification is considered.

Plates of some arms are uniserially arranged, whereas other arm plates are biserially arranged. Moreover, simple arms are consistently uniserial but pinnulate arms are commonly biserial. Paleontologists are confident that the uniserial arrangement is ancestral to the biserial arrangement. Moreover, even though portions of a crinoid arm may be biserial, the bases are invariably uniserial. This latter feature provides a good way to differentiate between crinoids and cystoids when arms are present, because cystoid arm plates are always biserial at their bases.

The partial biserial condition of crinoid arms is thought to have arisen according to a plan shown in Figure 14.14.3. In the simplest condition the brachial plates are more or less quadrate throughout the length of the arms (Fig. 14.14.1). The first modification in shape of brachial plates appears at the tips of the arms where wedge-shaped or cuneate plates arise (Fig. 14.14.3a), although the arm remains uniserial. Brachials in the lower portions of the same arm remain quadrate, however. As the cuneate condition progresses, the plates near the tips of the arms change from trapezoidal to triangular and thereby arise at the boundary between uniserial and biserial arrangement (Fig. 14.14.3b). At this stage plates at the tip are triangular, plates near the base are quadrate, and plates in the middle are trapezoidal. Continued crowding downward of plates at the tips of arms eventually results in a truly biserial arrangement along some or most of an arm, although basal portions always remain uniserial and the intermediate stages may not occupy much of the arm (Fig. 14.14.3c). The sequence just described and illustrated is an ontogenetic series. Moreover, similar changes are known to correspond with stratigraphic succession in various strains of crinoids; hence, details in construction of arms are accorded considerable significance in identifying crinoid species and in unraveling their evolutionary history.

The change from uniserial to biserial arms was advantageous to any crinoid because it increased the flexibility as well as the strength of arms. In the case of pinnulate arms, it also brought the pinnules closer together by eliminating intervening portions of brachial plates and thereby increased the food-gathering efficiency of the arms.

Perhaps the most effective food-gathering device known among crinoids is the net of *Crotalocrinites* (Fig. 14.14.4) which developed when the tips of the pinnules of one ramus fused with the tips of the pinnules of an adjacent ramus. On the other hand, it seems incredible that *Petalocrinus* could have survived when its arm plates were largely fused into five solid masses like petals of a flower (Fig. 14.14.5). It is thought that the arms of *Petalocrinus* and the distally expanded arms of *Eretmocrinus* (Fig. 14.14.6) served as paddles or as swim fins.

Calyx. That part of a crinoid which contains the viscera is the **calyx**. It is attached by its dorsal side to the stem and the arms project ventrally. It is convenient to differentiate between the portion of the calyx below the arms (the **dorsal cup** or just "the cup") and the ventral domelike roof (the **tegmen**). Calyces fundamentally are sacs composed of polygonal plates embedded in soft tissue. If sutures between plates are smooth the calyx is rigid, whereas plates of flexible calyces articulate one with another on ridged and grooved sutural surfaces.

Primitive calyces mostly are globular or steep-sided, whereas bases of specialized crinoids are flat or even concave and the stem is inserted within a distinct depression. This evolutionary trend for development of a basal concavity is known among many genetically different strains of crinoids, some of which lived at different times.

Dorsal cups, irrespective of their shapes, are constructed according to one or the other of two somewhat different plans. In both cases each arm is attached to a facet on one plate in a ring of five large plates. These plates occupy the ambulacral rays and are accordingly the **radial plates**. Beneath the radials in both groups there is a circlet of five **basal plates** which alternate in position with the radials and therefore occupy interambulacral rays. In one group, however, there are two circlets beneath the radials; the upper circlet contains five basal plates as in the first group, but the lower circlet contains three to five **infrabasal plates**. Infrabasals alternate in position with basals but naturally line up with radial plates and the arms. Crinoids with infrabasals obviously have two rows of plates beneath the radials, so they are **dicyclic** crinoids, whereas the other crinoids with one row of plates beneath the radials are **monocyclic** crinoids. The difference between monocyclic and dicyclic plans is universally accepted as one of the fundamental distinctions between crinoids of otherwise smiliar appearance.

In spite of the acknowledged importance of distinguishing monocyclic from dicyclic crinoids, there is still no clear-cut evidence as to which group is ancestral to the other. The number of basals in a few monocyclic crinoids is reduced from five to three, and the number of infrabasals in many dicyclic crinoids is reduced from five to three or even two. If there is evolutionary significance in the tendency toward reduction in number of plates, then dicyclic crinoids might have given rise to monocyclic forms by elimination of the infrabasal cycle. The possibility has not been proved by paleontologic evidence, however, and both structural plans are represented in about equally ancient rocks.

A second major distinction separates crinoids in which the arms are entirely free from the calyx above their articulation with the radials, from crinoids in which the calyx grows up ventrally and incorporates some brachial plates within the cup. Calyces of the former kind characterize **inadunate crinoids** (that is, "not united" arms), whereas calyces of the latter kind are present among **adunate crinoids** ("united" arms). Evolutionary progression in this case clearly goes from inadunate to adunate forms.

In some adunate crinoids only the primibrachials are incorporated within the calyx, whereas in other adunate crinoids arm plates up in the secundibrachial or tertibrachial series may be involved. Further modification of calyces is necessary in adunate crinoids because the space formerly present between adjacent free arms must be filled with special **interbrachial plates.** Moreover, the spaces between adjacent secundibrachials or tertibrachials then becomes occupied by **intersecundibrachials** or **intertertibrachials.** In general, presence of space fillers such as interbrachials signifies a primitive condition. The evolutionary principle of modification by reduction in number of plates operates with regard to calyces; hence, calyces of advanced type may show progressive simplification of construction. It is not unusual, therefore, for arm plates of adunate crinoids to be wide or laterally in contact with each other. Of course, few accessory plates are present between or within arms in those cases.

Many crinoids have what seems to be a large extra plate in the radial cycle, but no arm is attached to this plate. Or a series of two or more plates occupies the same interradial position as the single extra plate just mentioned. In both cases the modifications are coordinated with the position of the anal opening; hence, the large single plate or large lowermost plate of a series of plates is referred to as the **anal plate.** It defines the position of the posterior interradius. In association with the anal plate there is commonly a **radianal plate** in the interradial position just above and to the right of the anal (a position which is also close below and to the left of the right posterior radial plate). Names are also assigned by specialists to higher plates in the anal series.

Much attention is given to the anal series because the exact position and number of plates in the anal system are of great taxonomic value and evolutionary significance. In general, the size of plates in the anal series progressively diminishes, the number of plates decreases, and the several elements occupy successively higher positions until they are no longer contained within the dorsal cup. In view of the importance of the structure of the posterior interray, crinoids in which it is exposed are more readily identified than are those in which extensive cleaning of the posterior interray is required.

Modifications of the ventral surface or tegmen are of considerable general interest, but the tegmenal plates are distributed with less order than are the plates in the dorsal cup. Nevertheless, several fundamental evolutionary trends are worth noting. The simplest tegmen consists merely of five large triangular plates, the **orals,** which occupy alternate positions with the radials (Fig. 14.15.1). Food grooves pass up the five sutures to the mouth which is located at the apex of the orals. As food-gathering mechanisms became increasingly complicated, numerous accessory plates were added to the periphery of the tegmen just above the dorsal cup and the orals clustered around the mouth and became relatively unimportant. Ambulacral plates which

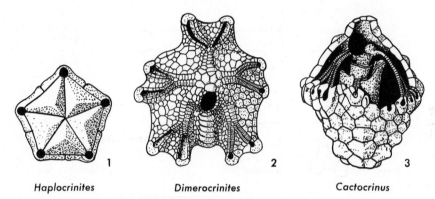

Haplocrinites   Dimerocrinites   Cactocrinus

Figure 14.15. Food Grooves of Crinoids.
1. Ventral surface of *Haplocrinites clio* in which food grooves follow the sutures between the five large oral plates, 9X, Devonian, New York. 2. Ventral surface of *Dimerocrinites inornatus* in which food grooves cross the surface of the tegmen and are roofed with cover plates, 2X, Silurian, Indiana. 3. Cut-away view of *Cactocrinus proboscidialis* showing food grooves as tubes sunk below the tegmen and leading to the "convoluted organ"; 1X, Mississippian, midcontinent.
(1 after Goldring, 1923. 2 after Wachsmuth and Springer, 1897. 3 after Meek and Worthen, 1873.)

roofed over the food grooves became incorporated within the surface of the tegmen (Fig. 14.15.2). At about this stage the tendency for calyces to grow upward ventrally affected the food grooves and the grooves were engulfed in the calyces of many crinoids. In the most specialized condition the food grooves of some crinoids eventually were represented by internal tubes which seem to have sunk beneath the tegmens (Fig. 14.15.3).

Lastly, the anal series, which had shown marked tendencies to shift upward ventrally, eventually became incorporated within the tegmen. In fact, anal openings tended to be located at the tips of tubular processes in many Genera. Some anal tubes were short and inconspicuous but others were produced into elongate columns which dominated the entire tegmen, reached above the tips of the arms, and in some cases were equipped with spines and other bizarrerie. Lower regions of the tegmen were subject to singular aberrations, too, as represented by long plates, or club-shaped processes, or just awesome spines around which and among which the delicate arms may have huddled as though for protection.

Specialists in the study of crinoids have devised systems of abbreviations for the designation of calical plates. According to the system most generally followed (revised by Moore and Laudon, 1941) each plate is given a short capitalized abbreviation, based upon letters common to the formal name of the plate. Thus, R stands for radial, PBr for primibrachial and IB for in-

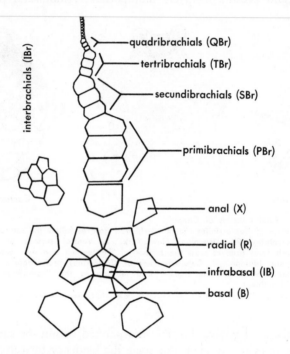

interbrachials (IBr)

quadribrachials (QBr)

tertribrachials (TBr)

secundibrachials (SBr)

primibrachials (PBr)

anal (X)

radial (R)

infrabasal (IB)

basal (B)

Figure 14.16. Terminology for Crinoid Calyces.
The radial diagnosis is of an imaginary crinoid which has structures characteristic of several different groups of crinoids.
(Partly after Moore and Laudon, 1941.)

frabasal. Plural abbreviations are formed by doubling the use of a significant letter in the same way that plural number or intensives are indicated in some languages by repeating an element. Thus RR means radials, PBrBr means primibrachials, and IBB means infrabasals. The plates described in the text, which are most necessary for intelligent reference to crinoid literature, are illustrated in Figure 14.16, together with their common abbreviations.

It is a nuisance to illustrate crinoids from various angles in order to show the distribution of all plates; therefore it has become customary for specialists to make expanded schematic representations of the calyces called **radial diagnoses** (Fig. 14.23.6). The need for these was appreciated as early as 1821 when J. S. Miller wrote the first major work on the group and coined the name Crinoidea for them. In a radial diagnosis a crinoid is viewed from the dorsal (basal) aspect and plates are depicted as if they occupied positions along the several rays and interrays. All sorts of modifications of the method are possible, chief of which is to show one ray and the posterior interray with the plates in normal contiguous position. Some diagnoses depict plate distribution as if the calyx were unrolled by rotation on a vertical axis. Moreover, various shading, hachuring, and stippling facilitate comparison of one diagnosis with another.

CLASSIFICATION. Classifications of crinoids down to Orders have been based upon the monocyclic or dicyclic character of the dorsal cup, the adunate or inadunate character of the arms, the degree of flexibility of the calyx, and the nature of the anal series. None of these characters seems to be of paramount importance, but the assemblage of characters can be used to organize crinoids into systematic categories which seem on the basis of all features to comprise homogeneous evolutionary or natural groups. The following key is restricted to Paleozoic crinoids because the Subclass Articulata is confined to post-Paleozoic rocks, in which crinoids are very rare.

KEY TO SUBCLASSES AND ORDERS OF PALEOZOIC CRINOIDS

I. Inadunate crinoids .... Subclass Inadunata
    1. Monocyclic .... Order Disparida
    2. Dicyclic .... Order Cladida
II. Adunate crinoids
    A. Calyx flexible .... Subclass Flexibilia
        1. Anal tube present .... Order Taxocrinida
        2. Anal tube absent .... Order Sagenocrinida
    B. Calyx rigid .... Subclass Camerata
        1. Monocyclic .... Order Monobathrida
        2. Dicyclic .... Order Diplobathrida

Crinoids are pelmatozoans whose calyces consist fundamentally of two or three cycles of plates on the dorsal side and of a ventral surface composed of many plates. Flexible branched arms with uniserial bases arise from the calyx. Stems generally are present.

SUBCLASS 1. INADUNATA

The Subclass Inadunata consists of crinoids whose arm plates are not incorporated within the calyx. It is one of the oldest groups of crinoids, extending back to the Medial Ordovician (Chazy). Even at that time the

Subclass was represented by two Orders based upon the monocyclic or di-cyclic character of the calyces.

Order a.   Disparida

The Disparida comprise the monocyclic inadunate‍ crinoids. In addition to their single distinguishing character, they are noteworthy for the presence of some unusual feature which differentiates one ray from the other rays. For instance, one radial plate may be unusually large; or some radial plates may be divided into two plates by extra sutures as in *Haplocrinites* (Fig. 14.17.3); or one arm may differ in structure from the others as in *Haly-siocrinus* (Fig. 14.17.1); *Halysiocrinus* is also noteworthy because the whole calyx is grossly asymmetrical.

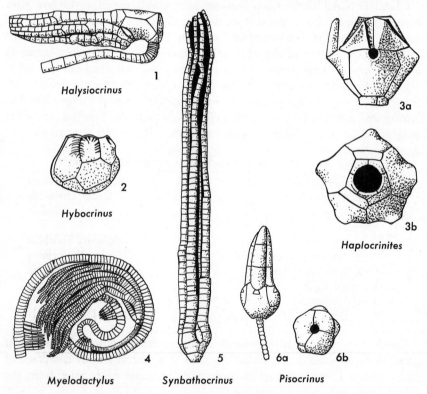

Figure 14.17.   Inadunate Crinoids (Disparida).
  1. Anterior view of *Halysiorcrinus dactylus*, 1X, Mississippian, Iowa. 2. Posterior view of *Hybocrinus eldonensis*, 2X, Ordovician, Ontario. 3a, 3b. Lateral and basal views of *Haplocrinites clio*, 9X, Devonian, New York. 4. Lateral view of *Myelodactylus keyserensis*, 1X, Silurian, West Virginia. 5. Posterior view of *Synbathocrinus dentatus*, 2/3X, Mississippian, Iowa. 6a, 6b. Lateral and basal views of *Pisocrinus quinquelobus*, 1X, Silurian, Tennessee.
  (1, 4, 6 after Springer, 1926. 2 after Springer, 1911a. 3 after Goldring, 1923. 5 after Moore and Laudon, 1943.)

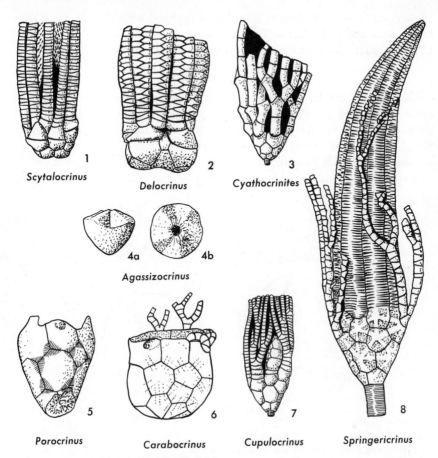

Figure 14.18.   Inadunate Crinoids (Cladida).
1. *Scytalocrinus validus*, 1X, Mississippian, Indiana.   2. *Delocrinus benthobatus*, 1X, Pennsylvanian, Texas.   3. *Cyathocrinites wilsoni*, 1 1/2X, Silurian, Indiana.   4a, 4b. Lateral and interior views of the fused infrabasals of *Agassizocrinus conicus*, 1X, Mississippian, midcontinent and Alabama.   5. *Porocrinus conicus* with cystoidlike pore rhombs, 1X, Ordovician, Ontario. 6. Posterior view of *Carabocrinus radiatus* showing three plates in the anal series, 1X, Ordovician, Ontario.   7. *Cupulocrinus humilis*, 1X, Ordovician, Ontario.   8. Posterior view of *Springericrinus doris* with most arms removed to reveal the enormous anal sac, 1X, Mississippian, Iowa.
(1 after Moore and Laudon, 1943.   2 after Moore and Plummer, 1939.   3 after Springer, 1926.   4 after Butts, 1926.   5, 6 after Billings, 1859.   7 after Springer, 1911a.   8 after Springer, 1911b.)

Hybocrinus is a globose form from the Ordovician (Fig. 14.17.2). It is notable because of its asymmetry and very primitive unbranched arms. Another strain of the Disparida is represented by *Pisocrinus* (Fig. 14.17.6). *Synbathocrinus,* from the Devonian and Mississippian, is typical of the numerous symmetrically constructed disparate crinoids (Fig. 14.17.5). *My-*

elodactylus is unusual because its calyx is enclosed within a recurved loop of the stem and is flanked by two densely packed rows of cirri on the stem (Fig. 14.17.4). The Order became extinct in the Permian.

Order b.   Cladida

Cladida are dicyclic inadunate crinoids. They are similar to the monocyclic inadunates in general appearance; hence, considerable attention to detail is required for their serious study. They show the classical evolutionary changes in shape of dorsal cup from conical into discoidal, with accompanying depression of the base. Infrabasals are large in primitive forms, but evolve into smaller and smaller plates which may be concealed beneath the stem;

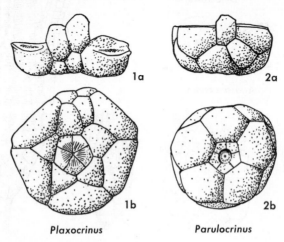

Figure 14.19.   Dorsal Cups of Delocrinids.
Posterior and dorsal views are shown for each species.
1a, 1b. *Plaxocrinus obesus* with three plates in the anal series, 1X, Pennsylvanian, Texas.   2a, 2b. *Parulocrinus compactus* with two plates in the anal series, 2/3X, Pennsylvanian, Kansas, Texas.

or the five plates may be fused into three plates. Arm structure is important and of some stratigraphic significance, for biserial arms are all post-Devonian in this Order. Moreover, number and strength of ridges on articular surfaces of plates are useful in separating Genera. An anal sac expanded above the tegmen is a characteristic feature, but it seems to have been too fragile to be preserved in any but the rarest cladids in post-Mississippian sediments. This Order has the longest range of any of the Paleozoic crinoids—from Medial Ordovician (Chazy) into the Triassic. Moreover, cladids are very important numerically, there being 234 Genera recognized in 1943.

Porocrinus (Fig. 14.18.5) is one of the most unusual of all crinoids because it retains pore rhombs reminiscent of the cystoids. It is therefore thought to be one of the most primitive crinoids.

Of the numerous characteristic Genera of cladids, *Cyathocrinites* (Fig.

14.18.3) and *Petalocrinus* (Fig. 14.14.5) represent strains with meager development of the anal sac, if any. On the other hand, about three-fourths of all the cladids resemble *Springericrinus* (Fig. 14.18.8), *Scytalocrinus* (Fig. 14.18.1), and *Cupulocrinus* (Fig. 14.18.7), all of which normally had well-developed anal sacs.

Agassizocrinus (Fig. 14.18.4) is a common Late Mississippian Genus in which all of the infrabasals are fused into one hemispherical plate; but even these single bases can be used for correlation of strata.

Late Paleozoic cladids such as *Delocrinus* and its relatives (Fig. 14.19) had strongly constructed dorsal cups but weakly built arms and anal sacs. Even so, delocrinids are useful index fossils. Genera can be recognized on

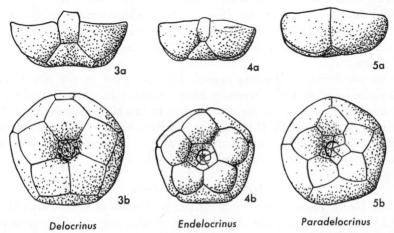

Delocrinus   *Endelocrinus*   *Paradelocrinus*

3a, 3b. *Delocrinus vulgatus*, in which the single anal plate rests firmly upon a basal, 1X, Pennsylvanian, Oklahoma, Texas. 4a, 4b. *Endelocrinus texanus*, in which the single anal plate barely touches a basal, 2/3X, Permian, Texas. 5a, 5b. *Paradelocrinus subplanus*, in which there is no anal plate in the dorsal cup, 1X, Pennsylvanian, Oklahoma, Texas.
(After Moore and Plummer, 1939.)

the basis of profiles of the cups, amount of concavity of the bases of cups, and number and position of plates in the anal series. In Figure 14.19, five Genera are arranged in a morphologic series to illustrate how the number of anal plates decreases from three to none and how the plates seem to occupy progressively higher positions up and out of the dorsal cups.

The Order became extinct during the Triassic when *Encrinus* and its relatives expired.

SUBCLASS 2. FLEXIBILIA

Flexible crinoids are appropriately named because they look flexible in spite of having prominent calical plates. They obviously were pliable enough to conform to the irregularities of the bottom on which they fell, without disassociation of the calyx. In addition to being flexible, all Flexibilia are characterized by having dicyclic calyces in which the infrabasal circlet consists of only three plates, or the infrabasal circlet is fused into one plate. Bases of the dorsal cup tend to become concave in advanced Genera. The arms are always uniserial and seem to be coarsely constructed because they lack pinnules. Calyces resemble little grasping fists because of the in-turned arms. Flexibilia are adunate crinoids in which several of the brachials are incorporated within the calyx without there being any surficial constriction at the juncture of the top of the dorsal cup and the base of the primibrachials.

It seems conclusive that the Flexibilia arose from the dicyclic inadunate crinoids—the Cladida, that is. In fact, the oldest of the Flexibilia, *Protaxocrinus,* occurs in strata of Medial Ordovician age along with a potential cladid ancestor, *Cupulocrinus* (Fig. 14.18.7), which seems to differ from *Protaxocrinus* only in having five instead of three infrabasal plates. Major evolutionary trends subsequently involved the character of the anal series of plates.

One problematic crinoidlike animal, *Edriocrinus,* is usually placed with Flexibilia, even though it seems to have a monocyclic calyx. Calical plates of *Edriocrinus* commonly are obscure, but its brachial plates are quite like those of flexible crinoids (Fig. 14.20.3). *Edriocrinus,* however, seems to have led an existence like that of a starfish, or at least it seems to have been unattached and to have carried itself ventral side down.

Order a.   Taxocrinida

The Order Taxocrinida is composed of six Genera of flexible crinoids in which the anal series is developed into a tubular projection. There is evidence that the fundamental number of primibrachials may increase from two in *Protaxocrinus* (Ordovician to Devonian) to three in *Taxocrinus* (Devonian and Mississippian) and even carry on this reversal of a normal crinoidal trend until as many as six primibrachials are present (as in *Onychocrinus* from the Mississippian and Pennsylvanian) (Fig. 14.20.4–6). The Order ranges from Medial Ordovician to Pennsylvanian and underwent two small flares, one in the Silurian and one in the Mississippian.

Order b.   Sagenocrinida

The Order Sagenocrinida contains 42 Genera of flexible crinoids in which there is no anal tube, but instead the anal series is firmly united to the right posterior ray. Unfortunately, scarcity of Early Paleozoic material makes it difficult to ascertain the origin of the Order, but it probably arose from the Taxocrinida rather than vice versa.

Among the highly diversified members of the Order, *Sagenocrinites* (Fig. 14.20.1) is notable for the extensive development of interbrachial plates, whereas other Genera such as *Ichthyocrinus* (Fig. 14.20.2) normally lack

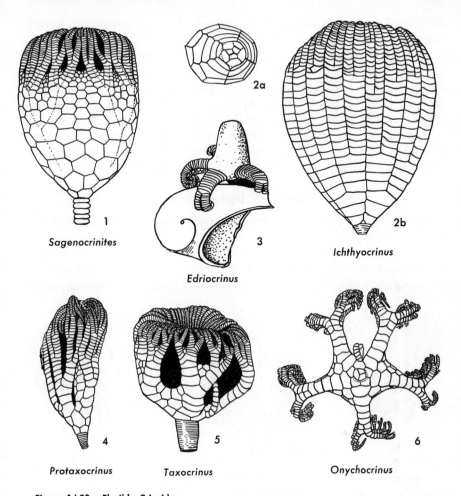

Figure 14.20. Flexible Crinoids.
   Sagenocrinida: 1, 2. Taxocrinida: 3-6. 1. *Sagenocrinites clarki*, 2/3X, Silurian, Tennessee.
2a, 2b. Some basal plates and lateral view of *Ichthyocrinus laevis*, 1X, Silurian, New York,
Ontario.   3. Reconstruction of *Edriocrinus sacculus*, 1X, Devonian, New York.   4. Posterior side of
Protaxocrinus elegans showing two primibrachial plates in each ray, 2X, Ordovician, Ontario.
5. Left posterior view of *Taxocrinus intermedius* showing three primibrachial plates in each ray,
2/3X, Mississippian, Iowa.   6. Dorsal view of *Onychocrinus ulrichi* showing more than three
primibrachial plates in each ray, 3/4X, Mississippian, Indiana.
   (1-3, 5 after Springer, 1920.   4 after Springer, 1911a.   6 after Kirk, 1911.)

interbrachials. Important flares of sagenocrinids took place during the Silurian and again during Late Paleozoic time.

SUBCLASS 3.   CAMERATA

Camerate crinoids are particularly characterized by the rigid articulation
of plates in both the dorsal cup and tegmen, a feature which causes them to

be referred to as "box crinoids." In addition, the food grooves are buried below the surface of the tegmen. Camerates are mostly adunate crinoids, but there is a persistent trend for simplification of the calyx and upward migration of plates so that in the most advanced forms such as *Platycrinites* the arms are free from the calyx. From their first appearance in mid-Ordovician (Chazy) strata the Camerata are divisible into monocyclic and dicyclic Orders. Most attention in classification is accorded variations in construction of the dorsal cup. Meager evidence such as similarity of interbrachial plates and construction of the ventral surface indicates a remote ancestral connection between the Inadunata and the Camerata.

Order a.   Diplobathrida

Diplobathrida are dicyclic camerate crinoids whose infrabasals are invariably five in number.

Reteocrinus, from the Chazy, exemplifies the primitive condition of members of the Order because it has numerous small interradial plates between the true radials (Fig. 14.21.1). *Gilbertsocrinus* (Devonian and Mississippian)

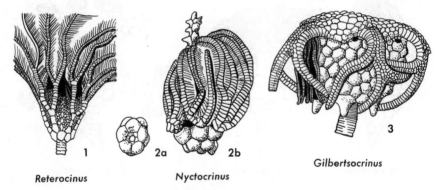

Reterocinus   *Nyctocrinus*   *Gilbertsocrinus*

Figure 14.21.   Camerate Crinoids (Diplobathrida).
1. *Reteocrinus onealli*, showing numerous interbrachial plates and a prominent raised anal ray, 1X, Ordovician, Ohio. 2a, 2b. Base and calyx of *Nyctocrinus magnitubus*, 1X, Silurian, Tennessee.   3. Lateral view of *Gilbertsocrinus tuberosus* with feeding arms shown only on the left side, 2/3X, Mississippian, Indiana.
(1, 3 after Wachsmuth and Springer, 1897. 2 after Springer, 1926.)

Figure 14.22 (opposite). Camerate Crinoids (Monobathrida).
1. *Glyptocrinus decadactylus*, 2/3X, Ordovician, Kentucky. 2. *Eucalyptocrinites crassus*, 1 1/3X, Silurian, midcontinent. 3. Dorsal cup of *Megistocrinus nodosus*, 2/3X, Devonian, midcontinent. 4. *Platycrinites hemisphericus*, 2/3X, Mississippian, Indiana. 5. Dorsal cup of *Dorycrinus missouriensis*, 2/3X, Mississippian, midcontinent. 6. Tegmenal spine of *Pterotocrinus bifurcatus*, 1X, Mississippian, Kentucky. 7. Calyx of *Pterotocrinus capitalis*, 1X, Mississippian, midcontinent. 8. Dorsal cup of *Batocrinus cantonensis* with long anal tube and arms attached to left side of cup, 1X, Mississippian, Indiana. 9. Dorsal cup and long anal tube of *Uperocrinus nashvillae*, 1/2X, Mississippian, midcontinent. 10a, 10b. Basal and lateral views of dorsal cup of *Talarocrinus ovatus*, 1 1/2X, Mississippian, midcontinent. 11. Calyx of *Dizygocrinus rotundus* with some arms removed to reveal spherical dorsal cup, 1X, Mississippian, midcontinent.
(10a after Weller, 1920. Others after Wachsmuth and Springer, 1897.)

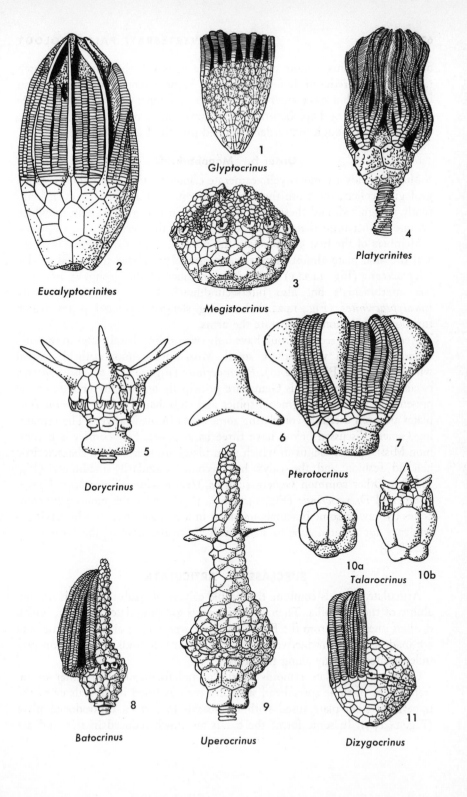

1

Glyptocrinus

2

Eucalyptocrinites

3

Megistocrinus

4

Platycrinites

5

Dorycrinus

6

7

Pterotocrinus

10a

Talarocrinus

10b

8

Batocrinus

9

Uperocrinus

11

Dizygocrinus

not only represents a more advanced stage in which the number of inter-radial plates is reduced, but the calyx has become remarkably spinose and is equipped with a spectacular umbrellalike anal apparatus (Fig. 14.21.3). At least 33 Genera of Diplobathrida are known, most of which lived during the Silurian, although the Order extended into the Late Mississippian.

Order b.   Monobathrida

Monobathrids are monocyclic camerate crinoids. Of all the crinoids which geologists collect, these are the most common. At least 95 Genera are currently recognized, and these can be arranged in two groups, both of which became extinct immediately prior to the end of the Permian.

Members of the first group retain the normal number of five basal plates, and the anal plate almost always has migrated up above the radial circlet. *Glyptocrinus* (Fig. 14.22.1) is an early member of the group; it not only has interbrachials but also intersecundibrachials and intertertibrachials. *Eucalyptocrinites* (Fig. 14.22.2) has long slender tegmenal plates which function as partitions to separate the arms.

Members of the second group have only two or three basal plates in the cup. *Talarocrinus* is a well-known, small, Mississippian, monobathrid crinoid with two basals (Fig. 14.22.10). *Pterotocrinus* (Fig. 14.22.6, 7) also had two basals, but members of this Genus are principally noteworthy because of the presence of prominent tegmenal spines and club-shaped plates. *Pterotocrinus* plates are even useful in correlating some strata in the Midwest. The remaining Genera discussed below have three basal plates. *Platycrinites* is a common Mississippian Genus in which stem plates are twisted in a characteristic helicoid fashion and the calyx has become secondarily inadunate (Fig. 14.22.4). Other common Genera such as *Megistocrinus, Batocrinus, Uperocrinus* and *Dizygocrinus* (Fig. 14.22.3, 8, 9, 11) typify the monocyclic camerates by having some brachials included in a boxlike calyx and by having a tendency for an anal tube to stand well above the level of the arms (Fig. 14.22.8, 9).

SUBCLASS 4.   ARTICULATA

Articulate crinoids combine the simple calyces of inadunates with the pliability of the Flexibilia. Their uniserial arms are pinnulate, however, which distinguishes them from the Flexibilia. Moreover, almost all of the Articulata are inadunates. Reproductive organs of articulate crinoids are borne on pinnules located midway along the arms.

Calyces of articulate crinoids consist of radials, basals, and either of infrabasals or of some specialized structure such as fused infrabasals or of the uppermost stem plate fused with infrabasals to form a **centrodorsal plate** (Fig. 14.23.5). In some forms the basals are much reduced in size and are

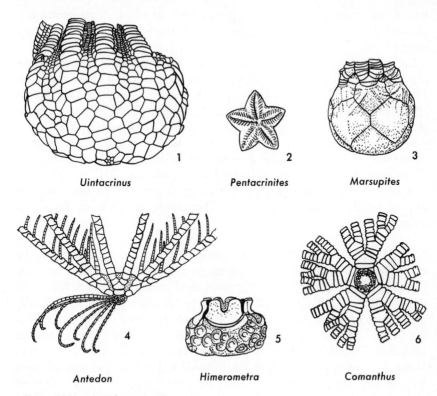

1   2   3

Uintacrinus   Pentacrinites   Marsupites

4   5   6

Antedon   Himerometra   Comanthus

Figure 14.23. Articulate Crinoids.
1. Oblique basal view of *Uintacrinus socialis*, 2/3X, Cretaceous, Kansas. 2. Articular face of a columnal plate of *Pentacrinites whitei*, 2X, Jurassic, western interior. 3. *Marsupites americanus*, 2/3X, Cretaceous, Mississippi. 4. Side view of the calyx and the bases of some arms of *Antedon* sp., about 2/3X, Recent. Some cirri have been removed from the centrodorsal plate and four arms are not shown on the far side of the calyx. 5. Side view of centrodorsal and radial plates of *Himerometra* sp., about 2X, Recent. 6. Radial diagnosis of *Comanthus* sp., 1X, Recent. Five narrow first primibrachials (1Br$_1$) surround the centrodorsal plate and four series of brachial plates are shown.
(1 after Springer, 1901. 2 after Clark and Twitchell, 1915. 3 after Springer, 1911b. 4-6 after Clark, 1915.)

fused into a star-shaped (**rosette**) plate in which only the tips of the rays may be visible on the surface. The ventral surface is always a leathery cover which often is studded with plates.

Two great groups of Articulata are recognized. The **pentacrinids** are typically stem-bearing forms whose star-shaped plates with stellate or petalloid patterns of crenellae are very commonly seen in some Mesozoic strata (Fig. 14.23.2). The pentacrinids may remain attached to their stems during their entire lives, or they may break away from the first stem and spend a period of free-living existence, after which they settle down and secrete a second stem to which they remain permanently attached. *Pentacrinites* is a common Mesozoic Genus. Living pentacrinids characteristically inhabit deep water.

Comatulids spend all but their larval life as free-swimming crinoids. Their centrodorsal plate bears cirri with which they can hold on to the substratum (Fig. 14.23.4). *Antedon,* which is one of the most commonly studied Recent crinoids, is a typical comatulid. Its graceful swimming movements are characteristic of this group to which the name "feather stars" so aptly applies.

One other stemless crinoid, *Uintacrinus,* has been found locally in great abundance in Upper Cretaceous sediments in Kansas and in Europe. It differs from other articulates in being distinctly adunate (Fig. 14.23.1).

Articulate crinoids are very rarely discovered as fossils on this continent but are locally important in Europe. They range in age from Triassic to Recent.

GEOLOGIC HISTORY. The crinoids that appeared suddenly in the early Medial Ordovician Period represented both the Inadunata and the Camerata (Fig. 14.24). Shortly thereafter the Flexibilia appeared, this being in Late Medial Ordovician time. Crinoid (or cystoid) stem plates are relatively common throughout Paleozoic sediments, but good Ordovician collecting localities for calyces are not known in America aside from occasional strata near Cincinnati, Ohio, and in eastern New York. Crinoids are common in the Silurian strata at Niagara Falls, Waldron, Indiana, and near Chicago, but the most famous Silurian crinoids have been collected on the island of Gotland in the Baltic Sea, where they are contributors to famous fossil biostromes. Crinoids are also well represented in the Silurian of Sweden. Devonian crinoids are locally common in several formations in New York State; in fact, the Becraft limestone was formerly called the "Encrinal limestone" because of the large number of crinoids which had been discovered in its upper part. No doubt the best-preserved Devonian crinoids have come from the black Bundenbach shale in Germany.

The greatest evolutionary burst of crinoids, however, occurred in the Early and Medial Mississippian (Kinderhook and Osage Epochs); therefore the Mississippian has been called the Age of Crinoids. Actually, the great burst is primarily due to extraordinary development of the monocyclic camerates, although many dicyclic inadunates and some of the Flexibilia participate in this notable culmination of the crinoids. Then, at the end of the Osage Epoch the crinoids went into a disastrous decline from which they never recovered. Upper Mississippian (Meramec and Chester Series) strata may contain abundant crinoids, of which the dicyclic inadunates (Cladida) are the most important and valuable representatives. Cladids were also the only important group of Pennsylvanian crinoids. In fact the Cladida actually survived into

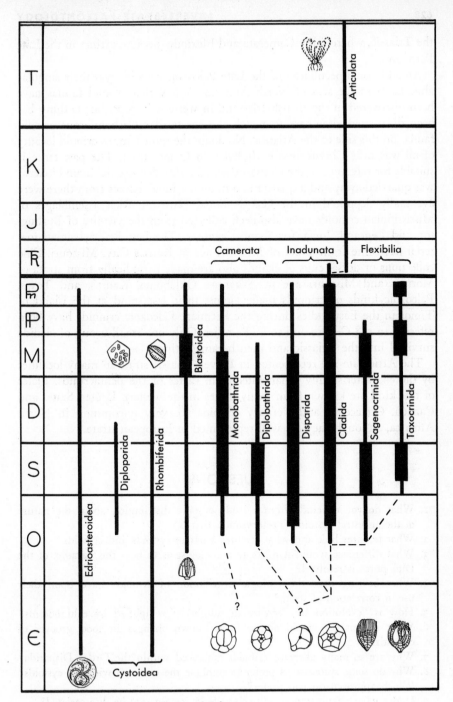

Figure 14.24. Geologic Distribution of Pelmatozoa.

the Triassic, whereas the Camerata and Flexibilia became extinct in the Late Permian.

An additional peculiarity of the Late Paleozoic crinoids was their singular abundance in the seas of North America. A few rich crinoid faunas have been discovered in the British Isles and in western Europe, but nothing has been discovered elsewhere to match the spectacular Carboniferous crinoid faunas on this side of the Atlantic. No doubt the most famous crinoid locality of all was near Crawfordsville, Indiana, in Osage strata. The past tense is suitable for reference to the Crawfordsville locality because the main bioherm was quarried away and a quarter of a million crinoid calyces from there were eventually deposited in the U.S. National Museum. Rich assemblages of Mississippian crinoids have also been collected from the vicinity of Burlington and Legrand, Iowa, for about a century. The best Pennsylvanian material has come from strata of Missouri age at Kansas City, Missouri. Fine collections of dorsal cups of cladids also are made periodically from strata of Morrow and Missouri age in Arkansas, Oklahoma, Kansas, and Texas. Paleozoic kinds of crinoids made almost their last stand at the island of Timor in the East Indies during the Permian. Paleozoic crinoids have been referred to 518 Genera and to 91 Families. Only one small group of cladids survived into the Triassic and then became extinct.

The Articulata are represented in Lower Triassic strata in many localities by the characteristically ornamented stem plates of the pentacrinids. Plates of this kind are known from many places in the western United States and Canada. Cretaceous and Tertiary crinoids are very uncommon in North America, although they are well represented in European strata.

QUESTIONS

1. What do you conclude from a study of pore distribution about the nature of the ancestral cystoids (protocystoids, that is)?
2. What features link and what features separate cystoids and crinoids?
3. What difference would it make to a zoologist as to how the Paradox of the Diplopores is resolved?
4. What bearing does the ecologic distribution of crinoids have upon their use in correlation of strata?
5. How is "evolution by decrease in number" exemplified by echinoderms?
6. What advantages would accrue from known changes in food grooves of crinoids?
7. Why are so many aberrant crinoids embraced within the Order Disparida?
8. Why do some systematists prefer to combine the blastoids with the cystoids? Which approach do you prefer?
9. Under what circumstances will echinoderm remains not be disassociated?

10. Why did the crinoids seem to experience one major flare just before a setback in the Medial Mississippian? Another setback near the close of the Permian?

BIBLIOGRAPHY

References to the Pelmatozoa are included with references to other echinoderms at the end of Chapter 15.

Chapter 15

UNATTACHED ECHINODERMS

PHYLUM XIV. ECHINODERMA (Continued)

Subphylum II. Eleutherozoa

The Subphylum Eleutherozoa includes the free-living echinoderms.

Class A.   Stelleroida

Starfish are among the most attractive and common marine creatures sought by visitors to beaches over the world, but are among the rarest of fossils, unless one counts the generally unrecognizable isolated plates which presumably are scattered through ancient sediments. Much attention has been given the Recent starfish because of their depredations in commercial oyster beds. A few of the 800 living species are so voracious in their assaults upon immature oysters that they materially threaten the survival of the oyster industry.

Living starfish consist of a central **disc** to which are attached five flexible **arms.** The mouth is at the point of convergence of the simple food grooves in the center of the oral surface of each arm. Particles of food are either washed down the grooves by ciliary action or are lifted toward the mouth by arching of the arms. Food consists of small molluscs, worms, barnacles, or of detrital organic debris on the ocean floor.

The surface generally is studded with large spinose plates, but minute pedicellariae also are present (Fig. 14.2.2–4). These stalked jawlike organs snap shut on any irritating body as a defensive mechanism. Respiration of many forms is largely through the fleshy tissue in which the skeletal plates are embedded; hence pedicellariae also may be busily engaged in cleaning sediment from the respiratory surface. Digestion takes place in a stomach which generally can be extruded from the mouth; hence an oyster which a starfish has pulled open is digested between its own two valves. Sexes are

630

separate and a characteristic larva develops after fertilization of the egg. It is a strange thing that although larvae of starfish retain their free-swimming habit for as long as three weeks and should be able to distribute a species very widely as they drift on ocean currents, the mature starfish occupy very restricted geographic ranges. Their sensitivity to their environment is such that they may only occupy a part of a bay or estuary; thus their value in stratigraphic correlations is reduced accordingly.

A madreporite on the **apical surface** affords access of sea water through an S-shaped **stone canal** to a circum-oral **ring canal**. Five single or paired **radial canals** traverse the lengths of the arms and send off **tube feet** at regular intervals (Fig. 14.2.1). Each tube foot passes through an **ambulacral plate** on the roof of the food groove through two pores because the middle portion of a tube foot is divided into two parallel tubes, although the two ends consist of single tubes. In some starfish the tube feet serve as locomotor organs which enable the animal to cross either rocky or muddy terrain. The suction-cup ends of the tube feet grasp the substratum, after which little pressure chambers (ampullae) inflate the tubes with sea water, and the body progresses as though on numerous rigid stilts. In other starfish the tube feet are much modified sensory organs or are even mostly lost.

The stelleroids display astonishing powers of survival and regeneration. A severed arm may live three months and heal itself without a body being attached; and a severed disc may regenerate another half, or a mutilated disc may regenerate five new arms.

CLASSIFICATION. Recent stelleroids are divided into two great groups —the true starfish (Asteroida) in which the arms are merged with the disc, and the brittle-stars (Ophiuroida) with arms distinctly differentiated from the disc. These groups merge somewhat through intermediate forms, so other classifications may be necessary. Accordingly, features such as size of marginal plates (**marginalia**) on the arms, mouth parts, pedicellariae, tube feet, genital slits, and form and position of the madreporite are also used to delimit groups.

SUBCLASS 1. SOMASTEROIDA

Somasteroids are characterized by having a pentagonal shape, and although they lack discrete arms, they bear ambulacra on the disc proper. Ambulacral rays are differentiated as a double row of ambulacral plates which alternate in position. The rest of the oral surface in the earliest forms consists of rod-shaped plates inclined obliquely to the ambulacra. In later forms marginalia were present. Spencer (1951) thought that these stelleroids fed by washing microscopic food particles toward the mouth by ciliary action, inasmuch as definite food grooves are not present.

Villebrunaster, the typical Genus, is the oldest stelleroid yet discovered

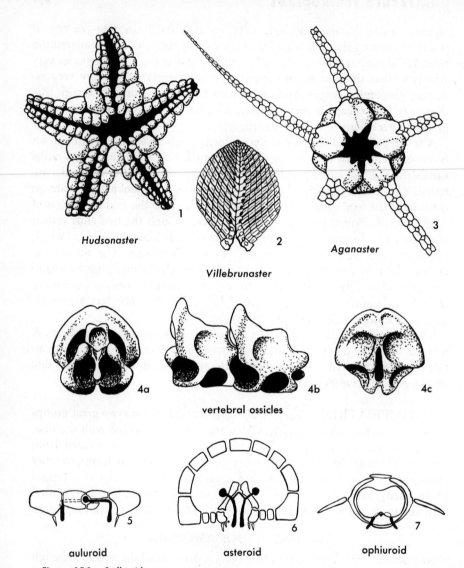

Hudsonaster

Villebrunaster

Aganaster

vertebral ossicles

auluroid   asteroid   ophiuroid

Figure 15.1. Stelleroida.
1. Oral surface of *Hudsonaster narrawayi*, 5X, Ordovician, Minnesota. 2. Reconstruction of the oral surface of one arm of *Villebrunaster thorali*, 1X, Ordovician, France. 3. Oral surface of *Aganaster gregarius*, 3X, Mississippian, Indiana. 4a, 4b, 4c. Aboral, lateral, and adoral views of vertebral ossicles from an ophiuroid, enlarged. 5. Cross section of an auluroid arm. 6. Cross section of an asteroid arm. 7. Cross section of an ophiuroid arm.
Tube feet in 6-7 are shown in solid black.
(1, 6 after Schuchert, 1915. 2 after Spencer, 1951. 3, 4 after Spencer, 1925. 5, 7 after Spencer, 1914.)

(Fig. 15.1.2). It is from Lower Ordovician strata in France. Other examples of the Subclass also have been discovered in Lower Ordovician strata in Europe.

SUBCLASS 2.   ASTEROIDA

Asteroida are the true starfish, characterized by having broad arms confluent with the disc and by deep food grooves on the arms. Skeletal plates are loosely united in a flexible body; hence, the plates usually are scattered after death. Asteroid arms typically consist of a hollow chamber bounded by stout marginalia and by small plates on the apical and oral surfaces. **Ambulacral plates,** which roof over the food grooves, are disposed in opposite pairs as in ophiuroids but unlike their distribution in somasteroids (Fig. 15.1.6).

The oldest asteroids, such as *Hudsonaster,* occur in Middle Ordovician rocks (Fig. 15.1.1) in the central and eastern United States and in southeastern Canada. Advanced forms evolved in part by increase in the number of plates but by decrease in the size of plates; presumably the new arrangement allowed more flexibility of the body. Progressive changes in the ambulacra were coordinated with the presence of more and more tube feet in the ambulacral grooves. Accordingly, the asteroids characteristically pass small particles of food along the grooves with tube feet. Some taxonomists recognize two Orders of Asteroida, depending upon whether the marginalia are large (Phanerozonida) or small (Cryptozonida). Asteroids with large marginalia are thought to be primitive because they not only antedate the others, but some Recent starfish with small marginalia pass through a stage in their development wherein they have large marginalia. Strangely, some asteroids lack a madreporite, and others have one on the oral surface instead of in the normal position on the aboral surface.

SUBCLASS 3.   OPHIUROIDA

Ophiuroids are the brittle-stars whose characteristic feature is the slenderness of their arms (Fig. 15.1.3). They ordinarily move by whiplike motion of the arms, but immature ophiuroids can swim. Moreover, many ophiuroids burrow into soft sediment and leave only the tips of their arms protruding. Their brittleness is manifested if they are disturbed because they can cast off their arms at will and regenerate them in the same way that crinoids can. The great flexibility of the arms arises through reduction of the marginalia and other exterior skeletal elements. Ultimately the ambulacrals become fused into a string of axial skeletal elements called **vertebral ossicles** (because their appearance resembles vertebrae of chordates) (Fig. 15.1.4). In conjunction with very active locomotion, tube feet decrease progressively in size and assume the status of sensory organs (Fig. 15.1.7).

Ophiuroids are more likely to occur as fossils than are the other stelleroids because many ophiuroids are burrowers. Moreover, their vertebral ossicles are more readily recognized than are ossicles of any other stelleroids. Even so, ophiuroids are not common fossils.

Ophiuroids comprise two groups which evolved in parallel fashion. In one group the ambulacral plates are paired, but in the other group they alternate. Moreover, many paleontologists find it desirable to separate almost all Paleozoic ophiuroids as a distinct group (auluroids) equal in rank to asteroids and ophiuroids, and characterized by having the radial canal of the water vascular system enclosed between ambulacral plates instead of lying beneath them (Fig. 15.1.5).

The Asteroida occur in rocks as old as the Ordovician. *Aganaster* is a Carboniferous Genus with typical ophiuroid form (Fig. 15.1.3). Ophiuroids are so common in Recent seas that Verrill reported dredging over 10,000 large specimens from a depth of about 1100 feet (367 m) off Martha's Vineyard, Massachusetts.

GEOLOGIC DISTRIBUTION OF STELLEROIDA. Stelleroids are rarely important rock-makers, the only exceptions being when local populations are discovered. In this way individuals have been discovered in considerable numbers in single quarries, as in the case of *Hudsonaster* (Ordovician) at Saugerties, New York; *Schoenaster* (Mississippian) at Legrand, Iowa; and various stelleroids in the famous roofing-slate quarries (Lower Devonian) at Bundenbach, Germany. An effort has been made to zone part of the Cretaceous System of England on the basis of fragments and isolated plates of stelleroids. Plates and spines are found occasionally in washed micropaleontologic material from the Tertiary, or in Recent samples of sediments, but expert skill usually would be needed to do more than to recognize that the fragments belonged to this Class.

Class B.   Echinoidea

Echinoids commonly are known in English as sea urchins or as sand dollars, or as sea apples in various European languages. They have been recognized longer than have most other fossils; indeed, they were prized for amulets by prehistoric inhabitants of Europe. Clues as to their probable value date from about the time of Christ, for Pliny recited a belief current in his time that these creatures (then called *brontia*) fell from the sky during thunderstorms and thereafter would safeguard their bearer from being struck by lightning. "Thunder stones" could weather out of Mesozoic and Cenozoic strata at many places in Europe, but they are said also to have been broadcast as erratics by the several ice sheets that plowed across the European continent during the Pleistocene. Living echinoids serve as a food source, either raw or cooked, in southern Europe and in many tropical areas. Fanciers crack open females to remove the roe (known as *rizzo di mer* or "sea rice" in Italy).

Echinoids, being of complex structure and being capable of diverse evolutionary modification, make excellent guide fossils. In the Coast Ranges of California, for instance, they rank in importance with Pectens and Turritellas as the most useful megafossils for field work in Upper Cenozoic rocks. Similar value is accorded them for stratigraphic work in Lower Cretaceous rocks of Texas. Fine, complete specimens are common, but specialization of anatomic features in the Class is so extensive that species can be identified accurately from selected fragments if the collector has taken pains to learn a few of the intricacies of the animals.

LIVING ECHINOIDS. Echinoid skeletons (**tests**) typically are globular, discoidal, or heart-shaped aggregations of plates surmounted by spines of various sizes. The calcareous plates which make up a test are arranged in more or less radial rows. Most tests are less than 10 centimeters in diameter.

The name Echinoderma characteristically is associated with the numerous slender radially arranged spines which are distributed over the outer surface of echinoids. Not only can these spines cause puncture wounds, but spines of some species may also be capable of poisoning the animal they penetrate. Echinoids with prominent spines commonly live in shallow water.

Many echinoids can be observed in the intertidal zone where they inhabit shallow holes which they excavate with their spines and teeth in solid rock. On the other hand, the heart urchins burrow down a few inches into soft sediment and construct a chamber into which they pump water and from which they ensnare food by long, fleshy, tentaclelike processes extending up the narrow entrance tube of the chamber. Various echinoids range down into the dark abysses of the ocean to depths in excess of 15,000 feet (5000 m) below sea level. All echinoids are strictly marine and are even intolerant of moderately brackish water. Echinoids browse on algae, hydroids, and worms, or crush small molluscs or barnacles, or ingest the bottom sediment and extract organic debris from it. Reproduction generally involves liberation of eggs, but a few echinoids are viviparous; that is, they bear their young alive.

MORPHOLOGY. Echinoid tests are composed of a spinose **corona** or main part of the test, surmounted by an **apical system** of plates on the aboral portion or summit. The corona rests upon or nearly upon the **basicoronal system** surrounding the mouth.

Fundamental bilateral symmetry of echinoids is readily apparent in the elongate "heart urchins," but is less notable in the circular forms. Both kinds, however, are oriented according to a system devised by Loven and based upon location of the madreporite. Loven proposed that echinoids should be oriented so that the madreporite would lie in the upper right-hand interambulacral ray when viewed from the dorsal or aboral side. Then the ten rays can be numbered counterclockwise, starting with the lower right-hand ambulacral ray. Loven used Roman numerals I-V for ambulacral rays and Arabic numerals 1-5 for interambulacral rays. In this way the madreporite always falls in ray 2, ray III is anterior, and ray 5 is posterior. The system is particularly useful in describing variations in the apical system of all echinoids and in the anatomy of ray 5 of the heart urchins (Fig. 15.2.1).

Spines. Spines range from long, slender, and pointed to short and club-shaped shafts. Some are smooth, some are flattened for digging, others are secondarily spinose, and some possess an unusual modification such as a recurved end or a poison gland. In life most spines are covered with ectoderm and are fastened to the corona by muscles and soft tissue; hence, the spines normally become detached from the test after death. Rarely, the fleshy cover dies back part of the way from the tips of spines, thus enabling sessile organisms to incrust the spines during the life of an individual echinoderm. Most spines bear a raised encircling band (**milled ring**) near the proximal (lower) end (Fig. 15.3.4). A conical array of muscles attached to the milled ring extend out obliquely and downward and are inserted on plates of the test; contraction of the muscles moves the spines. In this fashion, echinoids are able to walk as though on stilts or to dig in sediment.

Spines occur in several sizes, of which large **primary spines** are most conspicuous. Bands of very small **miliary spines** occur in roughly circular patterns around the summit or around the anal opening.

In among the various spines are the microscopic jawlike pedicellariae (Fig. 14.2.2–4). Pedicellariae normally lie with their jaws agape, but if stimulated by contact, the jaws snap shut on an offending object. Waste particles are passed along by pincerlike action of adjacent pedicellariae until they reach the widest part of the corona (**ambitus**), where they are dumped overside. On the other hand, living tissue of intruding creatures is grasped firmly and not released, even if pedicellariae are torn away from the echinoid. Zoologists attach great systematic value to the shape of jaws of pedicellariae and recognize several general types, depending upon the shape and number of the jaws. Paleontologists, however, have made little use of pedicellariae because these minute structures rarely remain attached to a corona in fossils. Never-

---

Figure 15.2 (opposite). Morphology of Echinoids.
1a, 1b. Aboral and oral surfaces of *Dendraster excentricus*, 3/4X, Pleistocene and Recent, Pacific Coast. 2. Vertical section through *Dendraster excentricus* showing pillars, 1X. 3. Equatorial section through *Dendraster excentricus* showing internal skeletal features, 2/3X. 4. Cut-away diagram of a sand dollar, showing digestive track, 2/3X, Recent, Atlantic Coast. 5. Aristotle's Lantern of *Strongylocentrotus dröbachiensis*, 3X, Recent, world-wide. 6. Lantern of *Pholidechinus brauni*, 2X, Mississippian, Indiana. 7. Perignathic girdle showing arched auricles to which muscles were attached; slightly enlarged; Recent.
(1 after Grant and Hertlein, 1938. 4 after Coe, 1912. 5, 6 after Jackson, 1912. 7 after Mortensen, 1935.)

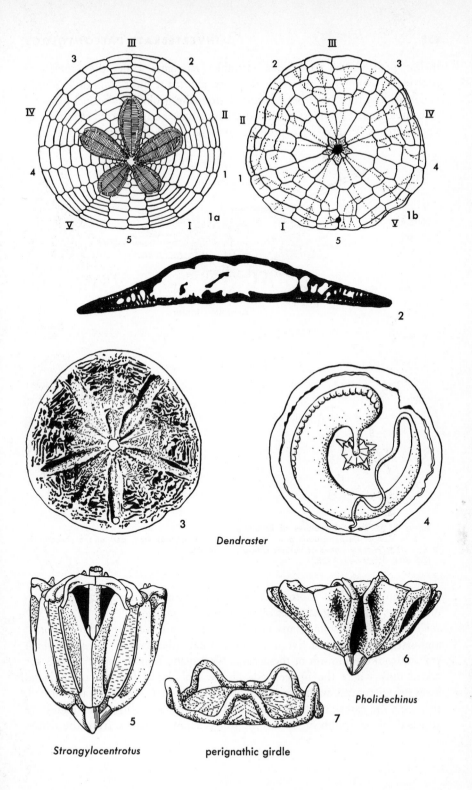

1a 1b 2

3 4

Dendraster

5 *Strongylocentrotus* perignathic girdle 7 6 *Pholidechinus*

theless, pedicellariae are of demonstrable systematic value; they consist of preservable calcareous material, they are abundant on certain living echinoderms, and they have been reported from the geologic column by several paleontologists. The oldest fossil pedicellariae have been collected from Mississippian rocks. Pedicellariae probably will be increasingly useful after they

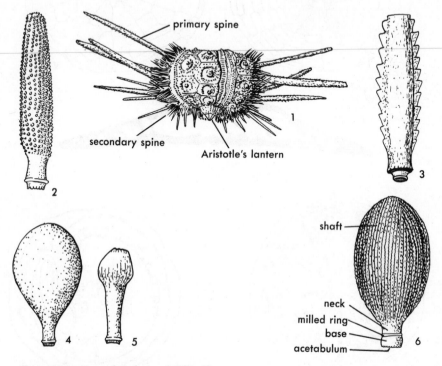

Figure 15.3.   External Features of Echinoids.
1. Side view of *Hesperocidaris panamensis* with spines removed from part of the corona, 1X, Recent.   2-6. Primary spines of various cidaroid echinoids, 1X.
(2-6 after Mortensen, 1928.)

have been studied in more detail and are commonly recognized by paleontologists examining samples of microscopic organisms.

Corona.   The corona of any post-Paleozoic Genus consists of five perforate **ambulacral areas** and of five imperforate **interambulacral areas,** all of which radiate from the summit of the corona. New plates in both kinds of areas are added only where the upper ends of the ambulacral and interambulacral areas are in contact with the plates of the summit. After plates are formed, their size increases and their shape and their contacts with other plates are adjusted by resorption or by secretion of calcium carbonate from the tissues in which they are embedded. Plates of the ambulacral areas increase in size as they literally flow down the rays during growth of the corona. Naturally, the plates are largest at the ambitus, and then they decrease in size by resorption as they move farther orally. Apparently a large proportion of the energy of an echinoid is devoted to shuffling calcium carbonate through its tissues in order to adjust the size of the plates.

Some taxonomic importance is attached to methods by which new plates are added and to positions at which they are added in the rays, particularly in Paleozoic echinoids. Except for the Genus *Tetracidaris,* post-Paleozoic echinoids all have two rows of plates in each of the ten areas. Plates in these areas interlock along a zigzag **median suture** as if they were parts of a hexagonal packing plan. But where adjacent areas meet along the **adradial suture** the hexagonal outline is modified to a pentagonal form by truncation of one angle, and straight outer sides of all plates are in contact along the adradial suture.

Ambulacral areas may be hard to distinguish from interambulacral areas on very spinose living echinoids, but in tests denuded of their spines the ambulacral areas are prominently outlined by pores from which tube feet once emerged. These pores almost always occur in pairs (hence, **pore pairs**) and have a strong tendency to crowd against the outer margins of ambulacral plates near the adradial sutures. Most commonly one row of pore pairs occurs on each margin of an ambulacrum, in which case the pore pairs are said to be **uniserial** (Fig. 15.4.1–6); but **biserial** pore pairs (Fig. 15.4.7, 8) are present among some post-Paleozoic echinoids and **multiserial** pore pairs are generally the rule among Paleozoic echinoids.

Conjugate pores are those in which two pores are included within a groove in a manner so much like the case of diplopores among cystoids that one naturally would suppose pores of cystoids and echinoids to serve identical purposes (Fig. 15.4.3). Pores in a pair tend to become closer as the intervening calcareous tissue diminishes, and eventually pores do not occur in pairs but are single (even though tube feet may or may not still be paired).

Great taxonomic importance is accorded the nature of the ambulacral plates themselves, according to whether they are simple or compound. Only variations in shape, such as involve equidimensional versus narrow plates, affect the simple or **cidaroid** plates (Fig. 15.4.1–3). On the other hand, compound plates are intricately contrived. Their sutural outlines commonly retain the pentagonal (modified hexagonal) form of most echinoid plates, but three or more plates make up the pentagon. Compound nature of plates can be determined most readily by counting the number of pore pairs in one pentagon, because each component plate has one pair of pores. Compound plates with the minimum number of three pore pairs are **oligoporous** (Fig. 15.4.5), whereas plates with four or more (up to about a dozen) pore pairs are **polyporous** (Fig. 15.4.6–9). Sutures between adjacent component plates in one pentagon generally are distinct at the porous region but die out toward the median suture (Fig. 15.4.6, 7, 9). Differentiation of sutural traces can be of very great importance, there being two main kinds of compound plates. In the **echinoid** pattern the largest component plate is the lowest plate. In the **diademoid** pattern the three plates are of subequal size (Fig. 15.4.5), and in

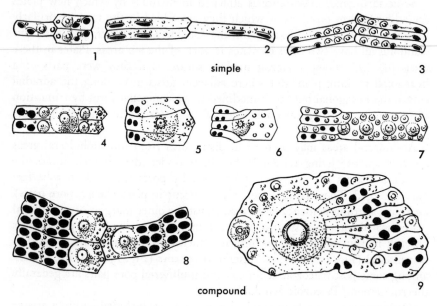

Figure 15.4. Ambulacral Plates.
1. Cidaroid type with round pores. 2. Cidaroid type with elongate pores. 3. Cidaroid type with conjugate pores. 4. Two plates sharing one primary spine base. 5. Diademoid plate with three long components. 6, 7. Arbacioid plates with a large central plate and three small demiplates; 6 is uniserial, 7 is biserial. 8. Advanced biserial compound plate of *Diplopodia* sp. 9. Polyporous echinoid type of plate from *Strongylocentrotus* sp.
  All plates are enlarged.
  (1-8 after Clark and Twitchell, 1915. 9 after Grant and Hertlein, 1938.)

the **arbacioid** pattern the largest plate is the one next above the lowest plate (Fig. 15.4.6).

Pores in ambulacra of globular echinoids such as sea urchins extend the length of each ambulacral area. In elongate echinoids such as heart urchins and sand dollars, however, the pores may be conspicuous only over part of each ambulacral ray. Partial rows of pores in each ambulacrum on the aboral surface commonly diverge away from each other and then swing back together above the ambitus. The poriferous ambulacral areas consequently resemble petals of a flower; hence, they are **petaloid** ambulacra (Fig. 15.2.1). The other ambulacral plates are present but they resemble interambulacral plates. In a few cases, however, ambulacral plates near the basicoronal system may again bear pores and may even resemble small-scale petaloid areas of the aboral surface. These latter, oral, petal-like groups are **phyllodes,** which, together with ridges which separate adjacent groups, are called **floscelles** (Fig. 15.11.1d, 2a).

Interambulacral plates normally are distinctly larger than the ambulacral plates are. Moreover, interambulacral plates are not compound. Although interambulacral plates always are arranged in double rows (except for *Tetracidaris*) near the ambitus of post-Paleozoic forms, they may be uniserial near the apical system. Some paleontologists think that this localized, uniserial, youthful condition is inherited from some ancestral Paleozoic echinoids which normally had only one row of interambulacral plates.

Spine bases are borne by all plates of the corona but are best developed on interambulacral plates, and especially near the ambitus of all rays. One large primary spine base, or several small ones, or combinations of large and small bases may be present on interambulacral plates, but the pattern and construction of spine bases are constant for a particular species. It will be remembered that the smallest spines of some irregular echinoids occur in characteristic circular rows; hence, the corresponding rows of minute spine bases (**miliary granules**) to which they are attached are reflected on the test by indented bands called **fascioles.** A **peripetalous fasciole** may circumscribe the tips of petaloid ambulacral areas (Fig. 15.13.1a), whereas a **marginal fasciole** may encircle the corona near the ambitus, and ringlike **anal** or **subanal fascioles** may surround or lie adjacent to the periproct.

A typical spine-bearing interambulacral plate consists of a flat base which carries a ball-like protuberance (**mamelon**) on a shaft (**boss**) (Fig. 15.5.1). The concave base of a spine fits snugly over the convex mamelon and the two elements are kept in place and also adjusted by the muscles which lead from the milled ring of the spine to a smooth depressed area (**aureole**) around the boss. If the spine is also kept in place by a short ligament, there is a dimple on the summit of the mamelon; hence, these are said to be **perforate** spine bases (Fig. 15.5.1, 3). **Imperforate** spine bases obviously lack the little hole (Fig. 15.5.2). Smaller **scrobicules** or secondary spine bases may surround the primaries, and even smaller ones, the **miliary granules,** may cover much of the remainder of a plate. Minute **granules** cover much of the surface and denote places to which pedicellariae were attached.

Spine bases on ambulacral plates resemble those on interambulacral plates in general features, except that many echinoids have compound ambulacrals. In this case a spine base may cover more than one plate. For instance, one pentagonal, compound, ambulacral plate may consist of three or more component plates, the sutures of which can be traced between the smaller spine bases and across the substance of a primary base (Fig. 15.4.5-7, 9).

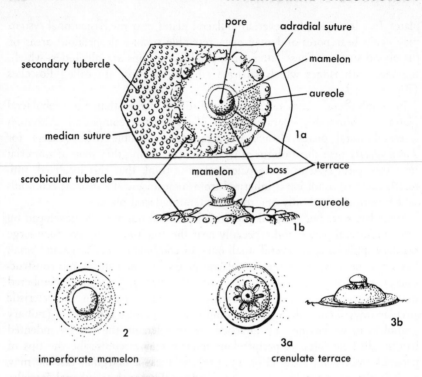

Figure 15.5.   Interambulacral Plates.
1. *Cidaris texanus.*   1a, plan view, 3X.   1b, side view of a tubercle, 5X.   2. Plan view of an imperforate mamelon, 10X.   3a, 3b. Plan and side views of a perforate and crenulate tubercle of *Hemiaster parastatus,* 20X.
(After Clark and Twitchell, 1915.)

Apical system.   All new plates of the corona originate at the summit around the margin of the apical system. The apical system of primitive echinoids consists of two discrete parts, of which the ten plates of the **oculo-genital ring** surround the **periproct.** Apical systems of this sort are said to be **endocyclic** (Fig. 15.6.1). In the more advanced (**exocyclic**) echinoids the periproct has migrated out of the apical system entirely and has come to occupy a position somewhere else on the aboral, or posterior, or even on the oral surface of the test. The position of the periproct in echinoids is of major taxonomic importance. The former position of the periproct in exocyclic echinoids is occupied either by expansion of the madreporite (Fig. 15.6.2) or by the plates of the oculo-genital ring which have expanded and fill the space.

The oculo-genital ring invariably is located at the summit of a corona. The ten plates of the ring are of two kinds and they coincide with the ten rays of the corona. **Genital plates,** which normally are the largest, are in line with interambulacral rays. They are characterized by the presence of a single distinct genital pore near the outer margin (Fig. 15.6.1, 2). Moreover, the genital plate in ray 2 is additionally modified by numerous minute perforations to serve as the madreporite (Fig. 15.6.2). **Ocular plates** bear a tiny perforation from which a fleshy feeler (not an eye) protruded in life (Fig. 15.6.1, 2). If ocular plates occupy positions on the periphery of an oculo-genital ring and merely slightly indent the sutural trace between adjacent genital plates the plates are said to be **exsert** (Fig. 15.6.1). On the other hand, oculars which extend into the inner edge of the ring are **insert**. In intermediate stages, Loven's system of numbering is applied when signifying which oculars are insert and

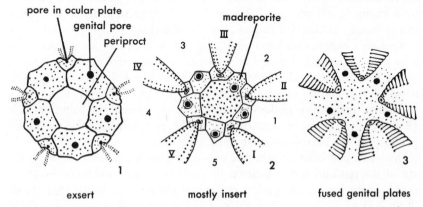

Figure 15.6. Apical Systems.
1. *Leiocidaris hemigranosus*, a regular echinoid, plates of the periproct have been removed from within the oculo-genital ring, 1X. 2. *Holectypus planatus*, an irregular echinoid, 6X. 3. *Encope macrophora*, an irregular echinoid, 5X.
(After Clark and Twitchell, 1915.)

which are exsert. Thus, all oculars in Figure 15.6.2 are insert except the ocular of ray IV. It appears that insert oculars evolved from exsert oculars among post-Paleozoic echinoids. On the other hand, oculars of Paleozoic echinoids are, paradoxically, typically insert, too.

In advanced stages of specialization the various genital plates may become fused together and serve as one large madreporite (Fig. 15.6.3). At the same time one or more of the genital pores may be aborted; and ocular plates may diminish in size to insignificance (Fig. 15.6.3).

From an evolutionary standpoint, a large apical system is more primitive than a small one and large oculars are more primitive than small ones.

Basicoronal system. The mouth is centrally located or is just anterior to the center of the oral surface, never occupying a very eccentric position. Among the common sea urchins of most coasts, the mouth opening is surrounded by a marvelously contrived chewing apparatus whose principal elements are five-pointed teeth. The apparatus can be protruded slightly below the base of the corona through a large circular aperture which is surrounded by a ring of calcareous plates, the **basicoronal plates** (Fig. 15.2.7). The teeth open and close like a pentameral "orange peel snapper" such as is used in oceanographic bottom sampling. Muscles operate a complicated system of struts and braces associated with the teeth (Fig. 15.2.5, 6). The whole calcareous contrivance has come to be known as Aristotle's lantern because Aristotle first drew the analogy between the 30 or 40 parts and the framework of horn lanterns of his time (which resemble gatepost lanterns of American colonial times). Similarities between lanterns of different echinoids are thought to afford unusually good evidence of relationship because lanterns are protected from changing external conditions and therefore presumably were not subject to much modification through natural selection.

Aristotle's lanterns are protruded from the peristome or are retracted into it by a ring of radially disposed muscles which are inserted on the lantern and on the basicoronal plates. Modification of the basicoronal ring (mostly of the terminal plates of the interambulacral rays) provides pedestals and arches of an internal **perignathic girdle** which facilitate insertion of the lantern muscles (Fig. 15.2.6). Details of construction of the perignathic girdle are of importance in the identification of some echinoids.

Unfortunately, after an echinoid dies the Aristotle's lantern normally falls out of the test and is disassociated by currents or by scavengers. Moreover, details of the perignathic girdle are internal phenomena; hence, they are difficult to examine. Accordingly, the oral region ordinarily is not studied except by specialists.

CLASSIFICATION. The main problem in classification of echinoids is not to discover some way in which various groups can be differentiated, but to reconcile various good ways. Few other groups of animals are so richly endowed with features of taxonomic value as are the echinoids. The difference in shape between sea urchins and heart urchins not only was recognized by Aristotle, but the underlying causes for the distinction still afford a major basis for differentiation. Recent authoritative classifications reflect excellent adjustment of zoologic and paleontologic features. Unfortunately for most student paleontologists and for field geologists, however, those definitive classifications either require knowledge of morphology which is rarely available to a paleontologist or necessitate the erection of taxonomic groups containing only creatures of extraordinary rarity. The strictly functional classification utilized herein is admittedly incomplete, even in view of the large comprehensive taxa it contains. Orders appropriate for a few unusual forms are omitted, such as for the Silurian *Echinocystites* which resembles the Perischoechinida but is exocyclic, and for the aberrant Triassic *Tiarechinus* which has three rows but only one tier of interambulacral plates.

KEY TO SUBCLASSES AND ORDERS OF ECHINOIDS

I. Test regular .... Subclass Regularia
    A. More than 20 rows of plates in test ..... Order Perischoechinida
    B. 20 rows of plates in test
        1. Ambulacral plates simple .... Order Cidarida
        2. Ambulacral plates compound .... Order Centrechinida
II. Test irregular .... Subclass Irregularia
    A. Ambulacra not petaloid .... Order Holectypida
    B. Ambulacra petaloid
        1. Floscelle present .... Order Cassidulida
        2. Floscelle absent
            a. Lantern present, test flattened .... Order Clypeasterida
            b. Lantern absent, test convex .... Order Spatangida

SUBCLASS 1.   REGULARIA

Regular echinoids are circular in plan view and are normally distinctly convex aborally, instead of being notably flattened. The periproct is endocyclic and the peristome contains an Aristotle's lantern.

Order a.   Perischoechinida

Perischoechinoids all have more than 20 rows of plates in the test, but the ways in which the rows can be arranged are diverse. In general there are as many as 14 rows of plates in the widest part of an interambulacrum and as many as 20 rows of plates with single pore pairs in the widest parts of the ambulacra. The size of the ancient echinoids (that is, width of rays) was adjusted by increase in the number of rows of plates from the apical system to the ambitus and then by decrease in the number of plates from the ambitus to the oral region. (Modern echinoids, on the other hand, retain only two rows of plates to a ray so the size of the test must be controlled by alteration in the sizes of the individual plates in the rays.) The Aristotle's lantern in the Perischoechinida is broadly V-shaped instead of being parallel-sided (Fig. 15.2.6).

The Order ranges from Mississippian to Permian, but recognizable specimens are very rare. Isolated plates probably occur in rocks of many Periods in the Paleozoic, but the plates cannot be determined to belong to the Perischoechinoida, if, indeed, they can be differentiated from ossicles of other echinoderms such as crinoids. As construed herein, the Perischoechinoida contain Genera which some authorities place in separate Orders.

Bothriocidaris, from the Upper Ordovician, is peculiar in possessing 15 rows of coronal plates, 2 in each ambulacral ray and 1 in each interambulacrum (Fig. 15.7.3). Inasmuch as there is only 1 plate at the summit of each interambulacral series in other echinoids, some paleontologists consider

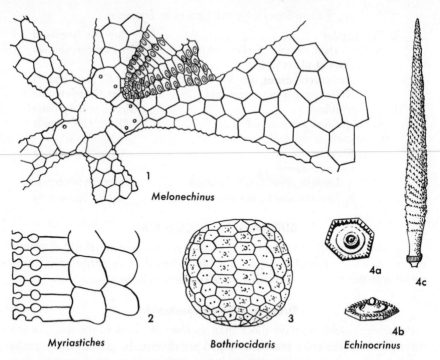

Figure 15.7.   Paleozoic Echinoids (Mostly Perischoechinida).
1. Expanded diagram of part of the summit of *Melonechinus indianensis*, 2X, Mississippian, midcontinent. 2. A few interambulacral and perforate ambulacral plates of the oldest echinoid, *Myriastiches gigas*, 12X, Ordovician, England. 3. Side view of *Bothriocidaris pahleni*, 2X, Ordovician, Russia. 4a, 4b, 4c. Plan and oblique views of an interambulacral plate, and a spine of *Echinocrinus* sp., 1X, Carboniferous, world-wide.
(1, 3, 4 after Jackson, 1912. 2 after Sollas, 1899.)

Bothriocidaris to be at the stem of the Class Echinoidea. On the contrary, other paleontologists now consider *Bothriocidaris* to be either a form of unknown ancestry which led to a dead end off the main line of echinoid evolution or a dead end developed as a highly specialized offshoot of diploporitan cystoids.

True echinoids contemporaneous with *Bothriocidaris* are unrelated to it, so the ancestral group of echinoids must be sought in older rocks. The oldest echinoid discovered is a single specimen from the Medial Ordovician of England; it is the basis of the Genus *Myriastiches*. This echinoid had a flexible test and more than 40 rows of interambulacral plates. Pore pairs lie in the sutures between adjacent ambulacral plates (Fig. 15.7.2).

Perhaps the most common specimens of Perischoechinoida are referable to *Melonechinus*, a Genus of cantaloupe-shaped Mississippian echinoids made famous by their discovery as a biostrome in a quarry at St. Louis, Missouri.

Order b.   Cidarida

Cidaroids are particularly characterized by the presence of a large, almost always perforate, primary spine base in the center of each large interambulacral plate (Fig. 15.8.1b, 4). Primary spines of cidaroids are almost unique in having a dense outer rind or cortex over a porous core. Although cidaroid spines may be wonderfully modified into large clubs, plates, saws, rasps, branches, hooks, and anastomosing intergrowths (Fig. 15.3), they are relatively light in weight because they may consist of only a little over one-third

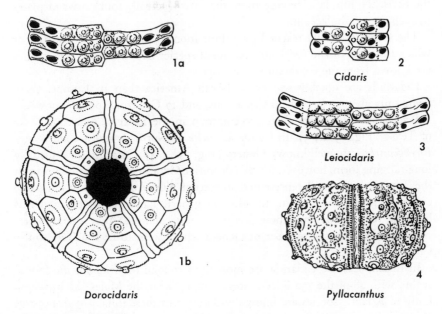

1a

Cidaris

2

Leiocidaris

3

1b

Dorocidaris   Pyllacanthus

4

Figure 15.8.   Cidarida.
   1. *Dorocidaris texanus*, Cretaceous, Gulf Coast. 1a, ambulacral plates, 6X. 1b, corona, 2/3X.   2. Ambulacral plates of *Cidaris splendens*, 5X, Eocene, Atlantic Coast. 3. Ambulacral plates of *Leiocidaris hemigranosus*, 5X, Cretaceous, Gulf Coast. 4. Side view of *Phyllacanthus mortoni*, 1X, Eocene, Atlantic Coast.
   (1-3 after Clark and Twitchell, 1915. 4 after Cooke, 1941.)

skeletal material—the rest being fleshy tissue. The narrow ambulacral areas of cidaroid coronas consist of simple plates which may lack spines. Cidaroids have an Aristotle's lantern.

Cidaroids are almost entirely modern types of echinoids; that is, with two rows of plates in each ray of a corona. The only exceptions to this rule are two or three Paleozoic Genera and the European Early Cretaceous Genus *Tetracidaris*. This latter Genus not only differs from all other post-Paleozoic cidaroids in having four rows of interambulacral plates in each ray, but it and the European Jurassic cidaroid, *Diplocidaris,* differ from other cidaroids in having overlapping biserial instead of uniserial pore pairs.

The oldest cidaroids so far discovered are from the Devonian of Iowa and Europe, but material of that age is extremely rare. By Carboniferous time, and to the end of the Paleozoic, cidaroids were relatively common, although they are usually represented by characteristic spine bases and spines of *Echinocrinus* (long known as *Archaeocidaris*). It seems that these ancient cidaroids had flexible tests with imbricating coronal plates—a condition not commonly encountered in post-Paleozoic echinoids. The Paleozoic cidaroids resemble the Perischoechinida in having more than two (actually four) rows of plates in each interambulacrum.

The Order Cidarida reached its culmination in the Jurassic of Europe at which time 251 of the 626 European fossil species lived. Another 228 species are known from the Cretaceous of Europe.

Cidaroids are notably scarcer in North America than in Europe, there being only about 3 Jurassic, 6 Cretaceous, and 17 Cenozoic species known.

Leiocidaris and *Dorocidaris* are common in the Lower Cretaceous rocks of Texas (Fig. 15.8.1, 3). In Cenozoic rocks of North America *Cidaris* and *Phyllacanthus* are well-known Genera (Fig. 15.8.2, 4). *Cidaris* is an unusually long-ranging form, however, for this primitive Genus not only is known from the Triassic but is still represented in Recent seas. About 45 post-Paleozoic cidaroid Genera are known. In addition generic names of 35 echinoderms bear the root *-cidaris* but these forms are not cidaroids; they therefore erroneously increase the number of Genera which seem to be referable to the Cidarida.

In Recent seas the Cidarida are most numerous in the Indo-Pacific faunal realm, with 48 of the 150 Recent species living near the Malay Archipelago. Only 16 Atlantic species are known and only 2 of these inhabit the ancestral cidaroid domain of Europe.

Order c.   Centrechinida

Regular echinoids with compound ambulacral plates are referred to the centrechinoids. Centrechinoids otherwise resemble the cidaroids very closely in general features and spinosity. Zoologists attach considerable importance to the structure of the lantern in this Order, using it as a basis for recognizing three Suborders. Unfortunately, these differences are based upon characters rarely preserved in fossils. The various Families are differentiated upon details of construction of the compound ambulacral plates. Diademoid-type and echinoid-type plates are recognized, and some systematists recognize several other modifications based upon the number of component plates and their distribution in the large compound units.

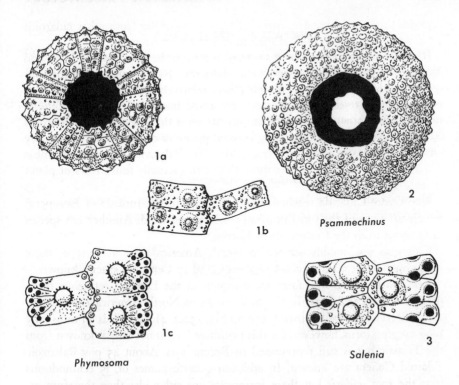

Figure 15.9. Centrechinida.
1. *Phymosoma texanum*, Cretaceous, Texas Gulf Coast. 1a, oral surface, 1X. 1b, interambulacral plates, 2X. 1c, ambulacral plates, 5X. 2. Oral surface of *Psammechinus philanthropus*, 1X, Miocene, Atlantic Coast. 3. Ambulacral plates of *Salenia texana*, 10X, Cretaceous, Texas Gulf Coast.
(After Clark and Twitchell, 1915.)

Phymosoma is probably the best-known extinct American centrechinoid (Fig. 15.9.1). It abounds locally in Lower Cretaceous strata on the Gulf Coast. *Phymosoma* can be differentiated from the cidaroids, which it closely resembles, by its imperforate tubercles, as well as by the compound ambulacral plates. The Order ranges from Jurassic to Recent.

Salenia is an Early Cretaceous Genus from Texas in which there is a dorsocentral plate in the center of the apical system, and the periproct is crowded over to one side. Ambulacral plates are of primitive construction (Fig. 15.9.3). *Arbacia* and *Psammechinus* (Fig. 15.9.2) are moderately common on the Atlantic Coast in Miocene rocks. *Strongylocentrotus* is a widespread Recent Genus which has been reported from Upper Cenozoic strata; its soft anatomy commonly is well known to student zoologists.

SUBCLASS 2.   IRREGULARIA

Irregular echinoids are rarely circular in plan view, but they may be subtly pentagonal; they are characteristically elongate, heart-shaped, and bilaterally symmetrical. The periproct is exocyclic. Some irregular echinoids bear a swollen and granular area on the oral surface in ray 5 which is called a **sternum.** An Aristotle's lantern is present in some groups and absent in others. All of the following four Orders are sometimes combined into the Order Exocycloida.

Order a.   Holectypida

Holectypoids are the least elongate and least bilaterally symmetrical of the exocyclic echinoids. Moreover, their ambulacral areas contain two rows

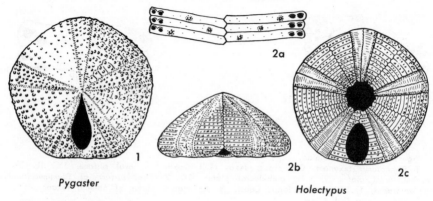

Pygaster

Holectypus

Figure 15.10.   Holectypida.
   1. Aboral surface of *Pygaster gresslyi,* 1X, Jurassic, France.   2. *Holectypus planatus,* Cretaceous, Texas Gulf Coast.   2a, ambulacral plates, 5X.   2a, 2b, posterior and oral views, 1X.
   (1 after Desor, 1858.   2 after Clark and Twitchell, 1915.)

of pores along their entire length, whereas petaloid ambulacra arise in the other three Orders. Holectypoids also tend to be rather convex aborally, or tent-shaped in profile. A lantern is present in many forms but tends to diminish in importance in the group and may be only in young individuals of some species. Concomitant reduction of the perignathic girdle accompanies decrease in the importance of the lantern.

Pygaster, from the Jurassic of Europe, is an unusually interesting form because it has a few compound plates and only a slightly exocyclic periproct; hence it has been considered as a possible link between the centrechinoid Regularia and the rest of the Irregularia (Fig. 15.10.1). *Holectypus* is the commonest example of the Holectypida (Fig. 15.10.2). It occurs abundantly in Lower Cretaceous strata on the Gulf Coast.

Order b.   Cassidulida

Cassiduloids are generally somewhat depressed on the aboral surface and normally contain radial partitions which support the upper surface. They tend to have petaloid or nearly petaloid ambulacra. An Aristotle's lantern is present in some Genera. Although most Genera have floscelles, they lack

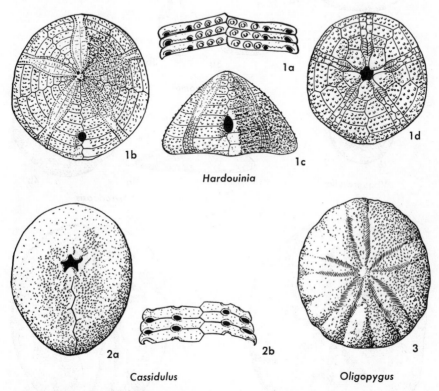

Figure 15.11. Cassidulida.
1. *Hardouinia florealis*, Cretaceous, Atlantic and Gulf Coastal Plains. 1a, ambulacral plates, 8X. 1b, 1c, 1d, aboral, posterior, and oral surfaces, 1X. 2. *Cassidulus conradi*, Eocene, Atlantic and Gulf Coastal Plains. 2a, oral surface, 1X. 2b, ambulacral plates, 8X. 3. Aboral surface of *Oligopygus haldemani*, 1X, Eocene, Georgia.
(After Clark and Twitchell, 1915.)

a sternum. The Order ranges from Jurassic to Recent.

Hardouinia occurs in Upper Cretaceous strata from New Jersey to Alabama (Fig. 15.11.1). *Cassidulus* is known from Cretaceous to Recent in many areas (Fig. 15.11.2). *Oligopygus* is a common Late Eocene Genus in the Atlantic Coastal Plain of Georgia and Florida (Fig. 15.11.3).

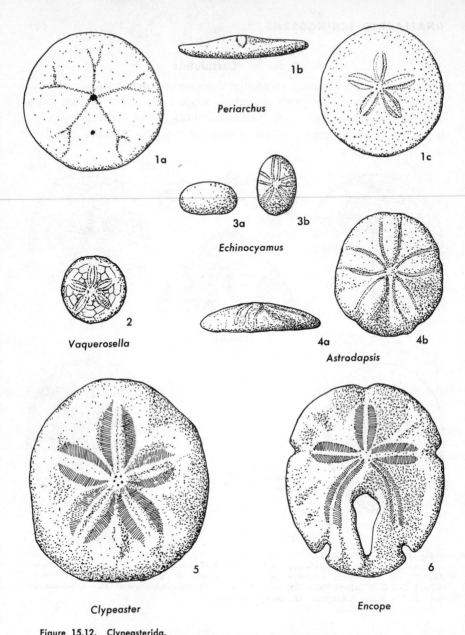

Periarchus

Echinocyamus

Vaquerosella

Astrodapsis

Clypeaster

Encope

Figure 15.12. Clypeasterida.
1. *Periarchus lyelli*, 1X, Eocene, Atlantic and Gulf Coastal Plains. 1a, 1b, 1c, oral, side, and aboral views. 2. Aboral surface of *Vaquerosella merriami*, 1X, Miocene, California. 3a, 3b. Side and aboral views of *Echinocyamus vaughani*, 2X, Oligocene, Georgia. 4a, 4b. Side and aboral surfaces of *Astrodapsis tumidus*, 1X, Miocene, California. 5. Aboral surface of *Clypeaster rogersi*, 2/3X, Oligocene, Atlantic and Gulf Coastal Plains. 6. Aboral surface of *Encope macrophora*, 1/2X, Pliocene, South Carolina.
(1, 3, 5, 6 after Clark and Twitchell, 1915. 2 after Grant and Hertlein, 1938. 4 after Kew, 1920.)

Order c. Clypeasterida

Clypeasteroids are the sand dollars. They are principally characterized by very flattened tests in which aboral surfaces are slightly convex but oral surfaces are usually plane or concave. Radially disposed pillars and laminae pervade the interior of the test and support the aboral surface (Fig. 15.2.2, 3). Spines are normally very small. An Aristotle's lantern is present, although it has 30 instead of the usual 40 pieces. Denuded tests normally bear conspicuous petaloid ambulacra. The periproct is on the oral surface, so the digestive track describes a large loop within the corona (Fig. 15.2.4). One group of Genera typified by *Encope* bears slots around the margin of the test.

Some of the most durable and stratigraphically useful fossils belong in this Order. Most of the representatives lived during the Cenozoic, although the group extends back to the Cretaceous time.

Echinocyamus (Cretaceous and Eocene to Recent) is unusual in having a more inflated shape than have the other members of the Clypeasterida (Fig. 15.12.3). *Periarchus* (Fig. 15.12.1) is very common in Upper Eocene strata from North Carolina to Louisiana, constituting the main element of the "*Scutella* beds." *Clypeaster* (Fig. 15.12.5) is pentagonal with rounded margins and a concave oral surface; it is common over the world from Eocene to Recent. *Vaquerosella* (Fig. 15.12.2) and *Astrodapsis* (Fig. 15.12.4) may be abundant in Miocene strata of California. In fact, a small species of *Vaquerosella* is so common locally that strata containing it are mapped as the "Button Beds." The culmination of the Order on the West Coast is met in *Dendraster* (Fig. 15.2.1–3), which was an important rock-maker in Pleistocene time and still lives off the California coast.

Order d. Spatangida

Heart urchins comprise the very abundant, diverse, and stratigraphically valuable Order Spatangida. The most characteristic features of the spatangoids are the notable bilateral symmetry and the presence of a sternum. In addition, some variable features such as the nature of fascioles, presence of petaloid as opposed to straight ambulacra, and aberrant development of some ambulacral rays are also very valuable for classification. No Aristotle's lantern is present. The Order appears in the Jurassic and is represented in Recent seas.

Holaster typifies a spatangoid group with linear rows of pores which have the same shapes in all of the ambulacra. Moreover, the ambulacra do not lie in grooves. The Genus contains valuable zonal fossils in the Lower Cretaceous of Texas and Oklahoma and occurs less commonly in outcrops on the Coastal Plain of the eastern states.

A second group of spatangoids is represented by *Enallaster, Macraster,*

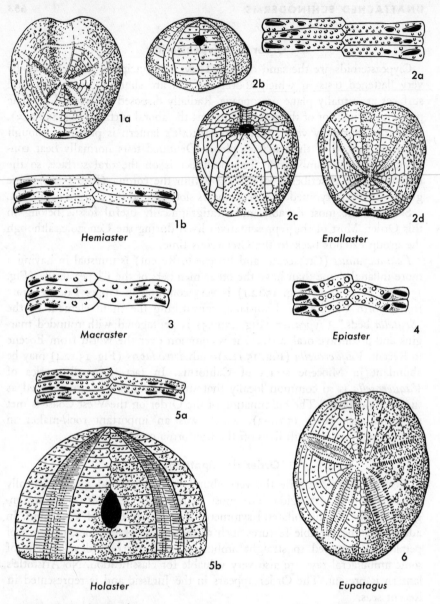

Figure 15.13. Spatangida.
1. *Hemiaster texanus*, Cretaceous, Texas Gulf Coast. 1a, aboral surface with fasciole, 2/3X. 1b, ambulacral plates, 8X. 2. *Enallaster texanus*, Cretaceous, Gulf Coastal Plain. 2a, plates from anterior ambulacrum, (III) 10X. 2b, 2c, 2d, posterior, oral, and oboral views, 1X. 3. Plates from the anterior ambulacrum of *Macraster elegans*, 5X, Cretaceous, Texas Gulf Coast. 4. Plates from the left anterolateral ambulacrum (IV) of *Epiaster whitei*, 8X, Cretaceous, Texas Gulf Coast. 5. *Holaster simplex*, Cretaceous, Gulf Coastal Plain. 5a, ambulacral plates, 3X. 5b, posteroir view 2/3X. 6. Aboral surface of *Eupatagus mooreanus*, 2/3X, Eocene, Florida. (After Clark and Twitchell, 1915.)

and *Epiaster* (Fig. 15.13.2–4) in the Lower Cretaceous of Texas. These Genera are characterized by the presence of shallow grooves on the corona, which contain at least some of the ambulacral rays. Moreover, pores in the different rays are differently shaped. In particular, ray III is long and contains one kind of pores, whereas the other four ambulacral rays are petaloid and all contain another pattern of pores. No fascioles are present.

The third group of spatangoids is characterized by the presence of fascioles. *Hemiaster* is a common Lower Cretaceous Genus on the Gulf Coast (Fig. 15.13.1), whereas Subgenera of *Eupatagus* are abundant in the Cenozoic strata of the southeastern United States (Fig. 15.13.6).

GEOLOGIC DISTRIBUTION OF ECHINOIDS. Although echinoids are known in rocks as old as Ordovician their remains are rarely encountered in strata older than Carboniferous. They may be locally abundant in carbonate sediments of the latter age. Paleozoic spines and tubercle-bearing hexagonal plates from disassociated tests are generally referred to *Echinocrinus* and to *Archaeocidaris*. Relatively complete Paleozoic specimens of echinoids are among the rarest of fossils.

After the extinction of the Paleozoic echinoids, or Perischoechinida, there was a nearly barren interval during the Triassic before the modern echinoids appeared in abundance in the Early Jurassic. North American Mesozoic echinoids are singularly abundant in Lower Cretaceous (Fredericksburg and Washita groups) sediments on the Gulf Coast. It is peculiar that echinoids are extremely rare in the Cretaceous deposits of the Rocky Mountain geosyncline, in spite of their great abundance to the south on the Gulf Coast. Only seven species have been reported from the western interior. Their scarcity may reflect their notable intolerance to brackish water or to changes in the salinity. In Europe, Cretaceous echinoids are abundant. Some of the best European echinoid fossils occur as silicified specimens in the Cretaceous chalk beds.

Cenozoic echinoids, both regular and irregular, are common in North America. They reached their peak of abundance and diversity on the southeastern Atlantic Coastal Plain during Late Eocene time, when about 61 of the 154 Cenozoic species of that region were living. Most of those species were only slightly flattened Irregularia. The peak of development on the Pacific Coast came a little later, during the Miocene and Pliocene Epochs, when flattened sand-dollar types were most abundant.

Some of the most interesting phenomena known in the science of geographic distribution are based upon the Cenozoic echinoids. It appears that echinoids on opposite sides of the Atlantic evolved from different stocks. By Eocene time the clypeasteroid stock dominated American waters, whereas the spatangoid stock dominated European seas. Then, in Miocene and Pliocene time, there was commingling of these two faunas on both sides of the Middle Atlantic. Oddly, however, the Late Tertiary faunas cannot be traced northward or southward around the Atlantic basin; they presumably were restricted to middle latitudes as a result of climatic control. It would appear, therefore, that echinoids must have migrated both eastward and westward across the mid-Atlantic. But a migration of this sort creates a paradox, because living echinoids are too sensitive to depth to migrate across the Atlantic basin, and the larval stages of echinoids do not last long enough for them to drift across. Yet shallow-water echinoids were able to populate both sides of the Atlantic Ocean in the Late Tertiary. As in the case of rudistoids and fresh-water molluscs and arthropods, the distribution of echinoids has been explained by land bridges, continental drift, and chance rafting of larvae or adult animals. The last two hypotheses (and especially the last) are currently defended by some or many biologists.

Class C.   Holothuroida

Holothurians are leathery sausage-shaped echinoderms which are principally characterized by their apparent lack of calcareous plates. Their shape, average size, and lengthwise banding of the ambulacral areas merit their common name of "sea cucumbers." Most of the holothurians rest on a slightly flattened side on the sea floor, but a few use tube feet to creep about or to burrow, and some even swim or float. They occur from the intertidal zone down to about 18,000 feet (6000 m). Although they may live in cool to cold water, they are most abundant in shallow tropical waters. Holothurians ingest sediments wholesale by pushing debris into the mouth with a ring of branching sticky tentacles. They are essentially scavengers. No doubt their digestive processes alter sediments materially in the course of extracting organic substances, after which the voided material possibly could be fossilized as castings.

The leathery skin of the holothurians generally contains microscopic calcareous **sclerites** in the form of wheels, anchors, tables, crosses, and spicular elements such as occur in sponges and in alcyonarian coelenterates (Fig. 15.14.2–9). Holothurian sclerites are useful in the recognition of Recent species, but not much has been published on their use in paleontology until recently. As micropaleontologic investigations are carried forward, holothurian sclerites presumably will be given increased attention.

Eocaudina, from the Medial Ordovician, is thought by some specialists to be the oldest known holothurian. It is represented by perforated sclerites (Fig. 15.14.7) which resemble sieve plates of larval crinoids; hence, other authorities think that *Eocaudina* may be a pelmatozoan. *Eothuria,* from Upper Ordovician strata of Scotland, is an unusual supposed holothurian with overlapping plates (Fig. 15.14.10). Fossil holothurian sclerites have been definitely identified in rocks as old as Mississippian and may be observed commonly in micropaleontologic materials from Carboniferous, Jurassic, and Cenozoic strata. Impressions of bodies are very rare, however, and generally have been questioned. Impressions have been reported from the Middle Cambrian of British Columbia and Ireland, but at least some of these fossils seem to be equally referable to the soft-bodied coelenterates such as the sea

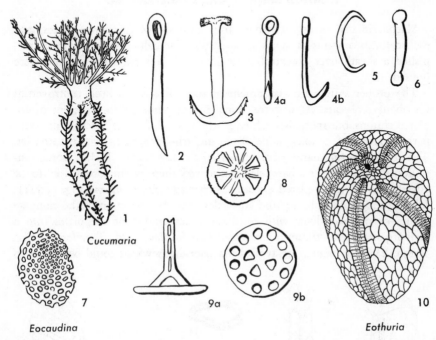

Cucumaria

Eocaudina   Eothuria

Figure 15.14. Holothurians.
 1. Side view of *Cucumaria* sp., showing oral tentacles and three rows of tube feet, about 1/3X, Recent. 2. Needle, enlarged, Mississippian, Scotland. 3. Anchor, 150X, Recent. 4a, 4b, two views of a hook, 25X, Jurassic, France. 5. C-shaped body, 20X, Jurassic, France. 6. Rod, 20X, Jurassic, Germany. 7. Wheel of *Eocaudina cribriformis*, one of the oldest holothurians, 20X, Ordovician, Illinois. 8. Wheel, 150X, Recent. 9a, 9b. Schematic side and basal views of a table, enlarged. 10. Reconstruction of *Eothuria* sp., a plated holothurian, 1X, Ordovician, Scotland.
 (1, 2, 4-7, 9 after Frizzell and Exline, 1955. 3, 8 after Clark, 1901. 10 after Macbride and Spencer, 1938.)

anemones. Several supposed body impressions are recorded from Jurassic strata in Europe, as at Solenhofen. About 1000 living species have been described.

Holothurians are used as food in southeast Asia under the names trepang and bêche-de-mer. This commodity is processed by splitting open the bodies and then drying, salting, or smoking them. Some holothurians are dredged commercially for food off western North America.

Holothurians are unique among echinoderms because a few of them have the ability to produce new individuals by budding. In company with this is their extraordinary power of regeneration. They may eviscerate themselves when disturbed and then regenerate an entirely new digestive track and parts of the water vascular system.

Incertae Sedis: Class Machaeridia

Machaeridians consist of two to four columns of calcareous plates, and each column contains as many as 60 plates. The columns seem to have furnished a sheath over a central space in which soft parts presumably were housed.

The proper systematic assignment of these fossils has been controversial for about 100 years. At first the remains were thought to represent multi-plated chitons, but specialists subsequently decided that the Machaeridia were parts of stems of cystoids, annelid worms, trilobites, or primitive barnacles. The consensus for many years supported the last theory. In fact, some outstanding authorities on barnacles considered these anomalous fossils to be ancestral to the many-plated Cretaceous barnacle, *Stramentum* (Fig. 13.9.11). It was thought that the lepadid barnacles arose by reduction of the elongate bodies of machaeridians with resultant concentration of the plates into a well-organized capitulum or crown. *Lepidocoleus* and *Turrilepas* (Fig. 15.15.1, 2) in particular are typical machaeridians which could be placed in

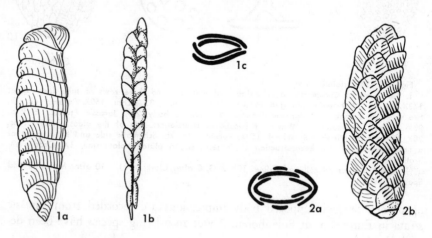

Lepidocoleus

Turrilepas

Figure 15.15. Machaeridia.
1a, 1b, 1c. Side view, edge view, and cross section of *Lepidocoleus sarlei*, 1X, Silurian, New York. 2a, 2b. Cross section and side view of *Turrilepas wrighti*, 1 2/3X, Silurian, England.
(1a, 1b after Clarke, 1896. 1c, 2b after Withers, 1915.)

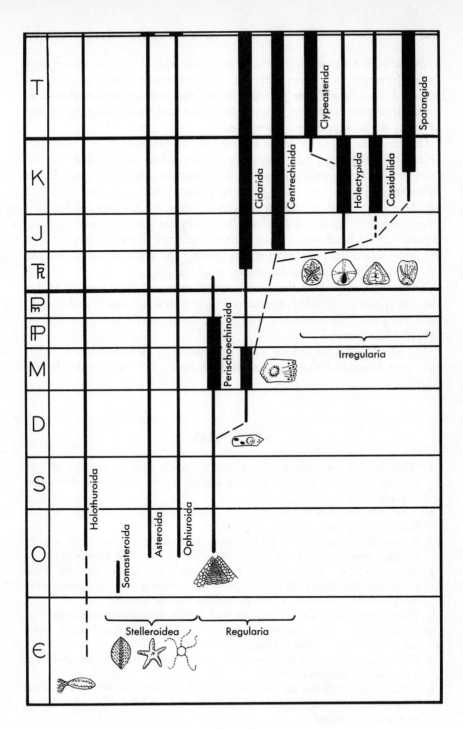

Figure 15.16. Geologic Distribution of Eleutherozoa.

a morphologic series leading up to lepadid barnacles. *Turrilepas,* as one may gather from the name, was supposed to be a barnacle when its name was coined. It is certainly true that the shapes and external ornamentation of machaeroid plates resemble plates of barnacles, and the overlapping pattern of plates is also suggestive of barnacles.

On the other hand, the plates of some of the Machaeridia are composed of calcite which comprises a single crystallographic unit. Ossicles of this kind are otherwise only known to be present among the Echinoderma. Moreover, the inner surfaces of plates may bear a netlike ornamental pattern which is reminiscent of interior surfaces of some echinoderm ossicles. It is interesting that remains of Machaeridia usually are associated with cystoids. Apparently the Machaeridia must either be referred to the Echinoderma, or we must believe that skeletal remains bearing the crystallographic features of echinoderms are present in another Phylum.

The latest theory about the nature and affinity of the Machaeridia is that they are distinctly different organisms which represent an early evolutionary offshoot of the Echinoderma, and in which the symmetry is strictly bilateral instead of pentameral.

The Machaeridia range from Early Ordovician to Medial Devonian. They have been found in Europe and in North America, but are exceedingly rare fossils.

QUESTIONS

1. What bearing does the distribution of echinoids have on theories of continental drift, land bridges, and the probability of transoceanic rafting of animals?
2. What characteristics of echinoids and crinoid stems plates would have made them awe-inspiring to medieval people?
3. If some Recent species of echinoids were differentiated on the basis of pedicellariae, how should a paleontologist handle problems of synonymy?
4. What conditions might have prevented the Gulf Coast echinoids from populating the Rocky Mountain geosyncline during the Cretaceous, even though cephalopods were common between the two areas?
5. What features diminish the usefulness of starfish in stratigraphic studies?
6. What evidence of a paleontologic nature seems to bear most directly upon the ancestry of the Class Echinoidea?
7. What characteristics of holothurian morphology and habit might encourage a paleontologist to study them?
8. What features enhance the value of echinoids in evolutionary studies? What features of echinoids enhance or diminish the usefulness of echinoids in stratigraphic studies?

9. How could recognized authorities fail so completely to agree upon the systematic assignment of the Machaeridia?

10. Why are ontogenetic series of fossil echinoids almost impossible to obtain?

BIBLIOGRAPHY

Barrande, J., 1887, Système Silurien du Centre de la Bohême: Recherches Paléontologiques, Echinodermes, pt. 1, Cystidées, v. 7, Praha.

Bassler, R. S., 1935, The classification of the Edrioasteroidea: Smithsonian Misc. Coll., v. 93, no. 8, pp. 1-11.

Bather, F. A., 1890-1892, British fossil crinoids: Annals Mag. Nat. Hist., ser. 6, v. 5, pp. 306-334, 373-388, 485, 486; ser. 6, v. 6, pp. 222-235; ser. 6, v. 7, pp. 35-40, 389-413; ser. 6, v. 9, pp. 189-226.

————, 1900, *in* Lankester, E. R., A treatise on zoology, pt. III, The Echinoderma: London, Adam and Charles Black.

Billings, E., 1858, On the Cystidae of the Lower Silurian rocks of Canada: Canada Geol. Survey, Canadian Org. Remains, dec. 3, pp. 9-74.

————, 1859, On the Crinoideae of the Lower Silurian rocks of Canada: Canada Geol. Survey, Canadian Org. Remains, dec. 4, pp. 7-66.

Branson, E. B., and Peck, R. E., 1940, A new cystoid from the Ordovician of Oklahoma: Jour. Paleont., v. 14, no. 2, pp. 89-92.

Butts, C., 1926, The Paleozoic rocks: Alabama Geol. Survey Spec. Rept. 14, pp. 41-230.

Caster, K. E., 1952, Concerning Enopleura of the Upper Ordovician and its relation to other carpoid Echinodermata: Bull. Amer. Paleont., v. 34, no. 141, pp. 5-47.

Clark, A. H., 1915-1931, A monograph of the existing crinoids: U. S. Nat. Mus., Bull. 82, vs. 1-3.

Clark, H. L., 1901, Synopses of North American invertebrates. XV. The Holothurioidea: Amer. Naturalist, v. 35, pp. 479-496.

Clarke, J. M., 1896, The structure of certain Paleozoic barnacles: Amer. Geol., v. 17, no. 3, pp. 137-143.

Cline, L. M., 1937, Blastoids of the Osage group, Mississippian: pt. II. The Genus *Cryptoblastus*: Jour. Paleont., v. 11, no. 8, pp. 634-649.

Coe, W. R., 1912, Echinoderms of Connecticut: Connecticut Geol. Nat. Hist. Survey, Bull. 19.

Cooke, C. W., 1941, Cenozoic regular echinoids of eastern United States: Jour. Paleont., v. 16, no. 1, pp. 1-62.

Croneis, C., and McCormack, J., 1932, Fossil Holothuroidea: Jour. Paleont., v. 6, no. 2, pp. 111-148.

Cuénot, L., 1891, Études Morphologiques sur les Echinodermes: Arch. Biol., v. 11, pp. 313-680.

Desor, E., 1858, Synopsis des Echinides Fossiles: Paris and Weisbaden, 490 pp., atlas.

Duncan, P. M., 1885, On the structure of the ambulacra of some fossil Genera and species of regular Echinoidea: Geol. Soc. London Quart. Jour., v. 41, pp. 419–453.

Durham, J. W., 1955, Classification of clypeasteroid echinoids: Univ. California Pubs. Geol. Sci., v. 31, no. 4, pp. 73–198.

——, and Melville, R. V., 1957, A classification of echinoids: Jour. Paleont., v. 31, no. 1, pp. 242–272.

Foerste, A. F., 1916, Comarocystites and Caryocrinites. Cystids with pinnuliferous free arms: Ottawa Naturalist (Canadian Field Naturalist), v. 30, pp. 69–79, 85–93.

Frizzell, D. L., and Exline, H., 1955, Monograph of fossil holothurian sclerites: Univ. Missouri Bull., Sch. Mines Metall., Tech. Ser., no. 89.

Galloway, J. J., and Kaska, H. V., 1957, Genus *Pentremites* and its species: Geol. Soc. America, Mem. 69.

Geis, H. L., 1936, Recent and fossil pedicellariae: Jour. Paleont., v. 10, no. 6, pp. 427–448.

Goldring, W., 1923, Devonian crinoids of New York: New York State Mus., Mem. 16.

Grant, U. S., IV, and Hertlein, L. G., 1938, The west American Cenozoic Echinoidea: Univ. California Pubs., Math. Phys. Sci., v. 2.

Gregory, J. W., 1892, The relations of the American and European echinoid faunas: Geol. Soc. America Bull., v. 3, pp. 101–108.

Hambach, G., 1903, Revision of the Blastoidea, etc.: Trans. St. Louis Acad. Sci., v. 13, pp. 1–68.

Hawkins, H. L., 1919, The morphology and evolution of the ambulacrum in the Echinoidea Holectypoida: Phil. Trans. Roy. Soc. London, ser. B., v. 209, pp. 377–480. (Contains bibliographic references to papers on evolutionary patterns in echinoids.)

——, 1944, Evolution and habit among the Echinoidea: some facts and theories: Geol. Mag., v. 99, pp. lii–lxxv.

Hudson, G. H., 1907, On some Pelmatozoa from the Chazy limestone of New York: New York State Mus., Bull. 107, pp. 97–152.

Jackson, R. T., 1912, Phylogeny of the Echini with a revision of Paleozoic species: Boston Soc. Nat. Hist., Mem., v. 7.

Kew, W. S. W., 1920, Cretaceous and Cenozoic Echinoidea of the Pacific Coast of North America: Univ. California Pubs., Bull. Dept. Geol., v. 12, no. 2, pp. 23–236.

Kirk, E., 1911, The structure and relationships of certain eleutherozoic Pelmatozoa: Proc. U. S. Nat. Mus., v. 41, pp. 1–137.

——, 1937, *Eupachycrinus* and related Carboniferous crinoid Genera: Jour. Paleont., v. 11, no. 7, pp. 598–607.

Laudon, L. R., in Weller, J. M., *et al.*, 1948, Correlation of Mississippian formations of North America: Geol. Soc. America Bull., v. 59, no. 1, pp. 91–196.

MacBride, E. W., and Spencer, W. K., 1938, Two new Echinoidea, etc.: Phil. Trans. Roy. Soc. London, ser. B, v. 229, no. 558, pp. 91–136.

Mead, A. D., 1901, The natural history of star-fish: Bull. U. S. Fish Comm., v. 19 (1899), pp. 203–224.

Meek, F. B., 1873, Description of invertebrate fossils of the Silurian and Devonian Systems: Ohio Geol. Survey, v. 1, pp. 1–243.

——, and Worthen, A. H., 1873, Descriptions of invertebrates from Carboniferous System: Illinois Geol. Survey, v. 5, pp. 324–619.

Moore, R. C., 1938, The use of fragmentary crinoidal remains in stratigraphic paleontology: Denison Univ. Bull., Jour. Sci. Labs., v. 33, pp. 165–250.

——, and Laudon, L. R., 1941, Symbols for crinoid parts: Jour. Paleont., v. 15, no. 4, pp. 412–423.

——, and Laudon, L. R., 1943, Evolution and classification of Paleozoic crinoids: Geol. Soc. America Spec. Paper 46.

——, and Plummer, F. B., 1939, Crinoids from the Upper Carboniferous and Permian strata in Texas: Univ. Texas Pub. 3945, pp. 9–468.

Mortensen, T., 1927, Handbook of the echinoderms of the British Isles: London, Oxford Univ. Press, 471 pp.

——, 1928–1948, A monograph of the Echinoidea, pts. I–IV: Copenhagen, C. A. Reitzel; London, H. Milford.

Schmidt, F., 1874, Über einige neue und wenig bekannte baltischsilurische Petrefacten: Mem. Acad. Imp. Sci. St. Petersburg, ser. 7, v. 21, no. 11.

Schuchert, C., 1904, On Siluric and Devonic Cystidea and Camarocrinus: Smithsonian Misc. Coll., v. 47, pp. 201–272.

——, 1915, Revision of Paleozoic Stelleroidea with special reference to North American Asteroidea: U. S. Nat. Mus., Bull. 88.

Smiser, J. S., 1933, A study of the echinoid fragments in the Cretaceous rocks of Texas: Jour. Paleont., v. 7, no. 2, pp. 123–163.

Sollas, W. J., 1899, Fossils in the University Museum, Oxford. I. On Silurian Echinoidea and Ophiuroidea: Geol. Soc. London, Quart. Jour., v. 55, pp. 692–715.

Spencer, W. K., 1914–1940, A monograph of the British Paleozoic Asterozoa, pts. I–X: Palaeontographical Society (London).

——, 1951, Early Paleozoic starfish: Phil. Trans. Roy. Soc. London, ser. B, no. 623, v. 235, pp. 87–129.

Springer, F., 1901, *Uintacrinus*: its structure and relations: Mus. Comp. Zool. (Harvard), Mem., v. 25, pp. 1–89.

——, 1911a, On a Trenton echinoderm fauna at Kirkfield, Ontario: Canada Dept. Mines, Geol. Survey Br., Mem. 15–P.

——1911b, Some new American fossil crinoids: Mus. Comp. Zool. (Harvard), Mem., v. 25, pp. 117–161.

——, 1917, On the crinoid Genus Scyphocrinus and its bulbous root Camarocrinus: Smithsonian Inst. Pub. 2440.

——, 1920, The Crinoidea Flexibilia: Smithsonian Inst. Pub. 2501.

——, 1926, American Silurian crinoids: Smithsonian Inst. Pub. 2871.

Storer, T. I., and Usinger, R. L., 1957, General zoology: New York, McGraw-Hill Book Co., 3rd ed., 700 pp.

Verrill, A. E., 1882, Notice of the remarkable marine fauna occupying the outer banks off the southern coast of New England: Amer. Jour. Sci., ser. 3, v. 23, pp. 135–142.

Volborth, A., 1846, Über die russischen Sphaeroniten, eingeleitet durch einige Betrachtungen über die Arme der Cystideen: Verhandl., kaiserl.-russ. Mineral. Ges. St. Petersburg, 1845–1846 (Vserossüskoe mineralogicheskoe obshchestvo, Leningrad, Zapiski), pp. 161–198.

Wachsmuth, C., and Springer, F., 1879–1885, Revision of the Palaeocrinoidea, pts. I–III: Proc. Acad. Nat. Sci. (Philadelphia).

Walcott, C. D., 1886, Second contribution to the studies of the Cambrian faunas of North America: U. S. Geol. Survey, Bull. 30.

Weller, S., 1920, The geology of Hardin County: Illinois Geol. Survey, Bull. 41.

Whitehouse, F. W., 1941, The Cambrian faunas of north-eastern Australia, pt. 4: Early Cambrian echinoderms similar to the larval stages of Recent forms: Mem. Queensland Mus., v. 12, pt. 1, pp. 1–28.

Withers, T. H., 1915, Some Paleozoic fossils referred to the Cirripedia: Geol. Mag., n. ser., dec. 6, v. 2, pp. 112–123.

———, 1926, Catalogue of the Machaeridia: London, British Mus. (Nat. Hist.).

Wood, E., 1909, A critical summary of Troost's unpublished manuscript on the crinoids of Tennessee: U. S. Nat. Mus., Bull. 64.

Woodward, H., 1865, On the discovery of a new Genus of Cirripedia in the Wenlock limestone and shale of Dudley: Geol. Soc. London Quart. Jour., v. 21, pp. 486–489.

COMPREHENSIVE QUESTIONS

1. What qualities of corals, brachiopods, cephalopods, and echinoderms enable their classification to be carried to minor taxa more readily than can the classifications of sponges, pelecypods, and gastropods?
2. What relationships might exist between ease of classification of fossils and their use in stratigraphic paleontology?
3. In what ways have some skeletal structures of various animals been modified to serve different functions?
4. What scientific developments possibly will transpire before some fossils referred to "Incertae Sedis" will be referred to some taxon with confidence?
5. Why should research involving mathematical, physical, or chemical examination of animals (living or extinct) be supported by competent studies of their nomenclature and systematics?
6. Why can complicated fossils be identified more readily, and be identified from less complete specimens, than can simply constructed animals?
7. What evidence indicates that some animals may have occupied different environments in the past than their descendants do today? How common is the phenomenon?
8. What are some paleontologic phenomena which bear on the philosophy of continental drift?
9. If you were in some remote place (even as a member of a space expedition) where our life forms are represented, and you needed to send back the smallest possible collection of fossils to a laboratory, what would you dispatch in order to convey the most significant information about:
   a. The complexity of evolution,
   b. The range of life from Cambrian to Recent,
   c. The diversity of environments.
10. By what academic study is paleontology likely to profit most in the future? Why? Which groups of invertebrates seem to offer the best opportunities for research in the geologic province in which you live?

INDEX

Genera and species are indicated by italics. Pages on which illustrations occur are indicated by boldface type.

Abdomen, 484, **525**, 564, **565**, 568
Acanthin, 91
Acanthodesia oblongula, **271**
Acanthopore, 265
Acanthoscaphites nodosus var. *brevis,* **453**
  roemeri, **453**
Acanthotelson, 563
  stimsoni, **565**
Acanthoteuthis, 472, **476**
Acarida, 535
Acceleration, 170, 387
Acetabulum, **638**
Acidaspis, 513
  romingeri, **514**
Acila, **342**, 343, **352**
  shumardi, **342**
Acline, 345
Acontia, **157**, 158
Acropora, 197, 239
  muricata, **198**
Actaeon, 400
  ovoides, **399**
Actaeonella, 400
  oviformis, **399**
Actinida, 193
Actinoceras, **414**
Actinophrys sol, **58**
Actinopoda, 91
Actinostroma, 147, 148
  clathratum, **147**
Actissa princeps, **58**
Adapertural, 408
Adapical, 408
Adductor muscles, of brachiopods, 282
  of pelecypods, 335
Adradial suture, 639, **642**
Adunate, 612
Adventitious, 435

Aechmina cuspidata, **551**
Aegialia, **571**
Aeglina, 495
  prisca, **494**
Aeschna, **571**
Aganaster, 634
  gregarius, **632**
Agaricia, 197, **199**
Agassizocrinus, 619
  conicus, **617**
Agathiceras, 440
  frechi, **441**
Aglaspida, 522
Aglaspis, 523
  spinifer, **522**
Aglaurides, **221**
Agnostids, 507
Agnostus, 492, 508
  interstrictus, **507**
Agoniatites vanuxemi, **439**
Ajacicyathus nevadensis, **119**
Alar pseudofossula, 169, **170**
Albertella helenae, **510**
Alcyonaria, 188
Alcyonidium polyoum, **249**
Alcyonium, **190**
Alectryonia, 352
  carinata, **353**
  falcata, **353**
Allomorphic, 345
Alternation of generations, in coelenterates, 125
  in foraminifers, 64
Alveolinid, 78, **84**, **86**
Alveolus, 71, **72**, **467**
Amaurellina, 396
  clarki, **398**
Ambitus, 636

667

Amblyomma, **534**
Amblysiphonella, 114
  barroisi, **115**
  prosseri, **115**
Ambonychia bellistriata, **346**
Ambulacral area, 594, 638
  petaloid, 640
Ambulacral groove, 586
Ambulacrum, 599
Amiskwia sagittiformis, **216**
Ammobaculites, 66
  flariformis, **67**
Ammonite, 458
Ammonites, 437
Ammonitina, 458
Ammonoidea, 429
  apertures, 429, **430**
  classification, 437
  extinction, 478
  geologic history, 462, **467**
  key, 438
  opercula, 432
  origin, 460
  ornamentation, 432
  ranges of sutural patterns, **464**
  shapes of conchs, 429
  siphuncle, 431
  sutures, 433, **434, 436**
  terminology for conchs, 430, **432**
Amoeba proteus, **59**
Amoebina, 59
Amorphognathus, **232**
Amphictene auricoma, **225**
Amphidetic, 338
Amphineura, 320
Amphipods, 564
Amphipora, 149, 150
  ramosa, **150**
Amphissites exiguus, **550**
Amphorellopsis, **93**
Amplexoid retreat, 171
Amplexopora pustulosa, 254, **257**
Amplexus, 171, 179
  bicostatus, **178**
  rockfordensis, **178**
Ampulla, 130, 587
Ampullaria, 383, 390, 404
Anaklinoceras reflexum, **452**
Anal sac, **617**, 618
Anaptychus, 431
Anarcestes, 462
Anarcestina, 439
Anascina, 266
Anastomopora, 261
  cinctuta, **261**
Ancestroecium, **241, 242**

Anchura lobata, **385**
Ancistroteuthis lichtensteini, **473**
Ancyrocrinus, 606
  spinosus, **607**
Ancyrodella, **230**
Andriopora, **267**
Animal Kingdom, composition, 4, **5**;
  qualitative, **7**; quantitative, **6**
Anisomyarian, 335
Anisomyariida, 345
Annelida, 217
  ancestor of trilobites, **506**
Annular ornamentation, 420
Anolotichia spinulifera, **248**
Anomia, 345
  epihippioides, **346**
Anomphalus, 378
Anostylostroma, 148
  hamiltonense, **147**
Ant, 571
Antedon, 606, **625**, 626
Antenna, **545**, 562
Antennule, 500, **501, 545**, 562
Anterior bar, **229**
Antetheca, 70
Anthocyrtium, 92
Anthozoa, 156
  classification, 159
  morphology, **157**
  skeletal features, 158
  zoological features, 156
Anthracoblattina, **571**
Anthracomya, 362
  elongata, **361**
Anthrapalaemon, 566
  gracilis, **565**
Antipathes subpinnata, **207**
Antipathida, 206
Antiquatonia hermosana, **315**
Anus, **334**, 372, **374**
Apatobolbina granifera, **549**
Apertural bar, **266, 267**
Apertural face, 260
Aperture, 267, **371**, 372, 379
  digitate, **380**
  entire, 379, **380**
  secondary, **267**
Apex, 167, **371**, 372, 466, **467**
Aphroid, 168
Apicad, 430
Apical, angle, 168, **371, 377**
  callus, **295**, 296
  plate, 242
  surface, 631
  system, 635, **643**

Appendages, of eurypterids, **527**
  of malacostracans, 565
  of trilobites, 499, **500**
Apterygota, 572
Aptychus, 431
Apus, **542**
Arabella, 223
Arabellites, 223
  alfredensis, **221, 222**
Arachnoid, 173
Arachnoida, 531
Araneida, 533
Arbacia, 649
Arca, **332, 340,** 343
  ponderosa, **344**
Arcestes, 447
  gabbi, **449**
Archaeoantennularia byersi, **128**
Archaeocidaris, 648, 655
Archaeocyatha, 118
  geologic distribution, **120**
Archaeocyathellus, **119**
Archaeogastropods, 391
Archaeolepas, **556, 558**
Archaeophiala, 390
  antiquissima, **389**
Archaeotrypa, 247
  prima, **246**
Archiannelida, 218
Archimedes, **259,** 262, 281
  distans, **259**
  invaginatus, **259**
Archiococeras, **416,** 421, 424
Architeuthis, 472
  princeps, **473**
Arcoid, 343
Arctinurus, 513
  boltoni, **514**
Arenicolites, 226
Argonauta, 474
  argo, **475**
Aristocystites, 592, 593, 598
  bohemicus, **591, 593**
Aristotle's lantern, 644
Armadillidium, 563
Arms, of coleoids, 465; sessile, 465; tentacular, 465, **469**
  of crinoids, 607, **609**; biserial, **609**; heterotomous, 608; isotomous, 608; pinnulate, **609**; unbranched, 608; uniserial, **609**
  of echinoderms, 586
  of stelleroids, 630
Arthroclema striatum, **261**
Arthropoda, 484
  classification, 486

Articular furrow, 491
Articular surface, 606
Articulata, 288, 624
  cardinal margin, 293, **295**
  classification, 298
  dorsal interiors, 297
  key, 301
  ornamentation, 292
  shape, 291
  shell structure, 288, **290**
  ventral interiors, 296
Articulate, 282
Ascandra reticulum, **100**
Ascaris, **216**
Ascoceras, 421, **425,** 428
  manubrium, **425**
Ascocerids, 421
Ascodictyon floreale, **249**
Asconoid, 102
Ascophorina, 266
Ascopore, 266
Ascus, 265
Asteractine, 106
Asteractinella, 110, **111**
  audax, **111**
Asteractis, 193
  expansa, **192**
Asterias, 605
Asteroblastus, 602
  stellatus, **602**
Asteroid, **632**
Asteroida, 633
Astraeospongium, 110
  meniscus, **111**
Astrhelia, 198
  palmata, **200**
Astrocoenia guadalupae, **198**
Astrocoeniina, 197
Astrodapsis, 653
  tumidus, **652**
Astroid, 168
Astrorhiza, **145**
Astrorhiza, **62,** 65
Astrorhizicae, 65, **66, 86**
Astylospongia, 110
  praemorsa, **109**
Atactrites, 466
  clavatulus, **467**
Athyris angelica var. *occidentalis,* **299**
  spiriferoides, **310**
Atlanta, 399
  cunicula, **401**
Atremida, 286
Atrina, **332**
Atrypa, 307
  reticularis, **299, 308**

Aturia, 427
  alabamensis, **426**
  curvilinea, **426**
  luculoensis, **426**
Aturoidea, 427
  paucifex, **426**
Aucella, 347
  piochii, **346**
Aulacoceras, 466
Aulacophyllum, 179
  sulcatum, **180**
Aulocera, 146, 149
  plummeri, **147**
Aulopora, 161
  elleri, **164**
Auloporidae, 161
Auluroid, **632**
Aurelia flavidula, **151**
Aureole, 641, **642**
Auricle, 348, **352, 372, 374**
Auriform, **376,** 377
Austinoceras, 421
Autocorallite, 163
Autotheca, 134, **135,** 136
Auxiliary, 435
Avicula, **328**
Avicularium, **241,** 243
Aviculoecium, 243, **267**
Aviculopecten. 348
  exemplarius, **350**
Axial filling, 74
Axial furrow, **488,** 489
Axial lobe, **488, 489**
Axial ring, 491
Axial section, **70**
Axillary, 608
Axis of divergence, 196
Aysheaia, 488
  pedunculata, **487**
Azygograptus, **140,** 141, 143

Bactrites, 462
  arkonensis, **462**
  schlotheimi, **462**
Baculites, 454, 456, **457**
  codyensis, **456**
  compressus, **456**
  grandis, 454, **456**
  ovatus, **452, 456**
Bairdia beedei, **550**
Balanus, 555, 558, **559**
  concavus chesapeakensis, **560**
  gregarius, 559
Bankia setacea, **359**
Bar, 228, **229**

Barbatia, 343
  phalarca, **344**
Barnacles, 554
  acorn, 555
  balanid, 558, **560**
  compartments, **559**
  lepadid, **556,** 557
  sessile, 554
Barnea, 357
  costata, **359**
Barrande, J., 381, 418, 502
Barroisia, 114
Basal disc, 195
Base, **638**
Basicoronal system, 635, 644
Basis, 558
Bassleratia typa, **550**
Bathysiphon parallelus, **66**
Batocrinus, 624
  cantonensis, **623**
Batostoma decipiens, **253**
  imperfecta, **257**
  variabile, **254**
  winchelli, **253**
Beak, 281, **412**
Beania mirabilis, **241**
Beecher, C. E., 500, 502
Beekite rings, 21
Belemnitella, 466
  americana, **467**
Belemnitida, 466
Belemnosis, 470, **476**
Belemnoteuthis, 472
Belinurus lacoei, **525**
Bellerophon, **393**
Bellerophontoids, 393
Beloitoceras lycum, **422**
Bembexia, 392
  sulcomarginata, **392**
Benthos, 29
Bernard, F., 338
Bethanyphyllum, 179
  robustum, **180**
Beyrichia fittsi, **546**
  moodeyi, **549**
Bigenerina, 66, 81
  nodosaria, **67**
Bighornia, 179
  parva, **178**
Billingsites, 423, **425**
Bilobites bilobus, **304**
Binomen, 14
Biofacies, 30
Biogenetic Law, 32

Bioherm, 202
Biologic niche, 167
Biostrome, 202
Biramous, 485
Birotule, 106
Black corals, 206
Blade, 228
Blastoidea, 598
  evolution, 602
  geologic distribution, 604, **627**
  melonlike, 604
  pentremitid, 604
  summits, **601**
  truncate, 604
  water vascular system, **600**
Blastoidocrinus, 602
  carchariadens, **602**
Blastostyle, 127
Blothrophyllum, 171, 181
  decorticum, **180**
Blue coral, 189
Bochianites, 454
Body wall, **157**
Body whorl, 371
Bolivina, 81
  interjuncta, **80**
Bollia burgeneri, **550**
Bolloceras, **424**
Book lungs, 520
Border, of ostracodes, 547
  of trilobites, **488, 489**
Borelis, 83
  melo, **84**
  schlumbergeri, **84**
Borings, 21
Boseites, 445
  scotti, 445, **446**
  texanus, 445, **446**
Boss, 641, **642**
Bothriocidaris, 645
  pahleni, **646**
Brachia, 279
Brachidium, 288
Brachiole, 590
Brachiophore, 298
Brachiopoda, 278
  classification, 285
  composition, 280
  geologic distribution, 320, **321**
  key, 301
  living animal, 278
  musculature, 282
  orientation, 281
Brachythyris subcardiiformis, **308**
Bradoria robusta, **542**
Branch, 260

Branchiopoda, 542
  egg capsules, **544**
  ornamentation, **544**
Branchipus, **542**
Brevicoceras, 417
Brevicone, **416, 417**
Brim, 489
Brontia, 634
Brood pouch, 550
Brooksella, 150
  alternata, **151**
Brown body, **241, 242, 254,** 260
Bryantodus, **230,** 234
Bryograptus, 139, **140,** 141
Bryozoa, 239
  classification, 243
  geologic distribution, **272, 273**
  growth, 250; bifoliate, 250; frondose, 250; incrusted, 250; massive, 250; ramose, 250; unilamellar, 250
  key, 244
  morphology, 241
  walls, 255; amalgamate, 255; integrate, 255
Buchia, 347
Budding, of coelenterates, **125;** calical, 168; lateral, 168; parricidal, 168
  of sponges, 103
  simultaneous, 242
  successive, 242
Bulimina, 81
  jacksonensis, **80**
Buliminicae, 79, **86**
Buliminid, 79
Bulla, 400
  striata waltonensis, **399**
Bumastus, 495, 511, 518
  barriensis, **512**
Buoyancy of conchs, 427, **457**
Burlingia, 497, 515
  hectori, **517**
Burrows, 21
Buskopora, **248**
Busycon canaliculatum, **395**
Butterfly, **571**
Byssal notch, 348, **352**
Byssal thread, 332, 335

Cacalydus, **571**
Cactocrinus proboscidialis, **613**
Cadulus, 365
  thallus, **363**
Caecum, 290, 410
Caecum, 381
  coronellum, **382**
Calantia, **556**

Calapoecia, 166
    canadensis, **162**
Calapoeciidae, 166
Calcarea, 114
Calcarina spengleri, **84**
Calceolid, 168
Calcification, 19
Calcispongea, 114
Calcioblast, 196
Callopora multitabulata, **256**
    subnodosa, **251**
Callus, 379
Calpidopora, 266, **267**
Calthrops, 105
Calymene, 499, 504
    senaria, **503**
Calyx, of Anthozoa, 159
    of Crinoidea, 611; dicyclic, 611; mono-
    cyclic, 611; terminology, **614**
Camarocrinus, **607**
Camarotoechia, 316
    congregata, **317**
Cambarus, 567
Cambrocyathus occidentalis, **119**
Cambrophyllum, 160
    problematicum, **162**
Camera, 409, 412
Cameral deposit, **414**
Camerata, 621
Campanularia, 127
    edwardsi, **128**
    flexuosa, **128**
Camptostroma, 150
Canal, 379
Cancellate, 333
Candona pagei, **555**
Caninophyllum, 171, 181
    incrassatum, **180**
Capitulum, 557
Carabocrinus radiatus, **617**
Carapace, 545
Carbonicola, 347, 362
    angulata, **361**
Carbonization, 17
Cardelle, 266
Cardinal area, 293
Cardinal extremities, 293
Cardinal margin, 293
Cardinal plate, 298, **319**
    divided, 298
    perforate, 298
Cardinal process, **284**
Cardinal shelf, 293, **295**
Cardinalia, 298
Cardioceras, 458
    cordiforme, **459**

Cardioids, 362
Cardium, 340
    medium, **358**
Carina, 262, 543, 557
Carpocystites, 598
Carpoids, **597**
Carpus, **565**
Carruthers, R. G., 174
Caryocrinites, 594, 598
    ornatus, **591**, **595**
Caryomanon, **109**, 110
Caryophylliina, 198
Cassidulida, 651
Cassidulus, 651
    conradi, **651**
Cast, 18
Castings, 21, 220
Catenipora, 163
    gracilis, **164**
Catophragmus, 558, **559**
Caudal appendix, **93**
Cellepora maculata, **271**
Centipede, 577
Central capsule, 91
Central carina, **229**
Central disc, 586
Centrechinida, 648
Centronella, 317, **319**, 320
    campbelli, **318**
Cephalic leg, **501**
Cephalon, **488**, 489
Cephalopoda, 407
    classification, **441**
    conch, 408
    geologic range, 477
    keys, 438, 465
Cephalothorax, 561
Ceratites, Age of, 463
Ceratites, 437
Ceratitida, 445
Ceratitina, 447
Ceratium, **56**
Ceratoid, 167
Ceratopea, 384
    keithi, **383**
Ceratopsis chambersi, **550**
Ceratospyris, **92**
Ceraurus, 515, 516
    pleurexanthemus, **517**
Cerianthida, 206
Cerianthus, 207
    americanus, **207**
Cerioid, 168
Chaetetes, 160, 161, **162**, 250
    eximius, **162**

Chaetetidae, 160
Chaetopleura apiculata, **331**
Chain corals, 161
Chamber, 60
Chancelloria, 110
  eros, **111**
Cheeks, 489
Cheiloporella flabellata, **246**
Cheilostomida, 262
  hydrologic apparatus, **265**
  morphology, **263**
Cheirusus, 515
  niagarensis, **517**
  welleri, **517**
Chela, 564
Chelicera, 520, **525, 527**
Chelicerata, 520
  classification, 521
  geologic range, 535, **536**
  key, 521
Cheliped, 564
Chilobolbina dentifera, **549**
Chilopod, 575
Chione, 356
Chirognathus, **232**
Chiton carbonarius, **331**
  squamosus, **331**
Chitons, 320
Choanoceras, 423, **425**
Choanocyte, 99
Choanoflagellida, **56, 57**
Choia ridleyi, **108**
Chomatum, **70, 71**
Chondrophore, 339
Chonetes, 314
  granulifer, **315**
Choristoceras, 447
  kelleyi, **450**
Chromatophore, 53, **55**
Chrysomonadida, 54 55
Cibicides, **62,** 81
  choctawensis, **82**
Cicada, **571**
Cicatrix, **599**
Cidarida, 647
Cidaris, 648
  splendens, **647**
Ciliata, 93
Cirripedia, 554
Cladida, 618
Cladochonus, 161
Classifications, artificial, 10
  comparison of, 11
  coordinate, 341
  natural, 10
  noncoordinate, 341

Clathrodictyon, 147, 148
  vesiculosum, **147**
Clathrodrillia, **396**
  incilifera, **395**
Clavulina, 66
  parisiensis, **67**
Climaticnites, 502
Clio, 400
  virgula, **401**
Cliona, 107
  celata, **108**
Clionites, 447
  americanus, **448**
Clionoides, 107
Clionolithes, 107
Clisiophyllids, 181
Clisiophyllum, 181
Clisiosaphites montanensis, **455**
  novimexicanus, **455**
Clithrum, 359
Clonograptus, 139, **140, 141**
Cloud, P. E., 296
Clymenia, 432, 444
Clymeniida, 443
Clypeaster, 653
  rogersi, **652**
Clypeasterida, 653
Cnidaria, 207
Coccolith, 54, **55**
Coccolithophore, 54
Cochloceras, 450
  fischeri, **450**
Cockroach, **571**
Codaster, 604
  pyramidatus, **601, 603**
Codonellopsis, **93**
Codonofusiella, 68, **69**
Codosiga, **56,** 57
Coelenterata, 123, 126
  classification, 125
  geologic distribution, 149, 166, 185
  keys, 160, 176, 197
  living organisms, 123
  morphology, **124**
Coelenteron, 123, **124, 157**
Coeloclema concentricum, **248**
Coelome, 215
Coeloptychium lobatum, **113**
Coenenchyme, 159, 189
Coenosarc, 193
Coenosteum, 144, 193, 247
Coiling, 375
Coleoidea, 464
  classification, 465
  key, 465
Coleopterida, 573

Collar, 93
Columella, 173, 193, **378**
Columellar fold, **380**
Columellar lip, 379
Columnal, 606
Columnariids, 177
Comanthus, **625**
Comarocystites, 596
  punctatus, **597**
Comatulids, 626
Commensal, 129
Compartments, **559**
Compensating sac, 265
Competition, 37
Composita, 310
  subquadrata, **310**
Conchasma, 92
Conchial furrow, **413**
Conchidium, 306
  laqueatum, **305**
Conchiolin, 327
Conchologist, 325
Conchopeltis, 153
  alternata, **152**
Conchostracans, 542
Conchs, of ammonoids, **430**
  of gastropods, 370, **372**
  of nautiloids, 408
Connecting ring, 410, **412, 413**
Conodontophoridia, 227
  assemblages, **229**
  evolution, **232**
  fibrous, 228, **232**
  geologic range, **232**
  laminar, 228, **232**
  morphology, 229
  taxonomic problems, 234
  zoologic affinities, 234
Conotheca, 466
Conradoceras, **424**
Constellaria, 250
  constellata, **251**
Constrictions, 433
Contact margin, 547
  bilamellar, **546,** 548
  monolamellar, **546,** 548
Continental shelf, 28
Continental slope, 28
Contractile vacuole, **58, 59**
Conularia, 153
  continens, **152**
  undulata, **152**
Conularioids, 151
Conus, 382
  floridanus, **395**
Convergence, **39,** 40

Convergent, 343
Convolute, 417
Convoluted organ, **613**
Cooper, G. A., 296, 300
Copepoda, 554
Coprolites, 21
Coralliochama, **332,** 362
  orcutti, **360**
Corallimorphida, 193
Corallimorphus profundus, **192**
Corallistes, 110
  nolitangere, **109**
Corallite, 159
Corallium, 189
  rubrum, **190**
Corbicula, 362
  umbonella, **361**
Corbisema, **56**
Corbula, 362
  undifera, **361**
Cordillerites angulatus, **449**
Cornellites emaceratus, **346**
Cornulites, 225
  flexuosus, **225**
Corona, 635
Correlation, 47
  by evolutionary position, 48
  by index fossils, 47
  by matching faunas, 47
  by relative abundance, 47
Cortex, **135,** 136
Coscinium latum, **261**
Coskinolina adkinsi, **84**
Costa, 65, 193, **196,** 266, **267,** 333, **352**
Costispirifer, 307
  arenosus, **299, 308**
Cover plate, 608
Coxopodite, 500
Cranidium, **488,** 490
Cranoceras, 421
Craspedacusta, 131
  ryderi, **132**
Craterina bohemica, **591**
Cravenoceras, 440
  hesperium, **441**
Crenella, 606
Crenulation, 337
Crepicephalus iowensis, **510**
Crepidula, 391
  fornicata, **391**
Cribrimorph, 267
Crinoidea, 605
  arms, 607, **609**
  calyx, 611, **614**
  classification, 615
  geologic distribution, **627**

Crinoidea—*Continued*
morphology, **585**, 606
roots, 606, **607**
stems, 606
Crinoids, Age of, 626
Crioceratites, **457**
Crisia pugeti, **246**
Crispella crispa, **295, 308**
Crotalocrinites, **609,** 610
Crucibulum, 391
costatum var. *pileolum,* **391**
Crural plate, 298
Crural point, **319**
Cruralium, 298
Crus, **283,** 298
Crustacea, 539
geologic distribution, 576
Cryptoblastus, 600, 604
melo, **601, 603**
Cryptocyst, 264
Cryptolithus, 490, 511, 513
tesselatus, **512**
Cryptomphalus, 378
Cryptostomida, 260
Cryptozonia, 633
Crystallization, center of, **196**
Ctenidium, 372
Ctenochasma, 570
Ctenocrinus nobilissimus, **609**
Ctenodonta, 342
planodorsata, **342**
Ctenolium, 348, **352**
Ctenophora, 206
Ctenostomida, 247
Cucullaea, 343
vulgaris, **344**
Cucumaria, **657**
Cuneate, 168
Cuniculus, 74
Cupulocrinus, 619, 620
humilis, **617**
Cushman, J., 87
Cyathaxonia, 178
dalmani, **177**
tantilla, **177**
venusta, **177**
Cyathaxoniids, 177
Cyathocrinites, 618
wilsoni, **617**
Cyathophyllids, 179
Cyathophyllum, 179, **180**
Cyclammina, 66
cancellata, **67**
Cycle of septa, 195
Cyclodont, 362
Cyclonema limatum, **398**

Cyclops, 554
Cyclosphaeroma, 563
trilobatum, **565**
Cyclostomida, 245
Cylindrical, 168
Cymbionites craticula, **587**
Cymbulia parvidentata, **401**
Cypraea heilprini, **395**
moneta, 325
Cypraeform, 376
Cypridea arvadensis, **555**
bisulcata, **555**
longispina, **555**
wyomingensis, **555**
Cyrtina, 310
alpenensis, **311**
Cyrtoceracone, 415, **416**
Cyrtoceras, 421
depressum, **422**
Cyrtoceratites, 415
Cyrtochoanitic, 420
Cyrtodonta, 343
saffordi, **344**
Cyrtograptus, **140,** 142
Cyrtospirifer, 307
whitneyi, **308**
Cyrtulus serotinus, **386**
Cystiphragm, 255
Cystiphyllids, 181
Cystiphylloides, 181
americanus, **183**
sulcatus, **183**
Cystoidea, 589
carpoids, **597**
geologic distribution, **627**
geologic significance, 598
pores, **591**
Cythere, 546
Cythereis americana, **552**
ciliata, **546**
exanthemata, **552**
fredericksburgensis, **549**
lemnicata, **552**
pennata, **552**
worthensis, **552**
Cytherella fredericksburgensis, **549**
Cytherelloidea alabamensis, **552**
Cytheridea ehlersi, **552**
ruginosa, **552**
Cytheropteron acutolobatum, **552**
Cytoplasm, 91
intracapsular, **58, 91**
extracapsular, **58, 91**
Cyzicus, **542, 543**
tetracerus, **544**

Dactyl, **565,** 566
Dactylioceras, **457**
Dactylopore, 130
Dall, W. H., 338
Dalmanellicae, 304
Dalmanites, 515
  limulurus, **517**
Dalmanitina, 499
Daraelites, 445, 447
  elegans, **446,** 447
  leonardensis, 445, **446**
  meeki, **444,** 445, **446**
Dawsonella meeki, **402**
Dawsonoceras hyatti, **422**
De Vries, H., 38
Decapods, 564
Decollation, 381, 418
Decurtaria, 268, **269**
Deep sea, 28
Deiphon, 516, 518
  forbesi, **517**
Dekayella praenuntia, **253**
Dekayia subfrondosa, **257**
Delocrinus, 619
  benthobatus, **617**
  vulgatus, **619**
Delthyris perlamellosus, **295**
  sulcatus, **295**
Delthyrium, 293, **295**
Deltidial plate, **283**
Deltidium, 294
  conjunct, 294
  discrete, 294
  fused, 294
Demospongea, 106, 239
Dendraster, **585,** 653
  excentricus, **637**
Dendrocystites, 598
  sedgwicki, **597**
Dendroida, 134
Dendrophrya, **62**
Dendrophylliina, 199
Dendrostomum, 220, 226
  pyroides, **219**
Dendrotion hanseni, **565**
Dental lamella **295,** 296
Dentalina, 78
  communis, **79**
Dentalium, 365
  attenuatum, **363**
  stenoschizum, **363**
Dentary, **222**
Denticle, apical, **229**
  lateral, **229**
Denticulate, 293
Depth zones, 28

Derbyia, 312
  crassa, **313**
Desmon, 105
Detorsion, 374
Dextral, **371,** 377
Diagenesis, 18
Diaperoecia floridana, **246**
Diaphanotheca, 71, **72**
Diaphragm, 255
  complete, 255
  perforate, 255
Diaphragmus, 316
Diatom, **59**
Dicanthaspis, 513
  secretus, **514**
Dichograptid, **135,** 139
Dichograptus, **140,** 141
Dicranella bicornis, **550**
Dicranograptus, **140,** 141, 143
Dicranurus, 513
  monstrosus, **514**
Dictyocha, **56**
Dictyoclostus, **284,** 316
  ivesi, **315**
Dictyoconus, 83
  americanus, **84**
  walnutensis, **84**
Dictyonema, 136, 139, **140**
  sociale, **135**
Dictyonine, 114
Dictyospongia, 112
  sceptrum, **113**
Didymograptus, 139, **140**
Dielasma, 318, 320
  bovidens, **295,** 318
  turgida, **319**
Dietella, **263,** 264
Difflugia, **59,** 60
Digestive gland, **157**
Digestive track, **334**
Dikelocephalus, 492, 509
  minnesotensis, **510**
Diluvarca, **339**
Dimerocrinites inornatus, **613**
Dimorphic, 125
Dimorphism, 373
Dimorphograptus, **140,** 142
Dimyarian, 335
Dinocochlea, 371
Dinoflagellida, **56**
Dipleura dekayi, **499**
Dipleurula, **587**
Diplobathrida, 622
Diplocidaris, 648
Diplograptid, **135,** 139

Diplograptus, 135, **140,** 141, 143
Diplopod, 575
Diplopodia, **640**
Diplopore, 590, **591**
Diplopore Paradox, 590
Diploporida, 592
Dipterida, 573
Disc, 630
Discinisca lugubris, **289**
Discoaster, 54, **55**
Discocoelia divaricata, **115**
Discoidal, 168, **376,** 377
Discophyllites patens, **451**
Discoporella umbellata, **271**
Discorbis, 30, **31,** 88, 89
  gravelli, 82
Disparida, 616
Dissepiment, of anthozoans, 172, **196;**
    angular, 172; concentric, 172; her-
    ringbone, 172; lonsdaleoid, 172
  of bryozoans, 260
  of graptolites, 136
  of stromatoporoids, 148
Dissepimentarium, 173
Distacodid, **230, 232**
Distacodus, 228, **230**
Distomum, 215
  hepaticum, **215**
Ditomopyge, 490
Divergence, **39**
Divergent, 343
Dizygocrinus, 624
  rotundus, **623**
Dodecaceria, 224, 225
  fistulicola, **225**
Döderlein, L., 338
Dollo, L., 42
Dolomitization, 19
Dorataspis, **92**
Dorocidaris, 648
  texanus, **647**
Dorsad, **430**
Dorsal cup, 611
Dorsal shield, **488,** 489
Dorsum, 409, **412, 430**
Dorycrinus missouriensis, **623**
Dosinia, **339**
Doublure, 489, **497**
Douvilleiceras, 460
  mammillatum, **459**
Douvillina, 312
  arcuata, **313**
Dragonfly, 571
Drillia, **395,** 396
Dufrenoya justinae, **459**
Duplicature, **546**

Dysodont, 337, 345
Dyssycus ananas, **100**

Ecdysis, 486
Echinocaris, 563
  socialis, **565**
Echinoconchus,` 316
  alternatus, **315**
Echinocrinus, **646,** 648, 655
Echinocyamus, 653
  vaughani, **652**
Echinocystites, 644
Echinoderma, 582
  attached, **588**
  classification, 588
  living positions, **583**
  morphology, **585**
  reproduction, 587
  skeleton, 584
  symmetry, 584
  unattached, 630
  water vascular system, 586
Echinoidea, 634
  apical system, 642, **643**
  basicoronal system, 643
  classification, 644
  corona, 638
  geologic distribution, **660**
  key, 645
  living, 635
  morphology, 635
  spines, 636, **638**
Echinolichas, 513
  eriopsis, **514**
Echinosphaerites, 594, 598
  aurantium, **595**
  infaustus, **591**
Echols, D. J., 89
Ecology, 2, 30
Ecphora quadricostata, **395**
Ectocyst, 264, **267**
Ectoderm, 99
Ectoproct, 240
Edge zone, 193
Edrioaster, **589**
Edrioasteroida, 588
Edriocrinus, 620
  sacculus, **621**
Edwardsia, **192,** 193-195
Egg capsule, **544**
Eggerella, **62**
Eiffelia, 110
  globosa, **111**
Eleutherozoa, 630
Ellesmeroceras, 418
Ellesmeroceratids, 421

Ellis, B. F., 60
Elphidium, 81
  crispum, **82**
Elrathia, 490
  kingi, **510**
Elytrum, 573
Emarginula, 391
  marylandica, **391**
Emmonsia, 165
  emmonsi, **162**
Enallaster, 653
  texanus, **654**
Encope, 653
  macrophora, **652**
Encrinurus, 515
  ornatus, **517**
Encrinus, 619
Endelocrinus texanus, **619**
Endemic population, 26
Endoceras, 420, 421, 427
  proteiforme, **422**
Endoceratids, 421
Endocone, 420
Endocyclic, 642
Endoderm, 100
Endogastric, 415, **416**
Endopachys, 200
  maclurii, **201**
Endopodite, 500
Endopuncta, 290
Endothyra, 67, 68, **69, 75**, 88
Endothyricae, 66, **86**
Endothyrid, 66
Engonoceras, 460
  subjectum, **461**
Enopleura, 596, 597
  popei, **597**
Entalophora proboscidea, **246**
Enteletes hemiplicatus, **304**
Enterolasma, 179
  strictum, **178**
Entoproct, 240
Entoprocta, **241**, 244
Environments, 29
  neritic, 29
  oceanic, 29
Eobelemnites, 466, **476**
Eocaudina, 656
  cribriformis, **657**
Eoconularia, 153
  loculata, **152**
Eocystites, 596, 598
  longidactylus, **591**
Eodiscids, 508
Eodiscus, 492, 509
  bellimarginatus, **507**

Eofletcheria, 161, **162**
Eoharpes, 494
Eoorthis, 302
  remnicha, **303**
Eoschubertella, 68, **69**
Eospirifer, 307
  niagarensis, **295**
  radiatus, **308**
Eothuria, 656, **657**
Eotomaria supracingulata, **392**
Eotrogulus fayoli, **534**
Epiaster, 655
  whitei, **654**
Epicanites, 445
  sandbergi, **446**
Epiphragm, 384
Epistereom, 590
Eponides antillarum, **82**
Eretmocrinus, 611
  remibrachiatus, **609**
Eridophyllum, 181
  seriale, **182**
Errantida, 221
Escutcheon, 338
Estheria, 543
Estivation, 383
Ethmophyllum, 121
  whitneyi, 119
Eucalyptocrinites, 624
  crassus, **623**
Eucladocrinus multibrachiatus, **609**
Eucope, 127
  diaphana, **128**
Eucrassatella marylandica, **358**
Eucythere byramensis, **552**
Eudea, 114
  pisum, **115**
Eumorphoceras, 440
  bisulcatum, **441**
Eumorphocystites multiporatus, **593**
Eunicea, 223
Eunicites, **221, 222**
Eupatagus, 655
  mooreanus, **654**
Euphemites, 393
  vittatus, **393**
Euphoberia armigera, **575**
Euplectella, 111
  aspergillum, **113**
  imperialis, **113**
  oweni, **113**
Euprimitia sanctipauli, **550**
Euproöps, 524
  thompsoni, **525**
Eurekia, 490
Eurycare, 493

Eurychilina reticulata, **550**
Eurypterida, 526
  anatomy, **527**
Eurypterus, 528, **529**
Eurysiphonate, 420
Eusarcus, **529**
Euscalpellum, **556**
Euthyneuran, 375
Eutrephoceras, 427
  cookanum, **426**
  dekayi, **426**
Evactinopora, 247
  radiata, **246**
  sexradiata, **246**
Evolute, 375, 417
Evolution, 35
Evolutionary patterns, **39**
Evolutionary theory, 35
Excurrent canal, 102
Exocyclic, 642
Exogastric, 415, **416**
Exogyra, 356
  arietina, **353**
  ponderosa, **353**, 356
Exopodite, 501
Exopuncta, 290
Exoskeleton, 484
Exsert, **643**
Eye, 372, **545**
  lateral, 533
  median, 533
  of trilobites, **488**, 489, 493; aggregate,
    495; compound, 493; holochroal, 494;
    schizochroal, 495; simple, 493
  ridge, **488**

Facial ridge, 489
Falcal arch, **222**
Falcus, **222**
Fan system, 196
Farrea, 114
  facunda, **113**
Fasciolaria acuta, **371**
  apicina, **386**
Fasciole, 641
  anal, 641
  peripetalous, 641
  subanal, 641
Faunal migration, 26
Faunal realm, 26
Favia, 198
  fragum, **200**
Faviina, 198
Favistella, 176, 186
  alveolata, **177**

Favosites, 165
  alpenensis, **162**
  gothlandicus, **162**
  turbinatus, **162**
Favositidae, 163
Fenestella, 261
  rudis, **259**
Fenestra, **267**
Fenestrapora occidentalis, **261**
Fenestrule, 260
Ferestromatopora larocquei, **145**
Ficus eopapyratia, **395**
Field techniques, 44
Filaria, **216**
Filter-feeders, 279, 334
Fission, 52, 125
Fissurella, 380, **381**, 391
Fistulipora, 247
  astrica, **248**
  crustula, **248**
  monticulata, **248**
  spinulifera, **246**
Fistuliporoid, 247
Fixed cheek, **488**, 489
Flabellum, 199
  cuneiforme, **200**
Flagellum, 53, **55**
Flank, **430**
Flexibilia, 619
Flexicalymene, 490, 497, 511
  meeki, **498, 512**
Flexure, 373, **374**
Float, 45
Floods, 87
Floridinella vicksburgica, **271**
Floscelle, 641
Floscularia, **217**
Flower, R. H., 417, 421
Fly, **571**
Fold, 281
Food grooves, 589, **595**, 599, **600, 609,**
  613
Foot, 334, 372, **374**
Foramen, **283**
Foramina, 60
Foraminiferida, 60
  apertures, 60, **64**
  classification, 65
  depth zones, 87
  economic paleontology, 90
  key, 65
  larger, 63
  living, 60
  origin, 85
  ornamentation, 64
  polymorphism, 63

Foraminiferida—*Continued*
  shape, 61
  skeletal features, 61
  smaller, 63
  stratigraphic distribution, **86**
Forams, 60
Fossilization, 17
Fossils, value of, 2
Fossula, 169
Free check, **488**, 489
Frizzell, D. L., 341
Frondicularia, **62**, 78
  goldfussi, **79**
Frontal lobe, 490
Fungia, 197, 198
  patella, 199
Fungiina, 197
Furca, **545**
Furrows, 466
Fuselle, **135**, 136
Fusiform, **376**, 377
Fusulina, **62**, 68, **75**
  acme, **69**
Fusulinella, 68, **69**, **75**
Fusulinids, 67, **86**
  morphology, **70**, **73**
  shapes of, **69**
  stratigraphic distribution, **75**

Galloway, J. J., 85
Gammarus, 564
Ganglion, 214
  cephalic, 372, **374**
  parietal, **374**
  visceral, **374**
Gape, 331
Gaspelichas, 513
  forillonia, **514**
Gastric mill, 563
Gastrioceras, 440
  branneri, **439**
Gastropoda, 370
  anatomy, **372**
  apertures, 379
  classification, 388
  conchs, 375
  fresh-water, 396
  geologic range, **404**
  key, 388
  morphology of conchs, **371**
  operculum, 383
  ornamentation, 384
  shapes of conchs, 375
  soft parts, 372
Gastropore, 130
Gastrostyle, 131

Gaudryina, 66
  subrotundata, **67**
Gemmule, 103
Geniculate, 167
Genital appendage, **527**
Geologic time scale, **3**
Gephyrea, 220, **227**
Gigantism, 359
Gilbertsocrinus, 622
  tuberosus, **622**
Gill chamber, **412**
Gill plate, **527**, 528
Gills, **334**, **372**, **374**, **412**, **469**
  of pelecypods, eulamellibranchial, 335;
    filibranchial, 335; protobranchial, 335;
    septibranchial, 335
Girtycoelia, 114
  beedei, **115**
Glabella, **488**, 489
Glabellar furrow, **488**, 489
Glabellar lobe, **488**, 490
Glabrocingulum, 392
  grayvillense, **392**
Glandulina, 78
  conica, **79**
Globigerina, 81, 94
  bulloides, **58**, **82**
Globose, **376**, 377
Globotruncana arca, **82**
Glottidia, **279**
Glycymeris, 343
  subovata, **344**
  veatchii, **344**
Glyptocrinus, 624
  decadactylus, **623**
Glyptocystites, **591**
Glyptopleura varicostata, **550**
Glyptosphaerites, 593, 594
  leuchtenbergi, **593**
Gnathodus, **228**, 233
  roundyi, **233**
Goldfingia hespera, **219**
Gomphoceras, 421
Gonad, **157**
Gondolella, 233
  neolobata, **233**
  symmetrica, **233**
Goniatite, **438**
Goniatites, 437, 440, 443
  choctawensis, **441**
Goniatitida, **438**
Goniatitina, 440
Gonotheca, 127, **134**
Gonozoid, 127, **128**
Gorgonia, 189
  flabellum, **190**

Gorgonin, 189
Grantia, 102
  compressa, **100**
Granule, 641
Graptogonophore, **135,** 136
Graptozoa, 133
  affinities, 143
  budding, 139
  evolution, 139, **140**
  modification of stipes and thecae, **138**
  morphology, 135
  reduction of branches, 137
  shape of rhabdosome, 137
  taxonomic problems, 142
  thecal shape, 137
  trends, 136
Grasshopper, **571**
Greenops, 494
  boothi, **494**
Gregarious, 99
Griffithides, 490
Growth lines, 171, 286
Gryphaea, 352, 354-356
  dumortieri, **354,** 355
  incurva, **354,** 355
  obliquata, **354,** 355
  washitaensis, 353
Guard, 465, **467**
Gumbelina plummerae, **82**
Gutschickia deltoidea, **555**
Gutter, **380**
Guttulina, 78, 79
  hantkeni, **79**
Gymnites, 447
  alexandrae, **449**
Gymnolaemata, 245
Gymnotoceras, 447
  beckeri, **449**
Gypidula, 306
  coeymansensis, **305**
Gypsina, 131, 148
  plana, **130,** 148
Gyraulus, 404
  utahensis, **402**
Gyroceracone, 415, **416**
Gyroceras, 415
Gyroceratites, 439
  gracilis, **439**

Hadrophyllum, 184
  orbignyi, **184**
Haeckel, E., 32
Halimeda, 202
Haliotis, 375, **376,** 380, 392
Halisarca, **56**

Hallopora, 250
  ramosa, **251, 253**
  rugosa, **251**
Halysiocrinus, 616
  dactylus, **616**
Halysites, 163, **164**
  labyrinthicus, **164**
Halysitidae, 161
Hamites, 454
  phaleratus, **452**
Hamulus onyx, **225**
Handlirsch, A., 574
Hanna, G. D., 57
Hansen, H. J., 575
Hantkenina alabamensis, **82**
Haplocrinites, 616
  clio, **613, 616**
Haplocytheridea wallacei, **552**
Haplophragmoides, 66
  concava, **67**
Haplopore, 590, **591**
Hapsiphyllum, 179
  calcariforme, **178**
Hardouinia, 651
  florealis, **651**
Haresiceras placentiforme, **459**
Harpoceras, 458
  aalense, **431**
  levinsoni, **431**
Harrington, H. J., 153
Hastigerina pelagica, **58**
Hayasakia, 161
Head, 484, 568
Hebertella, 302
  sinuata, **303**
Hebetoceras, 423, **425**
Helcionella subrugosa, **389**
Helicoid, 377
Heliolites, 165
  interstrictus, **162**
Heliolitidae, 165
Heliophyllum, 181
  halli, **182**
Heliopora, 165, 189
  cerulea, **190**
Heliozoida, 92
Helix, 404
  pomatia, **404**
Helopora harrisi, **261**
Hemiaspis, 524
  limuloides, **525**
Hemiaster, 655
  texanus, **654**
Hemicythere jollaensis, **552**
Hemiphragm, 255

Hemiphragma irrasum, **253**
  ottawaense, **253**
  whitfieldi, **256**
Hemipteroids, 573
Hemiseptum, 260
Hemitrypa, 262
  proutana, **259**
Hercoglossa, 427
  harrisi, **426**
Heredity, 36
Hesperocidaris panamensis, **638**
Hesperonoë adventor, **219**
Hesperorthis tricenaria, **299, 303**
Heteractine, 106
Heteractinellida, 110
Heterocoralla, 188
Heterodont, 337
Heterodontida, 356
Heterophyllia, 188
  reducta, **188**
Heteropod, 398
Heterostegina, 83
  texana, **84**
Heterotrypa subramosa, **254**
Hexacoralla, 191
Hexactine, 105
Hexactinella, 114
  tubulosa, **113**
Hexactinellid, 111, 148
Hexagonaria, 181
  cedarensis, **182**
  percarinata, **182**
Hexalonche, **92**
Hexameroceras, 421, **424**
Hexaphyllia, **188**
Hibbardella, **230**
Hibernation, 383
Himerometra, **625**
Hincksina jacksonica, **271**
Hindeodella, **228, 230,** 234
Hinge, 336
  line, 293
  margin, **546,** 547
  plate, **283**
Hipponicharion confluens, **542**
Hippurites, **360,** 362
Hirudinea, 218
Hirudo, 218
  medicinalis, **218**
Holaster, 653
  simplex, **654**
Holectypida, 650
Holectypus, 650
  planatus, **650**
Hollina spiculosa, **550**
Hollinella radiata, **550**

Holothuroida, 656
  geologic range, **659**
  morphology, **585**
Holotype, 16
Homalophyllum ungulum, **178**
Homing instinct, 566
Homoeodeltidium, 287
Homoeomorph, 40
Homoeomorphy, 39, 40
Homoeospira evax, **295**
Homonym, 15
Homotrypa flabellaris, **257**
  minnesotensis, **251**
Hood, **409,** 412
Horizontal, 137, **138**
Hormotoma, 392
  trentonensis, **392**
Horridonia subhorrida, **315**
Howell, B. F., 508
Hudsonaster, 633
  narrawayi, **632**
Hughmilleria, **529**
Hustedia, 311
  mormoni, **311**
Hyalospongea, 111
Hyalotragos patella, **109**
Hybocrinus, 617
  eldonensis, **616**
Hydnoceras, 112
  phymatodes, **113**
Hydra, **124, 127, 128**
  carnea, **128**
Hydractinia, 129, 130, 148
  multispinosa, **128**
  polyclina, **128**
Hydrocorallida, 130
Hydroid, 125
Hydroida, 127
Hydropore, 583, **600**
Hydrorhiza, 29
Hydrospire, **600**
Hydrotheca, 127
Hymenopterida, 573
Hydrozoa, 127, 239
Hydrozoid, 127, **128**
Hyolithes, 400
  princeps, **401**
Hyperstrophic, 394
Hyponome, 408, **409, 412, 469**
Hyponomic sinus, 408, **413**
Hypostome, 491, **497**

Ichthyocrinus, 620
  laevis, **621**
Idmonea magna, **246**
Idraites, **222**

Imago, 569
Imitoceras, 440
  rotatorium, **441**
Immature region, **252,** 254
Impressed zone, 417, **430**
Impressions, 17
Impunctate, 288, **290**
Inadunata, 615
Inadunate, 612
Inarticulate, 282
Incertae sedis, Coelenterata, 149
  Porifera, 114
Increase, **169**
Incurrent canal, 102
Inoceramus, 328
  sagensis, **346**
Index fossils, 47
Indoceras, 460
  baluchistanensis, **461**
Inductura, 379
Induration, 19
Infusoria, 93
Inner lip, **371,** 379
Inner margin, **546,** 549
Inner wall, 118
Inocellia, **571**
Insecta, 568
  classification, 572
  geologic occurrence, 574, **576**
  origin of flying, 574
Insects, Age of, 5
Insert, **643**
Instar, 486, 550
Interambulacral area, 594, 639
Interambulacral plate, **642**
Interarea, 293, **295**
Interfacial angle, 152
Interseptal ridge, **170**
Interspace, 352
Intertidal region, 28
Intervale, 543, **544**
Introtorsion, 137, **138**
Invertebrate paleontology, **1**
Involute, 377, 417
Involutina, 65
  exsertus, **66**
  incertus, **66**
Inyoites, 447
  oweni, **448**
Irregularia, 650
Irreversibility of evolution, 42
Ischadites, 118
  iowensis, **117**
Isodont, 345
Isolate, **138,** 139
Isomyarian, 335

Isopods, 518, 563
Isorophus, 589
  cincinnatiensis, **589**
Isotelus, 490, 492, 495, 499, 511, 518
  gigas, **499, 512**
Israelsky, M. C., 89
Iterative evolution, 40, 450
  compound, **39,** 41
  simple, **39,** 41

Jellyfish, 150
Jerea, 110
  tesselata, **109**
Jugum, 309
Juresania nebrascensis, **315**
Juvavites, 447
  strongi, **449**
Juvenarium, 74

Keel, 433
Keen, A. M., 341, 388
Kellettina montosa, **550**
Keratosida, 107
Keriotheca, 71, **72**
Kiderlen, H., 153
Kidney opening, **374**
Kingena, 318
  wacoensis, **318**
Kionoceras austini, **422**
Kirkbya symmetrica, **550**
Kirklandia, 131
Kleinpell, R. M., 90
Knightina harltoni, **550**
Kobayashi, T., 508, 542
Kossmatia, 458
Kozlowskia splendens, **315**
Kummel, B., 417, 421
Kutorgina, 302
  cingulata, **302**

Labechia, 146
  conferta, **147**
Labial palp, **334**
Laboratory techniques, 46
Lacazella, 312
Lacewing, **571**
Lacuna, 163
Lagena, 78
  elliptica, **79**
  humerifera, **79**
  sulcata spirata, **79**
Lagenicae, 78, **86**
Lagenid, 78
Lamella, 146, 173
  ascending, **319**
  descending, **319**
  outer, **546,** 548

Lamellibranch, 340
Lamina, 146
Lancet plate, 599, **600**
Lang, W. D., 268
Lappet, 431
Laqueus, 279
Larvae, actinula, 131
  cyphonautes, 240, **241**
  cypris, **556,** 557
  dipleurula, **587**
  metanauplius, 485
  nauplius, 485
  planula, **124,** 125
  protaspid, 502
  trochophore, **217**
  veliger, 326, **353**
Larval ridge, 502
Larwood, G. P., 268
Lateral costa, **229**
Lateral line, 152
Latilamina, **145,** 146
Latus, 557, 558
Laudon, L. R., 614
Leaching, 18
Leaia, 543
  tricarinata, **544**
  williamsoniana, **544**
Lecthaylus, 220
Legs, 562
  thoracic, 500, **501,** 545
  walking, 520, **525**
Leiocidaris, 648
  hemigranosus, **647**
Leioclema monroei, **256**
Leiodorella, 110
  expansa, **109**
Leiorhynchus, 316, 317
  rockymontanus, **317**
Lensal pit, 494
Lepas, 554, **556, 557,** 558
  hilli, **556**
Leperditia fabulites, **550**
Lepiditta alta, **544**
Lepidocoleus, 658
  sarlei, **658**
Lepidocyclina, 83, 85
  mantelli, **84**
  peruviana, **84**
Lepidocyclus, 316
  capax, **317**
Lepidolina, 74
  multiseptata, **73**
Lepidopterida, 574
Leptaena, 312, 314
  rhomboidalis, **299, 313**
Leptodus americanus, **313**

Leptograptus, **140,** 141, 143
Leptotrypa discoidea, **253**
Leptotrypella aequabilis, **256**
Leucodora, **190**
Leuconoid, 102
Lichas, 513
Lichenaria, 160
Liesegang rings, 21
Ligaments, 338
  alivincular, 340
  duplivincular, 340
  internal, 340
  multivincular, 340
  parivincular, 340
Ligonodina, **230**
Lima, **339**
Limacina, 400
  scaphoides, **401**
Limax, 404
  antiquorum, **402**
Limulus, 515, 523, 524, 526, 528
  polyphemus, **525**
Lindberg, R. G., 566
Lindstroemella, 288
  aspidium, **289**
Lindstroemoceras, 423, **425**
Lindström, G., 495
Line of concrescence, **546,** 549
Lineage, 39
Lingula, 278, 280, 281, 286, **287,** 322
  anatina, **287, 290**
  lepidula, **287**
Lingulella, 286
  acuminata, **287**
  ampla, **287**
Linnaeus, C., 14
Linoproductus, 316
  prattenianus, **315**
Liometopum, **571**
Liostracus, 504
  linnarssoni, **503**
Liostrea irregularis, **354,** 355
Lips of gastropod apertures, 379
  columellar, 379
  inflected, 379, **380**
  inner, 379
  outer, 379
  parietal, 379
  reflected, 379, **380**
Lira, 333
Lissochonetes, 314
  geinitzianus, **315**
Listriolobus pelodes, **219**
Listrium, 288
Lithistida, 107

Lithofacies, 30
Lithostrotion genevievensis, **183**
Lithostrotionella, 181
castelnaui, **183**
Lithothamnium, 202
Littorina, 390
littorea, 27, **383**
Lituites, 417
Lituiticone, **416,** 417
Lituolicae, 66, **67, 84, 86**
Lituolids, 66
Living chamber, 408, **412, 430**
Lobate, 137, **138**
Lobe, 433
adventitious, **434**
auxiliary, **434**
dorsal, **434,** 435
first lateral, **434,** 435, **455**
second lateral, **434**
umbilical, 435
Lobobactrites, 462
Loculus, 170
Loligo, 472
pealei, **473**
vulgaris, **473**
Loligopsis, 472, **476**
Lonchodina, **230**
Lonchodomas, 513
halli, **512**
Longitudinal section, **252**
Lonsdaleia, 171
Lonsdaleoid retreat, 171
Loop, 283, 298
centronelliform, 320
growth and metamorphosis, **319**
Lopadolith, 54, **55**
Lophophore, of brachiopods, **279**
of bryozoans, 240
of phoronids, 274
Lophophyllidium, 184
proliferum, **185**
Lophophyllids, 184
Lorica, 57, 93, 216
Loven, S. L., 636
Loxoconcha claibornensis, **552**
Lucina occidentalis ventricosa, **358**
Lumbriconereites, **222**
Lumbricus, 220
Lumen, 606
Lunarium, 247, **248**
Lunule, **336,** 338
Lychniskid, 114
Lymnaea, 404
bonnevillensis, **402**
Lyramula, **56**
Lyropecten, 351

Lyropora, 262
quincuncialis, **259**
ranoscula, **259**
Lytocrioceras, **457**
Lytoceratina, 453

Machaeridia, 658
Mackenzia, 193, 195
costalis, **192**
Maclurites, 394
logani, **394**
Macluritoid, 394
Macraster, 653
elegans, **654**
Macrocheira, 564
Macula, 250, 491
Madreporite, 583, 631
Malacologist, 325
Malacostraca, 561
fresh-water, 567
Malkin, D., 89
Malocystites murchisoni, **593**
Malthus, T. R, 36
Mamelon, **145,** 641, **642**
imperforate, **642**
Mandalaoceras, **424**
Mandible, **545,** 562
Manticoceras, 439
simulator, **439**
Mantle, 280, 326, 372
Mantle lobe, **412**
Manus, **565,** 566
Marginal flange, 492
Marginal furrow, **488,** 489
Marginalia, 631
Marginopora, 83
vertebralis, **84**
Marginulina, 78
texana, **79**
Marine environments, **28**
Marsupites americanus, **625**
Mastax, 217
Mastigophora, 53, **55**
Matherella saratogensis, **394**
Mature region, **252,** 254
Maxilla, **545, 562**
Maxilliped, 562
Mazosphaera, **92**
Meandroid, 193
Median septum, **283, 295,** 296, **319**
Median suture, 639, **642**
Medlicottia burckhardti, **444**
Medusoid, 125
Meekella striatocostata, **284, 313**
Meekoceras, 447
gracilitatis, **448**

Meekospira, 396
　peracuta, **397**
Megafossils, 44
Megasclere, 104
Megistocrinus, 624
　nodosus, **623**
Melina maxillata, **339**
Melonechinus, 646
　indianensis, **646**
Membranipora, **241**, 266, **267**, 268
Mendel, G., 36
Merostomata, 521
Merus, **565**
Mesalia, 396
　martinezensis, **397**
　seriatim-granulata, **397**
Mesenchyme, 100
Mesentery, 123, 156, **157**
　digestive, 194
　edwardsian, 194
Mesocorallite, 163
Mesoderm, 214
Mesogastropods, 391
Mesogloea, 100
Mesolobus, 314
　mesolobus, **315**
Mesonacids, 504
Mesonacis, 493, 504, 506
　fremonti, **505**
　vermontana, **505**
Mesopore, 247, 250, **252**
Mesosoma, 520, **527**
Messina, A. R., 60
Metacypris angularis, **555**
Metalegoceras, 440
　evolutum, **439**
Metamere, 218
Metamorphosis, 569
　complete, 569
　incomplete, 569
　of arthropods, 484
　of brachiopods, 280
　of bryozoans, 240
Metasoma, 520, **527**
Metazoa, 102
Metoicoceras whitei, **461**
Metridium, **192**, 193
Michelinoceras, 415, 421
　sociale, **422**
Michelinoceratids, 421
Microforaminifers, 63
Micropaleontology, 1
Microporella ciliata, **271**
Microsclere, 104
Microspongia, 110
　fibrosa, **109**

Midline, 152
Midumbonal line, 347
Miliary granule, 641
Miliolicae, 76, **84, 86**
Miliolid, 76
Milled ring, 636, **638**
Millepora, 130, 131, 148, 239
　alcicornis, **130**
Milleporidium, 149
　remesi, **150**
Miller, Hugh, 530
Miller, J. S., 615
Millerella, 68, **69, 75**
Millipede, 577
Mimoceras, 462
Miraspis, 495, 518, 573
　mira, **494**
Mischoptera, **571**, 572
Mitella, **556**, 557, 559
Mixopterus, 528, **529**
Modiolopsis, 347
　excellens, **346**
Modiomorpha, 347
Mold, 18
Mollusca, 325
　classes, **327**
　classification, 320
　composition and structure, 327, **328**
Molluscoidea, 243
Molt stages of trilobites, 502
　holaspid period, 502
　meraspid period, 502
　protaspid period, 502
Monactinellida, 107
Monaxon, 104
Moniliform, 254
Monobathrida, 624
Monocyathus, **119**
Monograptid, **135**, 139
Monograptus, **140**, 142, 143
Monomyarian, 335
Monosiga, **56**
Monotis subcircularis, **346**
Monotrypa benjamini, **256**
　cumulata, **253**
Monotroypella aequalis, **257**
Monticule, 250
Monticulipora, 250
　arborea, **256**
　mammulata, **251**
Monticuliporoid Controversy, 250
Montlivaltia, 198
　norica, **200**
Montyoceras, 422, **425**
Moore, R. C., 153, 614
Mooreoceras, 421, **422**

Morphologic equivalents, 40
Mortoniceras, 460
　shoshonensis, **459**
Mother-of-pearl, 328
Mouth, **157, 334, 372, 374, 469, 525,**
　527
Mucrospirifer, 307
　mucronatus, **308**
Munier-Chalmas, E. C. P. A., 338
Munsteroceras parallelum, **441**
Mural pore of fusulinids, 71
Murex chipolanus, **397**
Muscle band, 158
Muscle scars, of brachiopods, 282, **283;**
　accessory diductor, 285; adductor, 282,
　283; adjustor, **283;** diductor, **283,** 284;
　pedicle, **283;** pedicle adjustor, 283;
　protractor, 285
　of ostracodes, **546**
　of pelecypods, 336; anterior adductor,
　336; posterior adductor, **336;** re-
　tractor, 336
Muscle track, 282, **283**
Mutation theory, 38
Mya, **332, 339**
　arenaria, **358**
Myagropora, 266, **267**
Myalina, 347
　copei, **349**
　goldfussiana, **349**
　lepta, **349**
　miopetina, **349**
　pliopetina, 349
　wyomingensis, **349**
Myelodactylus, 606, 617
　keyserensis, **616**
Myenia, 107
　fluviatilis, **108**
　millsi, **108**
Myocoele, **222,** 223
Myriapoda, 577
　geologic distribution, **576**
Myriastiches, gigas, **646**
Mytiloid, 345
Mytilus, **332,** 340, 347
Myxospongida, 107
Myzostoma, 220
Myzostoma, **219**

Nahecaris sturtzi, **565**
Naiadites, 362
　carbonarius, **361**
Names, 14
　generic, 14
　specific, 14
　trivial, 14

Natica, 396
　precursor, **383**
Naticoid, **376,** 377
Natural selection, 37
Nautilicone, **416,** 417
Nautilids, 424
Nautiloidea, 411
Nautilus, 408, 409, 411, **412,** 417-420, 424,
　427, 464, 478
　pompilius, 409, **426,** 427
Nebalia, 563, **565**
Neck, 638
Nekton, 29
Nema, **135,** 136
Nemathelminthes, 215
Nematocyst, **124,** 125
Nematotheca, 134, **135**
Nemodon, 343
　grandis, **344**
Neogastropods, 391
Neokoninckophyllum, 181
　simplex, **183**
Neolenus pugio, **510**
Neolimulus, 524
Neopilina, 389, 390
　galatheae, **389**
Neopterica, 573
Neoshumardites, 443
Neospirifer, 307
　triplicatus, **308**
Neotremida, 287
Neozaphrentis, 179
　tenella, **178**
Nephridium, **279**
Nereidavus, **222**
Nereis, **221**
Nerinaea, 381
　trochea, **382**
Nerita tampaensis, **382**
Neritina, **382**
Nerve commissure, **372**
Neumayr, M., 338
Neupterida, 573
Neupteroids, 573
Neusina, 51
Nevadacyathus septaporus, **119**
Nevadia, 506
　weeksi, **505**
Nevadites, 447
　whitneyi, **448**
Neverita duplicata, **378**
Nipponitella, 68, **69**
Nipponites, 454
Nodosarella, 81
　paucistriata, 80

Nodosaria, **62,** 78
  latejugata, **79**
  obliquata, **79**
Nomenclature, 13
  binominal, 14
Nonionella cockfieldensis, **82**
Nonreef corals, 202
Nostoceras, 454
  crassum, **452**
  stantoni, **452**
Notch, 379
Notocorbula, **332**
Nucleocrinus, 604
  verneuili, **603**
Nucleus, **58, 59,** 373
Nucula, 342
Nuculana, 333, 342
  acuta, **342**
  senaria, **342**
Nuculoids, 342
Nuculopsis girtyi, 342
Nummulites, **62,** 81, 83
  ghizehensis, **84**
Nyctocrinus magnitubus, **622**
Nymph, 569

Obconical, **376,** 377
Obolella, 320
Obolus, 286, 287
  celatus, **287**
Obovate, **376,** 377
Occipital furrow, 490
Occipital lobe, 490
Occipital ring, **488,** 490
Ocellus, 494
Ochetosella jacksonica, **271**
Octactine, 106
Octameroceras, **424**
Octocoralla, 188
Octomeris, 558
Octopodida, 474
Octopus bairdii, **475**
  macropus, **475**
  piscatorum, **475**
Oculina, 198
  mississippiensis, **200**
Oculo-genital ring, 642
Oenenites, **222**
Oesophagus, **124, 157**
Oistodus, **228, 230**
Okulitch, V. J., 186
Olenelloides armatus, **506**
Oleneothyris, 318
  harlani, **318**
Oligopygus, 651
  haldemani, **651**

Olivella alabamensis, **395**
Ommastrephes, 472, 476
  illecebrosus, **473**
Ommatidium, 493
Omphalotrochus cochisensis, **378**
Oncoceras, 417, 421
Oncoceratids, 421
Ontogenesis, 32
Ontogeny, 30
Onychocrinus, 620
  ulrichi, **621**
Onychophora, 487
Onychoteuthis, 474
  banksii, **473**
Ooecium, 240, 263
Ooze, diatomaceous, 95
  globigerine, 94
  pteropod, 94, 400
  radiolarian, 94
Opercular membrane, 558
Operculinoides vicksburgensis, **84**
Operculum, of balanids, 558
  of bryooans, **263, 267**
  of chelicerates, **525, 527,** 528
  of coelenterates, 168
  of gastropods, **372, 383,** 384
Ophiuroid, **585, 632**
Ophiuroidea, 633
  morphology, **585**
Opisthobranchia, 399
Opisthocline, 345
Opisthodetic, 338
Opisthogyre, 333
Opisthoparian, 496, 509
Orad, **430**
Oral surface, **157**
Orbiculoidea, 288
  missouriensis, **289**
Orbitoids, **86**
Orbitolinids, **86**
Orbitremites, 601, 604
  norwoodi, **601**
Orbulina, **62,** 81
  universa, **82**
Ornamentation, antispiral sinus, 384
  costa, 293
  costellum, 293
  filum, 292
  frill, 292
  growth line, 292, 384
  lamella, 292
  nodose-reticulate, 385
  of brachiopods, 292
  of gastropods, 384, **386**
  plica, 293

Ornamentation—*Continued*
  reticulate, 293
  ruga, 292
  sinus, 384
  spine, 292
  spiral, **371, 384**
  spiral sinus, 384
  transverse, **371,** 384
Orophocrinus, 604
  stelliformis, **601, 603**
Orthicae, 302
Orthid brachiopods, 302
Orthina, 302
Orthis, **284**
  michaelis, **303**
Orthoceracone, 415, **416**
Orthoceras, **414,** 415
  truncatum, 418, **422**
Orthochoanitic, 420
Orthogenesis, 41
Orthogyre, 333
Orthopteroids, 573
Orthostrophia, 302
  strophomenoides, **283, 303**
Orthostrophic, 394
Orthotetes, 312
Oscule, 102
Osphradium, **372**
Ossicle, 584
  microstructure, **585,** 586
Ostracoda, 545
  appendages, **545**
  dimorphism, 549
  fresh-water, **555**
  terminology, **546**
Ostrea, **328,** 352
  gravitesta, 352
  titan, 352
  virginica, **353**
Ostreoid, 351
Ottoia prolifica, **219**
Outer lip, 371, 379
Ovarian impression, 280, **283**
Overlap, 547
Ovicell, 240, 263
Owenites, 447
  koeneni, 448
Oxytropidoceras, 460

Pachynion scriptum, **109**
Pachyphyllum, 181
  woodmani, **180**
Pachyteuthis, 466, **476**
  densus, **467**

Paedeumias, 498, 506
  robsonensis, **506**
  transitans, **498**
Pagetia, 509, 515
  clytia, **507**
Palaeocaris typus, **565**
Palaeoctopus, 474
  newboldi, **475**
Palaeopantopus maucheri, **531**
Palaeophonus, 533
  hunteri, **532**
  nuncius, **532**
Palaeotremida, 301
Paleobotany, 1
Paleoecology, 2
Paleofavosites, 165
  aspera, **162**
Paleontology, 1
  methods, 21
Paleopterica, 572
Paleozoology, 1
Palicolumella, 173
Pallial, cavity, 372
  complex, 372
  markings, 280, **283**
  sinus, 280, **336**
Palliseria robusta, **394**
Palmatodella, **230**
Palmatolepis, **230**
Palpebral lobe, 496
Palynology, 1
Panderodella, **230**
Paraconularia, 153
  missouriensis, **152**
Paracypris dentonensis, **552**
Paradelocrinus subplanus, **619**
Paradox of the Trepostomes, 255
Paradoxides, 490, 499
  harlani, **498, 510**
Parafusulina, 74, **75**
  nosonensis, **73**
Paragastric cavity, 102
Paralegoceras texanum, **439**
Parallel descent, **39,** 40
Parallelodon, 343
  rugosum, **344**
  tenuistriatus, **344**
Paramoecium, **93**
Paranomia, 345
  scabra, **346**
Parapachydiscus, **436,** 460
Paraparchites cyclopeus, **550**
Parapodium, 218
Paraschwagerina fosteri, **73**
  gigantea, **73**

Parasmilia, 199
  austinensis, **200**
Parazoa, 102
Paries, 118
Parietal lip, 379
Parulocrinus compactus, **618**
Patella, 376, 391
Patelliform, **376**, 377
Patellina corrugata, **58**
Patelloid, 391
Paterina, 287
  bella, **289**
Pearson, J. C., 388
Pecten, 332, 351
  circularis var. *aequisulcatus*, **352**
  estrellanus, **352**
  hemphilli, **350**
  jeffersonius, **350**
  madisonius, **350**
  peckhami, **350**
  quinquecostatus, **350**
Pectenoids, 347
  morphology, **352**
Pectinirhomb, **591**, **592**
Pedalion, **217**
Pedicellaria, **585**, 586, 636
Pedicellina cernua, **241**
Pedipalp, 520
Pedipalpida, 533
Peduncle, 557
Pedunculate, 554
Pelagia cyanella, **151**
Pelecypod adaptations, 332
  burrowing, 332
  mobile, 332
  sedentary, 332
Pelecypod teeth, 337
  cardinal, **336**
  lateral, **336**
Pelecypoda, 331
  adaptations, **332**
  anatomy, **334**
  classification, 340
  dentition, 337
  external features, 333
  geologic distribution, **364**
  gills, **334**, 335
  internal skeletal features, 336
  key, 341
  ligaments, 338, **339**
  nonmarine, 362
  sculpture, 333
  terminology of valves, **336**
Pelma, 268
Pelmatopora, 268, **269**
Pelmatozoa, 588

Pemphicyclus ortoni, **544**
Pen, 471
Pendent, 137, **138**
Penis, **372**
Pennatula, 189
  aculeata, **190**
Pentacrinids, 625
Pentacrinites, 626
  whitei, **625**
Pentameral symmetry, 582
Pentamerina, 305
Pentameroceras, **424**
Pentamerus, 316
  laevis, **305**
Pentremites, 604, 605
  angustus, **603**
  conoideus, **603**
  godoni, **603**
  pyriformis, **600**, **603**
  sulcatus, **603**
Perditocardinia dubia, **304**
Periarchus, 653
  lyelli, **652**
Peridinium, **56**
Peridionites navicula, **587**
Perigastrella plana, **271**
Perignathic girdle, **637**, 644
Periostracum, 327
Peripatoides, **487**, 488
Peripatus, **487**
Peripheral surface, 606
Periproct, 592, 642, **643**
Perisarc, 125
Perischoechinoida, 645
Perna, **339**, 340
Peronidella metabronni, **115**
Peronopsis, 508
  montis, **507**
Perrinites, 443
  hilli gouldi, **442**
  hilli hilli, **442**, 443
  hilli multistriatus, **442**
  hilli tardus, **442**
Petalocrinus, 611, 619
  mirabilis, **609**
Petrocrania, 288
  scabiosa, **289**
Phaceloid, 168
Phacops, 492, 515
  cristata, **499**
  rana, **494**, **495**, **517**
Phalangida, 535
Phaneromphalus, 378
Phanerozonia, 633
Phellia, **157**
Phillipsia, 490

Pholadidea, 332, 357
  penita, **359**
Pholadoid, 357
Pholidechinus brauni, **637**
Phoronida, 273
Phoronis architecta, **274**
Phragmoceras, 415
Phragmocone, 409, **412**, **430**, 465, **467**
Phylactolaemata, **241**, 245
Phyllacanthus, 648
  mortoni, **647**
Phyllocarids, 563
Phylloceras, 451
  grossicostatum, **451**
Phylloceratina, 451
Phyllode, 641
Phyllograptus, **140**, 141, 143
Phylloporina, 260, 261
  corticosa, **258**
  sublaxa, **258**
Phylogenesis, 32
Phylogenetic tree, 39
Phymosoma, 649
  texanum, **649**
Physa gyrina, **402**
Physalia, 132
  arethusa, **132**
Pilina, 389
  unguis, **389**
Pillar, 146
Pinna, **328**
Pinnaretepora conferta, **259**
Pinnule, 608
Pisocrinus, 617
  quinquelobus, **616**
Pitar, 356
Placenticeras, 460
  meeki, **461**
  placenta, **461**
Plaesiomys subquadrata, **283**, **284**
Plagioglypta, 365
  canna, **363**
  meekianum, **363**
Planaria, **215**
Planispiral, 377
Plankton, 29
Planocaprina trapezoides, **360**
Planulina taylorensis, **82**
Plasmodium, 93
Plate, adambulacral, 594
  ambulacral, 631, 633
  basal, 599
  brachial, 608
  deltoid, 599
  gill, **527**, 528
  hydrospire, 600

Plate—*Continued*
  outer side, 599
  radial, 599, **600**
  side, 599, **600**
  under-lancet, 599, **600**
Plates, of crinoids, 611; anal, 612, **614**;
    basal, 611, **614**; centrodorsal, 624, **625**;
    infrabasal, 611, **614**; interbrachial, 612,
    614; intersecundibrachial; 612; inter-
    tertibrachial, 612; oral, 613; primi-
    brachial, 610, **614**; quadribrachial, 610,
    614; radial, 611, **614**; radianal, 612;
    rosette, 624; secundibrachial, 610, **614**;
    tertibrachial, 610, **614**
  of echinoids, 639; arbacioid, 640; cidar-
    oid, 639; compound, **640**; diademoid,
    640; echinoid, 640; genital, 642, **643**;
    madreporite, **643**; ocular, **643**; oligo-
    porous, 639; polyporous, 640; simple,
    640
Platform, 297
Platform conodonts, 231
  parallel evolution of, **233**
Platyclymenia americana, **443**
Platycrinites, 606, **607**, 622, 624
  hemisphericus, **623**
Platyhelminthes, 214
Platyostoma lineata, **398**
Platyrachella, 307
  oweni, **295**, **308**
Platystrophia, 302, 307
  acutilirata, **303**
Plaxocrinus obesus, **618**
Plectofrondicularia, 81
  californica, **80**
Plectronoceras, **416**, 418, 421
Plerophyllum, 185
  australe, **185**
Pleural, angle, **371**, 377
  furrow, **488**, 491
  lobe, **488**, 489
  ridge, 491
Pleurobrachia rhododactyla, **207**
Pleurocyst, 264
Pleurocystites, 596, 597
  filitextus, **597**
Pleuron, **488**, 491
Pleurotomaria, 392
  adansoniana, **392**
Pleurotomarioids, 392
Plica, 333
Plicatostylus, 357
  gregarius, **360**
Pliomerops canadensis, **512**
Plumatella, **241**
Pneumatocyst, **135**, 136

Pneumatophore, 132
Pocillopora, 197
　eydouxi, **198**
Poecilasma inequilaterale, **556**
Polyaxon, 106
Polychaeta, 221
Polycoeliids, 184
Polydesmus erythropygus, **575**
Polydiexodina, 74
　afghanensis, **73**
　shumardi, **73**
　-Verbeekina zone, **75**
Polygnathid, **230, 232**
Polygnathus, 230, 231, 234
Polygordius, 218
Polygyra, 404
　albolabris, **402**
Polylophodonta, **230,** 231
Polymorphic, 132
Polymorphina, **62**
Polynices, 396
　heros, **398**
Polypide, 239
Polypoid, 125
Polypora nodocarinata, **259**
Polyzoa, 243
Pomatoceras, **225**
Popanoceras, 443
　bowmani, **442**
Pore pairs, 639
Pore rhomb, 591
Pores, echinoderms, 586
　echinoids, 639, **642**; biserial, 639; conju-
　　gate, 639; multiserial, 639; uniserial,
　　639
　fusulinids, 70
　mural, **72,** 159, 165
　oral, 123, **124**
　Ostracodes, **546,** 549; normal, 549;
　　radial, 549
　Sponges, 102
Porifera, 99, 106
　classification, 106
　geologic distribution, **120**
　morphology, **100**
　skeletal structures, 103
Porites, 198
　porites, **199**
Porocrinus, 618
　conicus, **617**
Porospora gigantea, 51
Porpites, 184
Porpitids, 184
Posidonia fracta, **350**
Post-thoracic segments, 493, **505**
Posterior canal, **371**

Posterior platform, **229**
Pourtalès plan, 200
Praedaraelites, 445
　culmiensis, **446**
Praelepas, **556,** 557
Prasopora simulatrix, **253, 256**
Preglabellar furrow, 489
Preoccipital furrow, 490
Prioniodella, **228**
Prioniodid, **230, 232**
Prioniodina, 228, **230,** 233
　camerata, **233**
Prioniodinid, **230,** 232
Prioniodus, 228, **230**
Prionocyclus, 460
Prionotropis woolgari, **459**
Priority, Law of, 15
Prismodictya, 112
　prismatica, **113**
Prismopora, 247
　trifolia, **246**
Proarthropods, **506**
Proboscidiella proboscidea, **315**
Prochoanitic, 432
Prodigality, 36
Prodissoconch, 333, 335
Prodromites, 445
　gorbyi, **444**
Prodryas, **571**
Productella, 316
　spinulicosta, **315**
Producticae, 314
Productids, 314
Productus, 316
　cestriensis, **315**
Proetus, 511
　nevadae, **512**
Profusulinella, 74, **75**
　munda, **73**
Prolecanites, 445, 447
　discoides, **444, 446**
Prolecanitina, 445
Proloculus, 61
Proostracum, 465, **467**
Proparian, 496, 514
Propodus, **565,** 566
Prorichthofenia, **315,** 316
Prosobranchia, 390
Prosocline, 345
Prosodetic, 338
Prosogyre, 333
Prosoma, 520, **525, 527**
Protarabellites, **222**
Protaxocrinus, 620
　elegans, **621**
Protegulum, 280

Proteroblastus, 594, 602
  schmidti, **593**
Proterospongia, **56, 57,** 106
Prothoracic flap, 570
Protocanites lyoni, **444**
Protocarus crani, **534**
Protoconch, 373, **386,** 409, **412, 430**
Protoecium, 242
Protogastropoda, 388
Protopharetra, 121
  raymondi, **119**
Protosepta, **170,** 174, 195
Protospongia fenestrata, **113**
  monomera, **113**
Protozoa, 51, 53
  classification, 52
  economic micropaleontology, 90
  stratigraphic distribution of foramini-
    fers, **86**
Protrachyceras lecontei, **449**
Protrematous, 300
Protremida-Telotremida, 302
Proverruca vinculum, **560**
Psammechinus, 649
  philanthropus, **649**
Pseudagnostus, 508
Pseudamusium, 351
Pseudascoceras, 423, 424, **425**
Pseudestheria emmonsi, 544
  multicostata, **544**
Pseudoammonites, 443, 464, 477
Pseudoceratites, 460, 464, 477
Pseudocrinites abnormalis, **595**
Pseudofossils, 17
Pseudomonotis, 348
  robusta, **350**
Pseudoparalegoceras williamsi, **441**
Pseudopodia, **58,** 59
  lobose, 59
  reticulate, 60
Pseudopunctate, **290,** 291
Pseudorthoceras, **414,** 421
  knoxense, **422**
Pseudoschwagerina, 68, **69,** 74, **75**
  gerontica, **73**
Pterinopecten, 348
  undosus, **350**
Pterocephalia, 511
  laticeps, **510**
Pteropod, 400
Pterotocrinus, 624
  bifurcatus, **623**
  capitalis, **623**
Pterygota, 572
Pterygotus, 526, 528, **529**
Ptilodictya magnifica, **261**

Pulmonata, 400
Puncta, 290, 491
Punctate, **290**
Punctospiricae, 310
Punctospirifer, 310
  pulcher, **311**
  transversus, **295, 311**
Pupa, 569
  muscorum, **402**
Pupaeform, **376,** 377
Purpurea, 325
Pycnogonida, 531
Pycnogonum littorale, **531**
Pygaster, 650
  gresslyi, **650**
Pygidium, **488,** 489
Pyrgo, 78
  comata, **77**
  fischeri, **77**
Pyrgulifera, 398
  humerosa, **398**
Pyritization, 20

Quadrants, 168, **170**
Quinqueloculina, **62,** 76, 78
  costata, **77**
  lamarckiana, **77**

Radial canal, 631
Radial diagnosis, 615, **625**
Radial trunk, **609**
Radiata, 584
Radiation, **39**
Radiolarian earth, 91
Radiolariida, 91
Radiolarite, 91
Radiolites, **360,** 362
Radula, **228,** 326, **412**
Rafinesquina, 312
  alternata, **289, 295, 313**
Ramule, 608
Ramus, 607
Rastrites, 137, **138**
Raw, F., 502
Ray, 586
Raymond, P. E., 195
Recapitulation, theory of, 32
Receptaculites, 116, 118
  mammillaris, **117**
  neptuni, **117**
  occidentalis, **117**
  oweni, **117**
Reclined, 137, **138**
Rectobolivina, 81
  monsouri, **80**

Red tide, 56
Reef corals, 202
Reesidella, **398**
Regularia, 645
Rejuvenescence, 168
Rensselaeria, 317
  marylandica, **318**
Replacement, 19
  penecontemporaneous, 20
Replica, 18
Reproduction, asexual, 52
  sexual, 52
Requienia, 362
  patagiata, **360**
Resilifer, 340
Resilium, 340
Resorption, 382
Resser, C. E., 508
Resserella meeki, **304**
Retardation, 387
Reteocrinus, 622
  onealli, **622**
Reticulariina, 311
  spinosa, **311**
Reticulate ornamentation, 65, 293
Retrochoanitic, 419
Reverse face, 260
Reworking, 236
Rhabdammina, **62**
Rhabdoceras, 450
  russelli, **450**
  suessi, **450**
Rhabdolith, 54, **55**
Rhadopleura, 144
Rhadosome, 133
Rhabdosphaera, **55**
Rhabdostichus buchoti, **544**
Rhagonoid, 103
Rhamphorhynchus, 570
Rhinidictya neglecta, **261**
Rhipidomella oweni, **304**
  thiemi, **299**
Rhizopoda, 59
Rhombiferida, 594
Rhombopora, 262
  lepidodendroides, **259**
Rhombopteria, 348
  mira, **350**
Rhombotrypa, 250
  quadrata, **251, 256**
Rhopalonaria attenuata, **249**
Rhyncholithes, 412
Rhynchonella, 316
Rhynchonellina, 316
Rhynchotrema, 316

Rhynchotreta, 316
  americana, **317**
Rhyniella, 572
Rib, 492
Richthofenia, 281, 316
Ring canal, 631
Rizzo di mer, 635
Robulus, 78
  euglypheus, **79**
Rootlets, 167
Ross, H. H., 570
Rostrospiricae, 310
Rostrum, 431, **497,** 498
Rotalia, **62,** 81
Rotaliicae, 81, **84, 86**
Rotaliid, 81
Rotifer, 217
Rudistoids, 357
  inverted, 357
  normal, 357
Ruedemann, R., 153
Ruga, **170**
Rugosa, 166
  classification, 176
  external features, 171
  geologic history, 185
  internal structures, 171
  key, 176
  morphologic trends, **187**
  ontogeny, 173
Rumina decollata, **382**
Rustella edsoni, **302**

Sacculina, 555
Sackenia, **571**
Saddle, 433
  first lateral, **434,** 435
  second lateral, **434,** 435
  ventral, **434,** 435
Sagenocrinida, 620
Sagenocrinites, 620
  clarki, **621**
Sagitta, 215
Salenia, 649
  texana, **649**
Salfeld, H., 40, 450
Salpingoeca, **56**
Sand dollar, 634
Sao, 504
  hirsuta, **503**
Sarcode, 57
Sarcodina, **57**
Saxolucina anodonta, **358**
Scacchinella, 312, **313**
Scalez, 384, 398
  petrolia, **398**

Scalpellum, 554, **556, 557,** 558
Scandent, 137, **138**
Scaphites, 454
  hippocrepis, **453**
  larvaeformis, 454, **455**
  leei var. *parvus,* **453**
  ventricosus, **455**
  warreni, 454, **455**
Scaphitid evolution, **455**
Scaphopoda, 362
Scenella, **389**
Schistoceras, 440
  missouriense, **439**
Schizambon, 287
  typicalis, **289**
Schizocrania, 288
  filosa, **289**
Schizophoria resupinoides, **304**
Schoenaster, 634
Schuchert, C., 296, 300
Schuchertella, 312
Schuchertoceras, 423
  anticostiense, 423, **425**
  iowaense, 423, **425**
Schwagerina, 68
  diversiformis, **69**
Scleractinida, 193
  classification, 196
  ecology, 202
  geologic history, 203
  insertion of mesenteries and septa, **194**
  key, 197
  septa, 196
Sclerite, 656
Scleroblast, 101
Sclerodermite, 196
Scolecodont, 222, 234
Scolithus, 220, 226, 234
  linearis, **219**
Scolopendra polymorpha, **575**
Scorpionida, 532
Scrobicularia, **332**
Scrobicule, **642**
Scrupocellaria scruposa, **241**
Sculpture, allomorphic, 345
  of pelecypods, 333; cancellate, 333; costa, 333; growth line, 333; lamella, 333; lira, 333; node, 333; plica, 333; ridge, 333; spine, 333
Scutella beds, 653
Scutum, **556,** 557, 558
Scyphocrinites, **607**
Scyphozoa, 150
Scytalocrinus, 619
  validus, **617**
Sea anemone, 193

Sea apple, 634
Sea cucumber, 656
Sea-fan, 189
Sea pen, 189
Sea urchin, 634
Sebargasia carbonaria, **115**
Secondary branchiae, 404
Segestria secessa, **534**
Selenizone, 379
Self-mutilation, 587
Selvage, **546**
Sepia, 470, 471, **476**
  officinalis, **469**
  orbignyana, **469**
Sepiida, 468
Sepium, 468
Septal anatomy, cephalopods, **413**
  corals, 196
Septal furrow, 70, **413**
Septal groove, **170**
Septal spine, 171
Septastrea, 198
  subramosa, 200
Septopora, 262
  subquadrans, **259**
Septula, 74, 264
Septum, of anthozoans, 169, **170;** alar, 169; carinate, 171; contratingent, 171; counter, 169; counter-lateral, 174; dilated, 171; major, 171; minor, 171; perforate, 171; rhopaloid, 171
  of cephalopods, 409, **412;** free portion, 410, **413;** mural portion, 410, **413;** septal foramen, 410, **413;** septal neck, 410, **413**
  of corals, 158
  of fusulinids, 70, **72;** fluted, 71
  of scleractinians, 196; dentate, 196; fenestrate, 196; laminar, 196; smooth, 196; structure, **196**
  tooth of, **196**
Seraphim, 530
Series, 22
  developmental, 30
  environmental, 28
  evolutionary, 34
  geographic, 26
  morphologic, 32
  stratigraphic, 22
Serpula, 224
  pervermiformis, **225**
Serpulites, 226
Seta, 218, 280, 485
Sethamphora, **92**
Shaft, **638**

Shape, discoidal, **75**
  fusiform, **75**
  of brachiopods, 291, 293
  schwagerine, **75**
  of foraminifers, 61, **62, 63**
Shastoceras, 454
  behemoth, **452**
Shell margin, **374**
Shell structure of Mollusca, 327
  foliated, 328
  nacreous, 328
  periostracum, 327
  prismatic, 328
Shoulder, 379
Shumardites, 443
Sicula, **135,** 136
Siderastrea siderea, **199**
Sieve plate, 587
Sigaloceras, **457**
Sigmoid, 137, **138**
Silicification, 20
Silicoflagellida, **56,** 57
Sinistral, **371,** 377
Sinus of pectenoids, **352**
Siphogenerina, 81
  branneri, **80**
Siphogenerinoides, **80,** 81
Siphonaria, 404
  acuta, **402**
Siphonia, 110
Siphonodentalium, **363**
Siphonoglyph, 123
Siphonophorida, 131, **132**
Siphonotreta, 288, **289**
Siphons, of gastropods, 372
  of pelecypods, 335; exhalant, **334,** 335;
    inhalant, **334,** 335
Siphuncle, 410, **412, 430, 467**
Siphuncular deposit, **414,** 420
Smith, G., 541
Smittina trispinosa, **271**
Sochkineophyllum, 184
  mirabile, **185**
Socket, **283**
Solen, **332**
Solenoceras reesidei, **452**
Somasteroida, 631
Somite, 218, 484
Sowerbyella rugosa, **313**
Spatangida, 653
Spathognathus, 233
  commutatus, **233**
Spencer, W. K., 631
Sphaeractinioids, 149
Sphaeragnostus similaris, **507**

Sphaerocystites, 596, 598
  multifasciatus, **595**
Sphaeronites, 594
Sphenodiscus, 460
  beecheri, **461**
Spicules, 101, 103
  of octocorals, 189, **190**
  of sponges, **105**
Spines, apertural, **267**
  of echinoids, 636, **638;** imperforate, 641;
    miliary, 636; perforate, 641; primary,
    636, **638;** secondary, **638**
  terminal, **267**
Spiracle, 600
Spiralium, 298
  athyroid, 306, 310
  atrypoid, 306
  metamorphosis and growth, **309**
  spiriferoid, 306, 307
Spire, **371**
Spirifer, 281, 293, 307
  centronatus, **308**
  increbescens, **308**
  rockymontanus, **308**
Spirifericae, 307
  development of spiralia, 307, **309**
Spiriferina, 306
Spiroglyphus, **376,** 377
Spiroplectammina, 66
  mississippiensis, **67**
Spirorbis, 224, 225
  spirillum, **225**
Spirotheca, 70, **72**
Spirula, 470, 471, **476**
  australis, **470**
  spirula, **470**
Spirulirostra, 470, 471, **476**
Spirulirostrina, 470, **476**
Spondylium, 297
  duplex, 297
  simplex, 297
Spongilla, 107
  lacustris, **108**
  purbeckensis, **108**
Spongin, 103
Sporozoa, 93
Springericrinus, 619
  doris, **617**
Squamula, 165
Squamularia perplexa, **310**
Statoblast, 241, 245
Steganomorph, 267
Steinkern, 17
Steinmann, G., 338
Stelleroida, 630
  classification, 631

Stelleroida—*Continued*
  geologic distribution, 634, **659**
  morphology, **585**
Stenosiphonate, 420
Stenosomella, **93**
Stentor, **93**
Stenzel, H. B., 12
Stephanocrinus, 603
Stereoconus, **232**
Sternum, 650
Stigmatella crenulata, **257**
  spinosa, **253**
Stigmatum, 532
Stipe, 133, **135**
Stomatopora, 245
  delicatula, **247**
  granulata, **247**
Stomodaeum, 123, **124**, **157**
Stone canal, 587, 631
Störmer, L., 530
Strabops, 523
  thacheri, **522**
Stramentum, 558, 658
  flabellum, **556**
Straparoloids, 393
Straparolus, 393
  subquadratus, **393**
Stratigraphic admixture, 236
Stratigraphic leak, 236
Stratigraphic range, 22
Stratigraphy, 2
Streblochondria, 348
  sculptilis, **350**
Streblus beccarii, **82**
Streptelasma, 179, 186
  rusticum, **178**
Streptocolumella, 173
Streptoneuran, 375
Stringocephalus, 317
  burtoni, **318**
Strobilocystites, 598
Stromatopora, **145**, 148, 149
  concentrica, **147**
Stromatoporoidea, 144
Strombus aldrichi, **395**
Strongylocentrotus, 585, 640, 649
  dröbachiensis, **637**
Stropheodonta, 312, **313**
Strophomena, 312
  planumbona, **313**
Strophomenicae, 311
Strophomenina, 311
Strophomenoid, 311
Stumm, E. C., 186
Stylaster, 131
  densicaulis, **130**

Stylonurus, 528, **529**
Stylopoma spongites, **271**
Subapical pit, **229**
Submargin, 352
Subsurface techniques, 46
Subulites, 396
  regularis, **397**
Succinea ovalis pleistocenica, **402**
Suffixes (*-oid, -id*), 13
Sulcus, 281
Survival of the fittest, 38
Sutural diagrams, 433, **434**
Sutures, of cephalopods, 410; ammonitic,
    436; asymmetrical, **434**; ceratitic,
    436; external, **430**, 433, **434**; goniati-
    tic, **436**; internal, 433, **434**
  of foraminifers, 65
  of gastropods, 371
  of trilobites, 496; connective, **497**, 498;
    facial, **488**, 489, 496, **497**; hypostomal,
    497, 498; marginal, **497**, 498; median,
    498; opisthoparian, 496; proparian,
    496; rostral, **497**, 498; terminology,
    497
Sycetta, 102
  primitiva, **100**
Sycon, 114
Syconoid, 102
Synapticula, **196**
Synbathocrinus dentatus, **616**
Syncoryne mutabilis, **128**
Synonym, 15
Syntrophiicae, 305
Syntrophina calcifera, **305**
Synura, 54, **55**
Syringaxon, 179
  acuminatum, **178**
Syringopora, **145**, 146, 161, **164**
  aculeata, **164**
Syringoporidae, 161
Systematics, 10

Tabella, 173
Tabula, of Anthozoa, **159**, 172
  of Archaeocyatha, 118
  of hydrocorallines, 131
  of stromatoporoids, **145**, 146
Tabulata, 159
  geologic history, 166
  key to Families, 160
Tabulipora carbonaria, **253**
Tachylasma, 185
  elongatum, **185**
Taenia, 215
Taeniodictya subrecta, **259**

Talarocrinus, 624
  ovatus, **623**
Talon, 167
Tamiosoma gregaria, 559, **560**
Tangential section, 252
Tarantula palmata, **534**
Tarphyceracone, 415, **416**
Tarphyceras, 414
Taxocrinida, 620
Taxocrinus, 620
  intermedius, **621**
Taxodont, 337
Taxodontida, 341
Taxon, 11
  standardized terminations, 13
Taxonomy, 10
Tectorium, inner, 71, **72**
  outer, 71, **72**
Tectum, 71, **72**
Tegmen, 611
Tellina tenuis, **334**
Telotrematous, 333
Telotremida, 302
Telson, 521, **525, 527**
Tentacles, of cephalopods, **412**
  of coelenterates, **124, 125, 157**
  of gastropods, **372, 374**
  of sepiids, **469**
Tentaculites, 400
  gyracanthus, **401**
  niagarensis, **401**
  scalariformis, **401**
Tenticospirifer cyrtiniformis, **308**
Tentorium, 569
Tercyathus, **119**
Terebra langdoni, **397**
Terebratalia obsoleta, **319**
Terebratula, 281
Terebratulina, 317
  development of loops, 318, **319**
Teredo, 332, 357
  norvegica, **359**
Teredolites, **357**
Tergum, 557, 558
Termen, 267
Terrace, **642**
  crenulate, **642**
Test, of cephalopods, **413, 430**
  of echinoids, 635
  of foraminifers, 60; agglutinated, 61;
    arenaceous, 61; calcareous, 61; chitin-
    ous, 61; complex, 61; fibrous, 61;
    granular, 61; hyaline, 61; imperforate,
    61; megalospheric, 63; microspheric,
    63; perforate, 61; porecellaneous, 61;
    siliceous, 61

Testacida, **59**
Tetracidaris, 639, 641, 647
Tetraclita, 558, **559**
Tetracoralla, 166
Tetractinellida, 107
Tetracystis fenestratus, **595**
Tetradidae, 161
Tetradium, 161, 250
  fibratum, **162**
Tetragraptus, 139, **140, 141, 143**
Tetraxon, 105
Teuthida, 471
Textularia, **62,** 66
  dibollensis, **67**
Thamnastraeoid, 168
Theca, 195
  of anthozoans, 158
  of graptolites, 134
  of hydroids, 127
Thecospira, 311
Thiele, J., 391
Thomas, H. D., 268
Thoracopora, 266, **267**
Thorax, 484, 488, 568
Thuiaria argentea, **128, 143**
Tiarechinus, 644
Tintinnid, 93
Tintinnopsis, **93**
Titanosarcolites, 362
Tolypammina tortuosa, **66**
Tornoceras, 440
  uniangulare, **441**
Tooth, of brachiopods, **283**
  of pelecypods, **336, 337**
Torsion, 373, **374**
Trabecula, **196;** compound, 196; simple,
  196
Trachea, 484, 520
Trachyceras, 447
Trachyleberis scabrocuneata, **546**
Trachylida, 131, **132**
Tracks, 21
Trails, 21
Transverse section, **252**
Trema, 380
Tremadictyon, 114
  reticulata, **113**
Tremalith, 54, **55**
Trematobolus, 288
  insignis, **289**
Trepostodmida, 247, 249
  external features, **251**
  morphology, **253**
  regeneration, **254**
  thin sections, **252**
Triaene, 105

Triarthus becki, 499, **501, 503**
Triaxon, 104
Tricephalophora, 268, **269**
Trichinella, **216**
Tricolpopora, **267**
Tridacna, 331
Trigonastrum, **92**
Trigonia, 333, 357
  thoracica, **358**
Trigonioids, 357
Trigonopora colligata, **271**
Trilobitae, 489
  adaptations, 516
  anatomy, **501**
  appendages, 499
  cephalon, 489
  classification, 504
  eyes, 493, **494**
  geologic history, **519**
  key, 504
  larvae, 502
  pygidium, 492
  sutures, 496, **497**
  terminology, 488
  thorax, 491
Triloculina, 76, 78
  schreiberiana, **77**
  trigonula, **77**
Trimerella, 286, 297
  ohioensis, **287**
Trimeroceras, **424**
Trimerus, 515
  delphinocephalus, **517**
Trinucleus, 511
Triplesia ortoni, 284, **295**
Triplophyllites, 179
  dalei, **178**
  lanceolatus, **178**
  spinulosus, **178**
Triticites, **75**
Triton corrugatus, **382**
Trochelminthes, 216
Trochiform, **376,** 377
Trochoceracone, **416,** 417
Trochoceras, 417
Trochocyathus, 199
  lunulitiformis, **200**
Trochoid, 394
Trocholites ammonius, **422**
Trochosphaera, **217**
Trochurus phylactainodes, **514**
Troostocrinus, 604
  reinwardti, **603**
Tropidoleptus carinatus, **304**
Tropigastrites, 447
  trojanus, **448**

Tryblidium, 388, 390
  reticulatum, **389**
Tube feet, 586, 631
Tubelelloides, 226
Tubercle, **642**
Tubicolida, 224
Tubipora, 189, **190**
Tubucellaria punctulata, **271**
Tunnel, 70
  accessory, 74
  angle, **70,** 71
Turbinaria, 200
  peltata, **201**
Turbiniform, **376,** 377
Turbinolia, 199
  pharetra, **200**
Turbo rhectogrammicus, **383**
Turonia constricta, **109**
Turriform, **376,** 377
Turrilepas, 658, 660
  wrighti, **658**
Turrilites, 454, **457**
  splendidus, **452**
Turritella, 383, **386,** 387, 397
  alabamensis, **397**
  arenicola, **397**
  broderipiana, **386**
  buwaldana, **386**
  cooperia, **386**
  humerosa, **397**
  mortoni, **397**
  plebeia, **397**
  postmortoni, **397**
  trilira, **397**
  uvasana, **386**
Turritelloid, 394
Tusk-shell, 363
Type specimens, 16
Tyrbula, **571**

Uddenites, 445
  schucherti, **444**
Uintacrinus, 626
  socialis, **625**
Ulrich, E. O., 2
Ulrichia bituberculata, **546**
Umbilical seam, **430, 433, 434**
Umbilical shoulder, **430, 434**
Umbilicus, 378, 417
  depth, **430**
  width, **430**
Umbo, 282
Uncinulus abruptus, **299**
Unio, 362
  belliplicatus, **361**
  endlichi, **361**

Uperocrinus, 624
  nashvillae, **623**
Urechis, 220, 226
  caupo, **219, 227**
Uropod, 562
Urosalpinx, 396
  cinereus, **397**
Ussaria, 447
  occidentalis, **449**
Ute syconoides, **100**
Uvigerina, 81
  hughesi, 80
  peregrina, 80

Vaginella chipolana, **401**
Vallacerta, **56**
Valves, of brachiopods; brachial, 281, **283**;
  composition, 280; length, 281; pedicle,
  281, **283, 293**; thickness, 281; width,
  281
  of ostracodes, 547
  of pelecypods, 333; beak, 333, **336, 352**;
  convexity, 333; equilateral, 333; gape,
  331; height, 333; inequilateral, 333;
  length, 333; margin, 333; midline,
  333; opisthogyre, 333; orthogyre, 333;
  prosogyre, 333; umbo, 333, **336, 352**
Valvulineria, 81, 91
  californica, **82**
Vaquerosella, 653
  merriami, **652**
Variation, 36
  definite, 36
  indefinite, 36
Vasseuria, 468
Velella, 132
Vellamo trentonensis, **302**
Velum, 127
Venericor densata, **346**
Veneroid, 356
Venter, 408, **412, 430**
Ventral shield, 489
Ventricle, **334, 372, 374**
Ventriculites, 114
  gracilis, **113**
Venus, 325, 332, 337, 356
  mercenaria, **336**
Venus' flower basket, 112
Verbeekina, 74
  heimi, **73**
Vermes, 214
Vermiform, **376, 377**
Verrill, A. E., 634
Verruca, 561
  pusilla, **560**
Verruculina, 110

Versluys, J., 575
Vertebral ossicles, **632,** 633
Vertebrate paleontology, 1
Vertigo loessensis, **402**
Vestibule, 260, **546,** 548
Vibraculum, 243
Villebrunaster, 631
  thorali, **632**
Vinella, 248
  repens, **249**
Virgula, 139
Visceral ganglion, **334**
Viviparus, 396
  intertextus, 383
  raynoldsanus, **398**
Voltzia, 469
Volution, 371
Volvula iota var. *patuxentia,* **399**
Vorticella, **93,** 217

Waagenoceras, 443
  guadalupensis, **442**
Waagenoconcha montpelierensis, **315**
Waldheimia, 299
  flavescens, **283**
Wall, frontal, 263
  of balanids, 558
  of central capsule, **58**
  of fusulinids, 71; fusulinellid, **72, 75**;
  profusulinellid, **72, 75**; schwagerinid,
  72, 75
  tertiary frontal, 267
Water ring, 586
Water vascular system, 583, **585**
Wedekindellina matura, **73**
Whitehouse, F. W., 588
Whitfieldella nitida, **310**
Whorl, **371**
  height, **430**
  section, 417
Wiwaxia corrugata, **219**
Worms, 214
Worthenopora spinosa, **259**

Xenaspis carbonaria, **446**
Xenocyathellus thedfordensis, **184**
Xenodiscus, 447
  waageni, **448**
Xiphosurida, 523

Yabeina, **75**
Yoldia, 342
  soror, **342**

Zacanthoides, 490
  idahoensis, **509**
Zaphrenthids, 178

Zaphrenthis, 179
Zaphrentites delanouei group, 174
  evolution, **175**
Zirphaea, **332**
Zoanthida, 191
Zoanthus, **192**
Zoarium, 239
Zones, 29
  abyssal, **28, 29**
  bathyal, **28, 29**
  Discorbis, 30, **31**, 88, 89
  Heterostegina, 30, **31**, 88, 89
  littoral, **28, 29**

Zones—*Continued*
  Marginulina, 30, **31**
  Nonionella cockfieldensis, 22, 89
  Olenellus, 22
  sublittoral, **28, 29**
Zooecium, 239, **252**
Zoogeography, 26
Zooid, 239
Zoology, 1
Zoophyte, 101
Zooxanthella, 202
Zygospira, 307, 309, 320
  modesta, 295, **308, 309**

Date Due